Ready® Common Core

Mathematics Teacher Resource Book 6

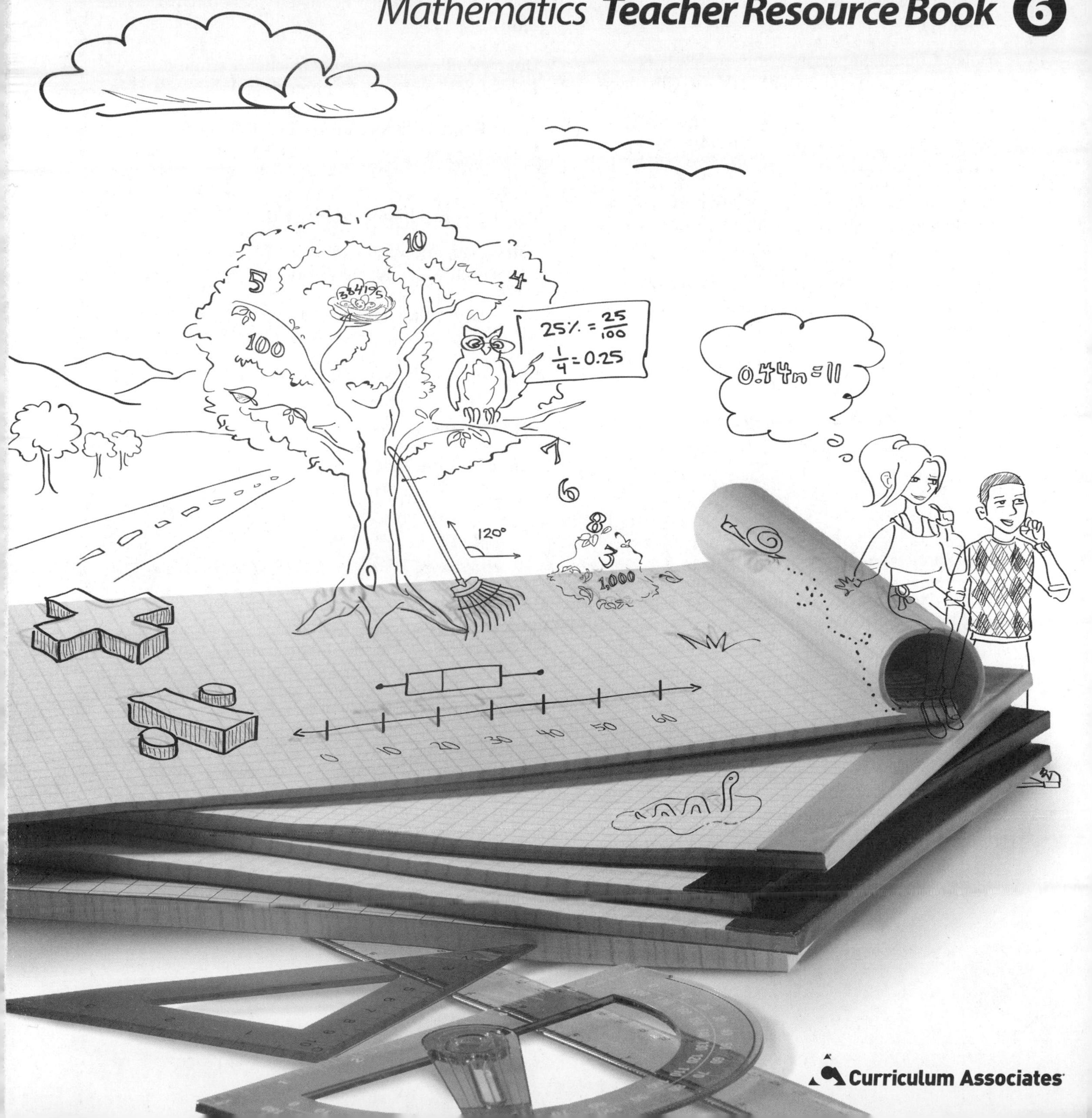

25% = $\frac{25}{100}$

$\frac{1}{4}$ = 0.25

0.44n = 11

Curriculum Associates®

Teacher Advisors

Crystal Bailey, Math Impact Teacher, Eastern Guilford Middle School, Guilford County Schools, Gibsonville, NC

Max Brand, Reading Specialist, Indian Run Elementary, Dublin City School District, Dublin, OH

Helen Comba, Supervisor of Basic Skills & Language Arts, School District of the Chathams, Chatham, NJ

Cindy Dean, Classroom Teacher, Mt. Diablo Unified School District, Concord, CA

Randall E. Groth, Ph.D, Associate Professor of Mathematics Education, Salisbury University, Salisbury, MD

Bill Laraway, Classroom Teacher, Silver Oak Elementary, Evergreen School District, San Jose, CA

Jennifer Lerner, Classroom Teacher, PS 57, New York City Public Schools, New York, NY

Susie Legg, Elementary Curriculum Coordinator, Kansas City Public Schools, Kansas City, KS

Sarah Levine, Classroom Teacher, Springhurst Elementary School, Dobbs Ferry School District, Dobbs Ferry, NY

Nicole Peirce, Classroom Teacher, Eleanor Roosevelt Elementary, Pennsbury School District, Morrisville, PA

Donna Phillips, Classroom Teacher, Farmington R-7 School District, Farmington, MO

Maria Rosati, Classroom Teacher, Harwood Elementary School, Warren Consolidated Schools, Warren, MI

Kari Ross, Reading Specialist, MN

Sunita Sangari, Math Coach, PS/MS 29, New York City Public Schools, New York, NY

Eileen Seybuck, Classroom Teacher, PS 57, New York City Public Schools, New York, NY

Mark Hoover Thames, Research Scientist, University of Michigan, Ann Arbor, MI

Shannon Tsuruda, Classroom Teacher, Mt. Diablo Unified School District, Concord, CA

Acknowledgments

Project Manager: Amy Chen
Revising Editor: Paul Meyers
Cover Designer and Illustrator: Julia Bourque
Book Designer: Scott Hoffman
Supervising Editor: Fran Fanning
Managing Editor: Nicole VanderLinden
Executive Editor: Kathy Kellman
Director–Product Development: Daniel J. Smith
Vice President–Product Development: Adam Berkin

ISBN 978-0-7609-8648-6

North Billerica, MA 01862

15 14 13 12 11 10 9 8 7 6 5 4 3

Table of Contents

M = Lessons that have a major emphasis in the Common Core State Standards
S/A = Lessons that have supporting/additional emphasis in the Common Core State Standards

M = Lessons that have a major emphasis in the Common Core State Standards
S/A = Lessons that have supporting/additional emphasis in the Common Core State Standards

CCSS Emphasis

M = Lessons that have a major emphasis in the Common Core State Standards
S/A = Lessons that have supporting/additional emphasis in the Common Core State Standards

Ready® *Common Core* Program Overview

Ready*® *Common Core is an integrated program of assessment and data-driven instruction designed to teach your students the Common Core State Standards (CCSS) for Mathematics. The program also teaches and assesses the Standards for Mathematical Practice. You can use the program in a supplemental way to address specific standards where your students need instruction and practice, or in a more comprehensive way to engage students in all the CCSS.

Built for the Common Core. Not just aligned.

Features

 Built with all-new content written specifically for the Common Core

 Uses a research-based, gradual-release instructional model

 Requires higher-order thinking and complex reasoning to solve multi-step problems and problems with more than one answer

 Integrates Standards for Mathematical Practice throughout every lesson

 Embeds thoughtful professional development

 Encourages students to develop deeper understanding of concepts and to understand and use a variety of mathematical strategies and models

Ready Common Core Instruction and *Ready Practice*

Ready Common Core Instruction provides differentiated instruction and independent practice of key concepts and skills that builds student confidence. Interim assessments give frequent opportunities to monitor progress.

Ready Common Core Practice provides extensive practice on the high-rigor items required by the Common Core, giving you a measure of student growth. The three full-length tests will strengthen students' skills, build their confidence, and ensure that they are ready to show their mastery of the Common Core.

Teacher Resource Book and Teacher Toolbox

Ready Common Core Teacher Resource Books support teachers with strong professional development, step-by-step lesson plans, and best practices for implementing the CCSS.

Ready Common Core Teacher Toolbox provides online lessons, prerequisite lessons from previous grades, and targeted best-practice teaching strategies.

i-Ready® *Diagnostic*

Built to support the Common Core and integrated with the ***Ready*** program, the ***i-Ready Diagnostic*** helps teachers track student growth and identify areas that need more work, pointing teachers to ***Ready*** lessons to use for remediation. See page A20 for details. (***i-Ready*** sold separately.)

NEW to the 2014 Edition

- More high-rigor test items reflecting latest guidance from SBAC and PARCC
- Updated item Depth of Knowledge (DOK) levels based on latest guidance

Supporting the Implementation of the Common Core

The Common Core State Standards (CCSS) were developed to make sure that by the time students graduate from high school, they are college- and career-ready. Therefore, the creators of the standards started with the expectations they had for students at the end of 12th grade and worked down to kindergarten. As a result of this backward design approach, the CCSS are more rigorous than most current standards. The creators of the standards want students at every grade to develop a deep mastery of fundamental math concepts; learn the coherence among seemingly different math concepts; demonstrate complex, higher-order thinking by solving more rigorous problems; and learn the mathematical practices that allow them to become confident, successful math students. ***Ready*® *Common Core*** is here to help.

Because every Common Core mathematics standard has been addressed with a clear, thoughtful pedagogy, you can use the ***Ready*** program as the main structure of a year-long program. Any other materials aligned to the CCSS can be easily woven into the curriculum.

Each ***Ready*** lesson covers the entirety of a particular skill, so classrooms can work through any lesson independently from the rest of the book. This gives teachers transitioning to the CCSS enormous flexibility, knowing that ***Ready*** lessons can be pulled out and applied to any implementation plan.

Keep Up to Date with the *Ready*® *Teacher Toolbox*

The online ***Ready Teacher Toolbox*** gives you access to a host of multilevel resources, such as instructional support, online lessons, and lessons for prerequisite skills. (See pages A18 and A19 for more.) You can access the latest version of ***Ready Practice*** there, as well.

Smarter Balanced Assessment Consortium (SBAC) and the Partnership for Assessment of Readiness for College and Career (PARCC) are state-led consortia developing assessments aligned to the Common Core. They are creating higher-rigor, innovative item types and assessments that can measure a student's mastery of the Common Core. (See page A10 to see the higher-level DOK items in ***Ready***, matching the consortia approach.) To match the differing approaches of the two consortia, we have created custom practice edition of ***Ready Practice***, one for PARCC and one for SBAC.

The situation will be changing rapidly as the consortia complete their work. We will make sure that ***Ready Practice*** addresses the most recent information released by the consortia. You can ensure you have access to the latest updates by visiting the ***Ready Teacher Toolbox*** (*www.teacher-toolbox.com*).

Helpful Resources for the Transition to the Common Core

http://www.corestandards.org/
The main website for the Common Core. Here you'll find the full text of the standards, plus frequently asked questions and resources.

http://www.smarterbalanced.org/ and ***http://www.parcconline.org/***
The testing consortia creating Common Core assessments for future implementation.

http://www.ascd.org/common-core-state-standards/common-core.aspx
A helpful list of all of ASCD's Common Core resources. A repository of evidence-based strategies, videos, and supporting documents that help educators transition to the Common Core.

http://commoncoretools.me/category/progressions/

http://www.parcconline.org/classroom-resources

http://www.utdanacenter.org/ccss/index.php

http://www.smarterbalanced.org/

http://illustrativemathematics.org/

http://www.hepg.org/hel/article/543#home

Answering the Demands of the Common Core with *Ready*®

THE DEMANDS OF THE COMMON CORE	HOW *READY*® DELIVERS
Focus: The Common Core State Standards for Mathematics focus on fewer topics each year, allowing more time to truly learn a topic. Lessons need to go into more depth to help students to build better foundations and understanding.	***Ready*** lessons reflect the same focus as the Common Core State Standards. In fact, the majority of the lessons in each grade directly address the major focus of the year. Furthermore, each lesson was newly-written specifically to address the Common Core State Standards. There is at least one lesson for each standard and only lessons that address the Common Core State Standards are included.
Coherent Connections (Building on Prior Knowledge): Instruction needs to provide logical ways for students to make connections between topics within a grade as well as across multiple grades. Instruction must **build on prior knowledge** and be organized to take advantage of the natural connections among standards within each cluster as well as connections across clusters or domains. This coherence is required for students to make sense of mathematics.	***Ready*** units are organized by domains following the cluster headings of the Common Core. Each lesson starts by referencing prior knowledge and making connections to what students already know, particularly reinforcing algebraic thinking and problem-solving. These connections are highlighted for teachers in the Learning Progressions of the Teachers Resource Book so teachers can see at a glance how the lesson connects to previous and future learning.
Rigor and Higher-Order Thinking: To meet the Standards, equal attention must be given to conceptual understanding, procedural skill and fluency, and applications in each grade. Students need to use **strategic thinking** in order to answer questions of varying difficulty requiring different cognitive strategies and higher-order thinking skills.	***Ready*** lessons balance conceptual understanding, skill and procedural fluency, and applications. Students are asked higher-order thinking questions throughout the lessons. They are asked to understand, interpret, or explain concepts, applications, skills and strategies. Practice questions match the diversity and rigor of the Common Core State Standards.
Conceptual Understanding: In the past, a major emphasis in mathematics was on procedural knowledge with less attention paid to understanding math concepts. The Common Core explicitly identifies standards that focus on conceptual understanding. Conceptual understanding allows students to see math as more than just a set of rules and isolated procedures and develop a deeper knowledge of mathematics.	***Ready*** includes conceptual understanding in every lesson through questions that ask students to explain models, strategies, and their mathematical thinking. In addition, a "Focus on Math Concepts" lesson is included for every Common Core State Standard that focuses on conceptual development—those standards that begin with the word "understand."
Mathematical Practices: The Standards for Mathematical Practice (SMP) must support content standards and be integrated into instruction. The content standards must be taught through intentional, appropriate use of the practice standards.	The Standards for Mathematical Practice are fully integrated in an age-appropriate way throughout each lesson. The Teachers Resource Book includes SMP Tips that provide more in-depth information for select practice standards addressed in the lesson. See pages A9 and A27 for more details.
Mathematical Reasoning: Mathematical reasoning must play a major role in student learning. Students must be able to analyze problems, determine effective strategies to use to solve them, and evaluate the reasonableness of their solutions. They must be able to explain their thinking, critique the reasoning of others, and generalize their results.	***Ready*** lessons build on problem-solving as a main component of instruction. Students work through a problem, discuss it, draw conclusions, make generalizations, and determine the reasonableness of their solutions. Guided Practice problems ask students to critique arguments presented by fictional characters and justify their own solutions.

The Standards for Mathematical Practice

Mastery of the Standards for Mathematical Practice (SMP) is vital for educating students who can recognize and be proficient in the mathematics they will encounter in college and careers. As the chart below shows, the SMPs are built into the foundation of ***Ready®* *Instruction***.

1. Make sense of problems and persevere in solving them:

Try more than one approach, think strategically, and succeed in solving problems that seem very difficult.

Each ***Ready*** lesson leads students through new problems by using what they already know, demonstrates multiple approaches and access points, and gives encouraging tips and opportunities for cooperative dialogue.

2. Reason abstractly and quantitatively:

Represent a word problem with an equation, or other symbols, solve the math, and then interpret the solution to answer the question posed.

Ready lessons lead students to see mathematical relationships connecting equations, visual representations, and problem situations. Each lesson challenges students to analyze the connection between an abstract representation and pictorial or real-world situations.

3. Construct viable arguments and critique the reasoning of others:

Discuss, communicate reasoning, create explanations, and critique the reasoning of others.

In ***Ready***, the teacher-led Mathematical Discourse feature guides students through collaborative reasoning and the exchange of ideas and mathematical arguments. ***Ready*** lessons also provide error-analysis exercises that ask students to examine a fictional student's wrong answer, as well as multiple opportunities to explain and communicate reasoning.

4. Model with mathematics:

Use math to solve actual problems.

Students create a mathematical model using pictures, diagrams, tables, or equations to solve problems in each ***Ready*** lesson. In the Teacher Resource Book, the Real-World Connection feature adds another dimension to understanding application of a skill.

5. Use appropriate tools strategically:

Make choices about which tools, if any, to use to solve a problem.

Ready lessons model the use of a variety of tools, including diagrams, tables, or number lines; Guided Practice problems may be solved with a variety of strategies.

6. Attend to precision:

Explain and argue, draw, label, and compute carefully and accurately.

Ready lessons guide students to focus on precision in both procedures *and* communication, including special error-analysis tasks and group discussion questions that motivate students to employ precise, convincing arguments.

7. Look for and make use of structure:

Build mathematical understanding by recognizing structures such as place value, decomposition of numbers, and the structure of fractions.

Each ***Ready*** Focus on Math Concepts lesson builds understanding of new concepts by explicitly reviewing prior knowledge of mathematical structure.

8. Look for and express regularity in repeated reasoning:

Recognize regularity in repeated reasoning and make generalizations or conjectures about other situations.

Each ***Ready*** lesson leads students to focus attention on patterns that reflect regularity. Where appropriate, students draw a conclusion or make a generalization and explain their reasoning by referencing the observed pattern.

Depth of Knowledge Level 3 Items in *Ready*® *Common Core*

The following table shows the ***Ready***® lessons and sections with higher-complexity items, as measured by Webb's Depth of Knowledge index.

Depth of Knowledge Level 3 Items in *Ready Common Core*

Lesson	Section	Item	Lesson	Section	Item
1	Guided Practice	11	16	Common Core Practice	5
1	Common Core Practice	6	16	Common Core Practice	6
2	Guided Practice	16	17	Guided Practice	28
2	Performance Task	17	17	Common Core Practice	5
3	Guided Practice	19	17	Common Core Practice	6
3	Common Core Practice	6	18	Guided Practice	23
4	Guided Practice	26	18	Guided Practice	24
5	Guided Practice	18	18	Performance Task	26
Unit 1	Interim Assessment	PT	19	Guided Practice	30
6	Guided Practice	17	19	Common Core Practice	5
6	Guided Practice	18	19	Common Core Practice	6
6	Guided Practice	19	20	Guided Practice	17
6	Performance Task	20	20	Common Core Practice	6
7	Guided Practice	28	21	Guided Practice	15
7	Common Core Practice	5	21	Common Core Practice	4
7	Common Core Practice	6	Unit 3	Interim Assessment	PT
8	Guided Practice	18	22	Guided Practice	17
8	Common Core Practice	6	22	Common Core Practice	5
9	Guided Practice	21	23	Guided Practice	18
9	Common Core Practice	5	23	Common Core Practice	5
9	Common Core Practice	6	23	Common Core Practice	6
10	Guided Practice	26	24	Guided Practice	24
10	Common Core Practice	5	24	Common Core Practice	4
11	Guided Practice	18	24	Common Core Practice	5
11	Common Core Practice	5	25	Guided Practice	18
11	Common Core Practice	6	25	Common Core Practice	5
12	Guided Practice	14	25	Common Core Practice	6
12	Performance Task	17	Unit 4	Interim Assessment	PT
13	Guided Practice	17	26	Guided Practice	11
13	Guided Practice	18	26	Guided Practice	12
13	Common Core Practice	4	26	Guided Practice	13
13	Common Core Practice	5	26	Performance Task	14
14	Guided Practice	23	27	Guided Practice	22
14	Common Core Practice	4	27	Common Core Practice	5
Unit 2	Interim Assessment	7	28	Guided Practice	22
Unit 2	Interim Assessment	PT	28	Common Core Practice	4
15	Guided Practice	19	29	Guided Practice	14
15	Common Core Practice	5	29	Common Core Practice	3
15	Common Core Practice	6	Unit 5	Interim Assessment	PT
16	Guided Practice	27			

Cognitive Rigor Matrix

The following table combines the hierarchies of learning from both Webb and Bloom. For each level of hierarchy, descriptions of student behaviors that would fulfill expectations at each of the four DOK levels are given. For example, when students compare solution methods, there isn't a lower-rigor (DOK 1 or 2) way of truly assessing this skill.

Depth of Thinking (Webb) + Type of Thinking (Revised Bloom)	DOK Level 1 Recall & Reproduction	DOK Level 2 Basic Skills & Concepts	DOK Level 3 Strategic Thinking & Reasoning	DOK Level 4 Extended Thinking
Remember	• Recall conversations, terms, facts			
Understand	• Evaluate an expression • Locate points on a grid or number on number line • Solve a one-step problem • Represent math relationships in words, pictures, or symbols	• Specify, explain relationships • Make basic inferences or logical predictions from data/observations • Use models/diagrams to explain concepts • Make and explain estimates	• Use concepts to solve non-routine problems • Use supporting evidence to justify conjectures, generalize, or connect ideas • Explain reasoning when more than one response is possible • Explain phenomena in terms of concepts	• Relate mathematical concepts to other content areas, other domains • Develop generalizations of the results obtained and the strategies used and apply them to new problem situations
Apply	• Follow simple procedures • Calculate, measure, apply a rule (e.g.,rounding) • Apply algorithm or formula • Solve linear equations • Make conversions	• Select a procedure and perform it • Solve routine problem applying multiple concepts or decision points • Retrieve information to solve a problem • Translate between representations	• Design investigation for a specific purpose or research question • Use reasoning, planning, and supporting evidence • Translate between problem and symbolic notation when not a direct translation	• Initiate, design, and conduct a project that specifies a problem, identifies solution paths, solves the problem, and reports results
Analyze	• Retrieve information from a table or graph to answer a question • Identify a pattern/trend	• Categorize data, figures • Organize, order data • Select appropriate graph and organize and display data • Interpret data from a simple graph • Extend a pattern	• Compare information within or across data sets or texts • Analyze and draw conclusions from data, citing evidence • Generalize a pattern • Interpret data from complex graph	• Analyze multiple sources of evidence or data sets
Evaluate			• Cite evidence and develop a logical argument • Compare/contrast solution methods • Verify reasonableness	• Apply understanding in a novel way, provide argument or justification for the new application
Create	• Brainstorm ideas, concepts, problems, or perspectives related to a topic or concept	• Generate conjectures or hypotheses based on observations or prior knowledge and experience	• Develop an alternative solution • Synthesize information within one data set	• Synthesize information across multiple sources or data sets • Design a model to inform and solve a practical or abstract situation

SBAC, 2012; adapted from Hess et al., 2009

Using *Ready*® Common Core

Use *Ready*® as Your Primary Instructional Program

Because every Common Core State Standard is addressed with clear, thoughtful instruction and practice, you can use ***Ready*® *Common Core*** as your primary instructional program for a year-long mathematics course. The lesson sequence is based on the learning progressions of the Common Core to help students build upon earlier learning, develop conceptual understanding, use mathematical practices, and make connections among concepts.

Instruct

Teach one ***Ready*® *Common Core Instruction*** lesson per week, using the Pacing Guides on pages A14 and A15 for planning.

Use the web-based, electronic resources found in the ***Teacher Toolbox*** to review prerequisite skills and access on-level lessons as well as lessons from previous grades. See pages A18 and A19 for more information.

Assess and Monitor Progress

Assess student understanding using the Common Core Practice and Interim Assessments in ***Ready Common Core Instruction***. See pages A29 and A46 for more information.

Monitor progress using the benchmark tests in ***Ready*® *Practice*** to assess cumulative understanding, identify student weaknesses for reteaching, and prepare for Common Core assessments.

Differentiate Instruction

Identify struggling students and differentiate instruction using the Assessment and Remediation pages at the end of each lesson in the ***Teacher Resource Book***. See page A23 for a sample.

Access activities and prerequisite lessons (including lessons from other grades) in the ***Teacher Toolbox*** to reteach and support students who are still struggling. See pages A18 and A19 for more details.

Use *Ready*® with the *i-Ready*® *Diagnostic*

You can add the ***i-Ready Diagnostic*** as part of your ***Ready*** solution.

- Administer the ***i-Ready Diagnostic*** as a cross-grade-level assessment to pinpoint what students know and what they need to learn.
- Use the detailed individual and classroom diagnostic reports to address individual and classroom instructional needs using the lessons in ***Ready Common Core Instruction*** and the ***Teacher Toolbox***.

See pages A20 and A21 for more information.

Using *Ready®* to Supplement Your Current Math Program

If your instructional program was not written specifically to address the Common Core State Standards, then your textbook likely does not include the concepts, skills, and strategies your students need to be successful. By supplementing with ***Ready® Common Core Instruction***, you'll be able to address these concerns:

- Filling gaps in mathematics content that has shifted from another grade
- Incorporating Common Core models and strategies into instruction
- Integrating the habits of mind that are in the Standards for Mathematical Practice
- Asking questions requiring students to engage in higher-level thinking, such as questions that ask students to explain effective strategies used to solve problems, critique the reasoning of others, and generalize their results
- Including lessons and questions that develop conceptual understanding
- Providing rigorous questions modeled on the latest Common Core assessment frameworks

Step-by-Step Implementation Plan

STEP 1 **IDENTIFY CONTENT NEEDS**	**How do I know what to teach?** • Identify the ***Ready*** lessons you need to include in your instructional plan. – First identify the ***Ready*** lessons that address standards that are a major emphasis in the Common Core. See page A16 or the Table of Contents to easily identify these ***Ready*** lessons. – Next, identify the Common Core State Standards in the table on page A17 that are not addressed in your current math program. • Identify the place in your scope and sequence to insert the ***Ready*** lessons. "Focus on Math Concepts" lessons should come before the lesson in your current book.
STEP 2 **INTEGRATE *READY***	**How do I make time to teach the *Ready* lessons?** • Remove lessons or units from your current instructional plan that are no longer covered in the Common Core State Standards at that grade level. • Replace lessons or units that do not teach topics using the models, strategies, and rigor of the Common Core with the appropriate ***Ready*** lessons.
STEP 3 **MEASURE STUDENT PROGRESS**	**How can I address gaps in student knowledge?** • Use the Interim Assessments in ***Ready*** to make sure your students are successfully able to meet the rigorous demands of the Common Core. • Use the benchmark tests in ***Ready® Practice*** to identify student weaknesses and gaps in students' knowledge. • Use the ***Ready® Teacher Toolbox*** to access activities, on-level lessons, and lessons from other grades to address gaps in students' background and learning. See pages A18 and A19 for more on the ***Teacher Toolbox***.

Ready Instruction Year-Long Pacing Guide

Week	*Ready*® *Common Core Instruction* Lesson	Days	Minutes/day
1	Practice Test 1 or *i-Ready* Baseline Diagnostic	3	60
2	L1: Ratios	5	30–45
3	L2: Understand Unit Rate	5	30–45
4	L3: Equivalent Ratios	5	30–45
5	L4: Solve Problems with Unit Rate	5	30–45
6	L5: Solve Problems with Percent	5	30–45
	Unit 1 Interim Assessment	**1**	**30–45**
7	L6: Understand Division with Fractions	5	30–45
8	L7: Divide with Fractions	5	30–45
9	L8: Divide Multi-Digit Numbers	5	30–45
10	L9: Add and Subtract Decimals	5	30–45
11	L10: Multiply and Divide Decimals	5	30–45
12	L11: Common Factors and Multiples	5	30–45
13	L12: Understand Positive and Negative Numbers	5	30–45
14	L13: Absolute Value and Ordering Numbers	5	30–45
15	L14: The Coordinate Plane	5	30–45
	Unit 2 Interim Assessment	**1**	**30–45**
16	Practice Test 2 or *i-Ready* Interim Diagnostic	3	60
17	L15: Numerical Expressions with Exponents	5	30–45
18	L16: Algebraic Expressions	5	30–45
19	L17: Equivalent Expressions	5	30–45
20	L18: Understand Solutions to Equations	5	30–45
21	L19: Solve Equations	5	30–45
22	L20: Solve Inequalities	5	30–45
23	L21: Dependent and Independent Variables	5	30–45
	Unit 3 Interim Assessment	**1**	**30–45**
24	L22: Area of Polygons	5	30–45
25	L23: Polygons in the Coordinate Plane	5	30–45
26	L24: Nets and Surface Area	5	30–45
27	L25: Volume	5	30–45
	Unit 4 Interim Assessment	**1**	**30–45**
28	L26: Understand Statistical Questions	5	30–45
29	L27: Measures of Center and Variability	5	30–45
30	L28: Display Data on Dot Plots, Histograms, and Box Plots	5	30–45
31	L29: Analyze Numerical Data	5	30–45
	Unit 5 Interim Assessment	**1**	**30–45**
32	Practice Test 3 or *i-Ready* Year-End Diagnostic	3	60

Ready® Instruction Weekly Pacing (One Lesson a Week)

Use ***Ready Common Core Instruction*** as the foundation of a year-long mathematics program. The Year-Long Sample Week (below) shows a recommended schedule for teaching one lesson per week. Each day is divided into periods of direct instruction, independent work, and assessment. Use the Year-Long Pacing Guide on page A14 for a specific week-to-week schedule.

	Day 1	Day 2	Day 3	Day 4	Day 5
	Introduction	**Modeled/Guided Instruction**	**Modeled/Guided Instruction**	**Guided Practice**	**Common Core Practice**
Whole Class	**Introduction**, including Vocabulary (30 minutes) **Mathematical Discourse** (10 min)	Discuss graphic and verbal representations of a problem. **Visual Support** (15 minutes)	Discuss graphic and verbal representations of a problem. **Concept Extension** (15 minutes)	Discuss a sample problem. (10 minutes)	
Small Group/ Independent	**Hands-On Activity** (where applicable)	Work the math with a symbolic representation and practice with **Try It** problems. (20 minutes)	Work the math with a symbolic representation and practice with **Try It** problems. (20 minutes)	Work three problems independently, then **Pair/Share**. (20 minutes)	Solve problems in test format or complete a **Performance Task**. (30 minutes)
Assessment	Discuss answer to the **Reflect** question. (5 minutes)	Discuss solutions to the **Try It** problems. (10 minutes)	Discuss solutions to the **Try It** problems. (10 minutes)	Check solutions and facilitate **Pair/ Share**. (15 minutes)	Review solutions and explanations. (15 minutes) **Assessment and Remediation** (time will vary)

Ready Instruction Weekly Pacing (Two Lessons a Week)

Target ***Ready Common Core Instruction*** lessons based on ***Ready Common Core Practice*** results to focus learning in a compressed time period. The chart below models teaching two lessons per week. The two lessons are identified as Lesson A and Lesson B in the chart below.

	Day 1	Day 2	Day 3	Day 4	Day 5
In Class	***Lesson A*** Introduction (15 minutes) Modeled Instruction (30 minutes)	***Lesson A*** Guided Instruction (15 minutes) Guided Practice (30 minutes)	***Lesson B*** Introduction (15 minutes) Modeled Instruction (30 minutes)	***Lesson B*** Guided Instruction (15 minutes) Guided Practice (30 minutes)	***Lesson A*** Review concepts and skills (20 minutes) ***Lesson B*** Review concepts and skills (20 minutes)
Homework (optional)		***Lesson A*** Common Core Practice		***Lesson B*** Common Core Practice	

Content Emphasis in the Common Core State Standards

Major Areas of Emphasis

Not all of the content in a given grade is emphasized equally in the Common Core State Standards. Some clusters of the standards require greater emphasis than others. This greater emphasis may be based on the depth of the ideas, the time that students need to master the concepts, the content's importance to future mathematics topics, or a combination of some or all of these. A greater focus on the most critical material at each grade allows for lessons to go more in-depth and for students to have more time to master concepts and mathematical practices.

The tables on these two pages identify the Major Clusters emphasized by the Common Core and assessments and those that are Supporting and Additional Clusters. In addition, the ***Ready***® lessons that correspond to these clusters are also identified.

Use the tables on these pages to help inform instructional decisions regarding the amount of time spent on clusters of varying degrees of emphasis. If you are using ***Ready*** as a supplement with another program, you may want to spend more time with the ***Ready*** lessons connected to clusters with a major emphasis.

The table below indicates the clusters of Major Emphasis in the Common Core.

Standard Clusters with Major Emphasis	Standards	*Ready* Lessons
RATIOS AND PROPORTIONAL RELATIONSHIPS		
Understand ratio concepts and use ratio reasoning to solve problems.	6.RP.A.1, 6.RP.A.2, 6.RP.A.3	1, 2, 3, 4, 5
THE NUMBER SYSTEM		
Apply and extend previous understandings of multiplication and division to divide fractions by fractions.	6.NS.A.1	6, 7
Apply and extend previous understandings of numbers to the system of rational numbers.	6.NS.C.5, 6.NS.C.6, 6.NS.C.7, 6.NS.C.8	12, 13, 14
EXPRESSIONS AND EQUATIONS		
Apply and extend previous understandings of arithmetic to algebraic expressions.	6.EE.A.1, 6.EE.A.2, 6.EE.A.3, 6.EE.A.4	15, 16, 17
Reason about and solve one-variable equations and inequalities.	6.EE.B.5, 6.EE.B.6, 6.EE.B.7, 6.EE.B.8	18, 19, 20
Represent and analyze quantitative relationships between dependent and independent variables.	6.EE.C.9	21

Supporting and Additional Areas of Emphasis

Although some clusters have greater emphasis in the Common Core State Standards, this does not mean that standards within the clusters identified as Supporting or Additional can be neglected during instruction. Neglecting material will leave gaps in students' skills and understanding and may leave students unprepared for the challenges of a later grade. Standards for topics that are not major emphases are written in such a way as to support and strengthen the areas of major emphasis. This allows for valuable connections that add coherence to the grade.

In addition, the Supporting and Additional clusters provide students with understanding that is essential for success on the Common Core assessments, though they are not a major focus of the assessments. The Common Core assessments will mirror the emphasis developed by the Common Core and highlighted here. Major clusters will represent the majority of the questions on the Common Core assessments, but it is important to note that items identified as being Supporting or Additional will also be included.

The table below indicates the clusters with Supporting or Additional Emphasis in the Common Core.

Standard Clusters with Supporting or Additional Emphasis	Standards	*Ready* Lessons
THE NUMBER SYSTEM		
Compute fluently with multi-digit numbers and find common factors and multiples.	6.NS.B.2, 6.NS.B.3, 6.NS.B.4	8, 9, 10, 11
GEOMETRY		
Solve real-world and mathematical problems involving area, surface area, and volume.	6.G.A.1, 6.G.A.2, 6.G.A.3, 6.G.A.4	22, 23, 24, 25
STATISTICS AND PROBABILITY		
Develop understanding of statistical variability.	6.SP.A.1, 6.SP.A.2, 6.SP.A.3	26, 27
Summarize and describe distributions.	6.SP.B.4, 6.SP.B.5	28, 29

Additional Resources

For more information on Content Emphases, see these helpful resources.

media.doe.in.gov/commoncore/docs/math_shifts_and_major_work_of_grade.pdf

www.parcconline.org/parcc-model-content-frameworks

www.smarterbalanced.org/wordpress/wp-content/uploads/2011/12/Math-Content-Specifications.pdf

engageny.org/resource/math-content-emphases/

Connecting with the *Ready*® *Teacher Toolbox*

Designed for use with the ***Ready*® *Common Core Instruction***, the Teacher Toolbox provides a host of multilevel resources teachers can use to differentiate instruction. If you purchased the Teacher Toolbox, you should have received an insert with access codes and information. Please contact Customer Service at (800) 225-0248 if you need this information. Visit *www.teacher-toolbox.com* to get started.

The Common Core builds on skills covered in the previous year's standards. Of course, many students will not have mastered those standards, and most students could use a review. ***Ready Common Core*** allows you to access lessons from previous ***Ready*** grades through the Teacher Toolbox.

How Do I Use the Teacher Toolbox?

Lessons are conveniently organized to match your print materials, making it easy to find additional resources for teaching the skills and standards associated with each lesson. All of these resources are perfect for use with any interactive whiteboard or other computer projection screen.

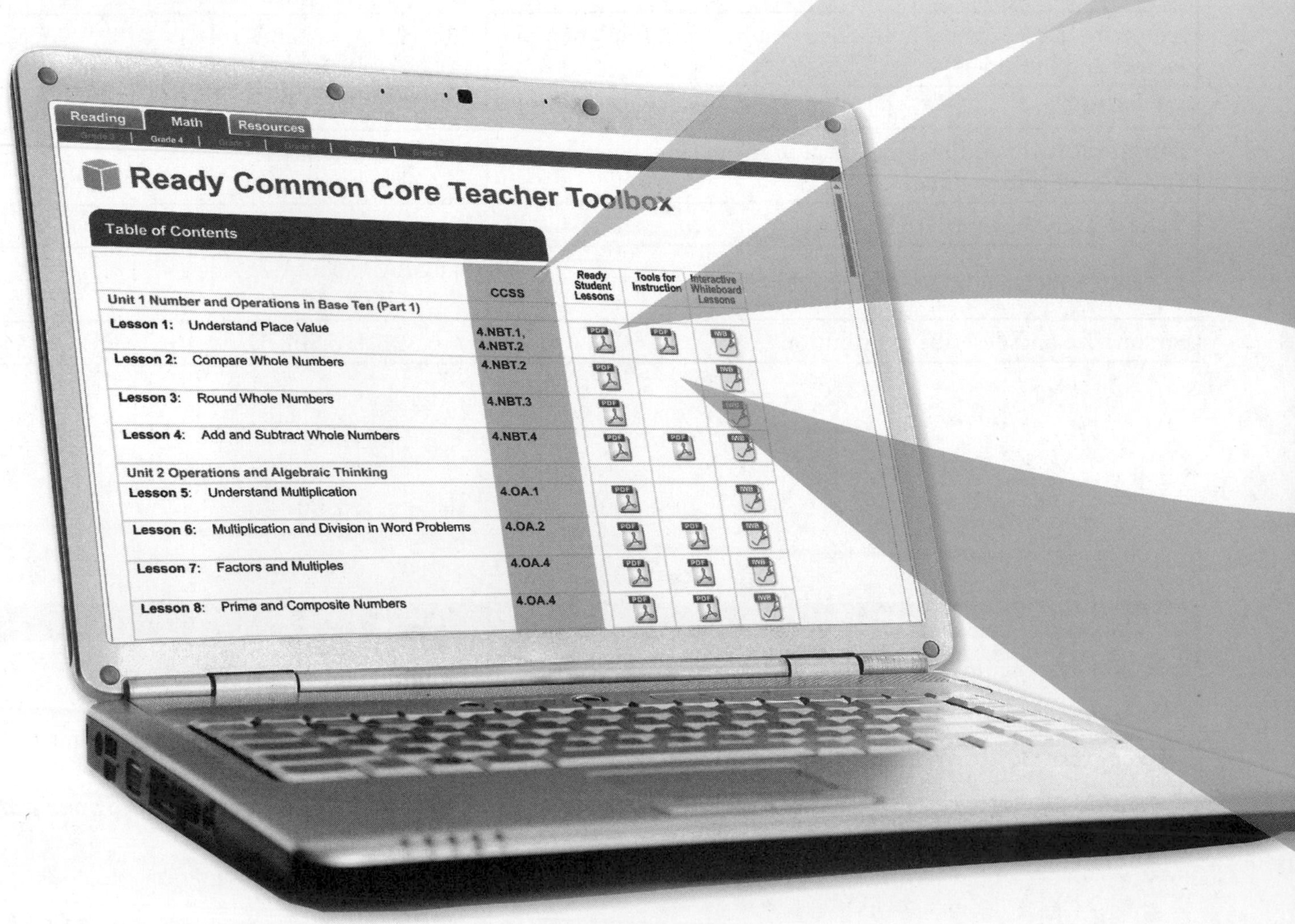

Downloadable *Ready*® Lessons

Downloadable ***Ready***® lessons make it easy for teachers to focus on particular skills, or even reteach skills that students may not have mastered at earlier grade levels. What you get:

- Every lesson in this book is available online as an individual PDF file, which you can project for whole-class and small-group use and access from any internet connection.
- Prerequisite student and teacher lessons are available from prior grades to address gaps in content coverage or strengthen prerequisite skills.

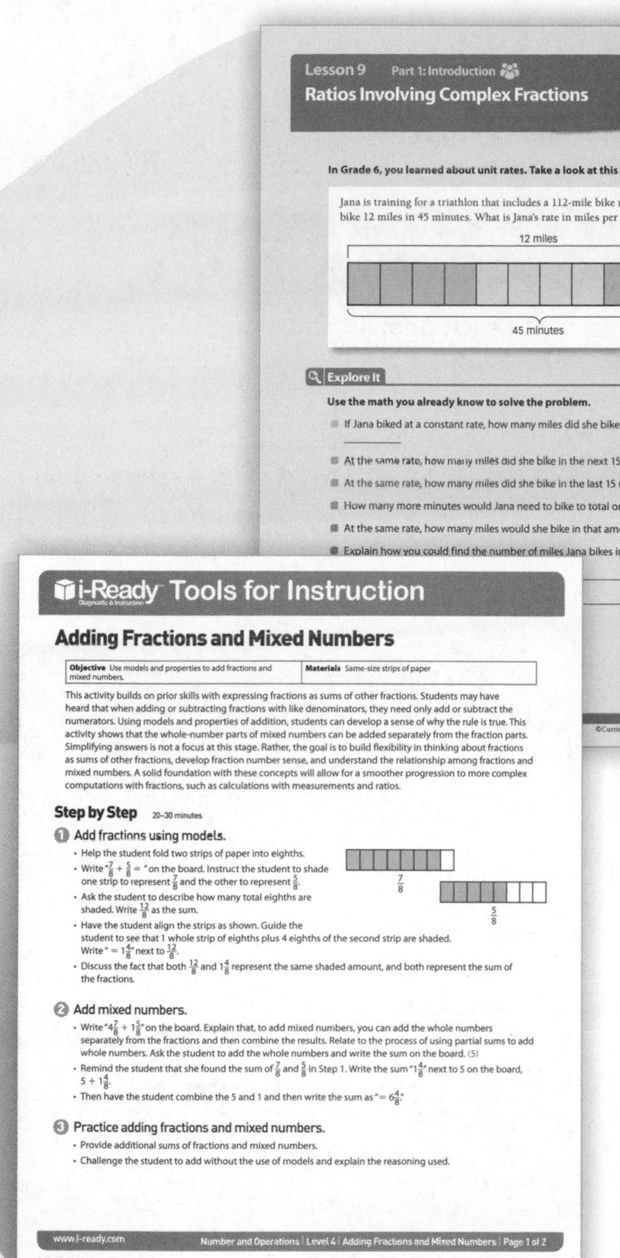

Develop Skills and Strategies

Lesson 9 Part 1: Introduction

Ratios Involving Complex Fractions

CCSS 7.RP.A.1

In Grade 6, you learned about unit rates. Take a look at this problem.

Jana is training for a triathlon that includes a 112-mile bike ride. Today, she rode her bike 12 miles in 45 minutes. What is Jana's rate in miles per hour?

12 miles

45 minutes

Explore It

Use the math you already know to solve the problem.

- If Jana biked at a constant rate, how many miles did she bike in the first 15 minutes? ________
- At the same rate, how many miles did she bike in the next 15 minutes? ________
- At the same rate, how many miles did she bike in the last 15 minutes? ________
- How many more minutes would Jana need to bike to total one hour? ________
- At the same rate, how many miles would she bike in that amount of time? ________
- Explain how you could find the number of miles Jana bikes in one hour.

©Curriculum Associates, LLC Copying is not permitted.

i-Ready Tools for Instruction

Adding Fractions and Mixed Numbers

Objective Use models and properties to add fractions and mixed numbers.	**Materials** Same-size strips of paper

This activity builds on prior skills with expressing fractions as sums of other fractions. Students may have heard that when adding or subtracting fractions with like denominators, they need only add or subtract the numerators. Using models and properties of addition, students can develop a sense of why the rule is true. This activity shows that the whole-number parts of mixed numbers can be added separately from the fraction parts. Simplifying answers is not a focus at this stage. Rather, the goal is to build flexibility in thinking about fractions as sums of other fractions, develop fraction number sense, and understand the relationship among fractions and mixed numbers. A solid foundation with these concepts will allow for a smoother progression to more complex computations with fractions, such as calculations with measurements and ratios.

Step by Step 20–30 minutes

1. Add fractions using models.
   - Help the student fold two strips of paper into eighths.
   - Write "$\frac{7}{8} + \frac{5}{8} =$ " on the board. Instruct the student to shade one strip to represent $\frac{7}{8}$ and the other to represent $\frac{5}{8}$.
   - Ask the student to describe how many total eighths are shaded. Write $\frac{12}{8}$ as the sum.
   - Have the student align the strips as shown. Guide the student to see that 1 whole strip of eighths plus 4 eighths of the second strip are shaded. Write "$= 1\frac{4}{8}$" next to $\frac{12}{8}$.
   - Discuss the fact that both $\frac{12}{8}$ and $1\frac{4}{8}$ represent the same shaded amount, and both represent the sum of the fractions.

   $\frac{7}{8}$ $\frac{5}{8}$

2. Add mixed numbers.
   - Write "$4\frac{7}{8} + 1\frac{5}{8}$" on the board. Explain that, to add mixed numbers, you can add the whole numbers separately from the fractions and then combine the results. Relate to the process of using partial sums to add whole numbers. Ask the student to add the whole numbers and write the sum on the board. (5)
   - Remind the student that she found the sum of $\frac{7}{8}$ and $\frac{5}{8}$ in Step 1. Write the sum "$1\frac{4}{8}$" next to 5 on the board, $5 + 1\frac{4}{8}$.
   - Then have the student combine the 5 and 1 and then write the sum as "$= 6\frac{4}{8}$."
3. Practice adding fractions and mixed numbers.
   - Provide additional sums of fractions and mixed numbers.
   - Challenge the student to add without the use of models and explain the reasoning used.

www.i-ready.com Number and Operations | Level 4 | Adding Fractions and Mixed Numbers | Page 1 of 2

©2012 Curriculum Associates, LLC

Tools for Instruction

Research-based, best-practice routines and activities that can be used with the whole class or small groups provide ways to teach or review standards and prerequisite skills.

Guided Interactive Tutorials

Guided interactive tutorials give teachers another engaging way to provide whole-class or small-group instruction. Lessons follow a consistent structure of explicit instruction and guided practice. Immediate corrective feedback continuously supports students.

Using *i-Ready*® *Diagnostic* with *Ready*® *Common Core*

If you have already purchased ***i-Ready*® *Diagnostic***, you can use its robust reporting to monitor students' overall and domain-specific mathematics proficiency as they move through ***Ready*® *Instruction***. Specifically, use the Student Profile report and the Instructional Grouping report to identify Next Step skills for student instruction.

i-Ready Diagnostic **available for Grades K–12**

Student Profile Report

The **Student Profile** report shows teachers students' performance levels for each domain and shows where they are struggling. Plus, it provides detailed recommendations and resources to support teacher-led instruction.

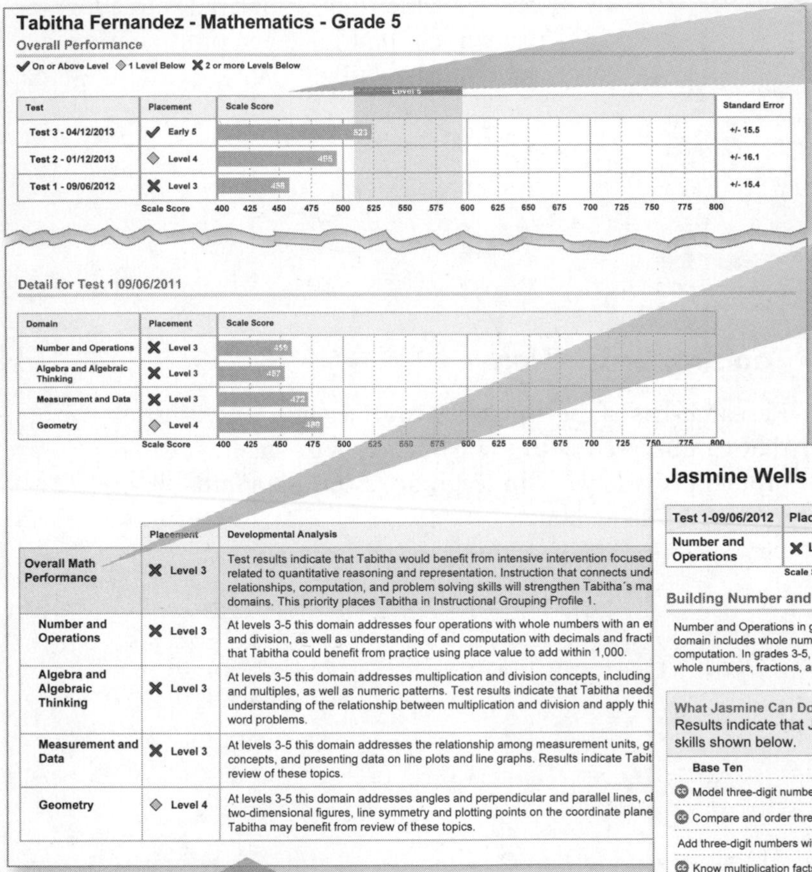

Tabitha Fernandez - Mathematics - Grade 5

Overall Performance

✔ On or Above Level ◇ 1 Level Below ✖ 2 or more Levels Below

Test	Placement	Scale Score	Standard Error
Test 3 - 04/12/2013	✔ Early 5	523	+/- 15.5
Test 2 - 01/12/2013	◇ Level 4	495	+/- 16.1
Test 1 - 09/06/2012	✖ Level 3	458	+/- 15.4

Level 5

Scale Score 400 425 450 475 500 525 550 575 600 625 650 675 700 725 750 775 800

Use the Overall Performance scores to measure growth over time.

Detail for Test 1 09/06/2011

Domain	Placement	Scale Score
Number and Operations	✖ Level 3	459
Algebra and Algebraic Thinking	✖ Level 3	457
Measurement and Data	✖ Level 3	472
Geometry	◇ Level 4	480

Scale Score 400 425 450 475 500 525 550 575 600 625 650 675 700 725 750 775 800

Drill down to see the performance details for each domain.

	Placement	Developmental Analysis
Overall Math Performance	✖ Level 3	Test results indicate that Tabitha would benefit from intensive intervention focused related to quantitative reasoning and representation. Instruction that connects und relationships, computation, and problem solving skills will strengthen Tabitha´s ma domains. This priority places Tabitha in Instructional Grouping Profile 1.
Number and Operations	✖ Level 3	At levels 3-5 this domain addresses four operations with whole numbers with an e and division, as well as understanding of and computation with decimals and fracti that Tabitha could benefit from practice using place value to add within 1,000.
Algebra and Algebraic Thinking	✖ Level 3	At levels 3-5 this domain addresses multiplication and division concepts, including and multiples, as well as numeric patterns. Test results indicate that Tabitha needs understanding of the relationship between multiplication and division and apply thi word problems.
Measurement and Data	✖ Level 3	At levels 3-5 this domain addresses the relationship among measurement units, g concepts, and presenting data on line plots and line graphs. Results indicate Tabit review of these topics.
Geometry	◇ Level 4	At levels 3-5 this domain addresses angles and perpendicular and parallel lines, c two-dimensional figures, line symmetry and plotting points on the coordinate plane Tabitha may benefit from review of these topics.

Detailed analysis of student needs provides the same information that a mathematics specialist would, but with ***i-Ready Diagnostic****, it's completely automated.*

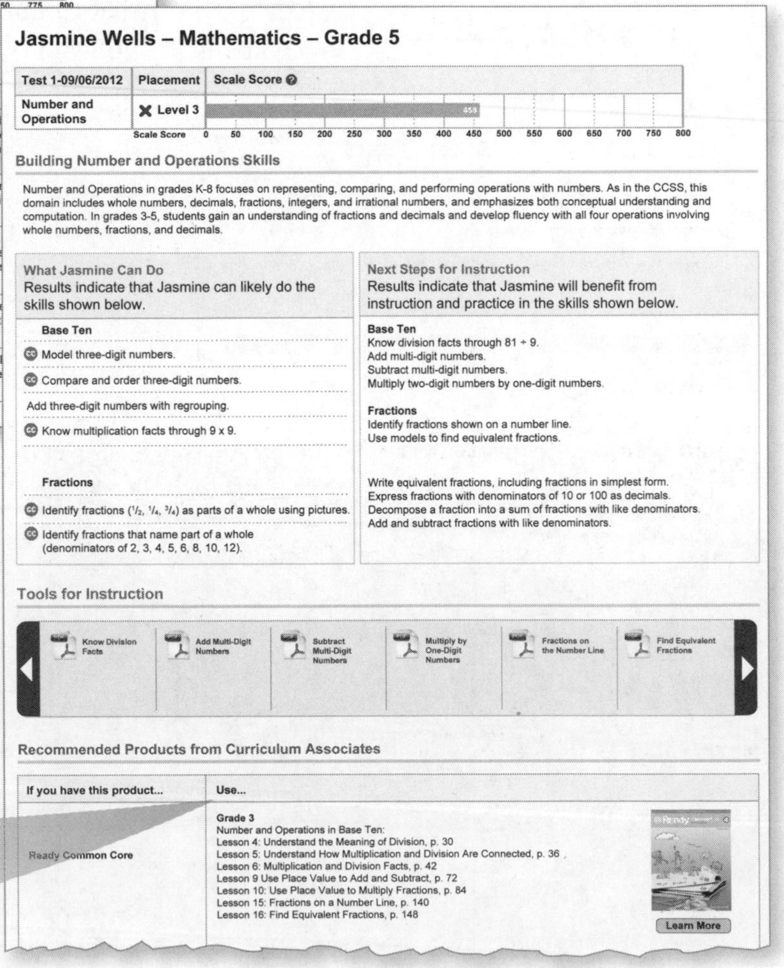

Jasmine Wells – Mathematics – Grade 5

Test 1-09/06/2012	Placement	Scale Score
Number and Operations	✖ Level 3	458

Scale Score 0 50 100 150 200 250 300 350 400 450 500 550 600 650 700 750 800

Building Number and Operations Skills

Number and Operations in grades K-8 focuses on representing, comparing, and performing operations with numbers. As in the CCSS, this domain includes whole numbers, decimals, fractions, integers, and irrational numbers, and emphasizes both conceptual understanding and computation. In grades 3-5, students gain an understanding of fractions and decimals and develop fluency with all four operations involving whole numbers, fractions, and decimals.

What Jasmine Can Do Results indicate that Jasmine can likely do the skills shown below.	Next Steps for Instruction Results indicate that Jasmine will benefit from instruction and practice in the skills shown below.
Base Ten Model three-digit numbers. Compare and order three-digit numbers. Add three-digit numbers with regrouping. Know multiplication facts through 9 x 9.	**Base Ten** Know division facts through 81 ÷ 9. Add multi-digit numbers. Subtract multi-digit numbers. Multiply two-digit numbers by one-digit numbers.
Fractions Identify fractions ($\frac{1}{2}$, $\frac{1}{4}$, $\frac{3}{4}$) as parts of a whole using pictures. Identify fractions that name part of a whole (denominators of 2, 3, 4, 5, 6, 8, 10, 12).	**Fractions** Identify fractions shown on a number line. Use models to find equivalent fractions. Write equivalent fractions, including fractions in simplest form. Express fractions with denominators of 10 or 100 as decimals. Decompose a fraction into a sum of fractions with like denominators. Add and subtract fractions with like denominators.

Tools for Instruction

Know Division Facts | Add Multi-Digit Numbers | Subtract Multi-Digit Numbers | Multiply by One-Digit Numbers | Fractions on the Number Line | Find Equivalent Fractions

Recommended Products from Curriculum Associates

If you have this product...	Use...
Ready Common Core	**Grade 3** Number and Operations in Base Ten: Lesson 4: Understand the Meaning of Division, p. 30 Lesson 5: Understand How Multiplication and Division Are Connected, p. 36 Lesson 6: Multiplication and Division Facts, p. 42 Lesson 9 Use Place Value to Add and Subtract, p. 72 Lesson 10: Use Place Value to Multiply Fractions, p. 84 Lesson 15: Fractions on a Number Line, p. 140 Lesson 16: Find Equivalent Fractions, p. 148 Learn More

Recommends specific lessons in ***Ready Common Core****.*

Instructional Grouping Profile

The **Instructional Grouping Profile** report shows teachers exactly how to group students so that students who are struggling with the same skills get the most out of small-group instruction. The report also gives effective instructional recommendations and resources for each group profile.

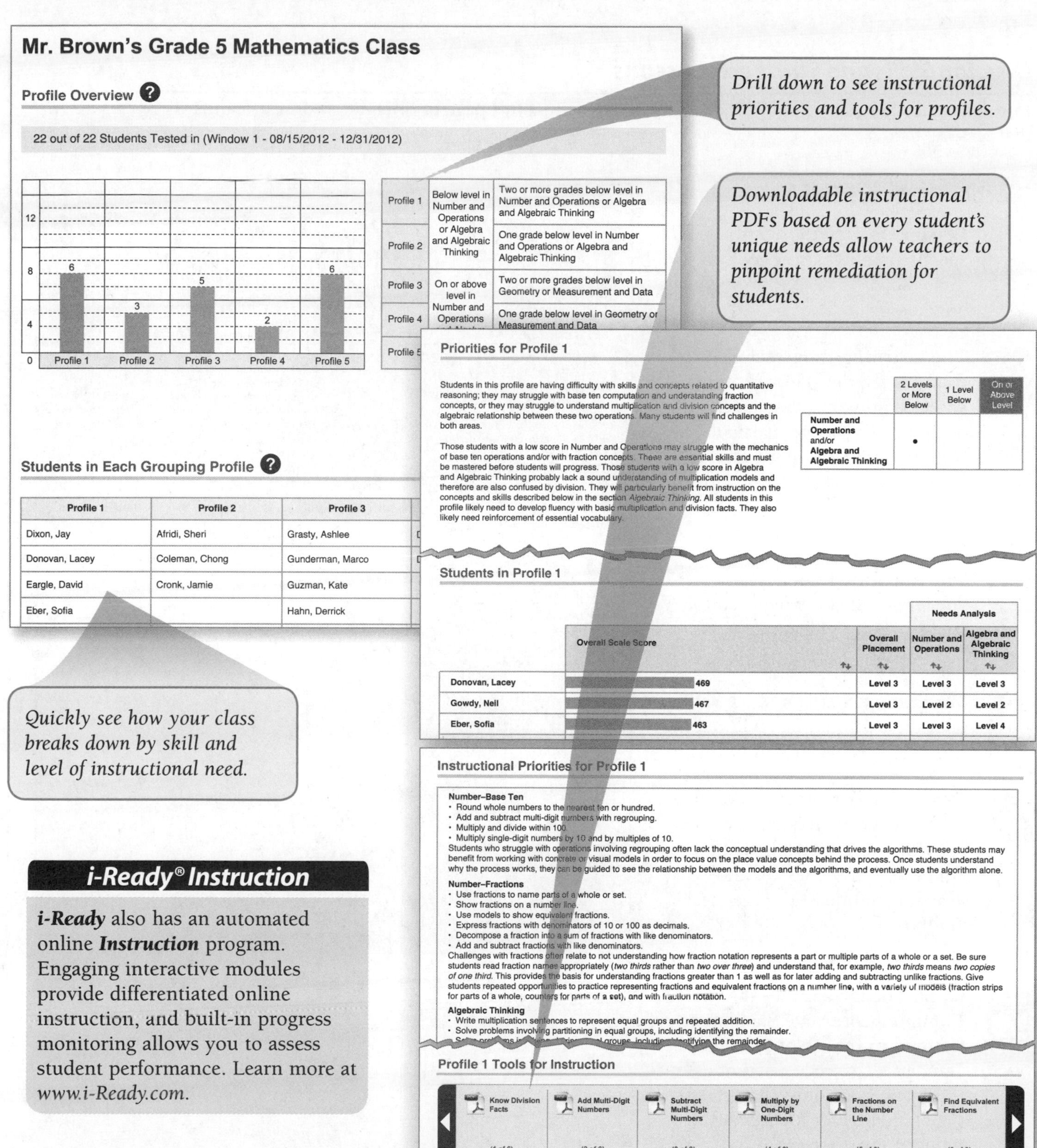

Mr. Brown's Grade 5 Mathematics Class
Profile Overview
22 out of 22 Students Tested in (Window 1 - 08/15/2012 - 12/31/2012)
Profile 1
Profile 2
Profile 3
Profile 4
Profile 5
Below level in Number and Operations or Algebra and Algebraic Thinking
Two or more grades below level in Number and Operations or Algebra and Algebraic Thinking
One grade below level in Number and Operations or Algebra and Algebraic Thinking
On or above level in Number and Operations
Two or more grades below level in Geometry or Measurement and Data
One grade below level in Geometry or Measurement and Data
Drill down to see instructional priorities and tools for profiles.
Downloadable instructional PDFs based on every student's unique needs allow teachers to pinpoint remediation for students.
Priorities for Profile 1
Students in this profile are having difficulty with skills and concepts related to quantitative reasoning; they may struggle with base ten computation and understanding fraction concepts, or they may struggle to understand multiplication and division concepts and the algebraic relationship between these two operations. Many students will find challenges in both areas.
Those students with a low score in Number and Operations may struggle with the mechanics of base ten operations and/or with fraction concepts. These are essential skills and must be mastered before students will progress. Those students with a low score in Algebra and Algebraic Thinking probably lack a sound understanding of multiplication models and therefore are also confused by division. They will particularly benefit from instruction on the concepts and skills described below in the section Algebraic Thinking. All students in this profile likely need to develop fluency with basic multiplication and division facts. They also likely need reinforcement of essential vocabulary.
2 Levels or More Below
1 Level Below
On or Above Level
Number and Operations and/or Algebra and Algebraic Thinking
Students in Each Grouping Profile
Profile 1: Dixon, Jay; Donovan, Lacey; Eargle, David; Eber, Sofia
Profile 2: Afridi, Sheri; Coleman, Chong; Cronk, Jamie
Profile 3: Grasty, Ashlee; Gunderman, Marco; Guzman, Kate; Hahn, Derrick
Students in Profile 1
Needs Analysis
Overall Scale Score
Overall Placement
Number and Operations
Algebra and Algebraic Thinking
Donovan, Lacey 469 Level 3 Level 3 Level 3
Gowdy, Neil 467 Level 3 Level 2 Level 2
Eber, Sofia 463 Level 3 Level 3 Level 4
Quickly see how your class breaks down by skill and level of instructional need.
Instructional Priorities for Profile 1
Number–Base Ten
• Round whole numbers to the nearest ten or hundred.
• Add and subtract multi-digit numbers with regrouping.
• Multiply and divide within 100.
• Multiply single-digit numbers by 10 and by multiples of 10.
Students who struggle with operations involving regrouping often lack the conceptual understanding that drives the algorithms. These students may benefit from working with concrete or visual models in order to focus on the place value concepts behind the process. Once students understand why the process works, they can be guided to see the relationship between the models and the algorithms, and eventually use the algorithm alone.
Number–Fractions
• Use fractions to name parts of a whole or set.
• Show fractions on a number line.
• Use models to show equivalent fractions.
• Express fractions with denominators of 10 or 100 as decimals.
• Decompose a fraction into a sum of fractions with like denominators.
• Add and subtract fractions with like denominators.
Challenges with fractions often relate to not understanding how fraction notation represents a part or multiple parts of a whole or a set. Be sure students read fraction names appropriately (two thirds rather than two over three) and understand that, for example, two thirds means two copies of one third. This provides the basis for understanding fractions greater than 1 as well as for later adding and subtracting unlike fractions. Give students repeated opportunities to practice representing fractions and equivalent fractions on a number line, with a variety of models (fraction strips for parts of a whole, counters for parts of a set), and with fraction notation.
Algebraic Thinking
• Write multiplication sentences to represent equal groups and repeated addition.
• Solve problems involving partitioning in equal groups, including identifying the remainder.
Profile 1 Tools for Instruction
Know Division Facts (1 of 6)
Add Multi-Digit Numbers (2 of 6)
Subtract Multi-Digit Numbers (3 of 6)
Multiply by One-Digit Numbers (4 of 6)
Fractions on the Number Line (5 of 6)
Find Equivalent Fractions (6 of 6)

i-Ready® Instruction

i-Ready also has an automated online ***Instruction*** program. Engaging interactive modules provide differentiated online instruction, and built-in progress monitoring allows you to assess student performance. Learn more at *www.i-Ready.com.*

Features of *Ready*® *Common Core Instruction*

This section guides teachers to the key features of the Student Book and Teacher Resource Book. Numbered boxes call out and describe the key features. Use this section to familiarize yourself with the overall structure of a ***Ready*® *Instruction*** lesson. There are two types of lessons in ***Ready***. Pages A22–A29 show a **Develop Skills and Strategies** lesson and pages A30–A37 show a **Focus on Math Concepts** lesson.

Develop Skills and Strategies Lessons

In the Teacher Resource Book, each lesson begins with a full page of orientation on the standards addressed in that lesson.

Teacher Resource Book

1 **Lesson Objectives** identify specific mathematical goals of the lesson.

2 **The Learning Progression** helps teachers see the standard in context, how the standard builds on prior knowledge, particularly from the previous grade, and how it leads to the expectations for the next year.

3 **Prerequisite Skills** list key concepts and skills required for success with the lesson.

4 **Vocabulary** that is new as well as terms that should be reviewed are provided with clear definitions.

5 ***Ready Teacher Toolbox*** identifies on-level and prerequisite lessons, activities, and tutorials that are connected to the lesson and available online in the Teacher Toolbox.

6 **CCSS Focus** identifies the Common Core State Standards featured in the lesson, Additional Standards covered in activities in the Teacher Resource Book, and the Standards for Mathematical Practice integrated into the lesson.

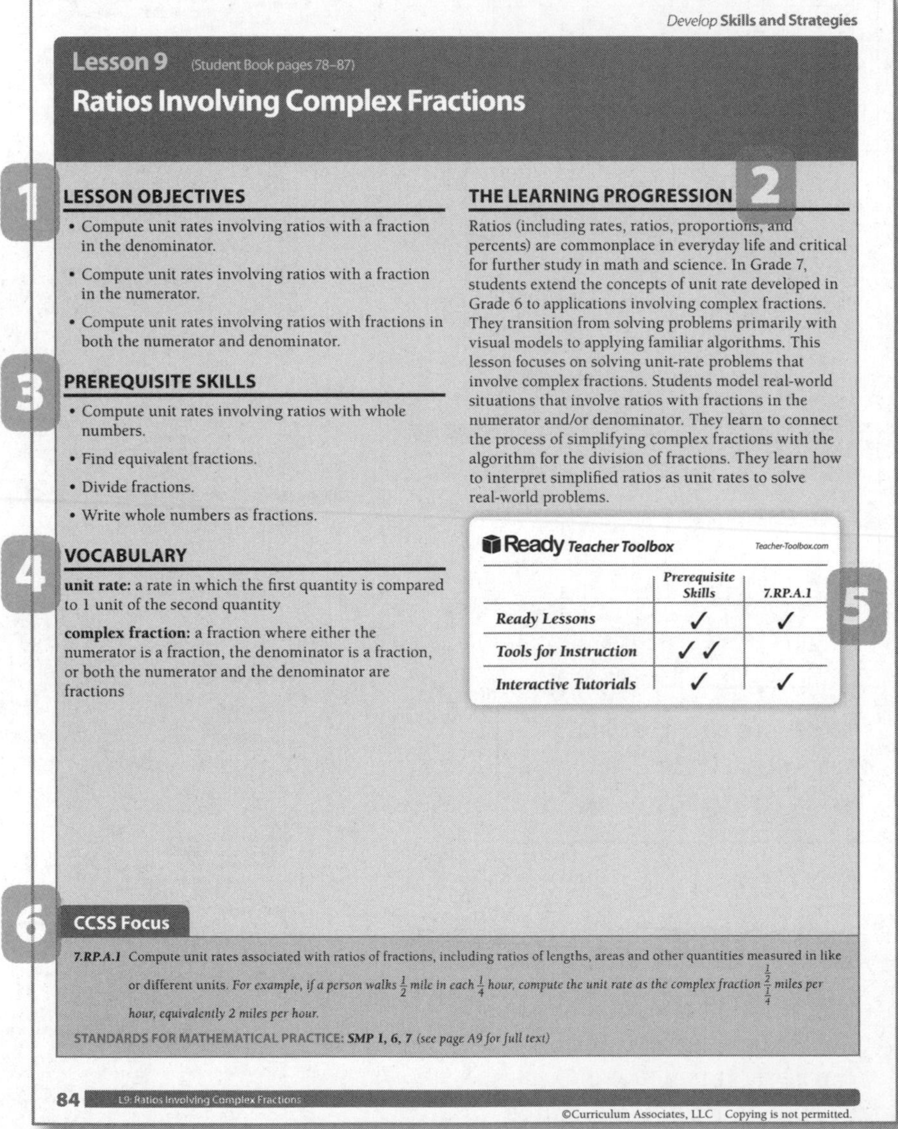

Develop **Skills and Strategies**

Lesson 9 (Student Book pages 78–87)

Ratios Involving Complex Fractions

1 **LESSON OBJECTIVES**

- Compute unit rates involving ratios with a fraction in the denominator.
- Compute unit rates involving ratios with a fraction in the numerator.
- Compute unit rates involving ratios with fractions in both the numerator and denominator.

3 **PREREQUISITE SKILLS**

- Compute unit rates involving ratios with whole numbers.
- Find equivalent fractions.
- Divide fractions.
- Write whole numbers as fractions.

4 **VOCABULARY**

unit rate: a rate in which the first quantity is compared to 1 unit of the second quantity

complex fraction: a fraction where either the numerator is a fraction, the denominator is a fraction, or both the numerator and the denominator are fractions

THE LEARNING PROGRESSION 2

Ratios (including rates, ratios, proportions, and percents) are commonplace in everyday life and critical for further study in math and science. In Grade 7, students extend the concepts of unit rate developed in Grade 6 to applications involving complex fractions. They transition from solving problems primarily with visual models to applying familiar algorithms. This lesson focuses on solving unit-rate problems that involve complex fractions. Students model real-world situations that involve ratios with fractions in the numerator and/or denominator. They learn to connect the process of simplifying complex fractions with the algorithm for the division of fractions. They learn how to interpret simplified ratios as unit rates to solve real-world problems.

Ready *Teacher Toolbox* Teacher-Toolbox.com 5

	Prerequisite Skills	*7.RP.A.1*
Ready Lessons	✓	✓
Tools for Instruction	✓✓	
Interactive Tutorials	✓	✓

6 **CCSS Focus**

7.RP.A.1 Compute unit rates associated with ratios of fractions, including ratios of lengths, areas and other quantities measured in like or different units. *For example, if a person walks $\frac{1}{2}$ mile in each $\frac{1}{4}$ hour, compute the unit rate as the complex fraction $\frac{\frac{1}{2}}{\frac{1}{4}}$ miles per hour, equivalently 2 miles per hour.*

STANDARDS FOR MATHEMATICAL PRACTICE: ***SMP 1, 6, 7*** *(see page A9 for full text)*

84 L9: Ratios Involving Complex Fractions

©Curriculum Associates, LLC Copying is not permitted.

Differentiated Instruction in *Develop Skills and Strategies* Lessons

Each **Develop Skills and Strategies** lesson concludes with Differentiated Instruction activities, giving you opportunities to extend and reinforce learning with all types of students.

Differentiated Instruction — Lesson 9

1 **Assessment and Remediation**

- A recipe calls for $2\frac{1}{4}$ cups of sugar for $1\frac{1}{2}$ dozen cookies. Have students find the amount of sugar per dozen cookies. [$1\frac{1}{2}$ cups]
- For students who are struggling, use the chart below to guide remediation.
- After providing remediation, check students' understanding. Have students find Carlos' rate in laps per minute if he runs $6\frac{1}{4}$ laps in 10 minutes. [$\frac{5}{8}$]
- If a student is still having difficulty, use ***Ready Instruction, Level 7,*** Lesson 6.

If the error is . . .	Students may . . .	To remediate . . .
$\frac{1}{8}$	have found the amount of sugar per cookie, not per dozen.	Have students reread the problem and state what they need to find. Have them explain why they do not need to convert $1\frac{1}{2}$ dozen to individual cookies.
$\frac{2}{3}$	have found the number of dozens per cup of sugar.	Write the ratio using words, $\frac{\text{sugar}}{\text{dozen}}$. Have students substitute numbers for words.
$3\frac{3}{8}$	have multiplied instead of divided.	Remind students that the fraction bar indicates division. Review the steps used to divide two fractions.
any other answer	have divided incorrectly.	Go over the student's work to make sure each step was done correctly.

2 **Hands-On Activity**

Use a paper model to find a unit rate.

Materials: small pieces of paper that are the same shape and size

On the board, write "Sheila buys $9\frac{1}{3}$ pounds of nuts for 4 gift baskets. How many pounds of nuts does Sheila buy per gift basket?" Distribute 10 pieces of paper to each student. Tell students that each piece represents a pound of nuts. Ask, *How can you represent $9\frac{1}{3}$ pounds using the paper?* [Tear one sheet in thirds and discard two of the thirds.] Direct students to distribute the paper into 4 piles so that there is the same amount of paper in each pile. It is acceptable to tear the paper into pieces that are the same size. When students have completed the task, write $\frac{9\frac{1}{3}}{4} = 2\frac{1}{3}$. Ask students what $2\frac{1}{3}$ represents.

Challenge Activity 3

Extend the concept of unit rate to solve problems.

Tell students that when Ginger made applesauce using $2\frac{1}{4}$ pounds of apples, she used $1\frac{1}{2}$ tablespoons of sugar. She now has 8 pounds of apples and wonders how much sugar she should use. Ask students how they could find and use the unit rate to solve the problem. [Possible answer: Find the unit rate by simplifying $\frac{1\frac{1}{2}}{2\frac{1}{4}}$, which is $\frac{2}{3}$. Then either create a ratio table or multiply $8 \times \frac{2}{3}$ to show that Ginger should use $5\frac{1}{3}$ tablespoons of sugar for 8 pounds of apples.]

L9: Ratios Involving Complex Fractions 93

©Curriculum Associates, LLC Copying is not permitted.

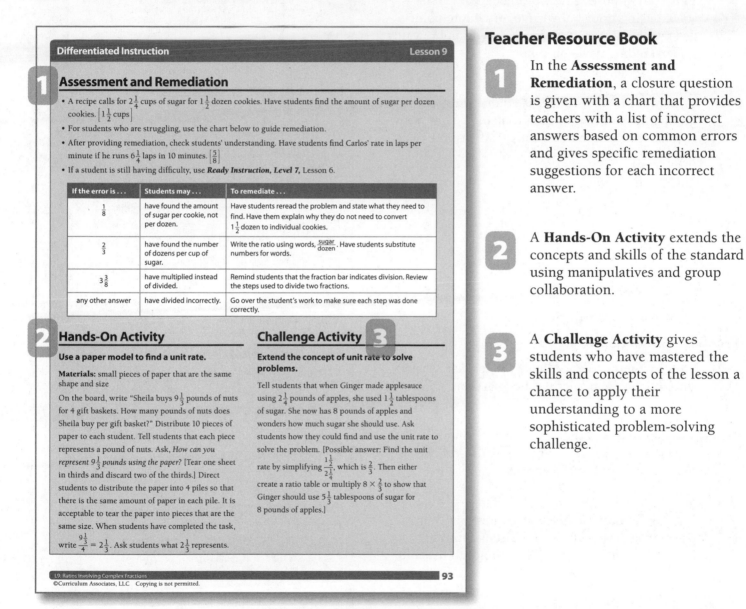

Teacher Resource Book

1 In the **Assessment and Remediation**, a closure question is given with a chart that provides teachers with a list of incorrect answers based on common errors and gives specific remediation suggestions for each incorrect answer.

2 A **Hands-On Activity** extends the concepts and skills of the standard using manipulatives and group collaboration.

3 A **Challenge Activity** gives students who have mastered the skills and concepts of the lesson a chance to apply their understanding to a more sophisticated problem-solving challenge.

Introduction in *Develop Skills and Strategies* Lessons

This section presents a problem designed to establish a connection between what students already know and what they are about to learn. Students can answer the Explore It questions individually, in pairs, or as a group.

Student Book

1 The CCSS covered in the lesson are given for easy reference.

2 This section poses a new problem that can be solved using prior knowledge, providing point-of-use review of prerequisites while working towards understanding new concepts.

3 In **Explore It**, the student is guided through finding the solution to the problem, usually with at least one question that asks students to explain their thinking.

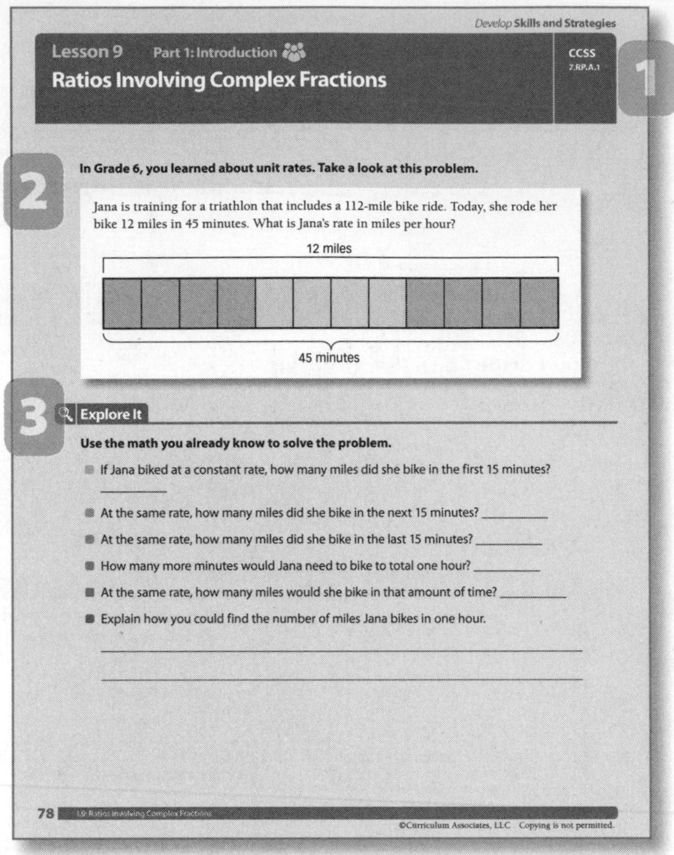

Develop **Skills and Strategies**

Lesson 9 Part 1: Introduction

Ratios Involving Complex Fractions

CCSS 7.RP.A.1

In Grade 6, you learned about unit rates. Take a look at this problem.

Jana is training for a triathlon that includes a 112-mile bike ride. Today, she rode her bike 12 miles in 45 minutes. What is Jana's rate in miles per hour?

Explore It

Use the math you already know to solve the problem.

- If Jana biked at a constant rate, how many miles did she bike in the first 15 minutes? ________
- At the same rate, how many miles did she bike in the next 15 minutes? ________
- At the same rate, how many miles did she bike in the last 15 minutes? ________
- How many more minutes would Jana need to bike to total one hour? ________
- At the same rate, how many miles would she bike in that amount of time? ________
- Explain how you could find the number of miles Jana bikes in one hour.

78 L9: Ratios Involving Complex Fractions

©Curriculum Associates, LLC Copying is not permitted.

Teacher Resource Book

1 **Step by Step** guidance helps the teacher support the students in answering the questions.

2 Use the **Visual Model** to encourage interactivity, engage visual learners, and give ELL students a new perspective on the concept.

3 The **Mathematical Discourse** questions help teachers lead rich classroom discussions and include answers as well as key topics to listen for in student responses.

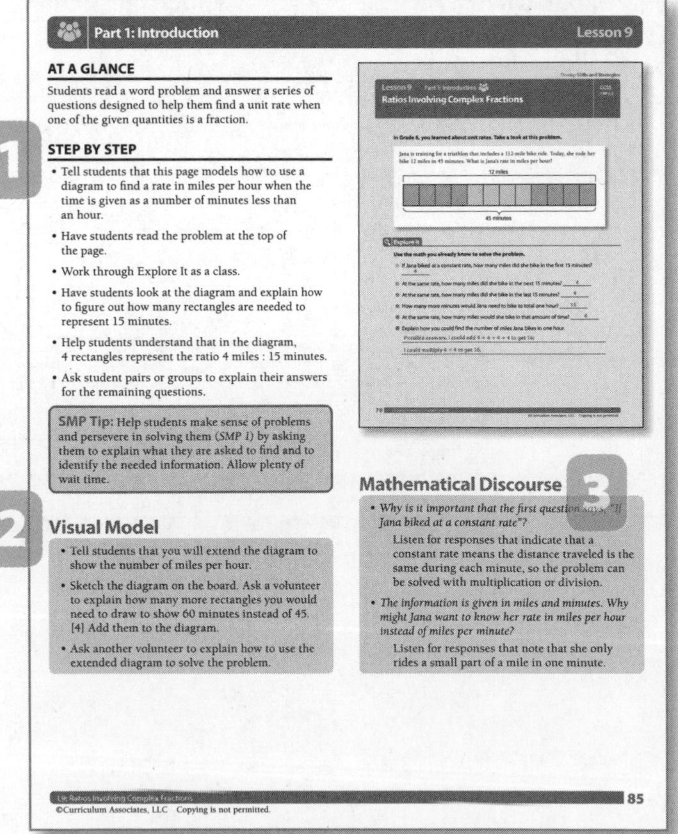

Part 1: Introduction Lesson 9

AT A GLANCE

Students read a word problem and answer a series of questions designed to help them find a unit rate when one of the given quantities is a fraction.

STEP BY STEP

- Tell students that this page models how to use a diagram to find a rate in miles per hour when the time is given as a number of minutes less than an hour.
- Have students read the problem at the top of the page.
- Work through Explore It as a class.
- Have students look at the diagram and explain how to figure out how many rectangles are needed to represent 15 minutes.
- Help students understand that in the diagram, 4 rectangles represent the ratio 4 miles : 15 minutes.
- Ask student pairs or groups to explain their answers for the remaining questions.

SMP Tip: Help students make sense of problems and persevere in solving them (*SMP 1*) by asking them to explain what they are asked to find and to identify the needed information. Allow plenty of wait time.

Visual Model

- Tell students that you will extend the diagram to show the number of miles per hour.
- Sketch the diagram on the board. Ask a volunteer to explain how many more rectangles you would need to draw to show 60 minutes instead of 45. [4] Add them to the diagram.
- Ask another volunteer to explain how to use the extended diagram to solve the problem.

Mathematical Discourse

- *Why is it important that the first question says, "If Jana biked at a constant rate"?*

  Listen for responses that indicate that a constant rate means the distance traveled is the same during each minute, so the problem can be solved with multiplication or division.

- *The information is given in miles and minutes. Why might Jana want to know her rate in miles per hour instead of miles per minute?*

  Listen for responses that note that she only rides a small part of a mile in one minute.

L9: Ratios Involving Complex Fractions 85

©Curriculum Associates, LLC Copying is not permitted.

Introduction in *Develop Skills and Strategies* Lessons

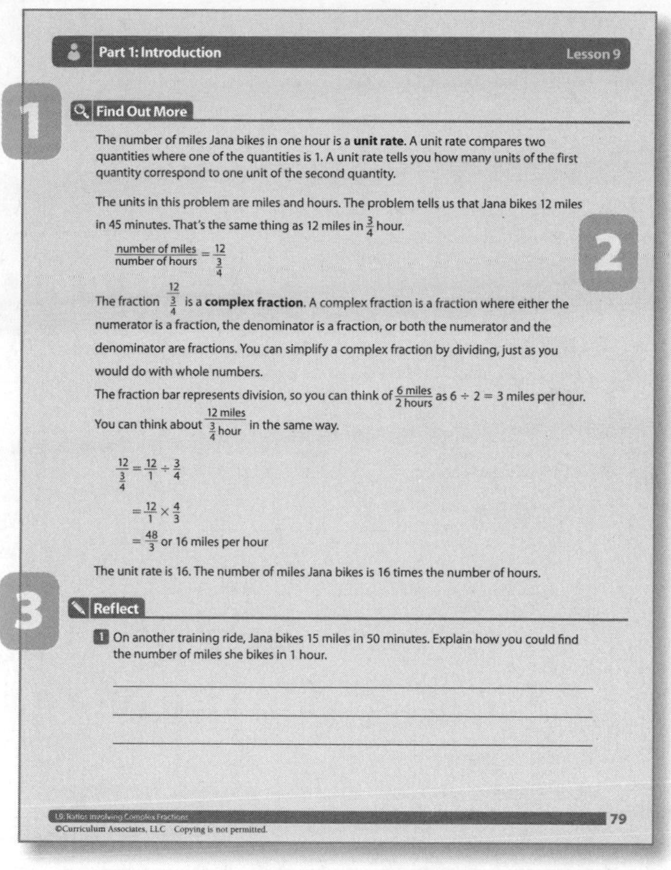

Part 1: Introduction — Lesson 9

1

Find Out More

The number of miles Jana bikes in one hour is a **unit rate**. A unit rate compares two quantities where one of the quantities is 1. A unit rate tells you how many units of the first quantity correspond to one unit of the second quantity.

The units in this problem are miles and hours. The problem tells us that Jana bikes 12 miles in 45 minutes. That's the same thing as 12 miles in $\frac{3}{4}$ hour.

2

$$\frac{\text{number of miles}}{\text{number of hours}} = \frac{12}{\frac{3}{4}}$$

The fraction $\frac{12}{\frac{3}{4}}$ is a **complex fraction**. A complex fraction is a fraction where either the numerator is a fraction, the denominator is a fraction, or both the numerator and the denominator are fractions. You can simplify a complex fraction by dividing, just as you would do with whole numbers.

The fraction bar represents division, so you can think of $\frac{6 \text{ miles}}{2 \text{ hours}}$ as $6 \div 2 = 3$ miles per hour.

You can think about $\frac{12 \text{ miles}}{\frac{3}{4} \text{ hour}}$ in the same way.

$$\frac{12}{\frac{3}{4}} = \frac{12}{1} \div \frac{3}{4}$$

$$= \frac{12}{1} \times \frac{4}{3}$$

$$= \frac{48}{3} \text{ or 16 miles per hour}$$

The unit rate is 16. The number of miles Jana bikes is 16 times the number of hours.

3

Reflect

1 On another training ride, Jana bikes 15 miles in 50 minutes. Explain how you could find the number of miles she bikes in 1 hour.

L9: Ratios Involving Complex Fractions 79

©Curriculum Associates, LLC Copying is not permitted.

Student Book

1 The teacher can use **Find Out More** to formally introduce the key vocabulary, notation, and concepts of the lesson.

2 In student-friendly language, this section describes the formal math the student used to solve the problem, and introduces related skills to be covered in the lesson.

3 Use the **Reflect** question to assess students' understanding about what they just learned.

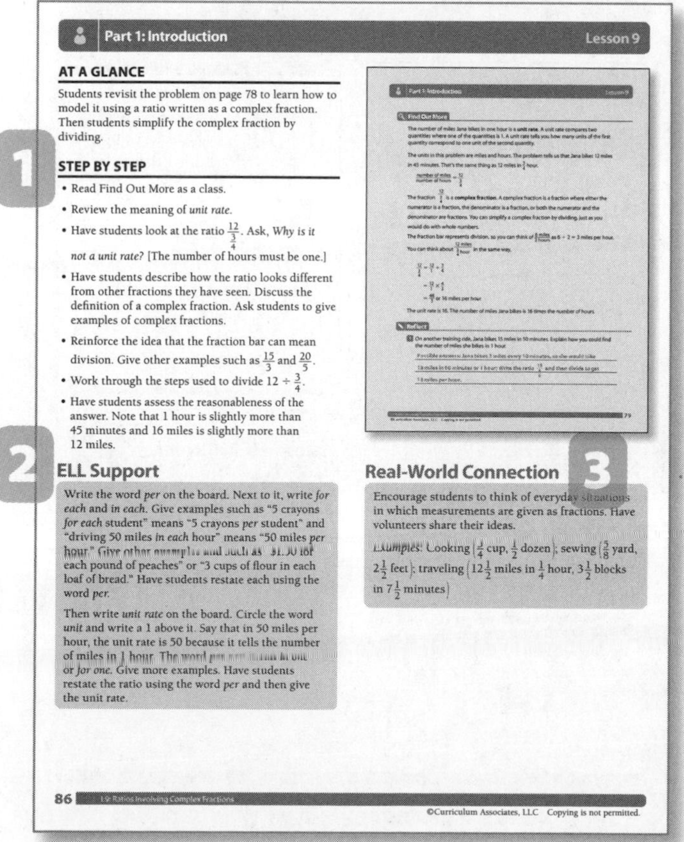

Part 1: Introduction — Lesson 9

AT A GLANCE

Students revisit the problem on page 78 to learn how to model it using a ratio written as a complex fraction. Then students simplify the complex fraction by dividing.

1

STEP BY STEP

- Read Find Out More as a class.
- Review the meaning of *unit rate.*
- Have students look at the ratio $\frac{12}{\frac{3}{4}}$. Ask, *Why is it not a unit rate?* [The number of hours must be one.]
- Have students describe how the ratio looks different from other fractions they have seen. Discuss the definition of a complex fraction. Ask students to give examples of complex fractions.
- Reinforce the idea that the fraction bar can mean division. Give other examples such as $\frac{15}{3}$ and $\frac{20}{5}$.
- Work through the steps used to divide $12 \div \frac{3}{4}$.
- Have students assess the reasonableness of the answer. Note that 1 hour is slightly more than 45 minutes and 16 miles is slightly more than 12 miles.

2

ELL Support

Write the word *per* on the board. Next to it, write *for each* and *in each.* Give examples such as "5 crayons *for each* student" means "5 crayons *per* student" and "driving 50 miles *in each* hour" means "50 miles *per* hour." Give other examples and such as "$1.50 for each pound of peaches" or "3 cups of flour in each loaf of bread." Have students restate each using the word *per.*

Then write *unit rate* on the board. Circle the word *unit* and write a 1 above it. Say that in 50 miles per hour, the unit rate is 50 because it tells the number of miles in 1 hour. The word *per* means *in one* or *for one.* Give more examples. Have students restate the ratio using the word *per* and then give the unit rate.

3

Real-World Connection

Encourage students to think of everyday situations in which measurements are given as fractions. Have volunteers share their ideas.

Examples: Looking ($\frac{1}{4}$ cup, $\frac{1}{2}$ dozen); sewing ($\frac{5}{8}$ yard, $2\frac{1}{2}$ feet); traveling ($12\frac{1}{2}$ miles in $\frac{1}{4}$ hour, $3\frac{1}{2}$ blocks in $7\frac{1}{2}$ minutes)

86 L9: Ratios Involving Complex Fractions

©Curriculum Associates, LLC Copying is not permitted.

Teacher Resource Book

1 **Step by Step** gives page-specific teaching suggestions that build student understanding.

2 Point-of-use **ELL Support** helps the teacher recognize strategies to use to enhance learning with English Language Learners.

3 **Real-World Connection** prompts teachers to help students connect the math to their own experiences.

Modeled Instruction in *Develop Skills and Strategies* Lessons

The teacher supports students as they explore different ways of solving a real-world or mathematical problem. The direction line above the problem identifies the learning objective.

Student Book

1. A problem is posed that can be solved efficiently by using the lesson's new skills and strategies.

2. Different ways of representing the problem create multiple access points to draw on prior knowledge.

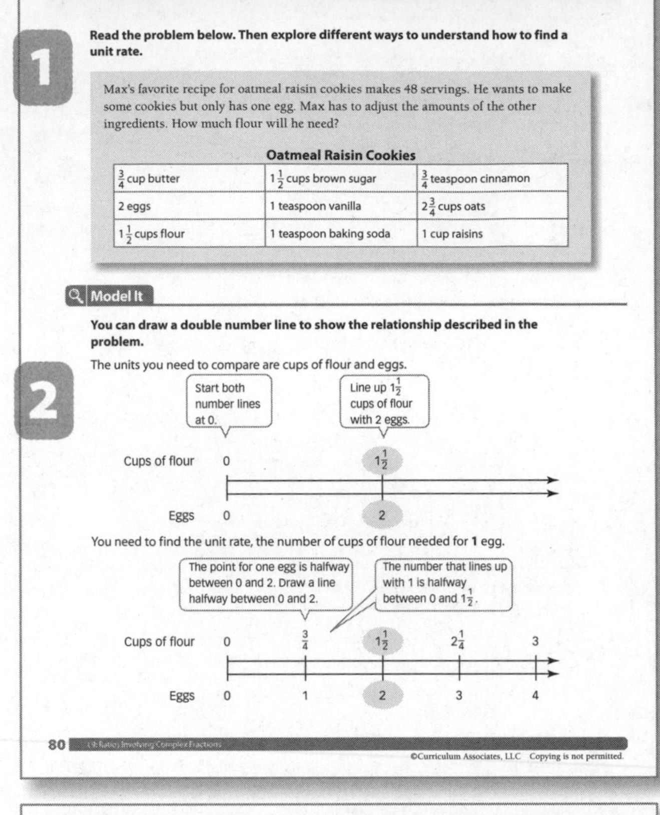

Part 2: Modeled Instruction — Lesson 9

1 **Read the problem below. Then explore different ways to understand how to find a unit rate.**

Max's favorite recipe for oatmeal raisin cookies makes 48 servings. He wants to make some cookies but only has one egg. Max has to adjust the amounts of the other ingredients. How much flour will he need?

Oatmeal Raisin Cookies

$\frac{3}{4}$ cup butter	$1\frac{1}{2}$ cups brown sugar	$\frac{3}{4}$ teaspoon cinnamon
2 eggs	1 teaspoon vanilla	$2\frac{3}{4}$ cups oats
$1\frac{1}{2}$ cups flour	1 teaspoon baking soda	1 cup raisins

Model It

2 **You can draw a double number line to show the relationship described in the problem.**

The units you need to compare are cups of flour and eggs.

Start both number lines at 0.
Line up $1\frac{1}{2}$ cups of flour with 2 eggs.
Cups of flour 0 $1\frac{1}{2}$
Eggs 0 2

You need to find the unit rate, the number of cups of flour needed for **1** egg.

The point for one egg is halfway between 0 and 2. Draw a line halfway between 0 and 2.
The number that lines up with 1 is halfway between 0 and $1\frac{1}{2}$.
Cups of flour 0 $\frac{3}{4}$ $1\frac{1}{2}$ $2\frac{1}{4}$ 3
Eggs 0 1 2 3 4

80 L9: Ratios Involving Complex Fractions

©Curriculum Associates, LLC Copying is not permitted.

Teacher Resource Book

1. **Hands-On Activities** suggest a differentiation option involving manipulatives.

2. The **Mathematical Discourse** questions help teachers lead rich classroom discussions and include answers as well as key topics to listen for in student responses.

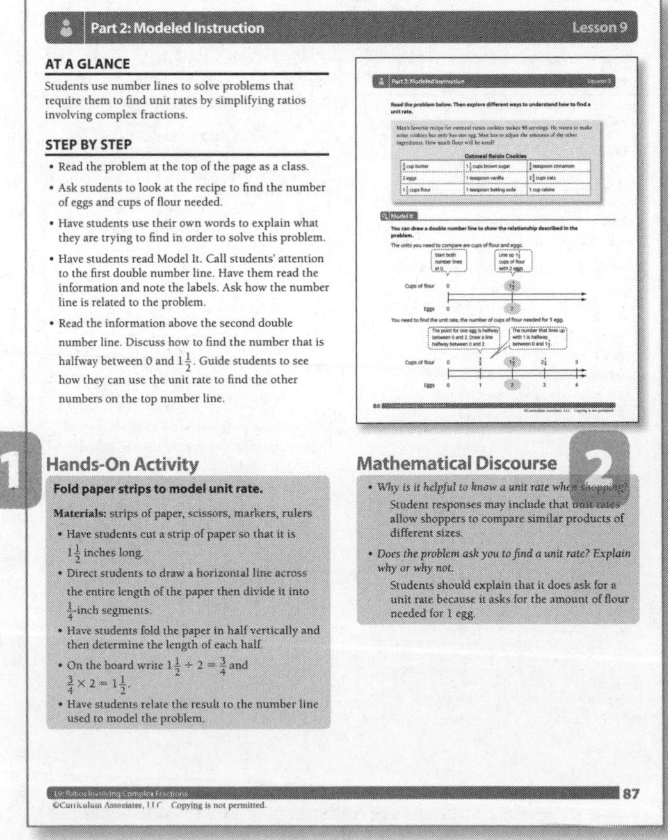

Part 2: Modeled Instruction — Lesson 9

AT A GLANCE

Students use number lines to solve problems that require them to find unit rates by simplifying ratios involving complex fractions.

STEP BY STEP

- Read the problem at the top of the page as a class.
- Ask students to look at the recipe to find the number of eggs and cups of flour needed.
- Have students use their own words to explain what they are trying to find in order to solve this problem.
- Have students read Model It. Call students' attention to the first double number line. Have them read the information and note the labels. Ask how the number line is related to the problem.
- Read the information above the second double number line. Discuss how to find the number that is halfway between 0 and $1\frac{1}{2}$. Guide students to see how they can use the unit rate to find the other numbers on the top number line.

1 **Hands-On Activity**

Fold paper strips to model unit rate.

Materials: strips of paper, scissors, markers, rulers

- Have students cut a strip of paper so that it is $1\frac{1}{2}$ inches long.
- Direct students to draw a horizontal line across the entire length of the paper then divide it into $\frac{1}{4}$-inch segments.
- Have students fold the paper in half vertically and then determine the length of each half.
- On the board write $1\frac{1}{2} \div 2 = \frac{3}{4}$ and $\frac{3}{4} \times 2 = 1\frac{1}{2}$.
- Have students relate the result to the number line used to model the problem.

Mathematical Discourse 2

- *Why is it helpful to know a unit rate when shopping?*
  Student responses may include that unit rates allow shoppers to compare similar products of different sizes.
- *Does the problem ask you to find a unit rate? Explain why or why not.*
  Students should explain that it does ask for a unit rate because it asks for the amount of flour needed for 1 egg.

L9: Ratios Involving Complex Fractions 87

©Curriculum Associates, LLC Copying is not permitted.

Guided Instruction in *Develop Skills and Strategies* Lessons

Scaffolded questions guide students to answer and sometimes extend the problem on the previous page. Students are then given an opportunity to practice what they learned.

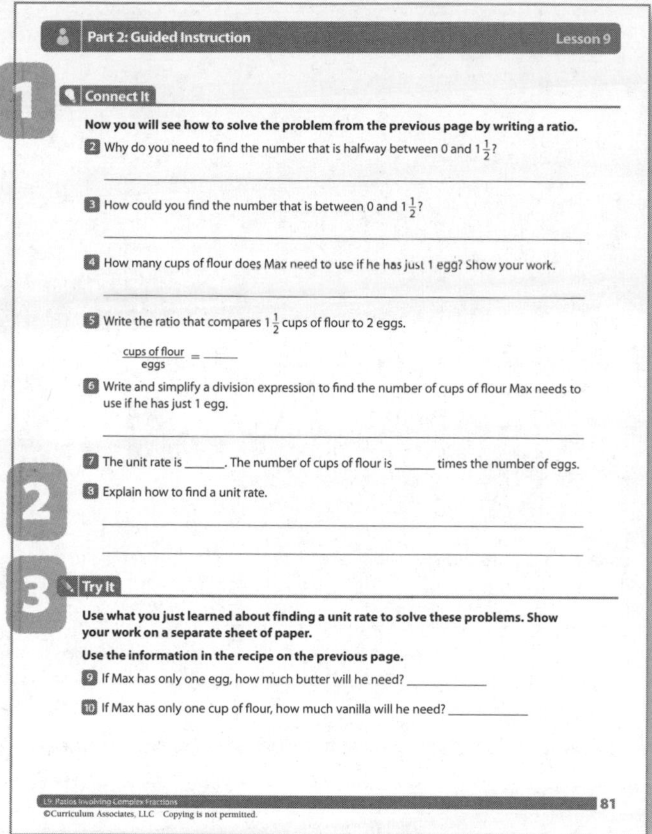

Part 2: Guided Instruction — Lesson 9

Connect It

Now you will see how to solve the problem from the previous page by writing a ratio.

2 Why do you need to find the number that is halfway between 0 and $1\frac{1}{2}$?

3 How could you find the number that is between 0 and $1\frac{1}{2}$?

4 How many cups of flour does Max need to use if he has just 1 egg? Show your work.

5 Write the ratio that compares $1\frac{1}{2}$ cups of flour to 2 eggs.

$\frac{\text{cups of flour}}{\text{eggs}} = $ ____

6 Write and simplify a division expression to find the number of cups of flour Max needs to use if he has just 1 egg.

7 The unit rate is ____. The number of cups of flour is ____ times the number of eggs.

8 Explain how to find a unit rate.

Try It

Use what you just learned about finding a unit rate to solve these problems. Show your work on a separate sheet of paper.

Use the information in the recipe on the previous page.

9 If Max has only one egg, how much butter will he need? ____

10 If Max has only one cup of flour, how much vanilla will he need? ____

L9: Ratios Involving Complex Fractions 81

©Curriculum Associates, LLC Copying is not permitted.

Student Book

1 In **Connect It**, students connect the representations on the previous page to a more symbolic representation of the problem and solution.

2 After working through the symbolic representation, students explain how to solve any similar problem.

3 In **Try It**, students apply what they learned to solve a similar problem.

For lessons addressing standards with multiple subskills, another two pages of Modeled and Guided Instruction are provided for each subskill.

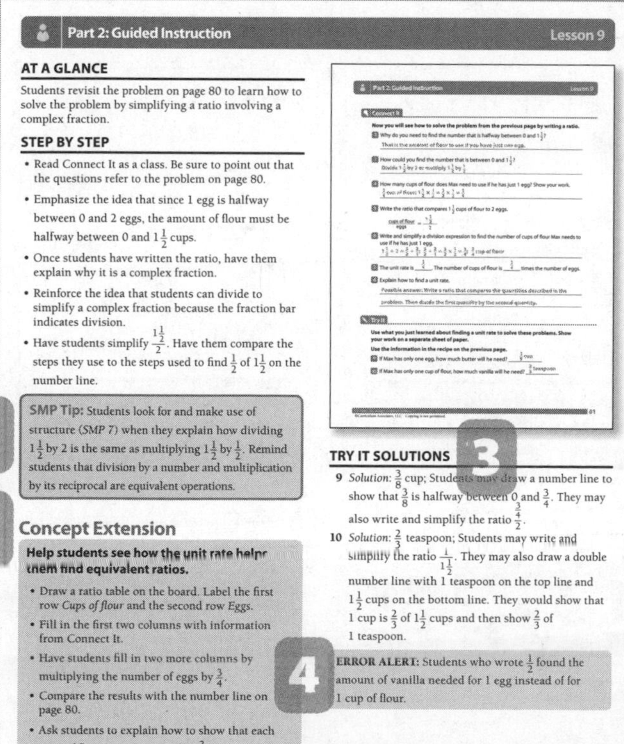

Part 2: Guided Instruction — Lesson 9

AT A GLANCE

Students revisit the problem on page 80 to learn how to solve the problem by simplifying a ratio involving a complex fraction.

STEP BY STEP

- Read Connect It as a class. Be sure to point out that the questions refer to the problem on page 80.
- Emphasize the idea that since 1 egg is halfway between 0 and 2 eggs, the amount of flour must be halfway between 0 and $1\frac{1}{2}$ cups.
- Once students have written the ratio, have them explain why it is a complex fraction.
- Reinforce the idea that students can divide to simplify a complex fraction because the fraction bar indicates division.
- Have students simplify $\frac{1\frac{1}{2}}{2}$. Have them compare the steps they use to the steps used to find $\frac{1}{2}$ of $1\frac{1}{2}$ on the number line.

SMP Tip: Students look for and make use of structure (*SMP 7*) when they explain how dividing $1\frac{1}{2}$ by 2 is the same as multiplying $1\frac{1}{2}$ by $\frac{1}{2}$. Remind students that division by a number and multiplication by its reciprocal are equivalent operations.

Concept Extension

Help students see how the unit rate helps them find equivalent ratios.

- Draw a ratio table on the board. Label the first row *Cups of flour* and the second row *Eggs*.
- Fill in the first two columns with information from Connect It.
- Have students fill in two more columns by multiplying the number of eggs by $\frac{3}{4}$.
- Compare the results with the number line on page 80.
- Ask students to explain how to show that each ratio of flour to eggs is equal to $\frac{3}{4}$.

TRY IT SOLUTIONS

9 *Solution:* $\frac{3}{8}$ cup; Students may draw a number line to show that $\frac{3}{8}$ is halfway between 0 and $\frac{3}{4}$. They may also write and simplify the ratio $\frac{\frac{3}{4}}{2}$.

10 *Solution:* $\frac{2}{3}$ teaspoon; Students may write and simplify the ratio $\frac{1}{1\frac{1}{2}}$. They may also draw a double number line with 1 teaspoon on the top line and $1\frac{1}{2}$ cups on the bottom line. They would show that 1 cup is $\frac{2}{3}$ of $1\frac{1}{2}$ cups and then show $\frac{2}{3}$ of 1 teaspoon.

ERROR ALERT: Students who wrote $\frac{1}{2}$ found the amount of vanilla needed for 1 egg instead of for 1 cup of flour.

88 L9: Ratios Involving Complex Fractions

©Curriculum Associates, LLC Copying is not permitted.

Teacher Resource Book

1 **SMP Tip** highlights a particular Standard for Mathematical Practice that is one of many practice standards integrated in the lesson.

2 Each **Concept Extension** suggests an optional strategy for going deeper into the concept behind the skill, or for connecting that concept to related understandings.

3 **Try It Solutions** provide complete solutions and brief explanations including multiple solutions to show different approaches.

4 **Error Alerts** explain a typical computational error, the wrong answer it might produce, and explanations to help students avoid those errors in the future.

Guided Practice in *Develop Skills and Strategies* Lessons

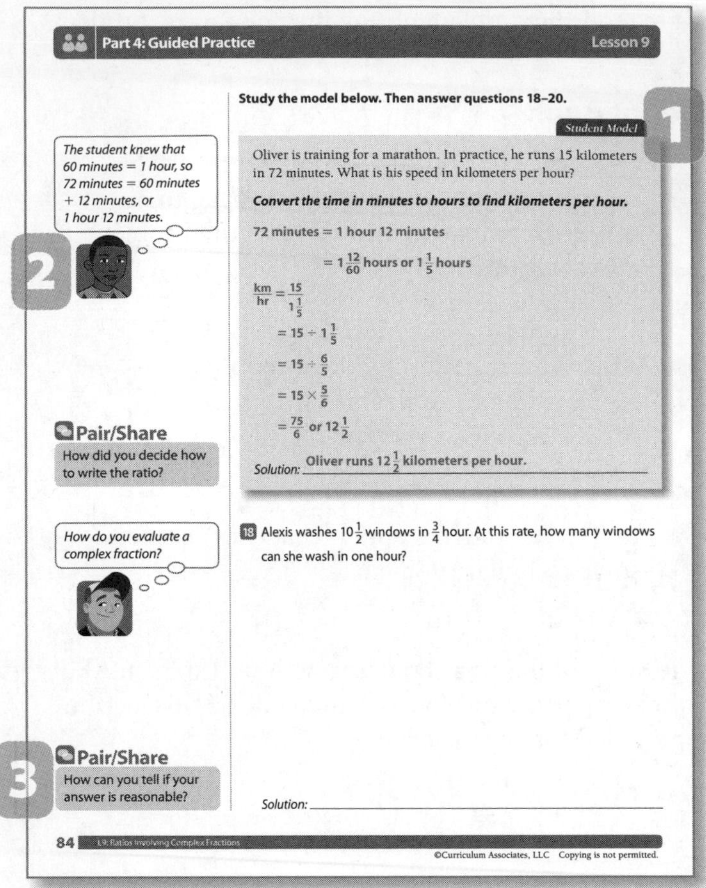

Part 4: Guided Practice — Lesson 9

Study the model below. Then answer questions 18–20.

Student Model

Oliver is training for a marathon. In practice, he runs 15 kilometers in 72 minutes. What is his speed in kilometers per hour?

Convert the time in minutes to hours to find kilometers per hour.

72 minutes = 1 hour 12 minutes

$= 1\frac{12}{60}$ hours or $1\frac{1}{5}$ hours

$\frac{km}{hr} = \frac{15}{1\frac{1}{5}}$

$= 15 \div 1\frac{1}{5}$

$= 15 \div \frac{6}{5}$

$= 15 \times \frac{5}{6}$

$= \frac{75}{6}$ or $12\frac{1}{2}$

Solution: Oliver runs $12\frac{1}{2}$ kilometers per hour.

The student knew that 60 minutes = 1 hour, so 72 minutes = 60 minutes + 12 minutes, or 1 hour 12 minutes.

Pair/Share How did you decide how to write the ratio?

How do you evaluate a complex fraction?

18 Alexis washes $10\frac{1}{2}$ windows in $\frac{3}{4}$ hour. At this rate, how many windows can she wash in one hour?

Pair/Share How can you tell if your answer is reasonable?

Solution: ______

84 L9: Ratios Involving Complex Fractions ©Curriculum Associates, LLC Copying is not permitted.

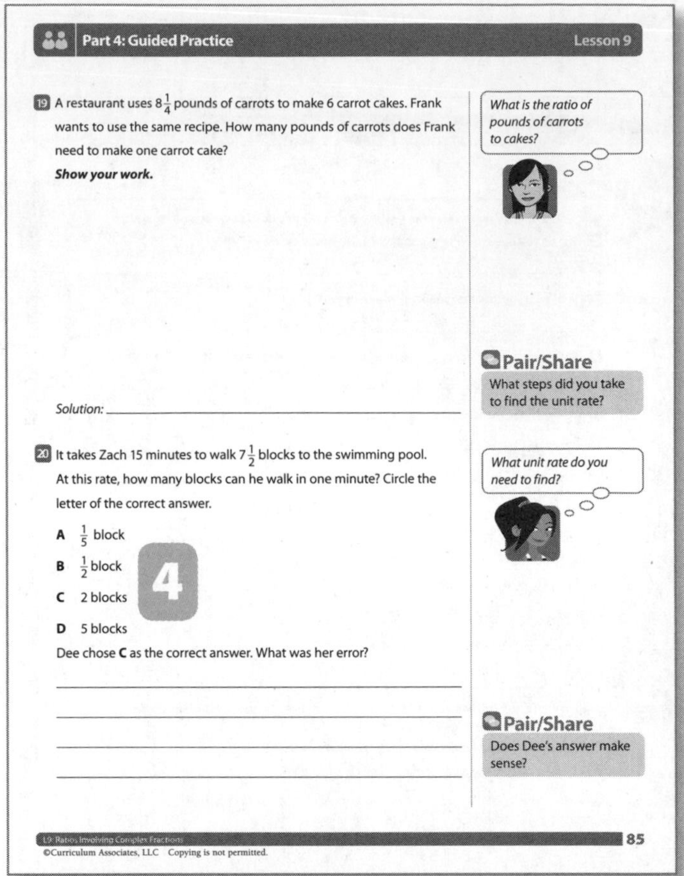

Part 4: Guided Practice — Lesson 9

19 A restaurant uses $8\frac{1}{4}$ pounds of carrots to make 6 carrot cakes. Frank wants to use the same recipe. How many pounds of carrots does Frank need to make one carrot cake?

Show your work.

What is the ratio of pounds of carrots to cakes?

Solution: ______

Pair/Share What steps did you take to find the unit rate?

20 It takes Zach 15 minutes to walk $7\frac{1}{2}$ blocks to the swimming pool. At this rate, how many blocks can he walk in one minute? Circle the letter of the correct answer.

A $\frac{1}{5}$ block

B $\frac{1}{2}$ block

C 2 blocks

D 5 blocks

Dee chose **C** as the correct answer. What was her error?

What unit rate do you need to find?

Pair/Share Does Dee's answer make sense?

L9: Ratios Involving Complex Fractions ©Curriculum Associates, LLC Copying is not permitted. 85

Student Book

1 The first problem is completed for students, modeling how they could show their work.

2 The Study Buddy models self-questioning and the habits of mind of proficient mathematics students.

3 The **Pair/Share** questions prompt students to discuss and analyze the problems on the page.

4 The last multiple-choice question asks students to analyze and explain a student error based on common misconceptions.

Teacher Resource Book

1 **Step by Step** support provides information and useful tips the teacher can use to build students' understanding of how to think about the problems.

2 Complete solutions at point-of-use provide a correct response and an explanation of how a student might solve the problem and also note the DOK level of each question.

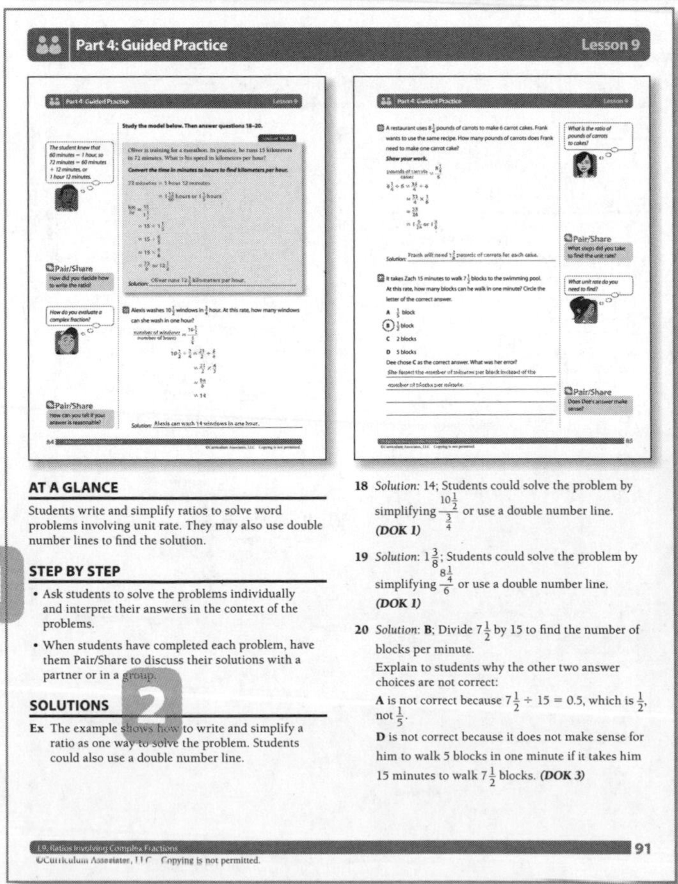

Part 4: Guided Practice — Lesson 9

AT A GLANCE

Students write and simplify ratios to solve word problems involving unit rate. They may also use double number lines to find the solution.

STEP BY STEP

- Ask students to solve the problems individually and interpret their answers in the context of the problems.
- When students have completed each problem, have them Pair/Share to discuss their solutions with a partner or in a group.

SOLUTIONS

Ex The example shows how to write and simplify a ratio as one way to solve the problem. Students could also use a double number line.

18 *Solution:* 14; Students could solve the problem by simplifying $\frac{10\frac{1}{2}}{\frac{3}{4}}$ or use a double number line. ***(DOK 1)***

19 *Solution:* $1\frac{3}{8}$; Students could solve the problem by simplifying $\frac{8\frac{1}{4}}{6}$ or use a double number line. ***(DOK 1)***

20 *Solution:* **B**; Divide $7\frac{1}{2}$ by 15 to find the number of blocks per minute.

Explain to students why the other two answer choices are not correct:

A is not correct because $7\frac{1}{2} \div 15 = 0.5$, which is $\frac{1}{2}$, not $\frac{1}{5}$.

D is not correct because it does not make sense for him to walk 5 blocks in one minute if it takes him 15 minutes to walk $7\frac{1}{2}$ blocks. ***(DOK 3)***

L9: Ratios Involving Complex Fractions ©Curriculum Associates, LLC Copying is not permitted. 91

Common Core Practice in *Develop Skills and Strategies* Lessons

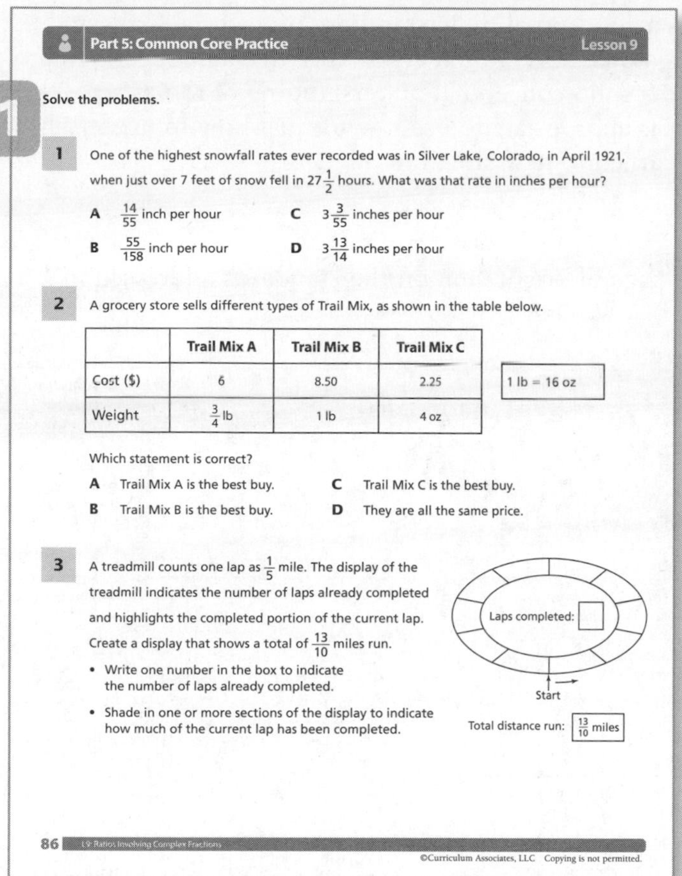

Part 5: Common Core Practice — Lesson 9

1 Solve the problems.

1 One of the highest snowfall rates ever recorded was in Silver Lake, Colorado, in April 1921, when just over 7 feet of snow fell in $27\frac{1}{2}$ hours. What was that rate in inches per hour?

A $\frac{14}{55}$ inch per hour C $3\frac{3}{55}$ inches per hour

B $\frac{55}{158}$ inch per hour D $3\frac{13}{14}$ inches per hour

2 A grocery store sells different types of Trail Mix, as shown in the table below.

	Trail Mix A	Trail Mix B	Trail Mix C
Cost ($)	6	8.50	2.25
Weight	$\frac{3}{4}$ lb	1 lb	4 oz

1 lb = 16 oz

Which statement is correct?

A Trail Mix A is the best buy. C Trail Mix C is the best buy.

B Trail Mix B is the best buy. D They are all the same price.

3 A treadmill counts one lap as $\frac{1}{5}$ mile. The display of the treadmill indicates the number of laps already completed and highlights the completed portion of the current lap. Create a display that shows a total of $\frac{13}{10}$ miles run.

- Write one number in the box to indicate the number of laps already completed.
- Shade in one or more sections of the display to indicate how much of the current lap has been completed.

Laps completed: ☐

Start

Total distance run: $\frac{13}{10}$ miles

86 L9: Ratios Involving Complex Fractions ©Curriculum Associates, LLC Copying is not permitted.

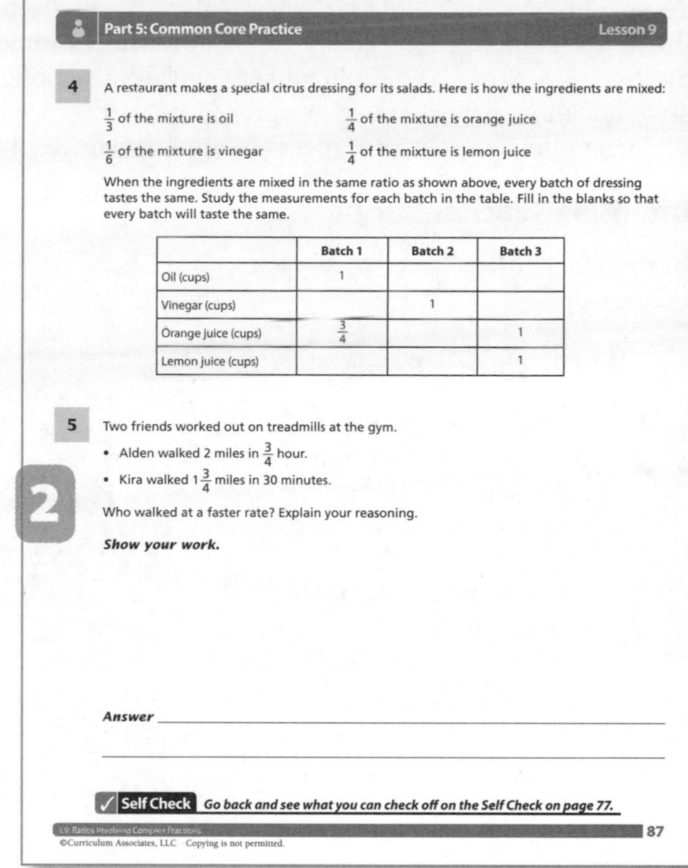

Part 5: Common Core Practice — Lesson 9

4 A restaurant makes a special citrus dressing for its salads. Here is how the ingredients are mixed:

$\frac{1}{3}$ of the mixture is oil $\frac{1}{4}$ of the mixture is orange juice

$\frac{1}{6}$ of the mixture is vinegar $\frac{1}{4}$ of the mixture is lemon juice

When the ingredients are mixed in the same ratio as shown above, every batch of dressing tastes the same. Study the measurements for each batch in the table. Fill in the blanks so that every batch will taste the same.

	Batch 1	Batch 2	Batch 3
Oil (cups)	1		
Vinegar (cups)		1	
Orange juice (cups)	$\frac{3}{4}$		1
Lemon juice (cups)			1

5 Two friends worked out on treadmills at the gym.

- Alden walked 2 miles in $\frac{3}{4}$ hour.
- Kira walked $1\frac{3}{4}$ miles in 30 minutes.

2 Who walked at a faster rate? Explain your reasoning.

Show your work.

Answer ______________________

Self Check *Go back and see what you can check off on the Self Check on page 77.*

L9: Ratios Involving Complex Fractions ©Curriculum Associates, LLC Copying is not permitted. 87

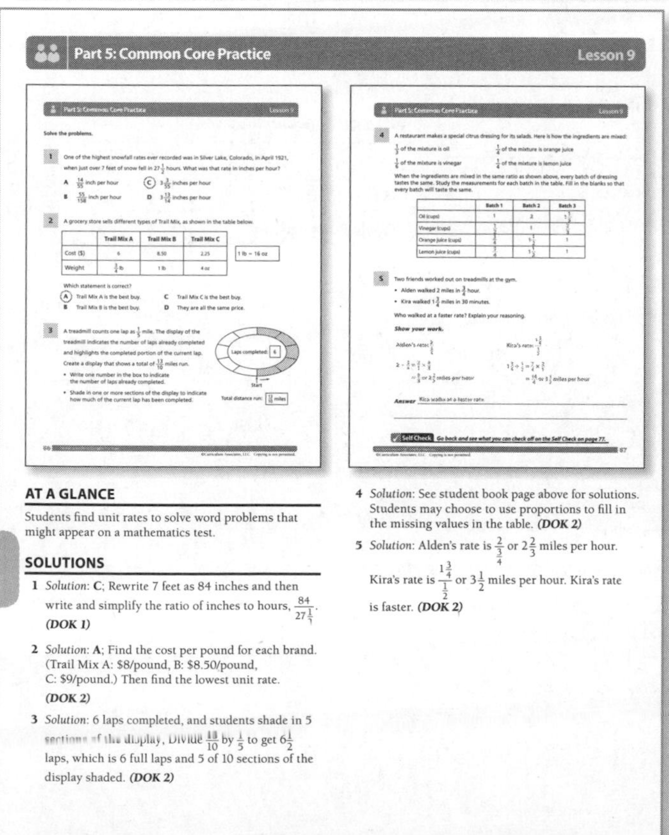

Part 5: Common Core Practice — Lesson 9

AT A GLANCE

Students find unit rates to solve word problems that might appear on a mathematics test.

1 **SOLUTIONS**

1 *Solution*: **C**; Rewrite 7 feet as 84 inches and then write and simplify the ratio of inches to hours, $\frac{84}{27\frac{1}{2}}$. ***(DOK 1)***

2 *Solution*: **A**; Find the cost per pound for each brand. (Trail Mix A: \$8/pound, B: \$8.50/pound, C: \$9/pound.) Then find the lowest unit rate. ***(DOK 2)***

3 *Solution*: 6 laps completed, and students shade in 5 sections of the display. Divide $\frac{13}{10}$ by $\frac{1}{5}$ to get $6\frac{1}{2}$ laps, which is 6 full laps and 5 of 10 sections of the display shaded. ***(DOK 2)***

4 *Solution*: See student book page above for solutions. Students may choose to use proportions to fill in the missing values in the table. ***(DOK 2)***

5 *Solution*: Alden's rate is $\frac{2}{\frac{3}{4}}$ or $2\frac{2}{3}$ miles per hour.

Kira's rate is $\frac{1\frac{3}{4}}{\frac{1}{2}}$ or $3\frac{1}{2}$ miles per hour. Kira's rate is faster. ***(DOK 2)***

92 L9: Ratios Involving Complex Fractions ©Curriculum Associates, LLC Copying is not permitted.

Student Book

1 **Common Core Practice** provides students with questions in a variety of Common Core assessment formats that integrate and extend concepts and skills.

2 Open-ended questions allow for multiple approaches and, when appropriate, more than one correct response.

Teacher Resource Book

1 Complete solutions at point-of-use provide a correct response and model at least one way to solve the problem in addition to providing the DOK level for each question.

Focus on Math Concepts Lessons

The Common Core State Standards demand a balance between conceptual understanding, procedural skills and fluency, and application. ***Ready*® Focus on Math Concepts** lessons, develop understanding through questioning, discussing, writing, and problem-solving. These lessons build a solid conceptual understanding of topics so students know why a strategy or procedure works or when it is appropriate to use it—not just how to use it. This understanding empowers students to apply what they have learned to new situations.

Intensive Teacher Support

In the Teacher Resource Book, each lesson begins with a full page of orientation on the standards addressed in that lesson.

Teacher Resource Book

1 **Lesson Objectives** identify specific mathematical goals of the lesson.

2 The **Learning Progression** helps teachers see the standard in context, how the standard build on prior knowledge, particularly from the previous grade, and how it leads to the expectations for the next year.

3 **Prerequisite Skills** list key concepts and skills required for success with the lesson.

4 **Vocabulary** that is new as well as terms that should be reviewed are provided with clear definitions.

5 ***Ready Teacher Toolbox*** identifies on-level and prerequisite lessons, activities, and animated videos that are connected to the lesson and available online in the Teacher Toolbox.

6 **CCSS Focus** identifies the Common Core State Standards featured in the lesson, Additional Standards covered in activities in the Teacher Resource Book, and the Standards for Mathematical Practice integrated into the lesson.

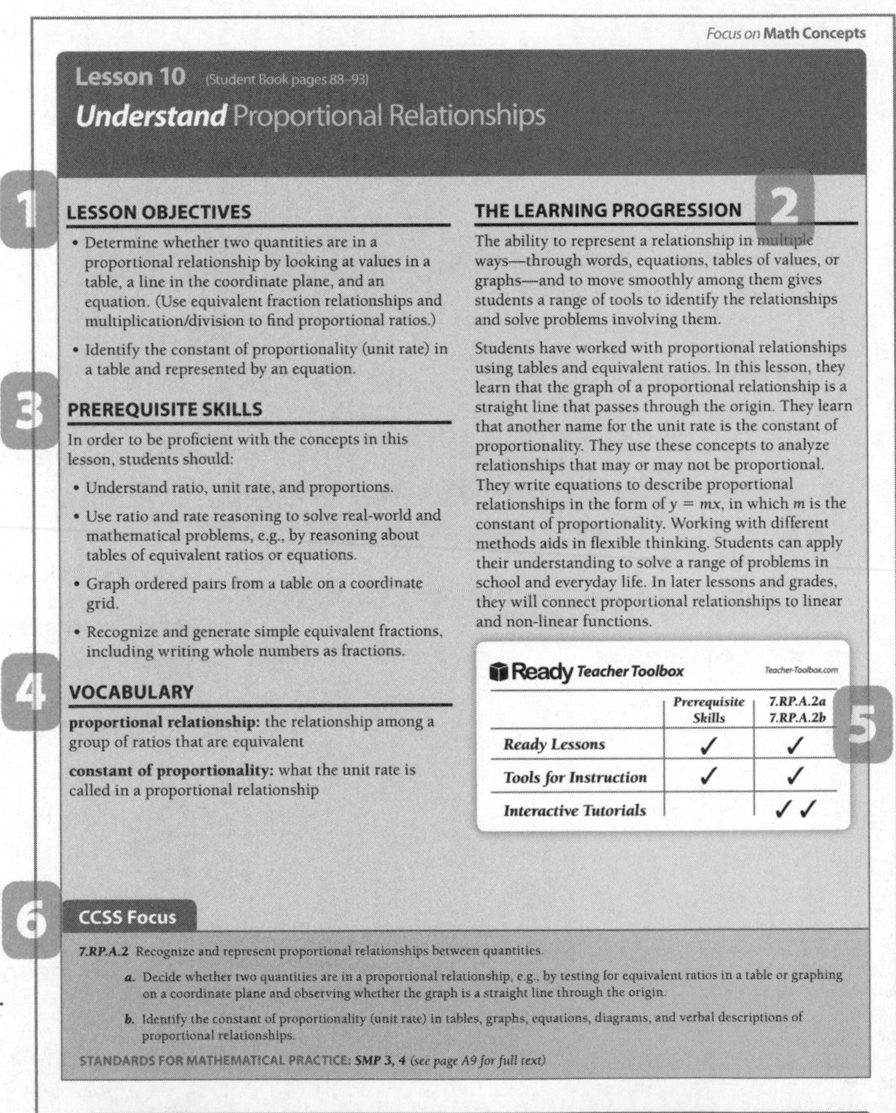
Focus on Math Concepts

Lesson 10 (Student Book pages 88–93)

Understand **Proportional Relationships**

1 **LESSON OBJECTIVES**

- Determine whether two quantities are in a proportional relationship by looking at values in a table, a line in the coordinate plane, and an equation. (Use equivalent fraction relationships and multiplication/division to find proportional ratios.)
- Identify the constant of proportionality (unit rate) in a table and represented by an equation.

3 **PREREQUISITE SKILLS**

In order to be proficient with the concepts in this lesson, students should:

- Understand ratio, unit rate, and proportions.
- Use ratio and rate reasoning to solve real-world and mathematical problems, e.g., by reasoning about tables of equivalent ratios or equations.
- Graph ordered pairs from a table on a coordinate grid.
- Recognize and generate simple equivalent fractions, including writing whole numbers as fractions.

4 **VOCABULARY**

proportional relationship: the relationship among a group of ratios that are equivalent

constant of proportionality: what the unit rate is called in a proportional relationship

THE LEARNING PROGRESSION 2

The ability to represent a relationship in multiple ways—through words, equations, tables of values, or graphs—and to move smoothly among them gives students a range of tools to identify the relationships and solve problems involving them.

Students have worked with proportional relationships using tables and equivalent ratios. In this lesson, they learn that the graph of a proportional relationship is a straight line that passes through the origin. They learn that another name for the unit rate is the constant of proportionality. They use these concepts to analyze relationships that may or may not be proportional. They write equations to describe proportional relationships in the form of $y = mx$, in which m is the constant of proportionality. Working with different methods aids in flexible thinking. Students can apply their understanding to solve a range of problems in school and everyday life. In later lessons and grades, they will connect proportional relationships to linear and non-linear functions.

Ready *Teacher Toolbox* Teacher-Toolbox.com 5

	Prerequisite Skills	*7.RP.A.2a 7.RP.A.2b*
Ready Lessons	✓	✓
Tools for Instruction	✓	✓
Interactive Tutorials		✓✓

6 **CCSS Focus**

7.RP.A.2 Recognize and represent proportional relationships between quantities.

a. Decide whether two quantities are in a proportional relationship, e.g., by testing for equivalent ratios in a table or graphing on a coordinate plane and observing whether the graph is a straight line through the origin.

b. Identify the constant of proportionality (unit rate) in tables, graphs, equations, diagrams, and verbal descriptions of proportional relationships.

STANDARDS FOR MATHEMATICAL PRACTICE: ***SMP 3, 4*** *(see page A9 for full text)*

94 L10: Understand Proportional Relationships

©Curriculum Associates, LLC Copying is not permitted.

Differentiated Instruction in *Focus on Math Concepts* Lessons

Each concept lesson concludes with Differentiated Instruction activities, giving you opportunities to extend and reinforce learning with all types of students.

Differentiated Instruction Lesson 10

1

Intervention Activity

Use graphs to model proportional and non-proportional relationships.

Materials: graph paper

Students will connect graphs, ratios, and proportional relationships.

Students should label the left half of a sheet of graph paper "Proportional" and draw and label a coordinate plane. They should plot 5 points that lie on a line passing through the origin. Beneath the graph, have them record the data in a table with rows labeled x and y. Have them find and simplify the ratios, x:y. Review the idea of the constant of proportionality and have them record their constant of proportionality below the table.

Have students label the right half "Not Proportional" and repeat the process with 5 points that are not part of a straight line passing through the origin. After they find and simplify the ratios, x:y, discuss why the data do not have a constant of proportionality.

On-Level Activity

Analyze real-world situations to see if they are proportional.

Materials: graph paper

Students will generate data from real-world situations and then analyze the relationships to see if they are proportional.

Write the following information on the board.

Video Plan A: \$2 for each video you rent

Video Plan B: \$1 for each video you rent plus a \$10 monthly fee

Have students make a table of data for each plan to show the amount it would cost to rent various numbers of videos in one month. After they have generated the data, ask students to describe two methods they can use to tell whether or not either plan represents a proportional relationship. Then have them work in pairs to analyze each set of data using both ratios and a graph. They should then explain why Plan A is a proportional relationship and name the constant of proportionality.

3

Challenge Activity

Develop and interpret a proportional relationship.

Materials: graph paper

Students will develop and interpret a proportional relationship from a point on a coordinate plane.

Have students plot one point such as (3, 6) or (5, 2) on a coordinate plane. They should connect the origin and their point and extend the line to the edge of the paper. Have them identify several other points on the line and enter the coordinates in a table with rows labeled x and y.

Have students work individually to find the following:

- the ratio of x to y in simplest form for each point
- the constant of proportionality
- an equation that relates x and y
- a real-world situation that could be modeled by their data

Have students share their work in small groups. They should explain how the graph, the table, the equation, and the real-world situation are related.

L10: Understand Proportional Relationships 101

Teacher Resource Book

1 **Intervention Activity** provides an opportunity to reteach the concepts and skills of the current lesson.

2 **On-Level Activity** has students apply the concepts of the lesson to new situations.

3 **Challenge Activity** gives students who have mastered the skills and concepts of the lesson a chance to extend their learning.

Introduction in *Focus on Math Concepts* Lessons

The introduction makes connections between what students already know and what they are about to learn. By making these connections, students develop a deeper understanding and see the relationship between mathematical concepts, rather than seeing everything as a separate, unrelated idea.

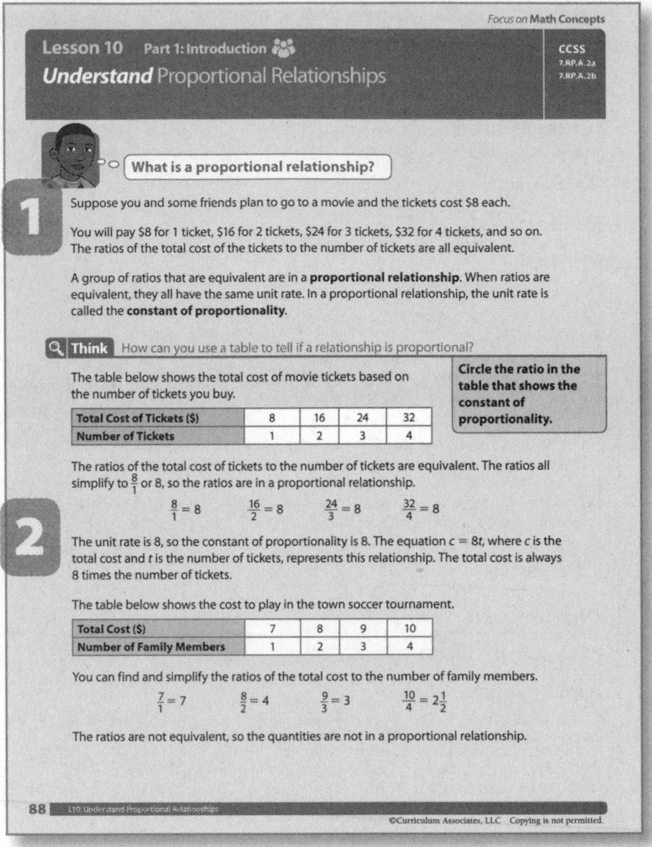

Focus on Math Concepts

Lesson 10 Part 1: Introduction

Understand Proportional Relationships

CCSS 7.RP.A.2a 7.RP.A.2b

What is a proportional relationship?

1 Suppose you and some friends plan to go to a movie and the tickets cost $8 each.

You will pay $8 for 1 ticket, $16 for 2 tickets, $24 for 3 tickets, $32 for 4 tickets, and so on. The ratios of the total cost of the tickets to the number of tickets are all equivalent.

A group of ratios that are equivalent are in a **proportional relationship**. When ratios are equivalent, they all have the same unit rate. In a proportional relationship, the unit rate is called the **constant of proportionality.**

Think How can you use a table to tell if a relationship is proportional?

The table below shows the total cost of movie tickets based on the number of tickets you buy.

Circle the ratio in the table that shows the constant of proportionality.

Total Cost of Tickets ($)	8	16	24	32
Number of Tickets	1	2	3	4

The ratios of the total cost of tickets to the number of tickets are equivalent. The ratios all simplify to $\frac{8}{1}$ or 8, so the ratios are in a proportional relationship.

$\frac{8}{1} = 8$ $\frac{16}{2} = 8$ $\frac{24}{3} = 8$ $\frac{32}{4} = 8$

2 The unit rate is 8, so the constant of proportionality is 8. The equation $c = 8t$, where c is the total cost and t is the number of tickets, represents this relationship. The total cost is always 8 times the number of tickets.

The table below shows the cost to play in the town soccer tournament.

Total Cost ($)	7	8	9	10
Number of Family Members	1	2	3	4

You can find and simplify the ratios of the total cost to the number of family members.

$\frac{7}{1} = 7$ $\frac{8}{2} = 4$ $\frac{9}{3} = 3$ $\frac{10}{4} = 2\frac{1}{2}$

The ratios are not equivalent, so the quantities are not in a proportional relationship.

88 L10: Understand Proportional Relationships

©Curriculum Associates, LLC Copying is not permitted.

Student Book

1 Each **Focus on Math Concepts** lesson begins with a key question that gets students thinking about the new concept.

2 Students develop deeper understanding by connecting new concepts to prior knowledge and skills.

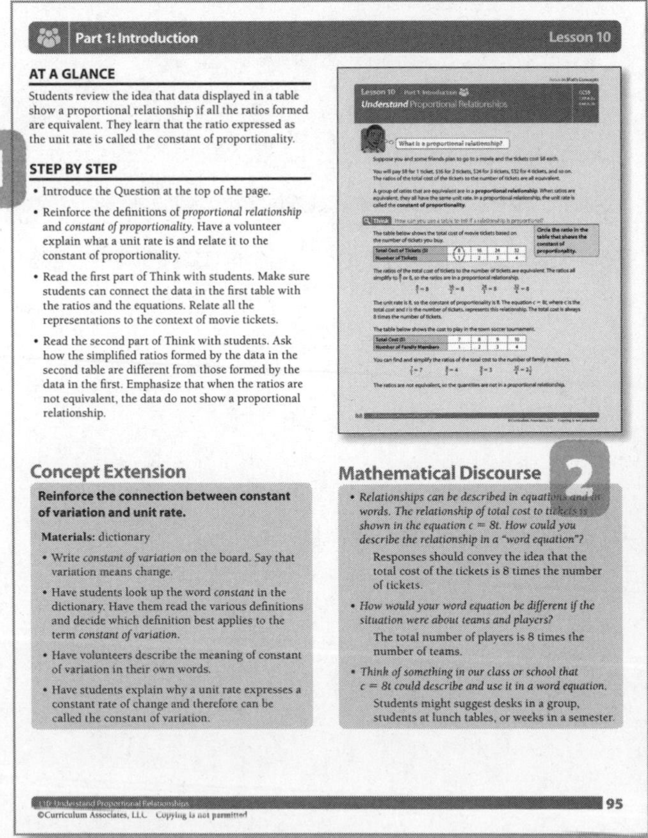

Part 1: Introduction Lesson 10

AT A GLANCE

Students review the idea that data displayed in a table show a proportional relationship if all the ratios formed are equivalent. They learn that the ratio expressed as the unit rate is called the constant of proportionality.

1 **STEP BY STEP**

- Introduce the Question at the top of the page.
- Reinforce the definitions of *proportional relationship* and *constant of proportionality*. Have a volunteer explain what a unit rate is and relate it to the constant of proportionality.
- Read the first part of Think with students. Make sure students can connect the data in the first table with the ratios and the equations. Relate all the representations to the context of movie tickets.
- Read the second part of Think with students. Ask how the simplified ratios formed by the data in the second table are different from those formed by the data in the first. Emphasize that when the ratios are not equivalent, the data do not show a proportional relationship.

Concept Extension

Reinforce the connection between constant of variation and unit rate.

Materials: dictionary

- Write *constant of variation* on the board. Say that variation means change.
- Have students look up the word *constant* in the dictionary. Have them read the various definitions and decide which definition best applies to the term *constant of variation.*
- Have volunteers describe the meaning of constant of variation in their own words.
- Have students explain why a unit rate expresses a constant rate of change and therefore can be called the constant of variation.

Mathematical Discourse 2

- *Relationships can be described in equations and in words. The relationship of total cost to tickets is shown in the equation $c = 8t$. How could you describe the relationship in a "word equation"?*

  Responses should convey the idea that the total cost of the tickets is 8 times the number of tickets.
- *How would your word equation be different if the situation were about teams and players?*

  The total number of players is 8 times the number of teams.
- *Think of something in our class or school that $c = 8t$ could describe and use it in a word equation.*

  Students might suggest desks in a group, students at lunch tables, or weeks in a semester.

L10: Understand Proportional Relationships 95

©Curriculum Associates, LLC Copying is not permitted.

Teacher Resource Book

1 **Step by Step** gives suggestions for leading class discussions for each section of the lesson.

2 **Mathematical Discourse** questions promote thoughtful dialogue and exchange of ideas and are specific to each page.

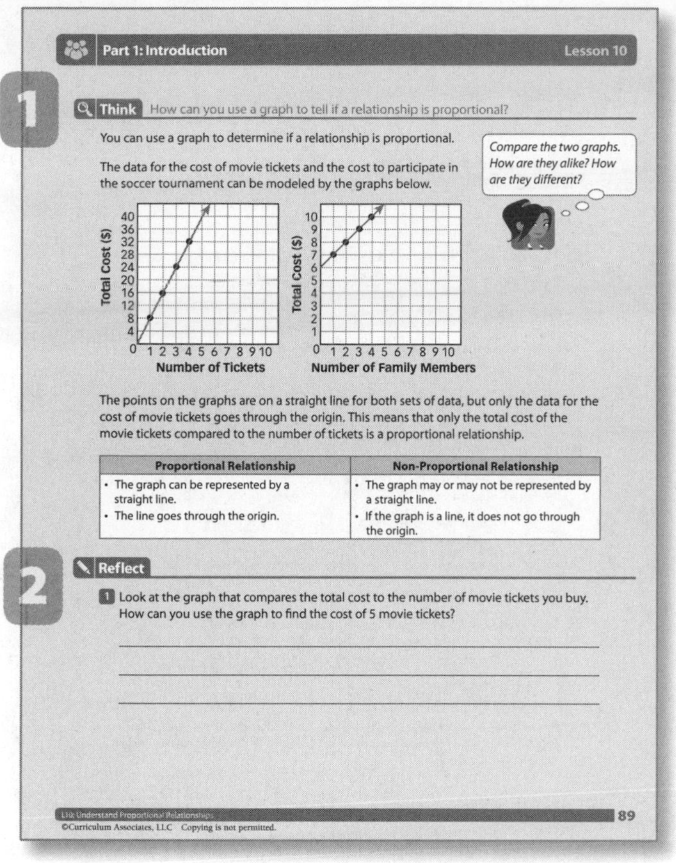

Part 1: Introduction Lesson 10

1

Think How can you use a graph to tell if a relationship is proportional?

You can use a graph to determine if a relationship is proportional.

The data for the cost of movie tickets and the cost to participate in the soccer tournament can be modeled by the graphs below.

Compare the two graphs. How are they alike? How are they different?

The points on the graphs are on a straight line for both sets of data, but only the data for the cost of movie tickets goes through the origin. This means that only the total cost of the movie tickets compared to the number of tickets is a proportional relationship.

Proportional Relationship	Non-Proportional Relationship
• The graph can be represented by a straight line. • The line goes through the origin.	• The graph may or may not be represented by a straight line. • If the graph is a line, it does not go through the origin.

2

Reflect

1 Look at the graph that compares the total cost to the number of movie tickets you buy. How can you use the graph to find the cost of 5 movie tickets?

L10: Understand Proportional Relationships 89

©Curriculum Associates, LLC Copying is not permitted.

Student Book

1 The **Think** sections of the introduction ask students to think about new concepts and connections.

2 The **Reflect** question asks students to summarize what they have learned by explaining the concept or describe how to use the concept in a new situation.

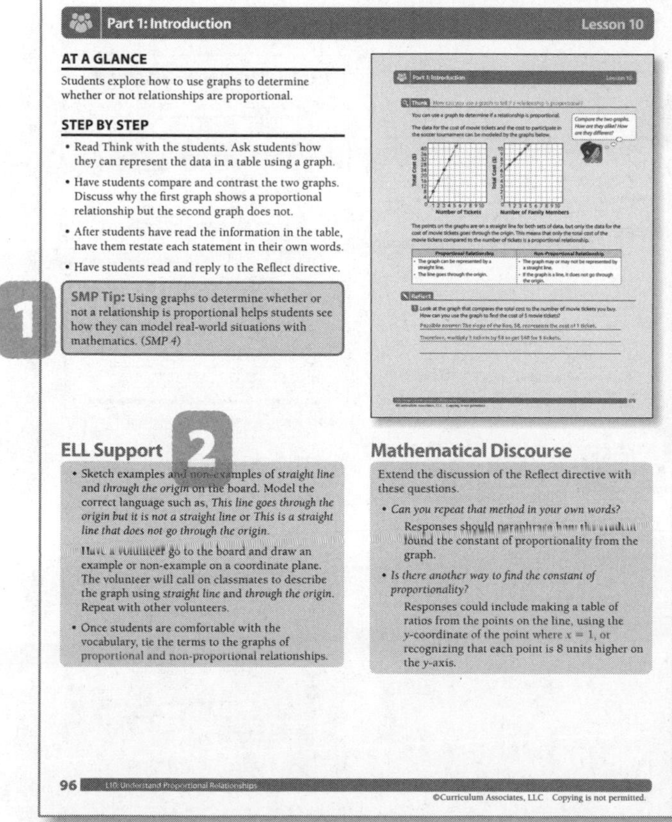

Part 1: Introduction Lesson 10

AT A GLANCE

Students explore how to use graphs to determine whether or not relationships are proportional.

STEP BY STEP

- Read Think with the students. Ask students how they can represent the data in a table using a graph.
- Have students compare and contrast the two graphs. Discuss why the first graph shows a proportional relationship but the second graph does not.
- After students have read the information in the table, have them restate each statement in their own words.
- Have students read and reply to the Reflect directive.

1

SMP Tip: Using graphs to determine whether or not a relationship is proportional helps students see how they can model real-world situations with mathematics. *(SMP 4)*

ELL Support 2

- Sketch examples and non-examples of *straight line* and *through the origin* on the board. Model the correct language such as, *This line goes through the origin but it is not a straight line* or *This is a straight line that does not go through the origin.*
  Have a volunteer go to the board and draw an example or non-example on a coordinate plane. The volunteer will call on classmates to describe the graph using *straight line* and *through the origin*. Repeat with other volunteers.
- Once students are comfortable with the vocabulary, tie the terms to the graphs of proportional and non-proportional relationships.

Mathematical Discourse

Extend the discussion of the Reflect directive with these questions.

- *Can you repeat that method in your own words?*
  Responses should paraphrase how the student found the constant of proportionality from the graph.
- *Is there another way to find the constant of proportionality?*
  Responses could include making a table of ratios from the points on the line, using the y-coordinate of the point where $x = 1$, or recognizing that each point is 8 units higher on the y-axis.

96 L10: Understand Proportional Relationships

©Curriculum Associates, LLC Copying is not permitted.

Teacher Resource Book

1 **SMP Tips** help teachers recognize a specific opportunity to reinforce one of the Standards for Mathematical Practice.

2 Point-of-use **ELL Support** helps the teacher recognize strategies to use to enhance learning with English Language Learners.

Student Book

1 In **Explore It**, students build understanding by answering thought-provoking questions about new problem-solving strategies and models.

2 Students apply what they have learned to new problems, explaining their solutions and often the reasons for using the strategies they choose.

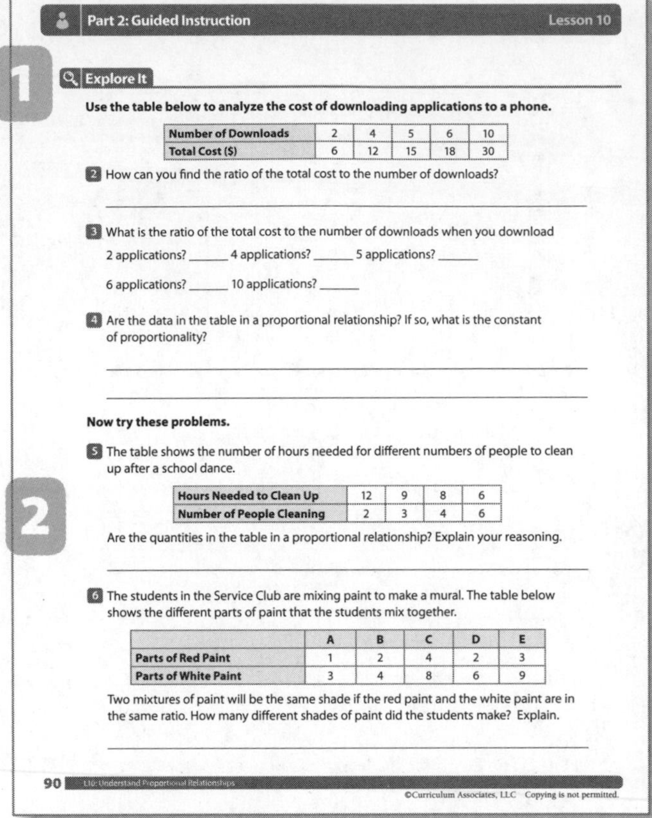

Part 2: Guided Instruction — Lesson 10

1 **Explore It**

Use the table below to analyze the cost of downloading applications to a phone.

Number of Downloads	2	4	5	6	10
Total Cost ($)	6	12	15	18	30

2 How can you find the ratio of the total cost to the number of downloads?

3 What is the ratio of the total cost to the number of downloads when you download 2 applications? _____ 4 applications? _____ 5 applications? _____ 6 applications? _____ 10 applications? _____

4 Are the data in the table in a proportional relationship? If so, what is the constant of proportionality?

Now try these problems.

2

5 The table shows the number of hours needed for different numbers of people to clean up after a school dance.

Hours Needed to Clean Up	12	9	8	6
Number of People Cleaning	2	3	4	6

Are the quantities in the table in a proportional relationship? Explain your reasoning.

6 The students in the Service Club are mixing paint to make a mural. The table below shows the different parts of paint that the students mix together.

	A	B	C	D	E
Parts of Red Paint	1	2	4	2	3
Parts of White Paint	3	4	8	6	9

Two mixtures of paint will be the same shade if the red paint and the white paint are in the same ratio. How many different shades of paint did the students make? Explain.

90 L10: Understand Proportional Relationships ©Curriculum Associates, LLC Copying is not permitted.

Teacher Resource Book

1 **Step by Step** gives teaching suggestions and questions for leading class discussions for each page.

2 **Student Misconception Alerts** notify teachers of errors in student thinking that produce conceptual misunderstanding.

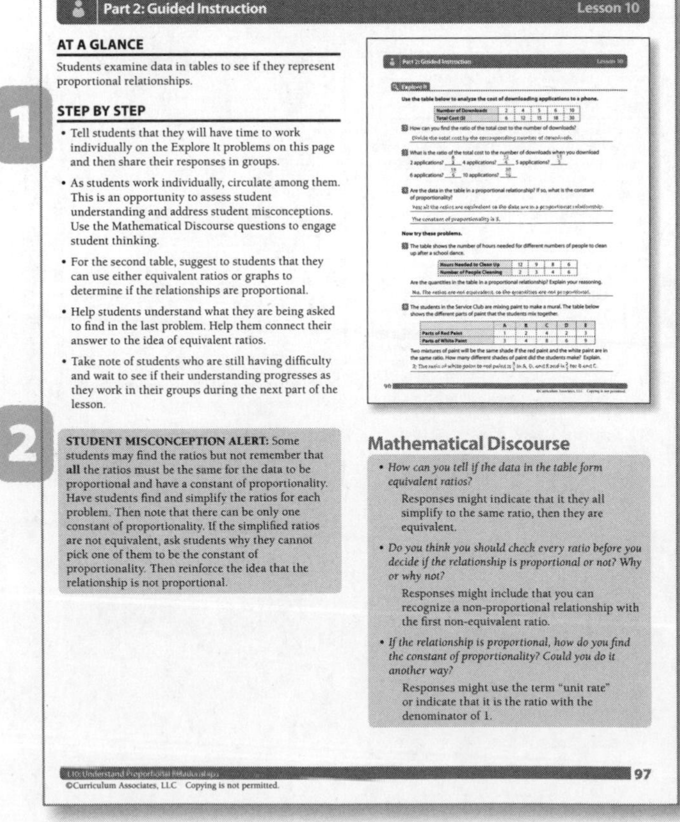

Part 2: Guided Instruction — Lesson 10

AT A GLANCE

Students examine data in tables to see if they represent proportional relationships.

1 **STEP BY STEP**

- Tell students that they will have time to work individually on the Explore It problems on this page and then share their responses in groups.
- As students work individually, circulate among them. This is an opportunity to assess student understanding and address student misconceptions. Use the Mathematical Discourse questions to engage student thinking.
- For the second table, suggest to students that they can use either equivalent ratios or graphs to determine if the relationships are proportional.
- Help students understand what they are being asked to find in the last problem. Help them connect their answer to the idea of equivalent ratios.
- Take note of students who are still having difficulty and wait to see if their understanding progresses as they work in their groups during the next part of the lesson.

2 **STUDENT MISCONCEPTION ALERT:** Some students may find the ratios but not remember that **all** the ratios must be the same for the data to be proportional and have a constant of proportionality. Have students find and simplify the ratios for each problem. Then note that there can be only one constant of proportionality. If the simplified ratios are not equivalent, ask students why they cannot pick one of them to be the constant of proportionality. Then reinforce the idea that the relationship is not proportional.

Mathematical Discourse

- *How can you tell if the data in the table form equivalent ratios?*

  Responses might indicate that it they all simplify to the same ratio, then they are equivalent.

- *Do you think you should check every ratio before you decide if the relationship is proportional or not? Why or why not?*

  Responses might include that you can recognize a non-proportional relationship with the first non-equivalent ratio.

- *If the relationship is proportional, how do you find the constant of proportionality? Could you do it another way?*

  Responses might use the term "unit rate" or indicate that it is the ratio with the denominator of 1.

L10: Understand Proportional Relationships 97 ©Curriculum Associates, LLC Copying is not permitted.

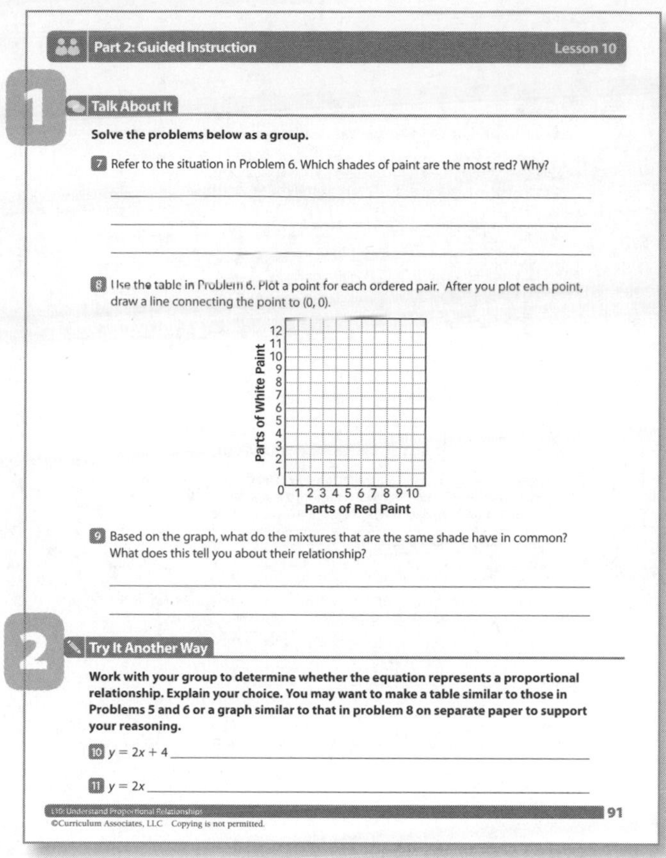

Part 2: Guided Instruction — Lesson 10

1 Talk About It

Solve the problems below as a group.

7 Refer to the situation in Problem 6. Which shades of paint are the most red? Why?

8 Use the table in Problem 6. Plot a point for each ordered pair. After you plot each point, draw a line connecting the point to (0, 0).

9 Based on the graph, what do the mixtures that are the same shade have in common? What does this tell you about their relationship?

2 Try It Another Way

Work with your group to determine whether the equation represents a proportional relationship. Explain your choice. You may want to make a table similar to those in Problems 5 and 6 or a graph similar to that in problem 8 on separate paper to support your reasoning.

10 $y = 2x + 4$

11 $y = 2x$

L10: Understand Proportional Relationships 91

©Curriculum Associates, LLC Copying is not permitted.

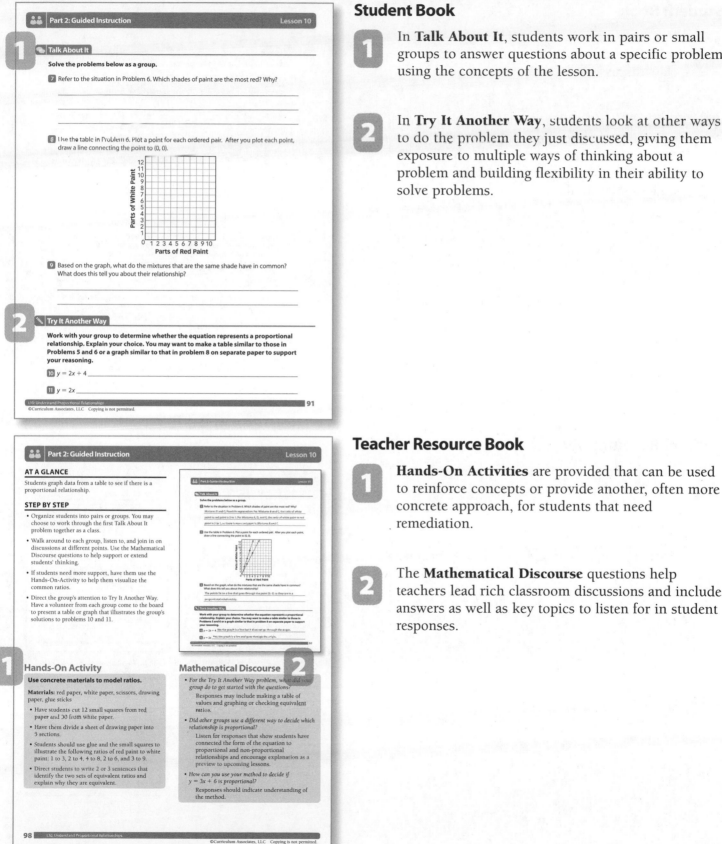

Student Book

1 In **Talk About It**, students work in pairs or small groups to answer questions about a specific problem using the concepts of the lesson.

2 In **Try It Another Way**, students look at other ways to do the problem they just discussed, giving them exposure to multiple ways of thinking about a problem and building flexibility in their ability to solve problems.

Part 2: Guided Instruction — Lesson 10

AT A GLANCE

Students graph data from a table to see if there is a proportional relationship.

STEP BY STEP

- Organize students into pairs or groups. You may choose to work through the first Talk About It problem together as a class.
- Walk around to each group, listen to, and join in on discussions at different points. Use the Mathematical Discourse questions to help support or extend students' thinking.
- If students need more support, have them use the Hands-On-Activity to help them visualize the common ratios.
- Direct the group's attention to Try It Another Way. Have a volunteer from each group come to the board to present a table or graph that illustrates the group's solutions to problems 10 and 11.

1 **Hands-On Activity**

Use concrete materials to model ratios.

Materials: red paper, white paper, scissors, drawing paper, glue sticks

- Have students cut 12 small squares from red paper and 30 from white paper.
- Have them divide a sheet of drawing paper into 5 sections.
- Students should use glue and the small squares to illustrate the following ratios of red paint to white paint: 1 to 3, 2 to 4, 4 to 8, 2 to 6, and 3 to 9.
- Direct students to write 2 or 3 sentences that identify the two sets of equivalent ratios and explain why they are equivalent.

Mathematical Discourse 2

- *For the Try It Another Way problem, what did your group do to get started with the questions?*

  Responses may include making a table of values and graphing or checking equivalent ratios.

- *Did other groups use a different way to decide which relationship is proportional?*

  Listen for responses that show students have connected the form of the equation to proportional and non-proportional relationships and encourage explanation as a preview to upcoming lessons.

- *How can you use your method to decide if $y = 3x + 6$ is proportional?*

  Responses should indicate understanding of the method.

98 L10: Understand Proportional Relationships

©Curriculum Associates, LLC Copying is not permitted.

Teacher Resource Book

1 **Hands-On Activities** are provided that can be used to reinforce concepts or provide another, often more concrete approach, for students that need remediation.

2 The **Mathematical Discourse** questions help teachers lead rich classroom discussions and include answers as well as key topics to listen for in student responses.

Student Book

1 In **Connect It**, students apply higher-order thinking skills and engage in meaningful class discussions.

2 Students develop deeper understanding by connecting to prior knowledge and skills. Students use the Standards for Mathematical Practice to solve problems designed to promote higher-order thinking.

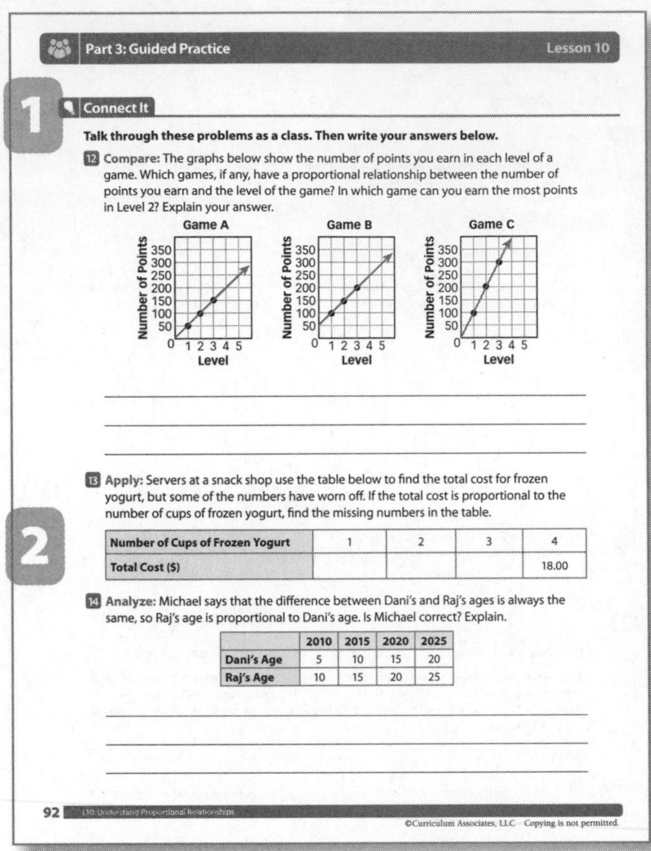

Part 3: Guided Practice — Lesson 10

1 **Connect It**

Talk through these problems as a class. Then write your answers below.

12 **Compare:** The graphs below show the number of points you earn in each level of a game. Which games, if any, have a proportional relationship between the number of points you earn and the level of the game? In which game can you earn the most points in Level 2? Explain your answer.

2

13 **Apply:** Servers at a snack shop use the table below to find the total cost for frozen yogurt, but some of the numbers have worn off. If the total cost is proportional to the number of cups of frozen yogurt, find the missing numbers in the table.

Number of Cups of Frozen Yogurt	1	2	3	4
Total Cost ($)				18.00

14 **Analyze:** Michael says that the difference between Dani's and Raj's ages is always the same, so Raj's age is proportional to Dani's age. Is Michael correct? Explain.

	2010	2015	2020	2025
Dani's Age	5	10	15	20
Raj's Age	10	15	20	25

92 L10: Understand Proportional Relationships ©Curriculum Associates, LLC Copying is not permitted.

Teacher Resource Book

1 **Step by Step** gives teacher support and suggestions for leading class discussions for each page.

2 **SMP Tips** help teachers recognize a specific opportunity to reinforce one of the Standards for Mathematical Practice.

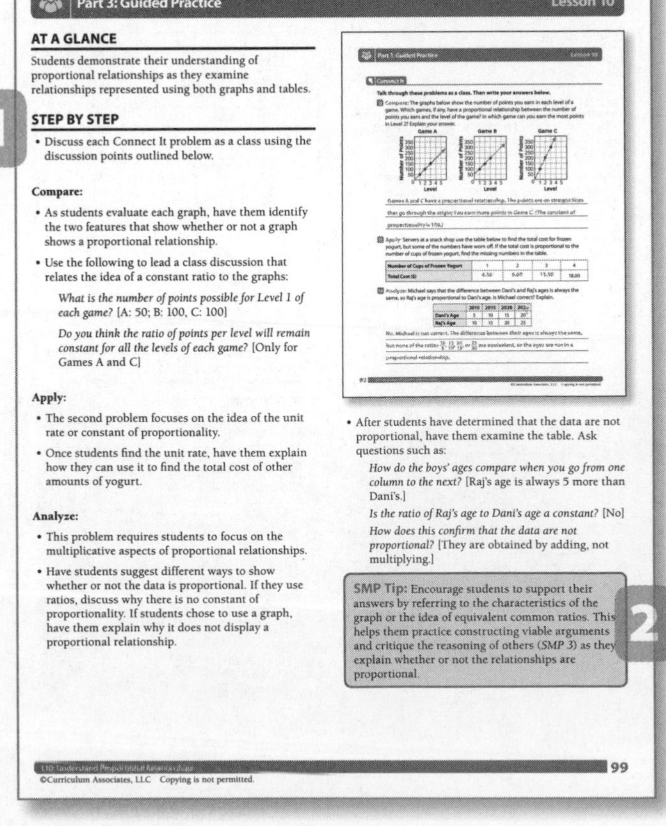

Part 3: Guided Practice — Lesson 10

AT A GLANCE

Students demonstrate their understanding of proportional relationships as they examine relationships represented using both graphs and tables.

1 **STEP BY STEP**

- Discuss each Connect It problem as a class using the discussion points outlined below.

Compare:

- As students evaluate each graph, have them identify the two features that show whether or not a graph shows a proportional relationship.
- Use the following to lead a class discussion that relates the idea of a constant ratio to the graphs:

  What is the number of points possible for Level 1 of each game? [A: 50; B: 100, C: 100]

  Do you think the ratio of points per level will remain constant for all the levels of each game? [Only for Games A and C]

Apply:

- The second problem focuses on the idea of the unit rate or constant of proportionality.
- Once students find the unit rate, have them explain how they can use it to find the total cost of other amounts of yogurt.

Analyze:

- This problem requires students to focus on the multiplicative aspects of proportional relationships.
- Have students suggest different ways to show whether or not the data is proportional. If they use ratios, discuss why there is no constant of proportionality. If students chose to use a graph, have them explain why it does not display a proportional relationship.
- After students have determined that the data are not proportional, have them examine the table. Ask questions such as:

  How do the boys' ages compare when you go from one column to the next? [Raj's age is always 5 more than Dani's.]

  Is the ratio of Raj's age to Dani's age a constant? [No]

  How does this confirm that the data are not proportional? [They are obtained by adding, not multiplying.]

SMP Tip: Encourage students to support their answers by referring to the characteristics of the graph or the idea of equivalent common ratios. This helps them practice constructing viable arguments and critique the reasoning of others (*SMP 3*) as they explain whether or not the relationships are proportional. 2

L10: Understand Proportional Relationships ©Curriculum Associates, LLC Copying is not permitted. 99

Common Core Performance Task in *Focus on Math Concepts* Lessons

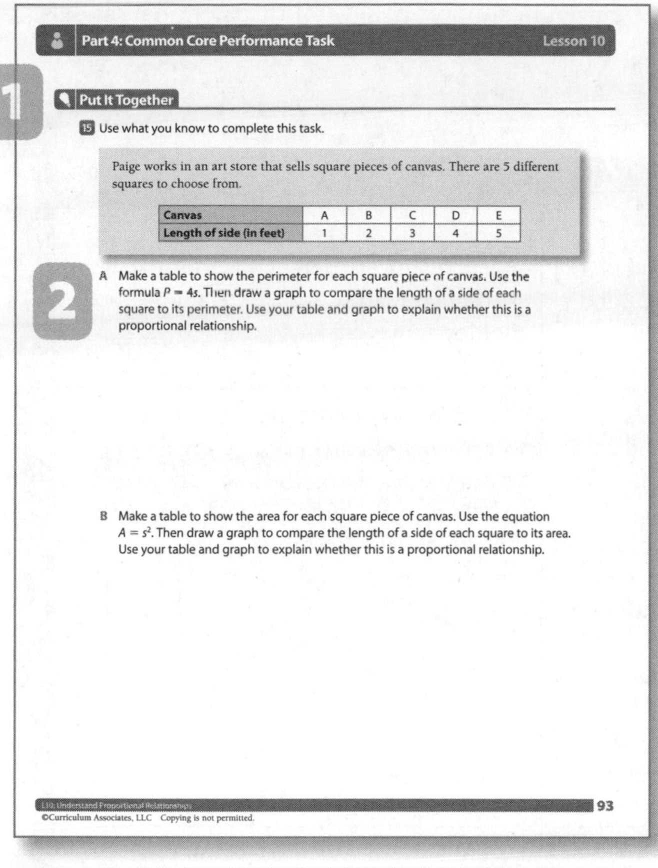

Part 4: Common Core Performance Task — Lesson 10

1 Put It Together

15 Use what you know to complete this task.

Paige works in an art store that sells square pieces of canvas. There are 5 different squares to choose from.

Canvas	A	B	C	D	E
Length of side (in feet)	1	2	3	4	5

2 A Make a table to show the perimeter for each square piece of canvas. Use the formula $P = 4s$. Then draw a graph to compare the length of a side of each square to its perimeter. Use your table and graph to explain whether this is a proportional relationship.

B Make a table to show the area for each square piece of canvas. Use the equation $A = s^2$. Then draw a graph to compare the length of a side of each square to its area. Use your table and graph to explain whether this is a proportional relationship.

L10: Understand Proportional Relationships 93
©Curriculum Associates, LLC Copying is not permitted.

Student Book

1 In **Put It Together**, students are asked to think through a critical-thinking problem that often has multiple entries and/or more than one correct answer.

2 The tasks are scaffolded. Part A is typically a simpler task, and Part B asks students to use information from Part A to answer a second question.

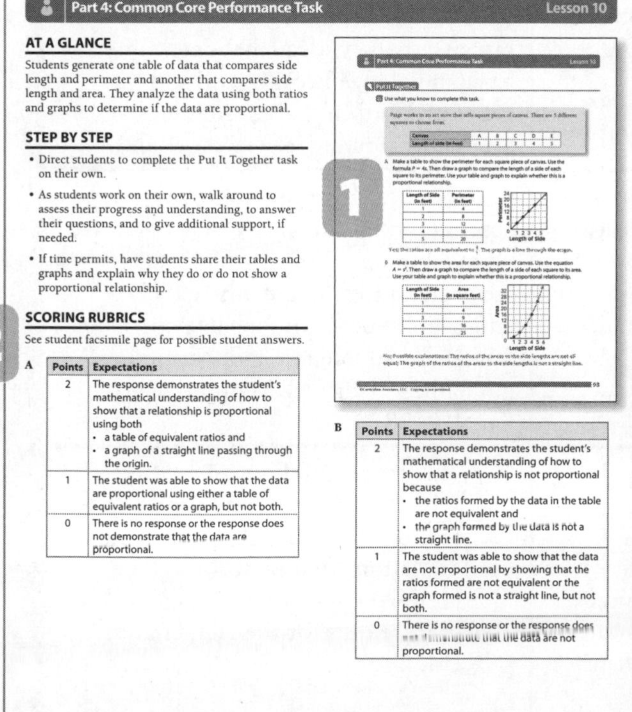

Part 4: Common Core Performance Task — Lesson 10

AT A GLANCE

Students generate one table of data that compares side length and perimeter and another that compares side length and area. They analyze the data using both ratios and graphs to determine if the data are proportional.

STEP BY STEP

- Direct students to complete the Put It Together task on their own.
- As students work on their own, walk around to assess their progress and understanding, to answer their questions, and to give additional support, if needed.
- If time permits, have students share their tables and graphs and explain why they do or do not show a proportional relationship.

2 **SCORING RUBRICS**

See student facsimile page for possible student answers.

A

Points	Expectations
2	The response demonstrates the student's mathematical understanding of how to show that a relationship is proportional using both • a table of equivalent ratios and • a graph of a straight line passing through the origin.
1	The student was able to show that the data are proportional using either a table of equivalent ratios or a graph, but not both.
0	There is no response or the response does not demonstrate that the data are proportional.

B

Points	Expectations
2	The response demonstrates the student's mathematical understanding of how to show that a relationship is not proportional because • the ratios formed by the data in the table are not equivalent and • the graph formed by the data is not a straight line.
1	The student was able to show that the data are not proportional by showing that the ratios formed are not equivalent or the graph formed is not a straight line, but not both.
0	There is no response or the response does not demonstrate that the data are not proportional.

100 L10: Understand Proportional Relationships
©Curriculum Associates, LLC Copying is not permitted.

Teacher Resource Book

1 Sample responses and worked-out solutions are provided for the performance task.

2 **Scoring Rubrics** offer guidance for evaluating students' responses.

Supporting Research

Overview

Ready*® *Common Core Mathematics is founded on research from a variety of federal initiatives, national literacy organizations, and literacy experts. As a result, this program may be used in support of several instructional models.

***Ready*® Uses . . .**	**Examples**	**Research Says . . .**
Instructional Strategies		
Scaffolded Instruction is the gradual withdrawal of support through modeled, guided, and independent instruction.	***Ready*** lessons follow the pattern of modeled and guided instruction, modeled and guided practice, and independent practice.	"Successful teachers help to create independent learners . . . . Contingent scaffolded instruction . . . is a powerful tool for achieving this goal." (Beed et al., 1991)
Mathematical Discourse in instruction uses questioning, listening, writing, and reflection to encourage conversation about mathematics.	***Ready*** lessons include regular verbal exchange of ideas and sharing of understanding in whole group, small group, and pair settings. **Talk About It** leads students through discussions of key ideas. **Pair/Share** prompts students to compare answers and reasoning to identify misconceptions. **Mathematical Discourse** in the Teacher Resource Book suggests thoughtful question prompts.	"The process of encouraging students to verbalize their thinking—by talking, writing, or drawing the steps they used in solving a problem—was consistently effective." (NCTM, 2007)
Applying Prior Knowledge These are experiences and knowledge that a student brings with himself or herself to learn about a topic.	In each lesson, **Explore It** introduces a new skill by guiding students to solve a new problem by applying prior knowledge.	"What and how students are taught should reflect not only the topics that fall within a certain academic discipline, but also the key ideas that determine how knowledge is organized and generated within that discipline." (Schmidt, Houang, & Cogan, 2002)
Collaborative Learning Students work together in pairs or small groups to attain their individual goals.	**Talk About It** leads students through discussions of key ideas. **Pair/Share** prompts students to compare answers and reasoning to identify misconceptions.	Collaborative learning improves computational skills. Use of cooperative or collaborative learning has been advocated in various mathematics education reports and in state curricular frameworks, policies, and instructional guidelines. (National Math Advisory Panel, 2008)
Visual Representation is using an image to help describe or define a mathematical problem or relationship, or to depict a real-life problem situation.	***Ready*** routinely uses pictorial (**Picture It**) and other visual models such as number lines (**Model It**) to illustrate mathematical concepts. **Visual Support** in the Teacher Resource Books suggests additional visual representations.	"Graphic representations of mathematical concepts and problems . . . are crucial components of programs used in nations that perform well on international comparisons, such as Singapore, Korea, or the Netherlands." (NCTM, 2007)

Ready® Uses . . .	Examples	Research Says . . .
Instructional Strategies (continued)		
Multiple Representations are the ways in which a teacher or student represents a math idea, including spoken, written, symbolic, and concrete formats.	***Ready*** routinely uses pictorial (**Picture It**) and visual models (**Model It**) to illustrate mathematical concepts. **Connect It** develops the symbolic representation. **Hands-On Activities** and **Visual Support** in the Teacher Resource Book offer suggestions for additional representations.	"The usefulness of numerical ideas is enhanced when students encounter and use multiple representations for the same concept." (National Research Council, 2001)
Formative Assessment (or **Progress Monitoring)** is a strategy that involves frequent, in-classroom progress checks of students' understanding and mastery of math concepts and skills.	**Solutions and Explanations** with **Error Alerts** in the Teacher Resource Books create ongoing formative assessment opportunities, with support for correcting misconceptions throughout each lesson. **Assessment and Remediation** charts at the end of the lesson help the teacher assess mastery of the skill, identify specific misconceptions, and remediate on the spot as necessary.	Teachers' regular use of formative assessment improves their students' learning, especially if teachers have additional guidance on using the assessment to design and to individualize instruction. (National Mathematics Advisory Panel, 2008)
Differentiated Instruction is an approach to teaching that gives students multiple ways to access and make sense of mathematical ideas.	***Ready*** student books provide verbal, visual, and symbolic representations of each new skill and concept. **Hands-On Activities**, **Visual Support**, **Concept Extension**, and **Challenge Activities** in the Teacher Resource Books provide additional differentiation options.	Many teachers and teacher educators have recently identified differentiated instruction as a method of helping more students in diverse classroom settings experience success. (Hall et al., 2003)
Hands-On Activities are any activities in which the student is handling manipulatives used to explore mathematical quantities, relationships, or operations.	Found throughout the Teacher Resource Book.	"The benefit of this [hands-on, manipulative] approach may be that its intensity and concreteness help students maintain a framework in their working memory for solving problems of this type." (NCTM, 2007)
ELL Support consists of tips to provide teachers the content knowledge and pedagogy to minimize obstacles to learning math due to language or cultural issues.	The ***Ready*** student book uses pictorial and visual representations combined with direct simple text to clearly present concepts. Point-of-use **ELL Support** tips for teachers are found throughout the Teacher Resource Book as appropriate.	Expanded opportunities should be available to English language learners (ELL students) who need them to develop mathematical understanding and proficiency. (NCTM, 2008)

Ready® Uses . . .	Examples	Research Says . . .
Instructional Features		
Standards for Mathematical Practice (SMPs) identify habits of mind and everyday ways of approaching math that are hallmarks of successful math students.	Throughout ***Ready*** Student Book, SMPs are built into the instruction and problems. Teacher Resource Books feature **SMP Tips** in every lesson to alert teachers to particular instances of each SMP.	"These practices rest on important 'processes and proficiencies' with longstanding importance in mathematics education." (CCSS, 2010)
Computational Fluency is having quick recall of number facts and knowledge and ability to apply multiple computational methods involving whole numbers, decimals, fractions, and other numbers as appropriate to the grade level.	***Ready*** lessons all directly address computation skills, develop the conceptual understanding to support computation, or provide applications of computation skills.	"Basic skills with numbers continue to be vitally important for a variety of everyday uses. They also provide a crucial foundation for the higher-level mathematics essential for success in the workplace, which must now also be part of a basic education." (Ball et al., 2005)
Conceptual Understanding is the knowledge of why math processes and rules work.	All ***Ready*** lessons begin by laying a foundation of conceptual understanding of the mathematical principles underlying the skill being addressed. Special **Focus on Math Concepts** lessons put a special emphasis on these principles. **Concept Extension** features in the Teacher's Resource Book further support conceptual understanding.	"To prepare students for Algebra, the curriculum must simultaneously develop conceptual understanding, computational fluency, and problem-solving skills." (National Mathematics Advisory Panel, 2008)
Problem Solving (or **Application**) is the process of formulating a real-life problem as a mathematical problem, then performing the calculations necessary, and interpreting the result to find the solution to the problem.	***Ready*** presents new math problems in real-world contexts and models finding the solution. (**Explore It**, **Picture It**, **Model It**, **Connect It**) Students then practice with similar problems in **Try It**. Practice problems always include real-world problems.	". . . An important part of our conception of mathematical proficiency involves the ability to formulate and solve problems coming from daily life or other domains, including mathematics itself." (National Research Council, 2001)
Answer Explanations for Students As a part of scaffolded instruction, students receive immediate feedback on their answer choices and the reasoning behind correct and incorrect answers.	In the **Guided Instruction**, **Guided Practice**, **Common Core Practice**, and **Interim Assessments** sections of the Teacher Resource Book, answer explanations are given for each question.	When students receive direct instruction about the reasons why an answer choice is correct or incorrect, they demonstrate long-term retention and understanding of newly learned content. (Pashler et al., 2007)

References

Ball, D. L., Ferrini-Mundy, J., Kilpatrick, J., Milgram, R. J., Schmid, W., & Schaar, R. (2005). Reaching for common ground in K–12 mathematics education. *Notices of the American Mathematical Society*, 52(9).

Beed, P. L., Hawkins, E. M., & Roller, C. M. (1991). Moving learners toward independence: The power of scaffolded instruction. *The Reading Teacher*, 44(9), 648–655.

Eastburn, J. A. (2011). The effects of a concrete, representational, abstract (CRA) instructional model on tier 2 first-grade math students in a response to intervention model: Educational implications for number sense and computational fluency. Dissertation. *ProQuest Information & Learning*, AAI3408708.

Furner, J. M., Yahya, N., & Duffy, M. L. (2005). 20 Ways to teach mathematics: strategies to reach all students. *Intervention in School and Clinic*, 41(1).

Hall, T., Strangman, N., & Meyer, A. (2003). Differentiated instruction and implications for UDL implementation. National Center on Accessing the General Curriculum. Accessed at: *http://aim.cast.org/learn/historyarchive/backgroundpapers/differentiated*

Hess, K. K., Carlock, D., Jones, B., & Walkup, J. R. (2009). *What exactly do "fewer, clearer, and higher standards" really look like in the classroom? Using a cognitive rigor matrix to analyze curriculum, plan lessons, and implement assessments.* Accessed at: *http://www.nciea.org/cgi-bin/pubspage.cgi?sortby=pub_date.*

National Council of Teachers of Mathematics. (2007). Effective strategies for teaching students with difficulties in mathematics. Accessed at: *http://www.nctm.org/news/content.aspx?id=8452.*

———. (2008). Teaching mathematics to English language learners. Accessed at: *http://www.nctm.org/about/content.aspx?id=16135*

National Governors Association Center for Best Practices and Council of Chief State School Officers. (2010). *Common Core State Standards for Mathematics.* Accessed at: *http://www.corestandards.org/the-standards.*

———. (2012). *Publisher's Criteria for the Common Core State Standards in Mathematics, K–8.* Accessed at: *http://www.corestandards.org/resources.*

National Mathematics Advisory Panel. (2008). Foundations for success: The final report of the National Mathematics Advisory Panel. Accessed at: *http://www2.ed.gov/about/bdscomm/list/mathpanel/index.html.*

National Research Council. (2001). *Adding it Up: Helping Children Learn Mathematics.* Mathematics Learning Study Committee: Kilpatrick, J., Swafford, J., & Findell, B. (eds.). Washington, D.C.: National Academy Press.

Partnership for Assessment of Readiness for College and Careers. (2011). *PARCC model content frameworks: English language arts/literacy grades 3–11.* Accessed at: *http://www.parcconline.org/parcc-model-content-frameworks.*

Pashler, H., Bain, P., Bottge, B., Graesser, A., Koedinger, K., McDaniel, M., & Metcalfe, J. (2007). *Organizing instruction and study to improve student learning* (NCER 2007–2004). Washington, D.C.: National Center for Education Research, Institute of Education Sciences, U.S. Department of Education. Retrieved from *http://ncer.ed.gov.*

Robertson, K. (2009). Math instruction for English language learners. *Colorín Colorado!* Accessed at: *http://www.colorincolorado.org/article/30570/.*

Schmidt,W., Houang, R., & Cogan, L. (2002). A coherent curriculum, *American Educator*, Summer, 2002.

Seethaler, P. M., Fuchs, L. S., Fuchs, D., & Compton, D. L. (2012). Predicting first graders' development of calculation versus word-problem performance: the role of dynamic assessment. *Journal of Educational Psychology* 104(1), 224–231.

Smarter Balanced Assessment Consortium. (2012). *General Item Specifications.* Accessed at: *http://www.smarterbalanced.org/wordpress/wp-content/uploads/2012/05/TaskItemSpecifications/ItemSpecifications/GeneralItemSpecifications.pdf.*

Common Core State Standards Coverage by *Ready*® Instruction

The table below correlates each Common Core State Standard to the ***Ready*® *Common Core Instruction*** lesson(s) that offer(s) comprehensive instruction on that standard. Use this table to determine which lessons your students should complete based on their mastery of each standard.

Common Core State Standards for Grade 6 — Mathematics Standards		Content Emphasis	*Ready*® *Common Core Instruction* Lesson(s)
Operations and Algebraic Thinking			
Ratios and Proportional Relationships			
Understand ratio concepts and use ratio reasoning to solve problems.			
6.RP.A.1	Understand the concept of a ratio and use ratio language to describe a ratio relationship between two quantities. *For example, "The ratio of wings to beaks in the bird house at the zoo was 2:1, because for every 2 wings there was 1 beak." "For every vote candidate A received, candidate C received nearly three votes."*	Major	1
6.RP.A.2	Understand the concept of a unit rate $\frac{a}{b}$ associated with a ratio a:b with $b \neq 0$, and use rate language in the context of a ratio relationship. *For example, "This recipe has a ratio of 3 cups of flour to 4 cups of sugar, so there is $\frac{3}{4}$ cup of flour for each cup of sugar." "We paid $75 for 15 hamburgers, which is a rate of $5 per hamburger.*	Major	2
6.RP.A.3	Use ratio and rate reasoning to solve real-world and mathematical problems, e.g., by reasoning about tables of equivalent ratios, tape diagrams, double number line diagrams, or equations.	Major	3, 4, 5
	6.RP.A.3a Make tables of equivalent ratios relating quantities with whole-number measurements, find missing values in the tables, and plot the pairs of values on the coordinate plane. Use tables to compare ratios.	Major	3
	6.RP.A.3b Solve unit rate problems including those involving unit pricing and constant speed. *For example, if it took 7 hours to mow 4 lawns, then at that rate, how many lawns could be mowed in 35 hours? At what rate were lawns being mowed?*	Major	4
	6.RP.A.3c Find a percent of a quantity as a rate per 100 (e.g., 30% of a quantity means $\frac{30}{100}$ times the quantity); solve problems involving finding the whole, given a part and the percent.	Major	5
	6.RP.A.3d Use ratio reasoning to convert measurement units; manipulate and transform units appropriately when multiplying or dividing quantities.	Major	4
The Number System			
Apply and extend previous understandings of multiplication and division to divide fractions by fractions.			
6.NS.A.1	Interpret and compute quotients of fractions, and solve word problems involving division of fractions by fractions, e.g., by using visual fraction models and equations to represent the problem. *For example, create a story context for* $\left(\frac{2}{3}\right) \div \left(\frac{3}{4}\right)$ *and use a visual fraction model to show the quotient; use the relationship between multiplication and division to explain that* $\left(\frac{2}{3}\right) \div \left(\frac{3}{4}\right) = \frac{8}{9}$ *because* $\frac{3}{4}$ *of* $\frac{8}{9}$ *is* $\frac{2}{3}$. *(In general,* $\left(\frac{a}{b}\right) \div \left(\frac{c}{d}\right) = \frac{ad}{bc}$.*) How much chocolate will each person get if 3 people share* $\frac{1}{2}$ *lb of chocolate equally? How many* $\frac{3}{4}$*-cup servings are in* $\frac{2}{3}$ *of a cup of yogurt? How wide is a rectangular strip of land with length* $\frac{3}{4}$ *mi and area* $\frac{1}{2}$ *square mi?*	Major	6, 7
Compute fluently with multi-digit numbers and find common factors and multiples.			
6.NS.B.2	Fluently divide multi-digit numbers using the standard algorithm.	Supporting/ Additional	8
6.NS.B.3	Fluently add, subtract, multiply, and divide multi-digit decimals using the standard algorithm for each operation.	Supporting/ Additional	9, 10

The Standards for Mathematical Practice are integrated throughout the instructional lessons.

Common Core State Standards for Grade 6 — Mathematics Standards	Content Emphasis	*Ready*® *Common Core Instruction* Lesson(s)
The Number System *(continued)*		
Compute fluently with multi-digit numbers and find common factors and multiples. *(continued)*		
6.NS.B.4 Find the greatest common factor of two whole numbers less than or equal to 100 and the least common multiple of two whole numbers less than or equal to 12. Use the distributive property to express a sum of two whole numbers 1–100 with a common factor as a multiple of a sum of two whole numbers with no common factor. *For example, express* $36 + 8$ *as* $4(9 + 2)$.	Supporting/ Additional	11
Apply and extend previous understandings of numbers to the system of rational numbers.		
6.NS.C.5 Understand that positive and negative numbers are used together to describe quantities having opposite directions or values (e.g., temperature above/below zero, elevation above/below sea level, credits/debits, positive/negative electric charge); use positive and negative numbers to represent quantities in real-world contexts, explaining the meaning of 0 in each situation.	Major	12, 13
6.NS.C.6 Understand a rational number as a point on the number line. Extend number line diagrams and coordinate axes familiar from previous grades to represent points on the line and in the plane with negative number coordinates.	Major	12, 14
6.NS.C.6a Recognize opposite signs of numbers as indicating locations on opposite sides of 0 on the number line; recognize that the opposite of the opposite of a number is the number itself, e.g., $-(-3) = 3$, and that 0 is its own opposite.	Major	12
6.NS.C.6b Understand signs of numbers in ordered pairs as indicating locations in quadrants of the coordinate plane; recognize that when two ordered pairs differ only by signs, the locations of the points are related by reflections across one or both axes.	Major	14
6.NS.C.6c Find and position integers and other rational numbers on a horizontal or vertical number line diagram; find and position pairs of integers and other rational numbers on a coordinate plane.	Major	12, 14
6.NS.C.7 Understand ordering and absolute value of rational numbers.	Major	13
6.NS.C.7a Interpret statements of inequality as statements about the relative position of two numbers on a number line diagram. *For example, interpret* $-3 > -7$ *as a statement that* -3 *is located to the right of* -7 *on a number line oriented from left to right.*	Major	13
6.NS.C.7b Write, interpret, and explain statements of order for rational numbers in real-world contexts. *For example, write* $-3°C > -7°C$ *to express the fact that* $-3°C$ *is warmer than* $-7°C$.	Major	13
6.NS.C.7c Understand the absolute value of a rational number as its distance from 0 on the number line; interpret absolute value as magnitude for a positive or negative quantity in a real-world situation. *For example, for an account balance of* -30 *dollars, write* $\|-30\| = 30$ *to describe the size of the debt in dollars.*	Major	13
6.NS.C.7d Distinguish comparisons of absolute value from statements about order. *For example, recognize that an account balance less than* -30 *dollars represents a debt greater than 30 dollars.*	Major	13
6.NS.C.8 Solve real-world and mathematical problems by graphing points in all four quadrants of the coordinate plane. Include use of coordinates and absolute value to find distances between points with the same first coordinate or the same second coordinate.	Major	14
Expressions and Equations		
Apply and extend previous understandings of arithmetic to algebraic expressions.		
6.EE.A.1 Write and evaluate numerical expressions involving whole-number exponents.	Major	15
6.EE.A.2 Write, read, and evaluate expressions in which letters stand for numbers.	Major	16
6.EE.A.2a Write expressions that record operations with numbers and with letters standing for numbers. *For example, express the calculation "Subtract y from 5" as* $5 - y$.	Major	16
6.EE.A.2b Identify parts of an expression using mathematical terms (sum, term, product, factor, quotient, coefficient); view one or more parts of an expression as a single entity. *For example, describe the expression* $2(8 + 7)$ *as a product of two factors; view* $(8 + 7)$ *as both a single entity and a sum of two terms.*	Major	16

Common Core State Standards for Grade 6 — Mathematics Standards		Content Emphasis	*Ready*® *Common Core Instruction* Lesson(s)
Expressions and Equations *(continued)*			
Apply and extend previous understandings of arithmetic to algebraic expressions. *(continued)*			
6.EE.A.2c	Evaluate expressions at specific values of their variables. Include expressions that arise from formulas used in real-world problems. Perform arithmetic operations, including those involving whole-number exponents, in the conventional order when there are no parentheses to specify a particular order (Order of Operations). *For example, use the formulas* $V = s^3$ *and* $A = 6s^2$ *to find the volume and surface area of a cube with sides of length* $s = \frac{1}{2}$.	Major	16
6.EE.A.3	Apply the properties of operations to generate equivalent expressions. *For example, apply the distributive property to the expression* $3(2 + x)$ *to produce the equivalent expression* $6 + 3x$*; apply the distributive property to the expression* $24x + 18y$ *to produce the equivalent expression* $6(4x + 3y)$*; apply properties of operations to* $y + y + y$ *to produce the equivalent expression* $3y$.	Major	17
6.EE.A.4	Identify when two expressions are equivalent (ie., when the two expressions name the same number regardless of which value is substituted into them). *For example, the expressions* $y + y + y$ *and* $3y$ *are equivalent because they name the same number regardless of which number* y *stands for.*	Major	17
Reason about and solve one-variable equations and inequalities.			
6.EE.B.5	Understand solving an equation or inequality as a process of answering a question: which values from a specified set, if any, make the equation or inequality true? Use substitution to determine whether a given number in a specified set makes an equation or inequality true.	Major	18, 20
6.EE.B.6	Use variables to represent numbers and write expressions when solving a real-world or mathematical problem; understand that a variable can represent an unknown number, or, depending on the purpose at hand, any number in a specified set.	Major	19
6.EE.B.7	Solve real-world and mathematical problems by writing and solving equations of the form $x + p = q$ and $px = q$ for cases in which p, q and x are all nonnegative rational numbers.	Major	19
6.EE.B.8	Write an inequality of the form $x > c$ or $x < c$ to represent a constraint or condition in a real-world or mathematical problem. Recognize that inequalities of the form $x > c$ or $x < c$ have infinitely many solutions; represent solutions of such inequalities on number line diagrams.	Major	20
Represent and analyze quantitative relationships between dependent and independent variables.			
6.EE.C.9	Use variables to represent two quantities in a real-world problem that change in relationship to one another; write an equation to express one quantity, thought of as the dependent variable, in terms of the other quantity, thought of as the independent variable. Analyze the relationship between the dependent and independent variables using graphs and tables, and relate these to the equation. *For example, in a problem involving motion at constant speed, list and graph ordered pairs of distances and times, and write the equation* $d = 65t$ *to represent the relationship between distance and time.*	Major	21
Geometry			
Solve real-world and mathematical problems involving area, surface area, and volume.			
6.G.A.1	Find the area of right triangles, other triangles, special quadrilaterals, and polygons by composing into rectangles or decomposing into triangles and other shapes; apply these techniques in the context of solving real-world and mathematical problems.	Supporting/ Additional	22
6.G.A.2	Find the volume of a right rectangular prism with fractional edge lengths by packing it with unit cubes of the appropriate unit fraction edge lengths, and show that the volume is the same as would be found by multiplying the edge lengths of the prism. Apply the formulas $V = lwh$ and $V = bh$ to find volumes of right rectangular prisms with fractional edge lengths in the context of solving real-world and mathematical problems.	Supporting/ Additional	25
6.G.A.3	Draw polygons in the coordinate plane given coordinates for the vertices; use coordinates to find the length of a side joining points with the same first coordinate or the same second coordinate. Apply these techniques in the context of solving real-world and mathematical problems.	Supporting/ Additional	23
6.G.A.4	Represent three-dimensional figures using nets made up of rectangles and triangles, and use the nets to find the surface area of these figures. Apply these techniques in the context of solving real-world and mathematical problems.	Supporting/ Additional	24

Common Core State Standards for Grade 6 — Mathematics Standards			Content Emphasis	*Ready®* *Common Core Instruction* Lesson(s)
Statistics and Probability				
Develop understanding of statistical variability.				
6.SP.A.1	Recognize a statistical question as one that anticipates variability in the data related to the question and accounts for it in the answers. *For example, "How old am I?" is not a statistical question, but "How old are the students in my school?" is a statistical question because one anticipates variability in students' ages.*		Supporting/ Additional	26
6.SP.A.2	Understand that a set of data collected to answer a statistical question has a distribution which can be described by its center, spread, and overall shape.		Supporting/ Additional	27
6.SP.A.3	Recognize that a measure of center for a numerical data set summarizes all of its values with a single number, while a measure of variation describes how its values vary with a single number.		Supporting/ Additional	27
Summarize and describe distributions.				
6.SP.B.4	Display numerical data in plots on a number line, including dot plots, histograms, and box plots.		Supporting/ Additional	28
6.SP.B.5	Summarize numerical data sets in relation to their context, such as by:		Supporting/ Additional	29
	6.SP.B.5a	Reporting the number of observations.	Supporting/ Additional	29
	6.SP.B.5b	Describing the nature of the attribute under investigation, including how it was measured and its units of measurement.	Supporting/ Additional	29
	6.SP.B.5c	Giving quantitative measures of center (median and/or mean) and variability (interquartile range and/or mean absolute deviation), as well as describing any overall pattern and any striking deviations from the overall pattern with reference to the context in which the data were gathered.	Supporting/ Additional	29
	6.SP.B.5d	Relating the choice of measures of center and variability to the shape of the data distribution and the context in which the data were gathered.	Supporting/ Additional	29

Interim Assessment Correlations

The tables below show the depth-of-knowledge (DOK) level for the items in the Interim Assessments, as well as the standard(s) addressed, and the corresponding ***Ready® Instruction*** lesson(s) being assessed by each item. Use this information to adjust lesson plans and focus remediation.

Ready® *Common Core* Interim Assessment Correlations			
Unit 1: Ratios and Proportional Relationships			
Question	**DOK[1]**	**Standard(s)**	***Ready®* *Common Core* Student Lesson(s)**
1	2	6.RP.A.2	2
2	2	6.RP.A.3d	4
3	2	6.RP.A.1	1
4	2	6.RP.A.3a	3
5	2	6.RP.A.3b	4
6	2	6.RP.A.3c	5
PT	3	6.RP.A.1, 6.RP.A.2, 6.RP.A.3b, 6.RP.A.3d	1, 2, 4
Unit 2: The Number System			
Question	**DOK**	**Standard(s)**	***Ready®* *Common Core* Student Lesson(s)**
1	2	6.NS.A.1	6, 7
2	1	6.NS.B.3	9, 10
3	2	6.NS.C.6b	14
4	2	6.NS.C.5	12
5	2	6.NS.C.7b, 6.NS.C.7c	13
6	2	6.NS.C.8	14
7	3	6.NS.B.4	11
PT	3	6.NS.A.1, 6.NS.B.3	6, 7, 9, 10
Unit 3: Expressions and Equations			
Question	**DOK**	**Standard(s)**	***Ready®* *Common Core* Student Lesson(s)**
1	1	6.EE.A.1	15
2	2	6.EE.B.7	19
3	2	6.EE.A.4	17
4	2	6.EE.C.9	21
5	1	6.EE.A.2c	16
6	2	6.EE.B.8	20
PT	3	6.EE.A.2a, 6.EE.A.2b, 6.EE.A.2c, 6.EE.B.7, 6.EE.C.9	16, 19, 21

[1]Depth of Knowledge levels:
1. The item requires superficial knowledge of the standard.
2. The item requires processing beyond recall and observation.
3. The item requires explanation, generalization, and connection to other ideas.

Ready® *Common Core* Interim Assessment Correlations *(continued)*			
Unit 4: Geometry			
Question	**DOK**	**Standard(s)**	***Ready®* *Common Core* Student Lesson(s)**
1	2	6.G.A.1	22
2	2	6.G.A.1	22
3	2	6.G.A.2	25
4	1	6.G.A.2	25
5	2	6.G.A.3	23
PT	3	6.G.A.2, 6.G.A.4, 6.RP.A.3a, 6.NS.B.3, 6.NS.B.4	3, 9, 10, 11, 24, 25
Unit 5: Statistics and Probability			
Question	**DOK**	**Standard(s)**	***Ready®* *Common Core* Student Lesson(s)**
1	2	6.SP.B.4	28
2	1	6.SP.A.3	27
3	2	6.SP.A.3, 6.SP.B.5c	27, 29
4	2	6.SP.A.1	26
5	2	6.SP.B.4	28
6	2	6.SP.B.5c	29
PT	3	6.SP.A.1, 6.SP.A.2, 6.SP.A.3, 6.SP.B.4	26, 27, 28

Unit 1: Ratios and Proportional Relationships

Which lessons are students building upon?

Grade 4, Lesson 23
Convert Measurements
4.MD.A.1

Grade 5, Lesson 15
Understand Multiplication as Scaling
5.NF.B.5a, 5.NF.B.5b

Grade 5, Lesson 20
Analyze Patterns and Relationships
5.OA.B.3

Grade 4, Lesson 23
Convert Measurements
4.MD.A.1

Grade 5, Lesson 12
Fractions as Division
5.NF.B.3

Grade 5, Lesson 17
Understand Division With Unit Fractions
5.NF.B.7a, 5.NF.B.7b

Grade 5, Lesson 12
Fractions as Division
5.NF.B.3

Grade 5, Lesson 17
Understand Division With Unit Fractions
5.NF.B.7a, 5.NF.B.7b

Grade 6, Lesson 1
Ratios
6.RP.A.1

Grade 5, Lesson 18
Divide Unit Fractions in Word Problems
5.NF.B.7c

Grade 6, Lesson 2
Understand Unit Rate
6.RP.A.2

Grade 6, Lesson 3
Equivalent Ratios
6.RP.A.3a

Grade 5, Lesson 12
Fractions as Division
5.NF.B.3

Grade 6, Lesson 2
Understand Unit Rate
6.RP.A.2

Unit 1

Which lessons are students preparing for?

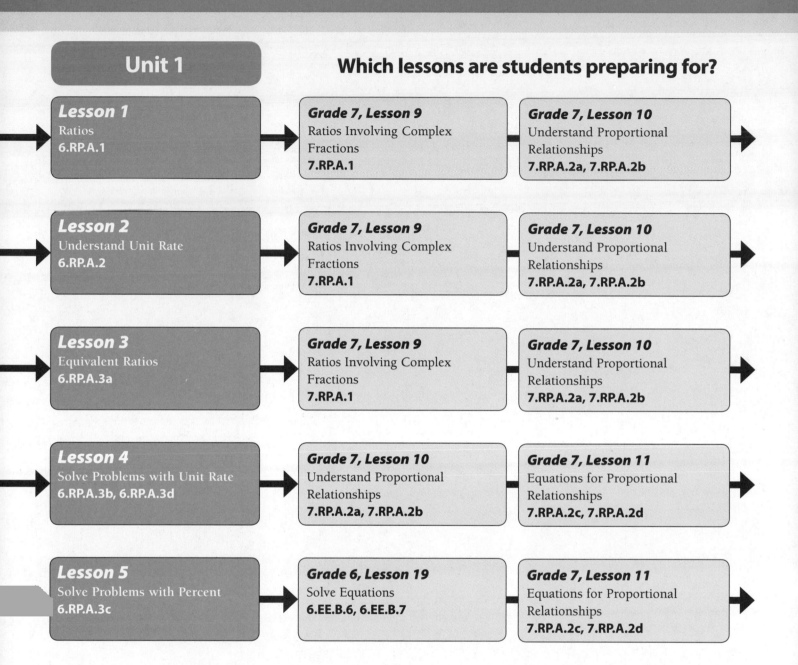

Unit 1	Preparing for	Preparing for
Lesson 1 Ratios **6.RP.A.1**	***Grade 7, Lesson 9*** Ratios Involving Complex Fractions **7.RP.A.1**	***Grade 7, Lesson 10*** Understand Proportional Relationships **7.RP.A.2a, 7.RP.A.2b**
Lesson 2 Understand Unit Rate **6.RP.A.2**	***Grade 7, Lesson 9*** Ratios Involving Complex Fractions **7.RP.A.1**	***Grade 7, Lesson 10*** Understand Proportional Relationships **7.RP.A.2a, 7.RP.A.2b**
Lesson 3 Equivalent Ratios **6.RP.A.3a**	***Grade 7, Lesson 9*** Ratios Involving Complex Fractions **7.RP.A.1**	***Grade 7, Lesson 10*** Understand Proportional Relationships **7.RP.A.2a, 7.RP.A.2b**
Lesson 4 Solve Problems with Unit Rate **6.RP.A.3b, 6.RP.A.3d**	***Grade 7, Lesson 10*** Understand Proportional Relationships **7.RP.A.2a, 7.RP.A.2b**	***Grade 7, Lesson 11*** Equations for Proportional Relationships **7.RP.A.2c, 7.RP.A.2d**
Lesson 5 Solve Problems with Percent **6.RP.A.3c**	***Grade 6, Lesson 19*** Solve Equations **6.EE.B.6, 6.EE.B.7**	***Grade 7, Lesson 11*** Equations for Proportional Relationships **7.RP.A.2c, 7.RP.A.2d**

Lesson 1 (Student Book pages 2–9)

Ratios

LESSON OBJECTIVES

- Understand the concept of a ratio as a way of expressing relationships between quantities.
- Write a ratio to describe the relationship between two quantities.
- Write a ratio using three different formats: a to b, $\frac{a}{b}$, a:b.
- Use ratio language, e.g., *for every, for each*.

PREREQUISITE SKILLS

- Compute with whole numbers and fractions.
- Understand equivalent fractions.

VOCABULARY

ratio: a way to compare two different quantities

THE LEARNING PROGRESSION

In Grade 6, students develop the concept of ratio and rate reasoning. They apply an understanding of fractions and of multiplication and division developed in previous grades as they work with ratios.

In Lesson 1, students learn to use ratios to compare part to whole as well as part to part. They express ratios both with words and with symbols. In Lessons 2 through 5, students learn to use rates, unit rates, equivalent ratios, and percents to solve various kinds of everyday problems.

In Grade 7, students focus on proportions and proportional reasoning. They solve ratios with complex fractions and use equations to solve problems involving proportional relationships.

In Grade 8 and up, students build upon what they have learned about ratios and proportional thinking as they study algebra and geometry and solve problems involving such things as similar figures and slopes of lines.

Ready *Teacher Toolbox* Teacher-Toolbox.com

	Prerequisite Skills	*6.RP.A.1*
Ready Lessons		✓
Tools for Instruction		✓
Interactive Tutorials		✓ ✓

CCSS Focus

6.RP.A.1 Understand the concept of a ratio and use ratio language to describe a ratio relationship between two quantities. *For example, "The ratio of wings to beaks in the bird house at the zoo was 2:1, because for every 2 wings there was 1 beak." "For every vote candidate A received, candidate C received nearly three votes."*

STANDARDS FOR MATHEMATICAL PRACTICE: ***SMP 4, 6*** *(see page A9 for full text)*

AT A GLANCE

Students read a problem involving making comparisons using ratios. They write both part-to-whole and part-to-part comparisons.

STEP BY STEP

- Tell students that this page models how to write comparisons of different quantities.
- Have students read the problem at the top of the page.
- Work through Explore It as a class.
- Point out the different ways to write ratios: fraction bar, the word *to,* and the colon.
- Ask student pairs or groups to explain their answers for the ratios they wrote.
- Discuss the last question. Which notation format do students find easiest to understand? Can they think of situations in which one format might be easier to use than another?

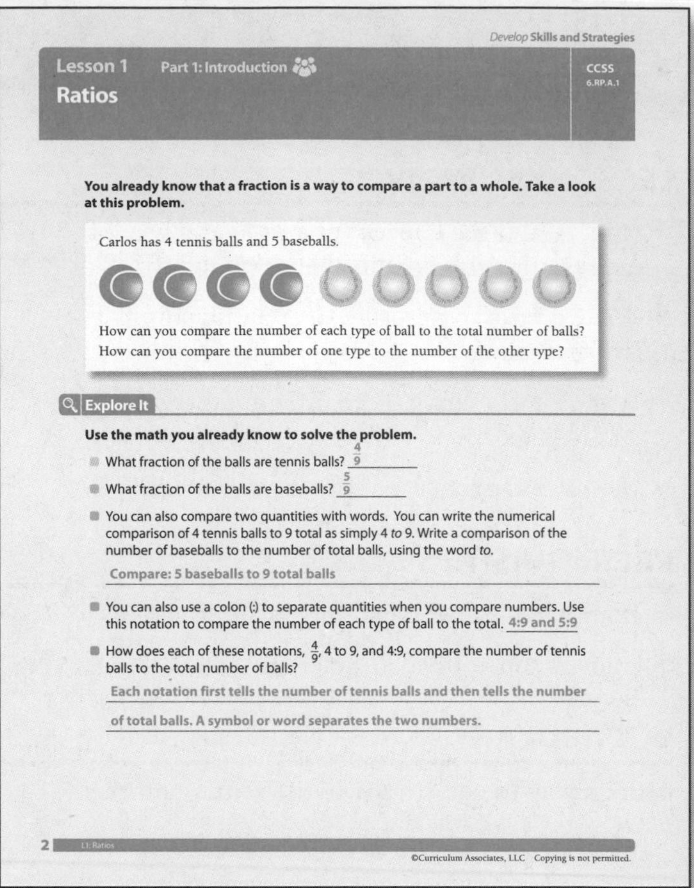

Develop Skills and Strategies

Lesson 1 Part 1: Introduction CCSS 6.RP.A.1

Ratios

You already know that a fraction is a way to compare a part to a whole. Take a look at this problem.

Carlos has 4 tennis balls and 5 baseballs.

How can you compare the number of each type of ball to the total number of balls?
How can you compare the number of one type to the number of the other type?

Explore It

Use the math you already know to solve the problem.

- What fraction of the balls are tennis balls? $\frac{4}{9}$
- What fraction of the balls are baseballs? $\frac{5}{9}$
- You can also compare two quantities with words. You can write the numerical comparison of 4 tennis balls to 9 total as simply 4 *to* 9. Write a comparison of the number of baseballs to the number of total balls, using the word *to.* Compare: 5 baseballs to 9 total balls
- You can also use a colon (:) to separate quantities when you compare numbers. Use this notation to compare the number of each type of ball to the total. 4:9 and 5:9
- How does each of these notations, $\frac{4}{9}$, 4 to 9, and 4:9, compare the number of tennis balls to the total number of balls? Each notation first tells the number of tennis balls and then tells the number of total balls. A symbol or word separates the two numbers.

2 L1: Ratios ©Curriculum Associates, LLC Copying is not permitted.

Visual Model

Use circles to show ratios.

Materials: two colors of chalk

- Write *4 tennis balls : 5 baseballs* on the board. Underneath, draw 4 yellow circles and 5 white circles separated with a colon to illustrate the ratio. Have students describe how the words and the pictures are related.
- Sketch 7 white circles and 3 yellow circles separated by a colon. Choose a volunteer to write the ratio using three different notations.
- Sketch 4 yellow circles and 2 white circles separated by a colon. Call on another volunteer to write the ratio using three different notations.
- Have volunteers come to the board and sketch their own ratios using pictures. Have them call on classmates to name the ratio illustrated.

Mathematical Discourse

- *Sometimes people talk about part-to-whole and part-to-part comparisons. What do you think they mean?*

  Students should use their own words to explain that *part-to-whole* means "comparing the number in a category with the total number within that same category." *Part-to-part* means "comparing the number in one category with the number in another category."

- *What is an example of a part-to-whole comparison? A part-to-part comparison? Explain your examples.*

  Students' examples will vary. Encourage them to justify their choices.

AT A GLANCE

Students learn about different types of ratios and ratio phrases and notation.

STEP BY STEP

- Read Find Out More as a class.
- Discuss the difference between part-to-whole and part-to-part comparisons.
- Write the three types of notation on the board. Emphasize that all three mean "compared to."
- Examine the table which illustrates types of ratios and types of notation. Point out that another way to think about ratios is by using the phrases *for each* and *for every.*
- Discuss Reflect with students. Emphasize that the additional ball affects only the whole-to-part ratio.

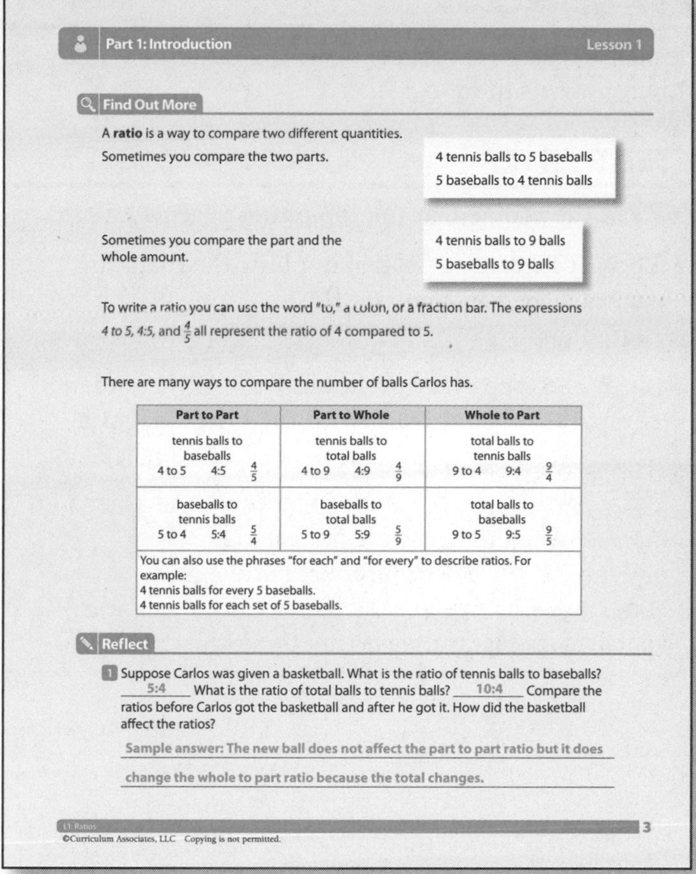

Part 1: Introduction Lesson 1

Find Out More

A **ratio** is a way to compare two different quantities.

Sometimes you compare the two parts.

4 tennis balls to 5 baseballs
5 baseballs to 4 tennis balls

Sometimes you compare the part and the whole amount.

4 tennis balls to 9 balls
5 baseballs to 9 balls

To write a ratio you can use the word "to," a colon, or a fraction bar. The expressions *4 to 5, 4:5,* and $\frac{4}{5}$ all represent the ratio of 4 compared to 5.

There are many ways to compare the number of balls Carlos has.

Part to Part	Part to Whole	Whole to Part
tennis balls to baseballs 4 to 5 4:5 $\frac{4}{5}$	tennis balls to total balls 4 to 9 4:9 $\frac{4}{9}$	total balls to tennis balls 9 to 4 9:4 $\frac{9}{4}$
baseballs to tennis balls 5 to 4 5:4 $\frac{5}{4}$	baseballs to total balls 5 to 9 5:9 $\frac{5}{9}$	total balls to baseballs 9 to 5 9:5 $\frac{9}{5}$
You can also use the phrases "for each" and "for every" to describe ratios. For example: 4 tennis balls for every 5 baseballs. 4 tennis balls for each set of 5 baseballs.		

Reflect

1 Suppose Carlos was given a basketball. What is the ratio of tennis balls to baseballs? 5:4 What is the ratio of total balls to tennis balls? 10:4 Compare the ratios before Carlos got the basketball and after he got it. How did the basketball affect the ratios?

Sample answer: The new ball does not affect the part to part ratio but it does change the whole to part ratio because the total changes.

L1: Ratios 3
©Curriculum Associates, LLC Copying is not permitted.

ELL Support

- Write *part* and *whole* on the board. Have volunteers explain the difference between the two terms.
- Hold up 3 red pens and 2 blue pens. Say, *One part is 3 red pens. Another part is 2 blue pens. The whole is 5 pens in all.*
- Hold up 1 red pen and 4 blue pens. Have students identify the parts and the whole.
- Ask students to use other classroom objects to model the terms *part* and *whole.*

SMP Tip: When students use standard notation to express ratios, they are attending to precision (*SMP 6*). It is important to continue to model standard notation and terminology throughout the year so that students can communicate concisely and accurately when talking about mathematics.

Real-World Connection

Discuss with the class some ways in which workers might use ratios in their jobs and ways the students might. Ask, *What are some ratios teachers might use when describing classrooms or schools? Cooks when describing ingredients or products? Truck drivers when describing their job? What are some ways you might use ratios?*

Examples:

Teachers: markers compared to students, minutes students are in class compared to at lunch, teachers in school compared to students in school

Cooks: pounds of meat compared to servings, amount of sugar compared to amount of flour

Truck drivers: miles traveled compared to gallons of gas used, miles traveled compared to hours driving, cost of a load compared to weight

Students: miles walked compared to minutes, hours on the Internet compared to hours in a day

AT A GLANCE

Students read a problem concerning ratios and study different ways to model it.

STEP BY STEP

- Read the problem at the top of the page as a class.
- Look at Picture It. Talk about how the diagram makes it easy to compare the amounts of each ingredient.
- Study the tape diagram in Model It. Have students compare and contrast it with the other diagram.

SMP Tip: Students learn to model with mathematics (*SMP 4*) when they use diagrams to help them understand a problem. Throughout the unit, encourage students to sketch diagrams to help them visualize problems they do not understand well.

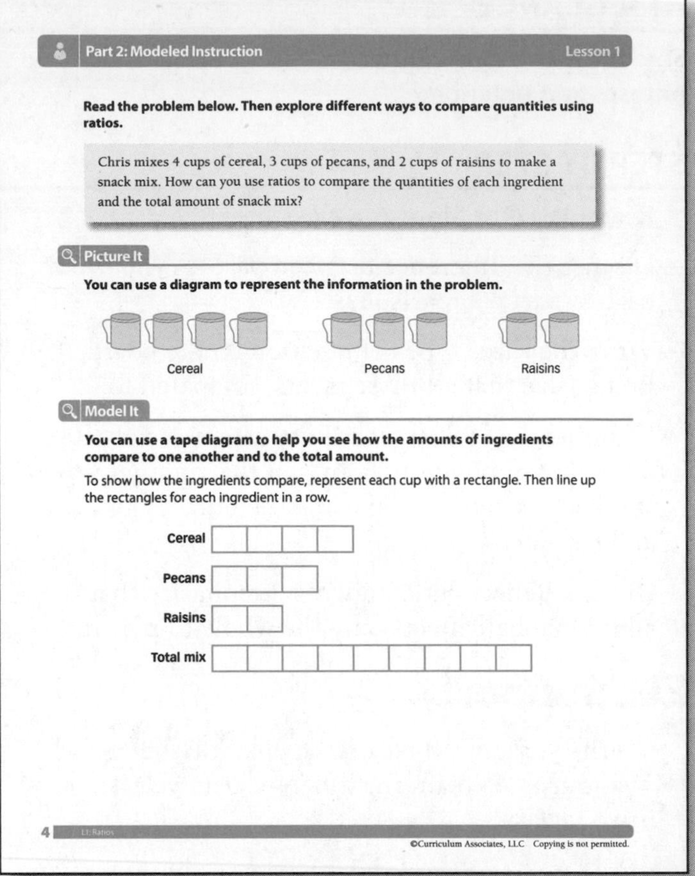

Part 2: Modeled Instruction Lesson 1

Read the problem below. Then explore different ways to compare quantities using ratios.

Chris mixes 4 cups of cereal, 3 cups of pecans, and 2 cups of raisins to make a snack mix. How can you use ratios to compare the quantities of each ingredient and the total amount of snack mix?

Picture It

You can use a diagram to represent the information in the problem.

Model It

You can use a tape diagram to help you see how the amounts of ingredients compare to one another and to the total amount.

To show how the ingredients compare, represent each cup with a rectangle. Then line up the rectangles for each ingredient in a row.

4 L1: Ratios

©Curriculum Associates, LLC Copying is not permitted.

Mathematical Discourse

- *Which diagram helps you understand the problem the best? Explain why.*

  Students' explanations should involve explaining which diagram makes it easier to compare the amounts.

- *What are some other ways you could illustrate the situation?*

  Students' responses will vary. Have volunteers show their ways on the board. One example: Draw three equal number lines marked off in 1s. Darken the line from 0 to the number of cups for each ingredient. Compare the lengths.

AT A GLANCE

Students revisit the problem on page 4 and use ratios to describe the relationships among quantities.

STEP BY STEP

- Read Connect It as a class. Be sure to point out that the questions refer to the problem on page 4.
- Review the three types of notation that can be used to write ratios. Talk about the differences between part-to-part, part-to-whole, and whole-to-part.
- Have students share their answers to the remaining questions. Have them justify the thinking that leads to their answers.
- Have students complete Try It on their own. Then ask volunteers to write their answers on the board. Encourage students to write their ratios in different ways. Discuss any questions or misconceptions that become evident.

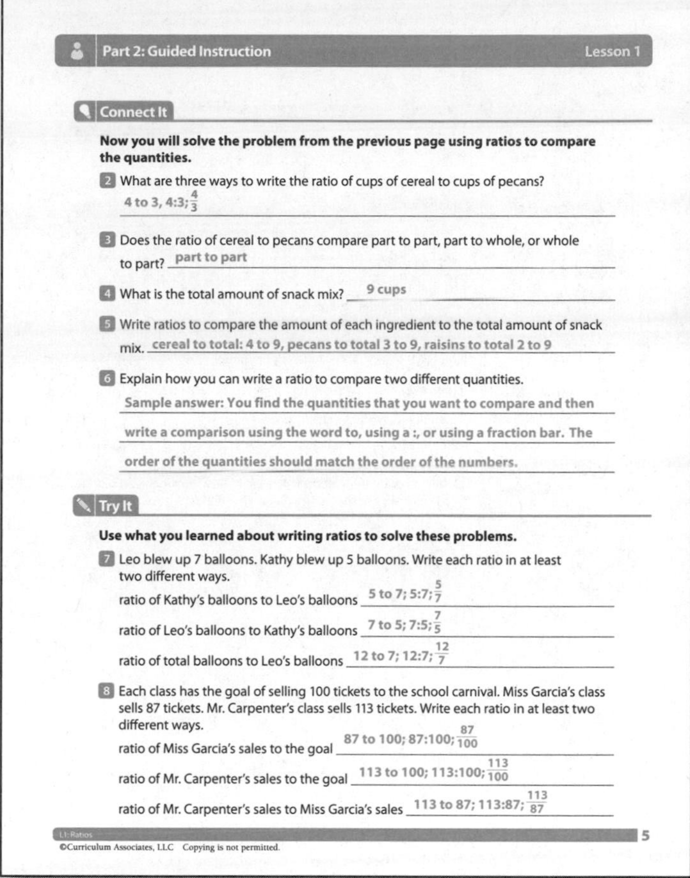

Part 2: Guided Instruction Lesson 1

Connect It

Now you will solve the problem from the previous page using ratios to compare the quantities.

2 What are three ways to write the ratio of cups of cereal to cups of pecans? 4 to 3, 4:3; $\frac{4}{3}$

3 Does the ratio of cereal to pecans compare part to part, part to whole, or whole to part? part to part

4 What is the total amount of snack mix? 9 cups

5 Write ratios to compare the amount of each ingredient to the total amount of snack mix. cereal to total: 4 to 9, pecans to total 3 to 9, raisins to total 2 to 9

6 Explain how you can write a ratio to compare two different quantities.
Sample answer: You find the quantities that you want to compare and then write a comparison using the word to, using a :, or using a fraction bar. The order of the quantities should match the order of the numbers.

Try It

Use what you learned about writing ratios to solve these problems.

7 Leo blew up 7 balloons. Kathy blew up 5 balloons. Write each ratio in at least two different ways.
ratio of Kathy's balloons to Leo's balloons 5 to 7; 5:7; $\frac{5}{7}$
ratio of Leo's balloons to Kathy's balloons 7 to 5; 7:5; $\frac{7}{5}$
ratio of total balloons to Leo's balloons 12 to 7; 12:7; $\frac{12}{7}$

8 Each class has the goal of selling 100 tickets to the school carnival. Miss Garcia's class sells 87 tickets. Mr. Carpenter's class sells 113 tickets. Write each ratio in at least two different ways.
ratio of Miss Garcia's sales to the goal 87 to 100; 87:100; $\frac{87}{100}$
ratio of Mr. Carpenter's sales to the goal 113 to 100; 113:100; $\frac{113}{100}$
ratio of Mr. Carpenter's sales to Miss Garcia's sales 113 to 87; 113:87; $\frac{113}{87}$

L1: Ratios 5
©Curriculum Associates, LLC Copying is not permitted.

TRY IT SOLUTIONS

7 *Solution:* 5 to 7, 5:7, or $\frac{5}{7}$; 7 to 5, 7:5, or $\frac{7}{5}$; 12 to 7, 12:7, or $\frac{12}{7}$; Students may use any 2 of the 3 ways to show each ratio.

8 *Solution:* 87 to 100, 87:100, or $\frac{87}{100}$; 113 to 100, 113:100, or $\frac{113}{100}$; 113 to 87, 113:87, or $\frac{113}{87}$; Students may use any 2 of the 3 ways to show each ratio.

ERROR ALERT: Students who wrote 87 to 200 for the ratio of Miss Garcia's sales and the goal used the total number of tickets sold by the two classes instead of the goal.

Concept Extension

Explore how ratios change when the quantities being compared change.

- Have students look at the diagrams on the previous page. Say that Chris changed his mind and only used 1 cup of raisins but added 2 cups of chocolate candy. Have students describe how the diagrams would change. [cereal would remain the same at 4; pecans would remain at 3; raisins would reduce to 1; new cups or tape would be added for 2 candies]
- Have students find each of these ratios and compare them with the ratios from the original problem: cereal : pecans cereal : total total : raisins.
- Discuss which ratios changed and which did not. Have students explain why. [Any part-to-whole or whole-to-part ratio changed because the total number of ingredients changed from 9 to 10.]

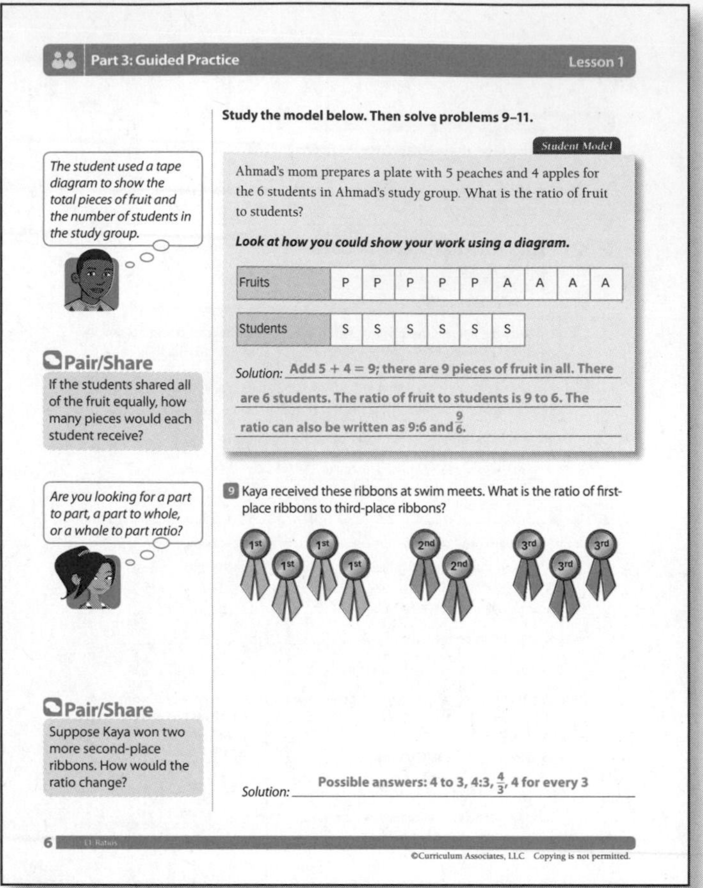

Study the model below. Then solve problems 9–11.

The student used a tape diagram to show the total pieces of fruit and the number of students in the study group.

Student Model

Ahmad's mom prepares a plate with 5 peaches and 4 apples for the 6 students in Ahmad's study group. What is the ratio of fruit to students?

Look at how you could show your work using a diagram.

Fruits	P	P	P	P	P	A	A	A	A

Students	S	S	S	S	S	S

Solution: **Add 5 + 4 = 9; there are 9 pieces of fruit in all. There are 6 students. The ratio of fruit to students is 9 to 6. The ratio can also be written as 9:6 and $\frac{9}{6}$.**

Pair/Share

If the students shared all of the fruit equally, how many pieces would each student receive?

Are you looking for a part to part, a part to whole, or a whole to part ratio?

9 Kaya received these ribbons at swim meets. What is the ratio of first-place ribbons to third-place ribbons?

1st 1st 1st 1st 2nd 2nd 3rd 3rd 3rd

Solution: **Possible answers: 4 to 3, 4:3, $\frac{4}{3}$, 4 for every 3**

Pair/Share

Suppose Kaya won two more second-place ribbons. How would the ratio change?

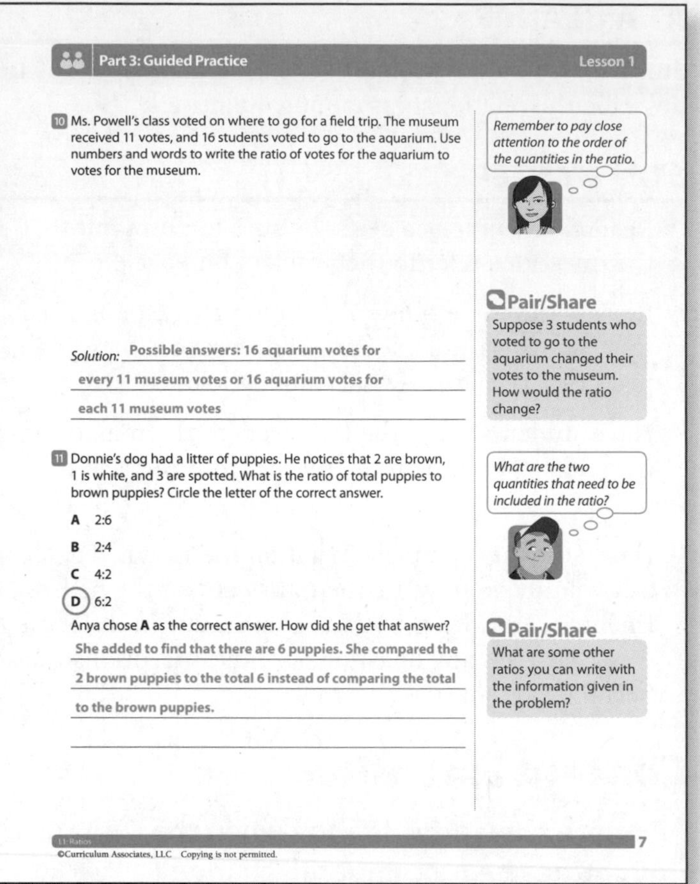

10 Ms. Powell's class voted on where to go for a field trip. The museum received 11 votes, and 16 students voted to go to the aquarium. Use numbers and words to write the ratio of votes for the aquarium to votes for the museum.

Remember to pay close attention to the order of the quantities in the ratio.

Solution: **Possible answers: 16 aquarium votes for every 11 museum votes or 16 aquarium votes for each 11 museum votes**

Pair/Share

Suppose 3 students who voted to go to the aquarium changed their votes to the museum. How would the ratio change?

11 Donnie's dog had a litter of puppies. He notices that 2 are brown, 1 is white, and 3 are spotted. What is the ratio of total puppies to brown puppies? Circle the letter of the correct answer.

What are the two quantities that need to be included in the ratio?

A 2:6

B 2:4

C 4:2

(D) 6:2

Anya chose **A** as the correct answer. How did she get that answer?

She added to find that there are 6 puppies. She compared the 2 brown puppies to the total 6 instead of comparing the total to the brown puppies.

Pair/Share

What are some other ratios you can write with the information given in the problem?

AT A GLANCE

Students use models and ratio notation to compare quantities.

STEP BY STEP

- Ask students to solve the problems individually using standard ratio notations.
- When students have completed each problem, have them Pair/Share to discuss their solutions with a partner or in a group.

SOLUTIONS

Ex Another way to solve the problem is to compute numerically: 5 + 4 = 9, ratio of fruit to students is 9:6.

9 *Solution:* Possible answers: 4 to 3, 4:3, $\frac{4}{3}$; Students could also use phrases *4 for every 3* or *4 for each 3.* ***(DOK 1)***

10 *Solution:* Possible answers: 16 to 11, or 16:11, or 16 aquarium votes for every 11 museum votes, or 16 aquarium votes for each 11 museum votes. ***(DOK 1)***

11 *Solution:* **D**; Anya mistakenly compared part to the whole.

Explain to students why the other two answer choices are not correct:

B is not correct because it compares brown puppies to the other puppies.

C is not correct because it compares the other puppies to brown puppies. ***(DOK 3)***

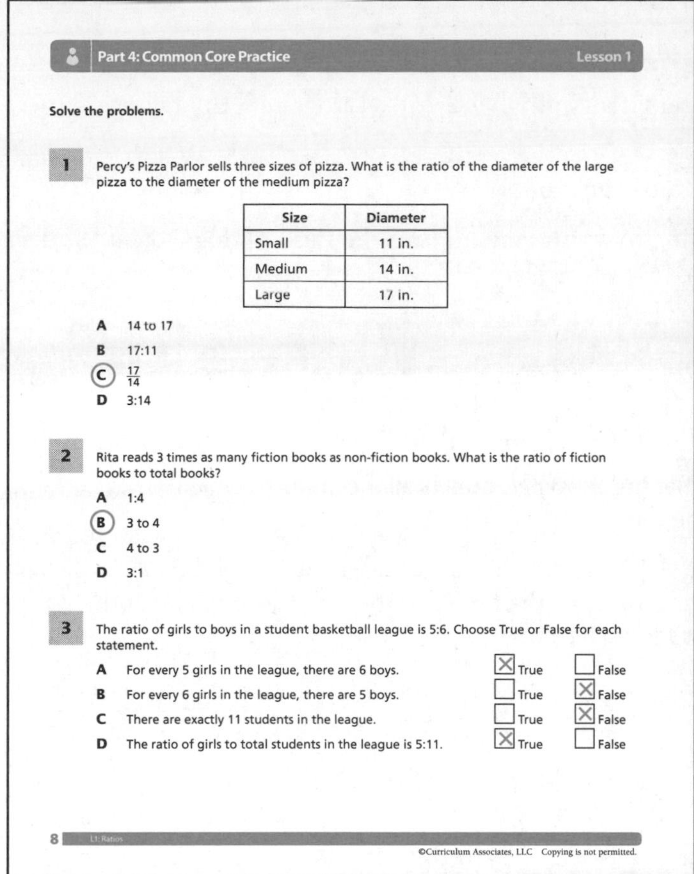

Part 4: Common Core Practice Lesson 1

Solve the problems.

1 Percy's Pizza Parlor sells three sizes of pizza. What is the ratio of the diameter of the large pizza to the diameter of the medium pizza?

Size	Diameter
Small	11 in.
Medium	14 in.
Large	17 in.

A 14 to 17

B 17:11

(C) $\frac{17}{14}$

D 3:14

2 Rita reads 3 times as many fiction books as non-fiction books. What is the ratio of fiction books to total books?

A 1:4

(B) 3 to 4

C 4 to 3

D 3:1

3 The ratio of girls to boys in a student basketball league is 5:6. Choose True or False for each statement.

A For every 5 girls in the league, there are 6 boys. ☒ True ☐ False

B For every 6 girls in the league, there are 5 boys. ☐ True ☒ False

C There are exactly 11 students in the league. ☐ True ☒ False

D The ratio of girls to total students in the league is 5:11. ☒ True ☐ False

8 L1: Ratios

©Curriculum Associates, LLC Copying is not permitted.

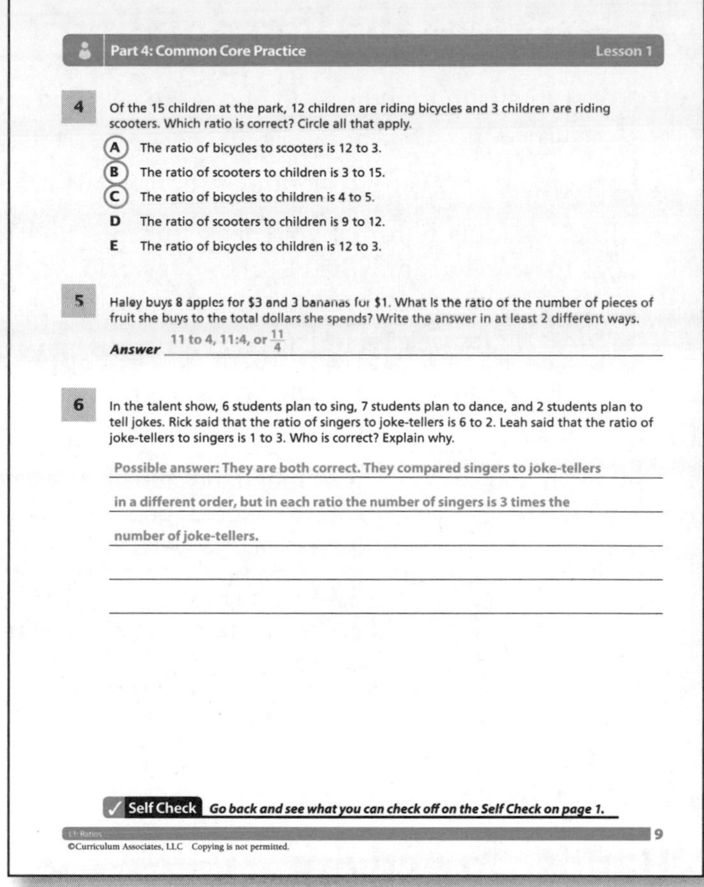

Part 4: Common Core Practice Lesson 1

4 Of the 15 children at the park, 12 children are riding bicycles and 3 children are riding scooters. Which ratio is correct? Circle all that apply.

(A) The ratio of bicycles to scooters is 12 to 3.

(B) The ratio of scooters to children is 3 to 15.

(C) The ratio of bicycles to children is 4 to 5.

D The ratio of scooters to children is 9 to 12.

E The ratio of bicycles to children is 12 to 3.

5 Haley buys 8 apples for $3 and 3 bananas for $1. What is the ratio of the number of pieces of fruit she buys to the total dollars she spends? Write the answer in at least 2 different ways.

Answer 11 to 4, 11:4, or $\frac{11}{4}$

6 In the talent show, 6 students plan to sing, 7 students plan to dance, and 2 students plan to tell jokes. Rick said that the ratio of singers to joke-tellers is 6 to 2. Leah said that the ratio of joke-tellers to singers is 1 to 3. Who is correct? Explain why.

Possible answer: They are both correct. They compared singers to joke-tellers in a different order, but in each ratio the number of singers is 3 times the number of joke-tellers.

✓ Self Check *Go back and see what you can check off on the Self Check on page 1.*

L1: Ratios 9

©Curriculum Associates, LLC Copying is not permitted.

AT A GLANCE

Students write ratios to solve word problems that might appear on a mathematics test.

SOLUTIONS

1 *Solution:* **C**; Find the diameters of the large and medium pizzas and compare them using ratio notation. ***(DOK 1)***

2 *Solution:* **B**; Conclude that *three times as many* means a ratio of 3 parts to 1 part and that the whole is 4. Then compare 3 parts to the whole using ratio notation. ***(DOK 1)***

3 *Solution:* A **True**; B **False**; C **False**; D **True** ***(DOK 1)***

4 *Solution:* **A**; Find the number of scooters and the total number of children and compare them using ratio notation.

B; Find the number of children riding scooters and the total number of children and compare them using ratio notation.

C; Find the number of children riding bicycles and the total number of children and compare them using ratio notation. ***(DOK 1)***

5 *Solution:* 11 to 4, 11:4, or $\frac{11}{4}$; Students should write the ratio in at least two different ways. ***(DOK 2)***

6 *Solution:* Both are correct; students could say the order of the words is different, so the order of the numbers must be different, and that one of the ratios is simplified. ***(DOK 3)***

Assessment and Remediation

- Ask students to find the ratio of dogs to cats and cats to pets if a family has 2 cats, 1 dog, and 4 parakeets. [1:2 and 2:7]
- For students who are struggling, use the chart below to guide remediation.
- After providing remediation, check students' understanding. Ask students to find the ratio of dogs to cats and dogs to pets if a family has 1 cat, 3 dogs, and 3 parakeets. [3:1 and 3:7]

If the error is . . .	Students may . . .	To remediate . . .
2:1 and 2:7	have found the ratio of cats to dogs.	Stress that the order is important in ratios. Have students note that they are to find the ratio of dogs to cats.
1:2 and 2:5	have found the ratio of cats to the other pets instead of total pets.	Point out that the word *pets* means all the animals, which includes the cats.
1:7 and 2:7	have found the ratio of dogs to pets instead of cats.	Have students describe the first ratio they are trying to find and note that it should be a part-to-part ratio.

Hands-On Activity

Write part-to-part and part-to-whole ratios.

Materials: 8 to 12 pennies for every pair of students

Give each pair of students several pennies. Have the students flip the pennies and separate them into a row of heads and a row of tails. They should record the number of heads and tails in a table similar to the one shown. Then have them write the ratios. Have the students flip the pennies several more times, recording the results and writing the ratios each time.

Heads	Tails	Heads: Tails	Tails: Heads	Heads: Coins	Tails: Coins

Challenge Activity

Explore three-part ratios.

Draw 3 circles, 2 triangles, and 4 rectangles on the board. Tell students that they can write three-part ratios using a colon or the word *to*. Give examples such as these.

triangles : circles : rectangles

2 : 3 : 4

rectangles to circles to triangles

4 to 3 to 2

Point out that the part-to-whole ratios will still be two-part ratios.

triangles : shapes

2 : 9

rectangles to shapes

4 to 9

$\frac{\text{circles}}{\text{shapes}}$

$\frac{3}{9}$

Write *4 apples, 5 bananas, and 2 grapefruit* on the board. Instruct students to write 3 three-part ratios comparing part to part to part and 3 two-part ratios comparing part to whole. Ask them to write each ratio using words and then using numbers. Remind them to use proper ratio notation.

Lesson 2 (Student Book pages 10–15)

Understand Unit Rate

LESSON OBJECTIVES

- Understand the concept of a unit rate.
- Use rate and unit rate language.
- Find rates and unit rate.

PREREQUISITE SKILLS

- Understand ratio concepts from 6.RP.A.1.
- Simplify fractions.
- Communicate relationships between two quantities using ratio notation.

VOCABULARY

ratio: a way to compare two different quantities

rate: an equivalent ratio that compares the first quantity in a ratio to only one of the second quantity

unit rate: the part of the rate that is being compared to 1

THE LEARNING PROGRESSION

Some educators use *ratio* to refer to a comparison of quantities with the same unit (green apples : apples, for example) and *rate* for comparisons of quantities with different units (revolutions : minute). The Common Core uses *ratio* to include both types of comparison. In the previous lesson, students were introduced to ratios by using ratio language to compare quantities. In this lesson students learn about rates and unit rates. They draw on their knowledge of ratios and on their fraction skills to find unit rates from ratios. Throughout this unit, students will use ratios, rates, and unit rates to solve real world and mathematical problems.

In future grades students will compute unit rates involving complex fractions. They will also reason about proportional relationships and use them to solve real world problems.

Ready *Teacher Toolbox* Teacher-Toolbox.com

	Prerequisite Skills	6.RP.A.2
Ready Lessons	✓	✓
Tools for Instruction	✓	✓
Interactive Tutorials		✓

CCSS Focus

6.RP.A.2 Understand the concept of a unit rate $\frac{a}{b}$ associated with a ratio $a{:}b$ with $b \neq 0$, and use rate language in the context of a ratio relationship. *For example, "This recipe has a ratio of 3 cups of flour to 4 cups of sugar, so there is $\frac{3}{4}$ cup of flour for each cup of sugar." "We paid \$75 for 15 hamburgers, which is a rate of \$5 per hamburger."*

ADDITIONAL STANDARDS **6.RP.A.3a, 6.RP.A.3b, 6.RP.A.3d, 6.RP.A.1** *(see page A42 for full text)*

STANDARDS FOR MATHEMATICAL PRACTICE: **SMP 2, 6, 7** *(see page A9 for full text)*

AT A GLANCE

Students explore comparisons of one quantity to another using ratios and related rates.

STEP BY STEP

- Introduce the Question at the top of the page.
- Discuss how the tape diagram represents the question. Note that the top of the tape represents cups of nuts and the bottom represents cups of dried fruit.
- Read the information about the ratio, rate, and unit rate as a class. Discuss that while they are all related, each is slightly different from the other two. Have students describe the differences. Be sure they see that the rate is stated in terms of 1 cup instead of 2 cups. The unit rate is like a summarized form of the rate. It includes only a number to describe how many for each 1. The "for each 1" is assumed and not written.
- Read Think as a class. Have students explain how the tape diagram shows the comparison. Discuss the meaning of rate and how rate is related to ratio.

SMP Tip: The terms ratio, rate, and unit rate have very specific meanings in mathematics. As you discuss each one, note that it is important to attend to precision (*SMP 6*) when using the terms.

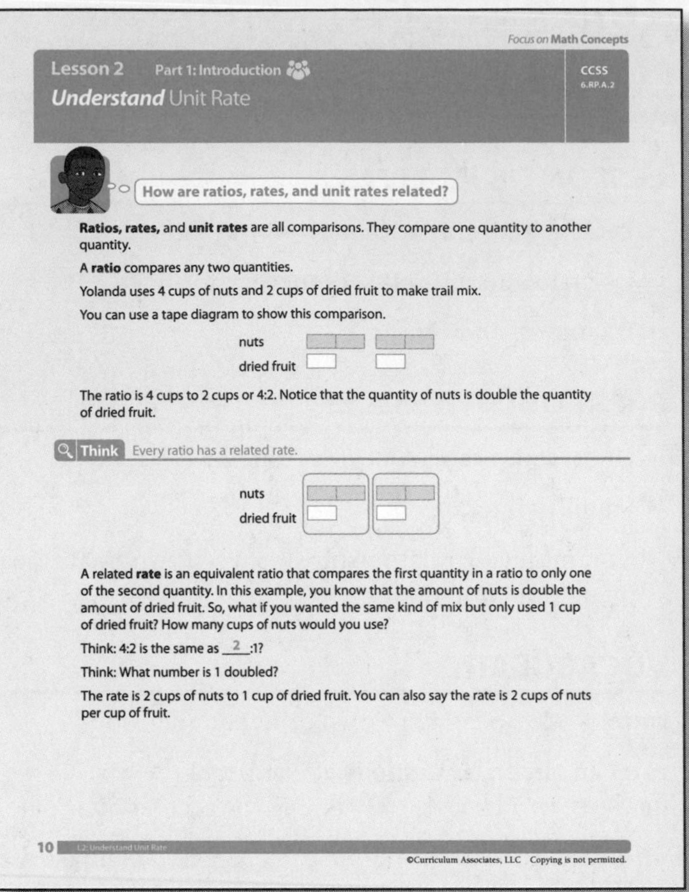

Focus on Math Concepts

Lesson 2 Part 1: Introduction CCSS 6.RP.A.2

Understand **Unit Rate**

How are ratios, rates, and unit rates related?

Ratios, rates, and **unit rates** are all comparisons. They compare one quantity to another quantity.

A **ratio** compares any two quantities.

Yolanda uses 4 cups of nuts and 2 cups of dried fruit to make trail mix.

You can use a tape diagram to show this comparison.

The ratio is 4 cups to 2 cups or 4:2. Notice that the quantity of nuts is double the quantity of dried fruit.

Think Every ratio has a related rate.

A related **rate** is an equivalent ratio that compares the first quantity in a ratio to only one of the second quantity. In this example, you know that the amount of nuts is double the amount of dried fruit. So, what if you wanted the same kind of mix but only used 1 cup of dried fruit? How many cups of nuts would you use?

Think: 4:2 is the same as _2_:1?

Think: What number is 1 doubled?

The rate is 2 cups of nuts to 1 cup of dried fruit. You can also say the rate is 2 cups of nuts per cup of dried fruit.

10 L2: Understand Unit Rate ©Curriculum Associates, LLC Copying is not permitted.

Mathematical Discourse

- *We use ratios all the time. In sports, we compare goals made to attempts. In school, we compare the number of teachers to students. What are other examples of ratios?*

  Responses may include other sports statistics, ratios for mixing ingredients, graduation rates.

- *In the trail mix problem, how can you use a bar model to find the rate?*

  Responses may include that the bar model is a visual way to show the comparison. You see how many rectangles on the top it takes to be the same length as one rectangle on the bottom.

Hands-On Activity

Illustrate the rates 2:1, 3:1, and 4:1.

Materials: sticky dots, drawing paper, crayons or markers

- Discuss the number of wheels on a bicycle, a tricycle, and a car. Write each as a rate of wheels : vehicle.
- Give each student a sheet of sticky dots and drawing paper. On the top of the paper, students should sketch several bicycles using sticky dots for the wheels. Underneath, they should record the ratio and the rate.
  __ wheels : __ bicycles = 2 wheels : 1 bicycle
- Repeat the activity for tricycles and for cars. Under each illustration they should show that the ratio and the rate are equivalent.

AT A GLANCE

Students explore rates and related unit rates. They also review the terms *ratio*, *rate*, and *unit rate*.

STEP BY STEP

- Read the problem at the top of the page with the class. Point out that it is the problem from Think on the facing page.
- Stress the difference between a ratio and a related rate. Challenge students to give examples of ratios and their related rates. (Examples: 10 passengers : 2 vans, 5 passengers : 1 van; 36 seats : 4 rows and 9 seats : 1 row)
- Read Think as a class. Use the terms *ratio, rate*, and *unit rate* in the context of the problem.
- Note the difference between the ratios in Think on this page and those in Think on the previous page. On this page the ratio compares two different units, dollars to hours, and on the previous page the ratio compares the same units, cups to cups.
- Have students read and reply to the Reflect directive.

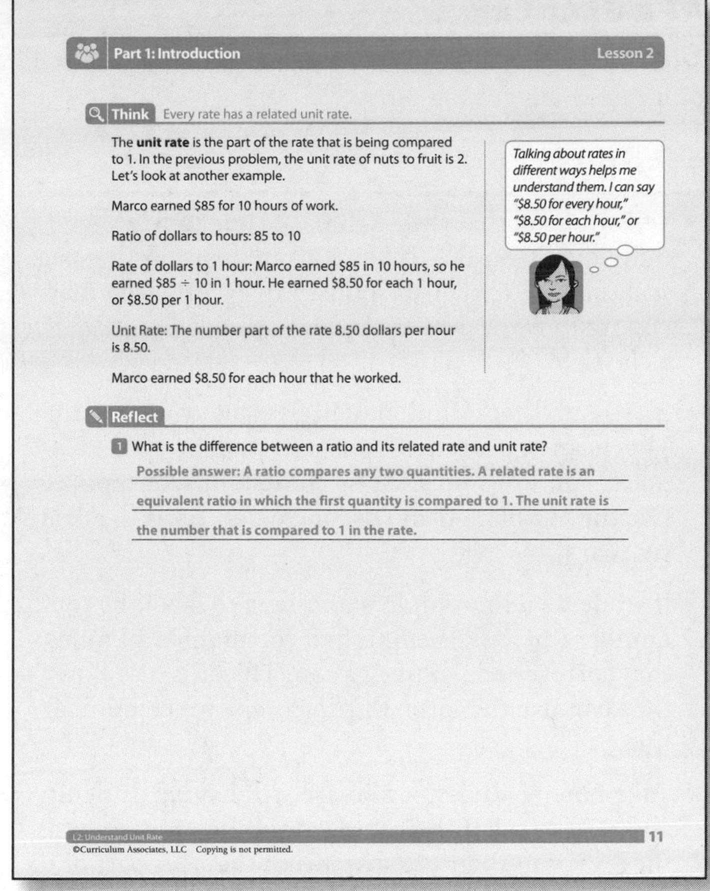

Part 1: Introduction Lesson 2

Think Every rate has a related unit rate.

The **unit rate** is the part of the rate that is being compared to 1. In the previous problem, the unit rate of nuts to fruit is 2. Let's look at another example.

Marco earned $85 for 10 hours of work.

Ratio of dollars to hours: 85 to 10

Rate of dollars to 1 hour: Marco earned $85 in 10 hours, so he earned $85 ÷ 10 in 1 hour. He earned $8.50 for each 1 hour, or $8.50 per 1 hour.

Unit Rate: The number part of the rate 8.50 dollars per hour is 8.50.

Marco earned $8.50 for each hour that he worked.

Talking about rates in different ways helps me understand them. I can say "$8.50 for every hour," "$8.50 for each hour," or "$8.50 per hour."

Reflect

1 What is the difference between a ratio and its related rate and unit rate?

Possible answer: A ratio compares any two quantities. A related rate is an equivalent ratio in which the first quantity is compared to 1. The unit rate is the number that is compared to 1 in the rate.

L2: Understand Unit Rate 11

©Curriculum Associates, LLC Copying is not permitted.

ELL Support

Make a table of ways to talk about a rate. Encourage students to look for these words in problems involving rates. Point out that sometimes we don't say the *1* when we say *for every, for each,* or *per,* e.g., 2 cups of nuts for each cup of fruit. Continue the table using other examples such as 4 legs and 1 table or 25 miles and 1 hour.

2 cups of nuts	**to**	1 cup of fruit
2 cups of nuts	**for every**	1 cup of fruit
2 cups of nuts	**for each**	1 cup of fruit
2 cups of nuts	**per**	1 cup of fruit

Mathematical Discourse

- *Explain why the ratio and the rate describing a situation have to be equivalent.*

  Students should see that they are equivalent since they describe the same situation. The rate is the ratio simplified so that the denominator is 1.

- *Suppose a school has 800 students and 40 teachers. What is the ratio of students to teachers, the rate, and the unit rate?*

  800 students to 40 teachers; 20 students to 1 teacher; 20

- *When might it be useful to give the ratio? The rate?*

  The ratio shows the size of the school as well. The rate is easier to understand and simpler to use.

AT A GLANCE

Students use a double number line to find the rate and unit rate when given a ratio.

STEP BY STEP

- Tell students that they will have time to work individually on the Explore It problems on this page and then share their responses in groups. You may choose to work through the first problem together as a class.
- As students work individually, circulate among them. This is an opportunity to assess student understanding and address student misconceptions. Use the Mathematical Discourse questions to engage student thinking.
- If students do not understand how to label the top number line, ask them to find the number of miles that corresponds to one gallon. Then discuss how they can use the ratio 30:1 to complete the number line.
- Take note of students who are still having difficulty and wait to see if their understanding progresses as they work in their groups during the next part of the lesson.

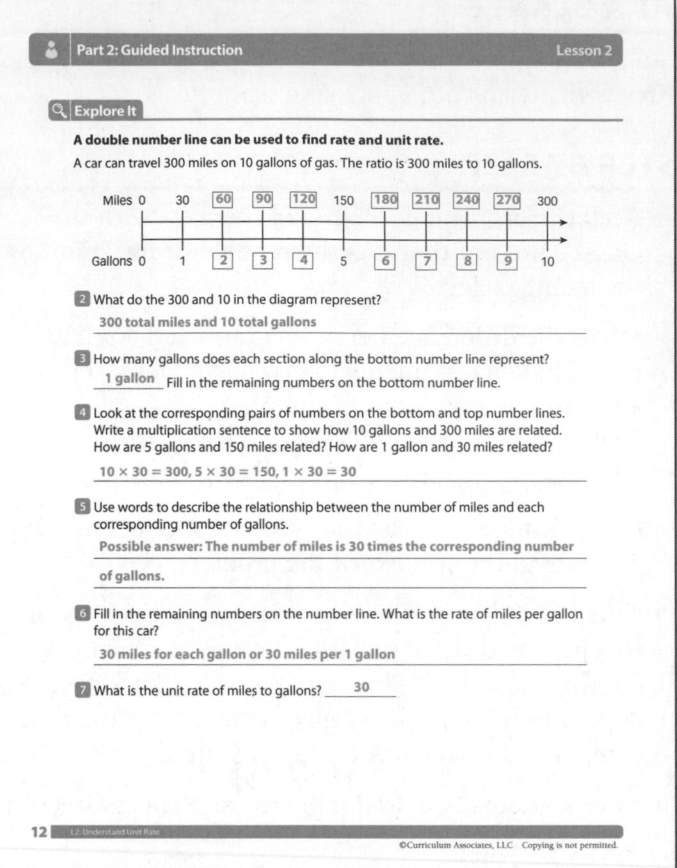

Part 2: Guided Instruction — Lesson 2

Explore It

A double number line can be used to find rate and unit rate.

A car can travel 300 miles on 10 gallons of gas. The ratio is 300 miles to 10 gallons.

Miles	0	30	60	90	120	150	180	210	240	270	300
Gallons	0	1	2	3	4	5	6	7	8	9	10

2 What do the 300 and 10 in the diagram represent?
300 total miles and 10 total gallons

3 How many gallons does each section along the bottom number line represent? **1 gallon** Fill in the remaining numbers on the bottom number line.

4 Look at the corresponding pairs of numbers on the bottom and top number lines. Write a multiplication sentence to show how 10 gallons and 300 miles are related. How are 5 gallons and 150 miles related? How are 1 gallon and 30 miles related?
$10 \times 30 = 300$, $5 \times 30 = 150$, $1 \times 30 = 30$

5 Use words to describe the relationship between the number of miles and each corresponding number of gallons.
Possible answer: The number of miles is 30 times the corresponding number of gallons.

6 Fill in the remaining numbers on the number line. What is the rate of miles per gallon for this car?
30 miles for each gallon or 30 miles per 1 gallon

7 What is the unit rate of miles to gallons? **30**

12 L2: Understand Unit Rate

©Curriculum Associates, LLC Copying is not permitted.

Visual Model

Use a model to find rate and unit rate.

- Draw an oval or other symbol for a gallon on the board. Have students read the Explore It problem and tell you how many gallon symbols you should draw in all.
- Ask how many miles are given in the problem. Say that the car travels the same distance on each gallon. Have students figure out how far the car travels on one gallon.
- Write 30 in each of the gallon symbols.
- Use the visual model to reinforce the relationship shown by the double number line.

Mathematical Discourse

- *We have used three different visual models for ratios—a bar model, tape diagram, and double number line. What is one way all are alike?*

  Responses may include that all show the ratio and can also be used to figure out the rate and unit rate.

- *How are they different?*

  Students may see that the bar model and number line are aligned so it is easy to see the unit rate. The tape diagram is for comparisons of the same unit, so the rectangles are the same size.

- *Is there one model that helps you see the relationship more clearly? What do you like about it?*

  Students' explanations should involve explaining which model helps them see the relationship more clearly.

AT A GLANCE

Students work with the double number line to reinforce the concepts of unit rate and rate in the context of the problem on page 12. They also use equivalent fractions to find rate and unit rate.

STEP BY STEP

- Organize students into pairs or groups. You may choose to work through the first Talk About It problem together as a class.
- Walk around to each group, listen to, and join in on discussions at different points. Use the Mathematical Discourse questions to help support or extend students' thinking.
- Note that there is often more than one way to describe a pattern. To make sure a pattern is valid, have students check to see if it is true for all the numbers on the double number line.
- Direct the group's attention to Try It Another Way. Have a volunteer from each group come to the board to explain the group's solutions to problems 12 and 13.

SMP Tip: Students look for and make use of structure (*SMP 7*) as they describe the patterns found on the double number line and in the related ratios. Occasionally ask them to describe the numeric patterns in other diagrams and ratio tables they are working with.

STUDENT MISCONCEPTION ALERT: Some students may reverse the two quantities. Have students read the problem and tell what it is asking for. Note that the word order is important because it tells what order the numbers should follow. It is sometimes helpful for the student to write the ratio as words before using the numbers in the problem.

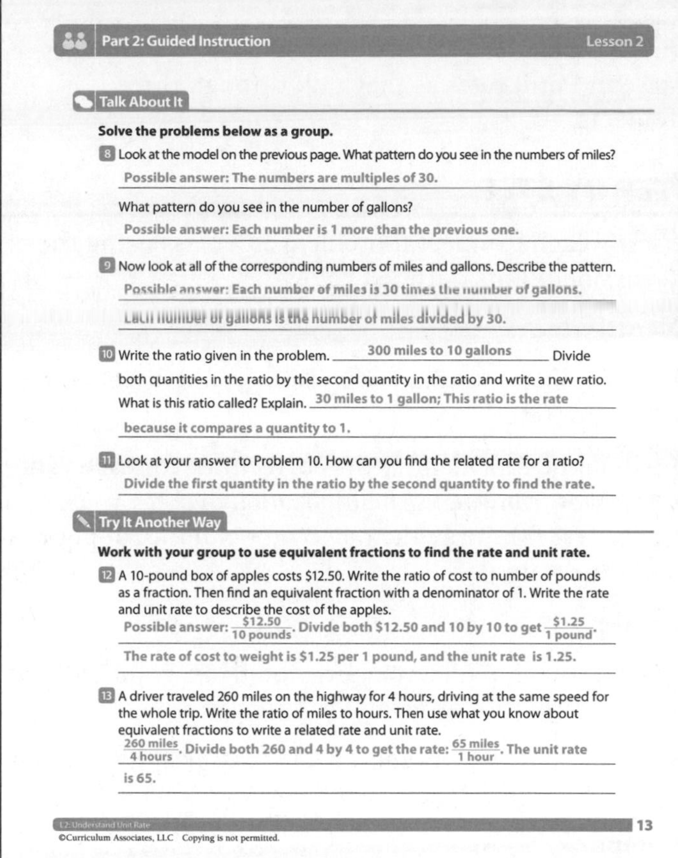

Part 2: Guided Instruction Lesson 2

Talk About It

Solve the problems below as a group.

8 Look at the model on the previous page. What pattern do you see in the numbers of miles?

Possible answer: The numbers are multiples of 30.

What pattern do you see in the number of gallons?

Possible answer: Each number is 1 more than the previous one.

9 Now look at all of the corresponding numbers of miles and gallons. Describe the pattern.

Possible answer: Each number of miles is 30 times the number of gallons. Each number of gallons is the number of miles divided by 30.

10 Write the ratio given in the problem. 300 miles to 10 gallons Divide both quantities in the ratio by the second quantity in the ratio and write a new ratio. What is this ratio called? Explain. 30 miles to 1 gallon; This ratio is the rate because it compares a quantity to 1.

11 Look at your answer to Problem 10. How can you find the related rate for a ratio?

Divide the first quantity in the ratio by the second quantity to find the rate.

Try It Another Way

Work with your group to use equivalent fractions to find the rate and unit rate.

12 A 10-pound box of apples costs \$12.50. Write the ratio of cost to number of pounds as a fraction. Then find an equivalent fraction with a denominator of 1. Write the rate and unit rate to describe the cost of the apples.

Possible answer: $\frac{\$12.50}{10 \text{ pounds}}$. Divide both \$12.50 and 10 by 10 to get $\frac{\$1.25}{1 \text{ pound}}$. The rate of cost to weight is \$1.25 per 1 pound, and the unit rate is 1.25.

13 A driver traveled 260 miles on the highway for 4 hours, driving at the same speed for the whole trip. Write the ratio of miles to hours. Then use what you know about equivalent fractions to write a related rate and unit rate.

$\frac{260 \text{ miles}}{4 \text{ hours}}$. Divide both 260 and 4 by 4 to get the rate: $\frac{65 \text{ miles}}{1 \text{ hour}}$. The unit rate is 65.

L2: Understand Unit Rate 13

©Curriculum Associates, LLC Copying is not permitted.

Mathematical Discourse

- *How can you use the pattern in numbers of miles and gallons to help you write the ratio or the rate?*

  Responses should indicate that the pattern tells how many miles can be driven with each gallon of gas, which is the same as the rate.

- *Will the rate always be a whole number? Explain or give an example.*

  Listen for responses that show the rate can be a fraction. For example, the associated rate for 7 miles in 2 hours is $3\frac{1}{2}$ miles for every 1 mile. The rate for 2 cups flour for 18 muffins is $\frac{1}{9}$ cup per muffin.

AT A GLANCE

Students demonstrate their understanding of ratios, rates, and unit rates as they talk through three problems.

STEP BY STEP

Discuss each Connect It problem as a class using the discussion points outlined below.

Identify:

- Have students explain why they would divide to find the unit rate.
- After students identify the correct rate for each ratio, ask, *How can you use multiplication to check your answers?* [Multiply the rate by the number of pounds in the original ratio.]

Create:

- Have students read the nutrition facts. Point out that the information is given for 2 crackers.
- Ask, *If you know a quantity for 2 crackers, how do you find the related quantity for 1 cracker?* [divide by 2]

Compare:

- The third problem focuses on using the unit rate to compare two ratios with different second quantities.
- Have students explain why they cannot compare the hourly earnings using the information as given.
- Have students explain why finding the rate is important in this problem.

SMP Tip: Students reason abstractly and quantitatively (*SMP 2*) as they compare two ratios with different second numbers by finding the related rates. They understand the meaning of the quantities in context and then work abstractly to calculate the related rates. They contextualize the rates they derived to compare the girls' earnings.

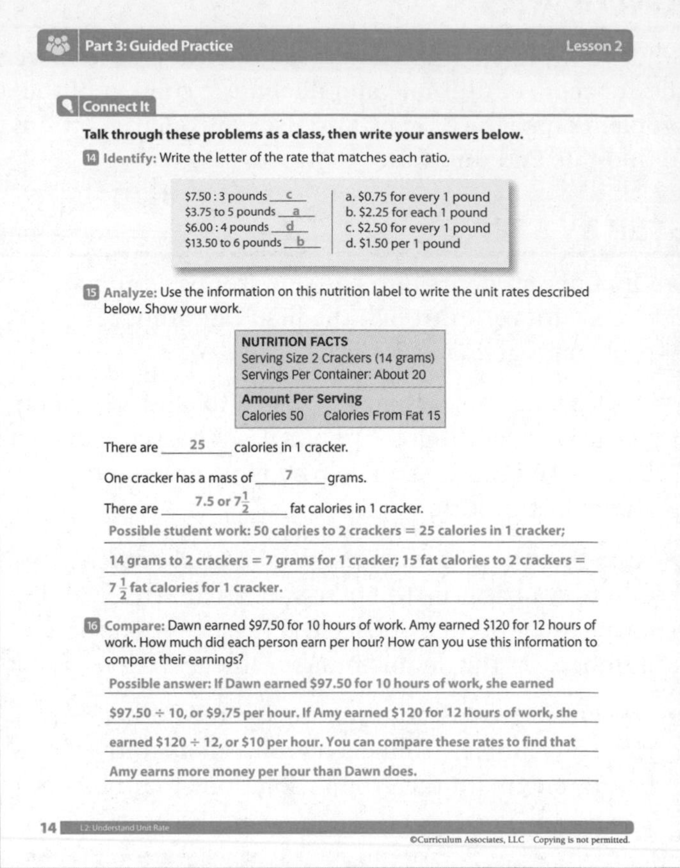

Part 3: Guided Practice Lesson 2

Connect It

Talk through these problems as a class, then write your answers below.

14 **Identify:** Write the letter of the rate that matches each ratio.

\$7.50 : 3 pounds __c__	a. \$0.75 for every 1 pound
\$3.75 to 5 pounds __a__	b. \$2.25 for each 1 pound
\$6.00 : 4 pounds __d__	c. \$2.50 for every 1 pound
\$13.50 to 6 pounds __b__	d. \$1.50 per 1 pound

15 **Analyze:** Use the information on this nutrition label to write the unit rates described below. Show your work.

NUTRITION FACTS
Serving Size 2 Crackers (14 grams)
Servings Per Container: About 20
Amount Per Serving
Calories 50 Calories From Fat 15

There are __25__ calories in 1 cracker.

One cracker has a mass of __7__ grams.

There are __7.5 or $7\frac{1}{2}$__ fat calories in 1 cracker.

Possible student work: 50 calories to 2 crackers = 25 calories in 1 cracker; 14 grams to 2 crackers = 7 grams for 1 cracker; 15 fat calories to 2 crackers = $7\frac{1}{2}$ fat calories for 1 cracker.

16 **Compare:** Dawn earned \$97.50 for 10 hours of work. Amy earned \$120 for 12 hours of work. How much did each person earn per hour? How can you use this information to compare their earnings?

Possible answer: If Dawn earned \$97.50 for 10 hours of work, she earned \$97.50 ÷ 10, or \$9.75 per hour. If Amy earned \$120 for 12 hours of work, she earned \$120 ÷ 12, or \$10 per hour. You can compare these rates to find that Amy earns more money per hour than Dawn does.

14 L2: Understand Unit Rate

©Curriculum Associates, LLC Copying is not permitted.

AT A GLANCE

Students work with the ratios of two ingredients to change the quantities needed when using a recipe.

STEP BY STEP

- Direct students to complete the Put It Together task on their own.
- Remind students that unit rates can be fractions and that fractional unit rates are found and used the same way as whole number unit rates are used.
- As students work on their own, walk around to assess their progress and understanding, to answer their questions, and to give additional support, if needed.
- If time permits, have students share the reasoning behind their solutions.

SCORING RUBRICS

See student facsimile page for possible student answers.

A

Points	Expectations
2	The response shows the correct ratio, rate, and unit rate.
1	The response shows either the correct ratio or the correct rate and unit rate, but not all three.
0	Incorrect response, or none given

B

Points	Expectations
2	The response shows the correct ratio, rate, and unit rate.
1	The response shows either the correct ratio or the correct rate and unit rate, but not all three.
0	Incorrect response, or none given

C

Points	Expectations
2	Student demonstrates the correct answer by multiplying by the unit rate, making a double number line, or using a table.
1	Student's work shows some evidence of proportional reasoning but is not well developed or contains a minor error.
0	Incorrect response, or none given

Part 4: Common Core Performance Task — Lesson 2

Put It Together

17 A recipe uses 3 cups of flour and 2 cups of sugar.

A Write the ratio of cups of flour to cups of sugar as a fraction: $\frac{3}{2}$ cups.

Divide the first quantity by the second quantity to find the related rate:

3 cups ÷ 2 cups = $\frac{3}{2}$ cups to 1 cup.

The unit rate is $\frac{3}{2}$.

B Now write a ratio of cups of sugar to cups of flour as a fraction: $\frac{2}{3}$ cups.

Divide the first quantity by the second quantity to find the related rate:

2 cups ÷ 3 cups = $\frac{2}{3}$ cups to 1 cup.

The unit rate is $\frac{2}{3}$.

C Imagine that the recipe is doubled and that 4 cups of sugar are used. Use the unit rate in A to find how much flour is needed if the recipe is made with 4 cups of sugar. Show your work.

Possible answer: $\frac{3}{2} \times 4 = 6$. If 4 cups of sugar are used, then 6 cups of flour are needed.

D Imagine that 6 cups of flour are used to make the recipe. Use the unit rate in B to find how much sugar is needed if the recipe is made with 6 cups of flour.

Possible answer: $\frac{2}{3} \times 6 = 4$. If 6 cups of flour are used, then 4 cups of sugar are needed.

E Compare your answers to C and D and explain how the two unit rates are related.

Possible answer: Both answers show that to double the recipe, you need 6 cups of flour and 4 cups of sugar. The unit rates include the same quantities, but the quantities are reversed. The unit rates are reciprocals.

L2: Understand Unit Rate 15

©Curriculum Associates, LLC Copying is not permitted.

D

Points	Expectations
2	Student demonstrates the correct answer by multiplying by the unit rate, making a double number line, or using a table.
1	Student's work shows some evidence of proportional reasoning but is not well developed or contains a minor error.
0	Incorrect response, or none given

E

Points	Expectations
2	The response indicates the student understands that the rates show an inverse relationship and some explanation of the relationship is given.
1	The response uses a word such as *reciprocal* but does not explain the relationship in depth.
0	The response does not recognize that the rates show an inverse relationship or no response is given.

Intervention Activity

Use concrete materials to find and apply a unit rate.

Materials: paper cups, paper clips, paper, pencils

Have students work in groups of 2 or 3. Give each group 4 cups and 24 paper clips. Have students find and record the ratio of paper clips to cups. Then have them place the paper clips into cups so that each cup contains the same number. Have them record the ratio of paper clips to one cup. Then have students find and record the ratio of paper clips to 2 cups and to 3 cups.

Ask students to identify and record the unit rate. Then have them explain how they could use the unit rate to find other ratios with the same unit rate without having to count the clips in the cups.

On-Level Activity

Draw and use a double number line to find a unit price.

Tell students that a package of 12 markers costs $3.00.

Have them draw a double number line with the top line labeled *Cost* and the bottom *Number of Markers*. Ask them how many vertical lines they would need to show all 12 markers. Have them draw the lines and label the bottom number line. Discuss how to find the cost of 1 marker. Emphasize that the cost of 1 marker is called the unit rate. Once students have found the unit rate, have them use it to number the top number line. Have students draw conclusions from the number line and share them with the class.

Challenge Activity

Find and compare unit rates.

Materials: index cards

On the board write,

For 6 fruit baskets, Ben used 24 oranges, 6 grapefruit, 18 apples, and 3 pounds of cherries.

For 8 fruit baskets, Bill used 24 oranges, 8 grapefruit, 32 apples, and 6 pounds of cherries.

For each type of basket, have students find the unit rate for each type of fruit. Have students compare the contents of the two types of basket.

Give students an index card. On the front, the students will state the number of baskets and the amount of each type of fruit used for all the baskets. On the back, the students will list the unit rate for each type of fruit they listed on the front. Students exchange cards and find the unit rates. They check their answers with the information on the back of the card. Encourage students to create their own similar problems using different numbers of baskets and contents, and exchange cards.

Lesson 3 (Student Book pages 16–25)

Equivalent Ratios

LESSON OBJECTIVES

- Use a table to find equivalent ratios.
- Find missing values in equivalent ratio tables.
- Plot the pairs of values in a table on a coordinate plane.
- Use a table and graph to reason about equivalent ratios.
- Use a table and graph to compare ratios.

PREREQUISITE SKILLS

- Understand ratio reasoning and relationships.
- Understand equivalent fractions.
- Use the four basic operations (+, −, ×, ÷).
- Represent equivalent ratios with ratio notation.

VOCABULARY

equivalent ratios: two or more ratios that are equal to one another

THE LEARNING PROGRESSION

Students have worked with the concept of a ratio as a way to compare two different quantities. They have learned to find rates and unit rates from a given ratio. In this lesson, they extend the idea of ratio to include equivalent ratios. When two ratios simplify to the same rate, they are equivalent.

Students work with equivalent ratios in tables and use multiplication and division to reason about them. They begin to use ratios to solve simple problems. In later lessons, students will extend their understanding of ratios to solve more complex problems and to understand different methods they can use to solve them.

Students will extend their understanding of ratio and proportion to include scale drawings and real-world percent problems in Grade 7 and slope in Grade 8.

Ready ***Teacher Toolbox*** Teacher-Toolbox.com

	Prerequisite Skills	6.RP.A.3a
Ready Lessons	✓	✓
Tools for Instruction	✓	✓
Interactive Tutorials		✓✓

CCSS Focus

6.RP.A.3 Use ratio and rate reasoning to solve real-world and mathematical problems, e.g., by reasoning about tables of equivalent ratios, tape diagrams, double number line diagrams, or equations.

a. Make tables of equivalent ratios relating quantities with whole-number measurements, find missing values in the tables, and plot the pairs of values on the coordinate plane. Use tables to compare ratios.

STANDARDS FOR MATHEMATICAL PRACTICE: ***SMP 1, 2, 4, 5, 7, 8*** *(see page A9 for full text)*

AT A GLANCE

Students use multiplication and division to find equivalent ratios, related rates, and unit rates.

STEP BY STEP

- Tell students that this page models how to use multiplication and division to solve problems involving ratios.
- Have students read the problem at the top of the page.
- Work through Explore It as a class.
- Remind students that ratios are comparisons of two quantities.
- Review the definitions of rate and unit rate and have students explain how to use each ratio to find the rate and unit rate.
- Ask student pairs or groups to explain their answers for the last question.

SMP Tip: Students must look for and express regularity in repeated reasoning *(SMP 8)* as they figure out that they double the amount of stock for 2 batches, they triple it for 3 batches, and they multiply it by 4 for 4 batches. You can extend the process by having them find the amount of stock needed for other numbers of batches. Then challenge them to state a general rule that they can use to find the stock needed for any number of batches.

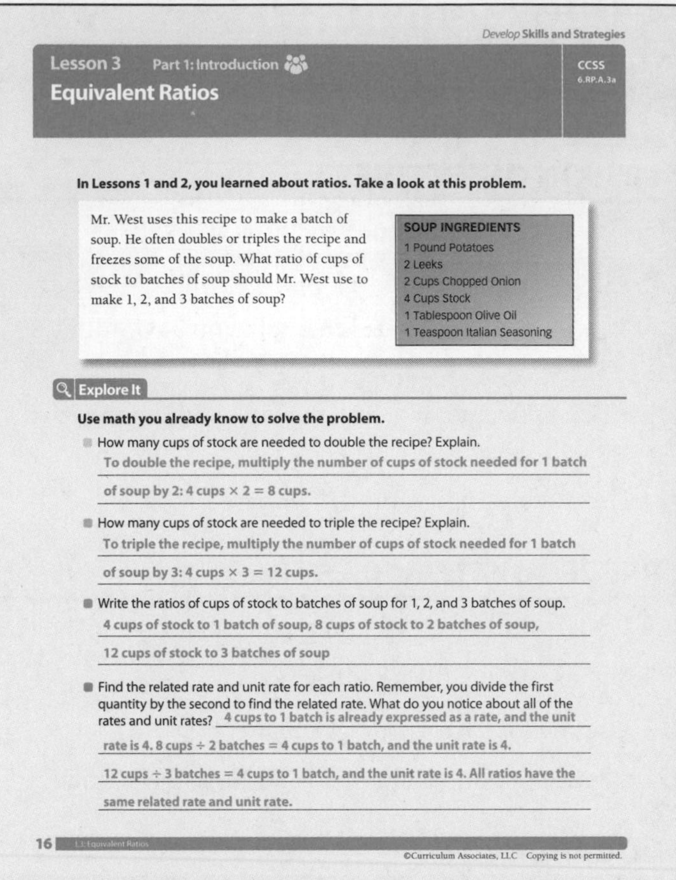

Develop Skills and Strategies

Lesson 3 Part 1: Introduction

Equivalent Ratios

CCSS 6.RP.A.3a

In Lessons 1 and 2, you learned about ratios. Take a look at this problem.

Mr. West uses this recipe to make a batch of soup. He often doubles or triples the recipe and freezes some of the soup. What ratio of cups of stock to batches of soup should Mr. West use to make 1, 2, and 3 batches of soup?

SOUP INGREDIENTS
1 Pound Potatoes
2 Leeks
2 Cups Chopped Onion
4 Cups Stock
1 Tablespoon Olive Oil
1 Teaspoon Italian Seasoning

Explore It

Use math you already know to solve the problem.

- How many cups of stock are needed to double the recipe? Explain.
  To double the recipe, multiply the number of cups of stock needed for 1 batch of soup by 2: 4 cups × 2 = 8 cups.
- How many cups of stock are needed to triple the recipe? Explain.
  To triple the recipe, multiply the number of cups of stock needed for 1 batch of soup by 3: 4 cups × 3 = 12 cups.
- Write the ratios of cups of stock to batches of soup for 1, 2, and 3 batches of soup.
  4 cups of stock to 1 batch of soup, 8 cups of stock to 2 batches of soup, 12 cups of stock to 3 batches of soup
- Find the related rate and unit rate for each ratio. Remember, you divide the first quantity by the second to find the related rate. What do you notice about all of the rates and unit rates? 4 cups to 1 batch is already expressed as a rate, and the unit rate is 4. 8 cups ÷ 2 batches = 4 cups to 1 batch, and the unit rate is 4. 12 cups ÷ 3 batches = 4 cups to 1 batch, and the unit rate is 4. All ratios have the same related rate and unit rate.

16 L3: Equivalent Ratios ©Curriculum Associates, LLC Copying is not permitted.

Mathematical Discourse

- *We used multiplication to find equivalent ratios and solve the problem. Could you add the same number to both the amount of stock and number of batches and get the same rate? Explain why or why not.*

  Students should explain why adding the same number to both terms of the ratio does not create equivalent ratios. Encourage them to find examples. $\left(\text{Ex: } \frac{1+3}{5+3} \neq \frac{4}{8}, \text{ but } \frac{1 \times 3}{5 \times 3} = \frac{3}{15} = \frac{1}{5}\right)$
- *How would you find the amount of potatoes, onions, and salt you would need for 2 batches of soup? For 3?*

  Multiply by the amount needed for 1 batch by 2 for 2 batches and by 3 for 3 batches.

AT A GLANCE

Students use tables to find equivalent ratios.

STEP BY STEP

- Read Find Out More as a class.
- Review the term *equivalent ratios.* Ask, *How can you show that the ratios in the table are equivalent?* (See if they all simplify to the same number.)
- Draw students' attention to the use of multiplication to find the amount of fruit needed in the second problem. Ask, "How is finding equivalent ratios for the table like finding equivalent fractions? (You are multiplying both parts of the ratio by the same number.)

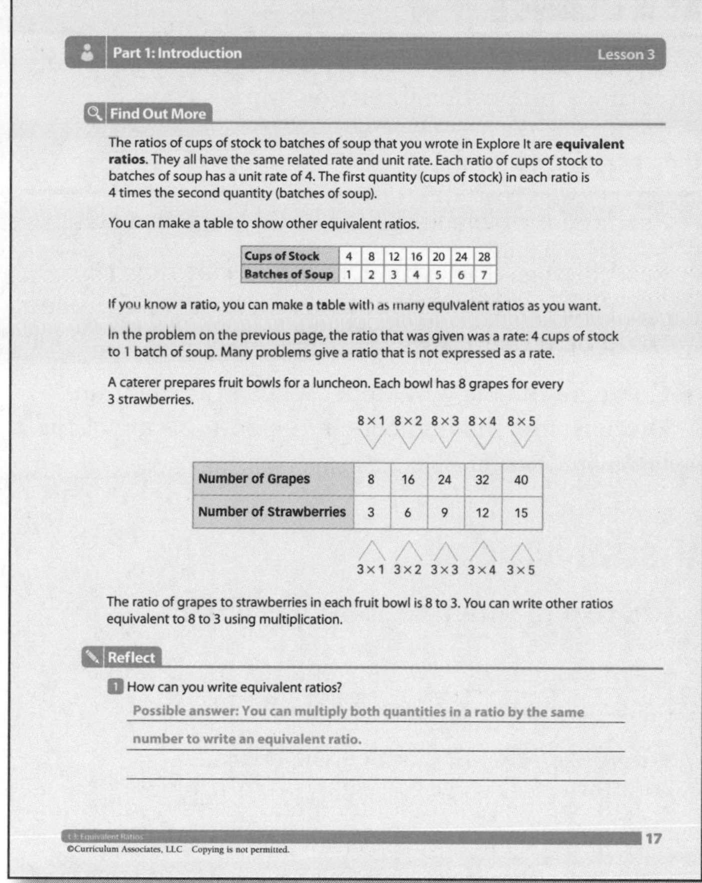

Part 1: Introduction Lesson 3

Find Out More

The ratios of cups of stock to batches of soup that you wrote in Explore It are **equivalent ratios.** They all have the same related rate and unit rate. Each ratio of cups of stock to batches of soup has a unit rate of 4. The first quantity (cups of stock) in each ratio is 4 times the second quantity (batches of soup).

You can make a table to show other equivalent ratios.

Cups of Stock	4	8	12	16	20	24	28
Batches of Soup	1	2	3	4	5	6	7

If you know a ratio, you can make a table with as many equivalent ratios as you want.

In the problem on the previous page, the ratio that was given was a rate: 4 cups of stock to 1 batch of soup. Many problems give a ratio that is not expressed as a rate.

A caterer prepares fruit bowls for a luncheon. Each bowl has 8 grapes for every 3 strawberries.

	8×1	8×2	8×3	8×4	8×5
Number of Grapes	8	16	24	32	40
Number of Strawberries	3	6	9	12	15
	3×1	3×2	3×3	3×4	3×5

The ratio of grapes to strawberries in each fruit bowl is 8 to 3. You can write other ratios equivalent to 8 to 3 using multiplication.

Reflect

1 How can you write equivalent ratios?

Possible answer: You can multiply both quantities in a ratio by the same number to write an equivalent ratio.

L3: Equivalent Ratios 17

©Curriculum Associates, LLC Copying is not permitted.

Hands-On Activity

Use visual models to understand equivalent ratios.

Materials: paper, scissors, red and green markers or crayons

- Have students each cut out a circle to represent a bowl. Direct them to draw 3 red strawberries and 8 green grapes on their circle.
- Draw a table that compares grapes to strawberries on the board. Have a volunteer come to the board and record the number of grapes and strawberries for one "bowl" in the table (8:3) and then record equivalent ratios that other students provide next.
- Have 4 students come to the front of the class. Ask them to use their models to figure out their combined number of grapes and of strawberries. Have the recorder enter the numbers they decide in the table.
- Repeat with groups of various sizes such as 2 students, 7 students, and 5 students.
- Once the table has at least 6 columns, have students find and simplify the ratio of grapes to strawberries for each column. Discuss why the ratios are equivalent.

Real-World Connection

Encourage students to think of everyday tasks that require them to use equivalent ratios. Have volunteers share their ideas.

Examples: Changing the amount of ingredients in cooking or the amount of materials needed for sewing and crafts; using a scale for such things as finding distance on a map, making a model airplane or an architectural drawing of different-sized rooms.

AT A GLANCE

Students use a diagram and a table to solve a problem involving a proportional relationship.

STEP BY STEP

- Read the problem at the top of the page as a class.
- Read Picture It. Have students describe how the diagram models the problem. Ask how the diagram could help them solve the problem.
- Compare the table in Model It with the diagram. Discuss how the numbers in the bottom row of the table are found.

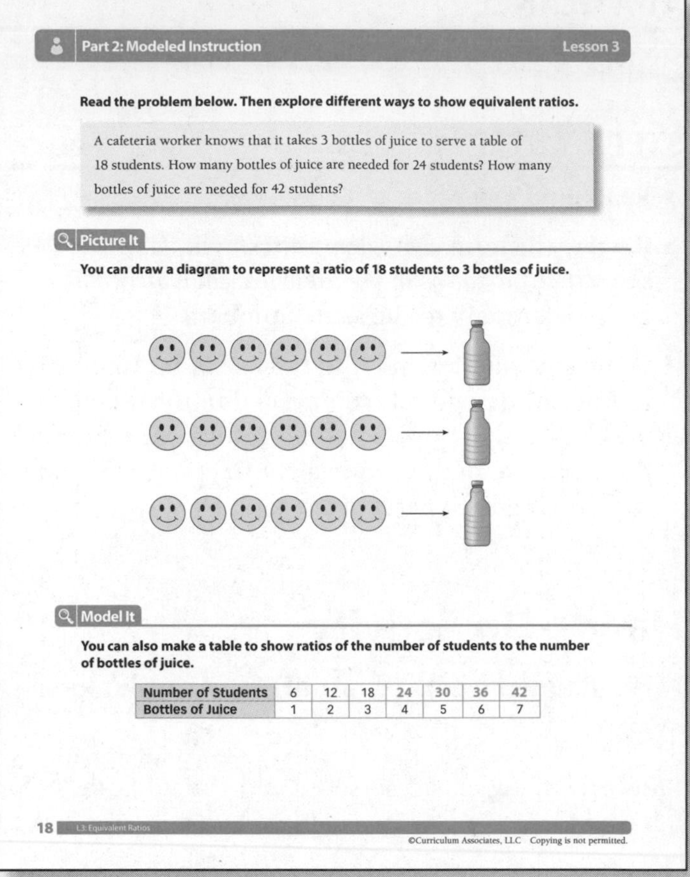

Part 2: Modeled Instruction Lesson 3

Read the problem below. Then explore different ways to show equivalent ratios.

A cafeteria worker knows that it takes 3 bottles of juice to serve a table of 18 students. How many bottles of juice are needed for 24 students? How many bottles of juice are needed for 42 students?

Picture It

You can draw a diagram to represent a ratio of 18 students to 3 bottles of juice.

Model It

You can also make a table to show ratios of the number of students to the number of bottles of juice.

Number of Students	6	12	18	24	30	36	42
Bottles of Juice	1	2	3	4	5	6	7

18 L3: Equivalent Ratios

©Curriculum Associates, LLC Copying is not permitted.

Visual Model

Add to a diagram to solve a problem.

- Tell students you will extend the bottle-and-students diagram to solve the problem.
- Replicate the diagram on the board.
- Add one more symbol for a bottle and 6 more symbols for students. Ask, "What does the new diagram represent?" (4 bottles for 24 students)
- Continue to add rows of symbols for 1 bottle per 6 students until you have 42 students. Have students explain why the extended diagram answers the second question of the problem.

Mathematical Discourse

- *In Picture It, is it important to have the same number of students next to each bottle of juice? Explain.*

  Yes, that is the idea of a proportional relationship. The number does not change.

- *Suppose 4 bottles of juice are needed for 20 students, how will the diagram be different?*

  It would show 4 bottles, each followed by 5 students.

- *How can you figure out how many students to draw next to each bottle if you know the total number of students and the total number of bottles?*

  Divide the number of students by the number of bottles to find the unit rate.

AT A GLANCE

Students revisit the problem on page 18 to learn how to create and use a ratio table to solve the problem. Then, students solve other problems using tables.

STEP BY STEP

- Read Connect It as a class. Be sure to point out that the questions refer to the problem on page 18. Review the terms *ratio, rate*, and *unit rate* in the context of the problem.
- Have students explain why multiplying the number of bottles by the unit rate is one way to complete the table.
- Use the table to answer the questions in the problem.
- Ask students how they can simplify the ratios $\frac{24 \text{ bottles}}{4 \text{ students}}$ and $\frac{42 \text{ bottles}}{7 \text{ students}}$ to check their answers.
- Have students work in pairs to solve the Try It problems. Invite pairs to show and explain how they did it.

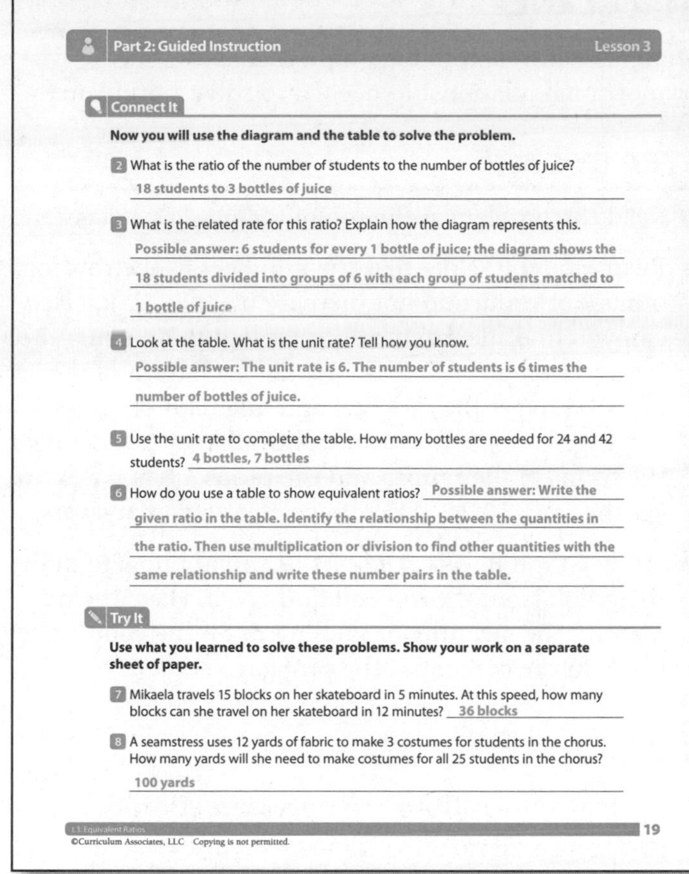

Part 2: Guided Instruction Lesson 3

Connect It

Now you will use the diagram and the table to solve the problem.

2 What is the ratio of the number of students to the number of bottles of juice? 18 students to 3 bottles of juice

3 What is the related rate for this ratio? Explain how the diagram represents this. Possible answer: 6 students for every 1 bottle of juice; the diagram shows the 18 students divided into groups of 6 with each group of students matched to 1 bottle of juice

4 Look at the table. What is the unit rate? Tell how you know. Possible answer: The unit rate is 6. The number of students is 6 times the number of bottles of juice.

5 Use the unit rate to complete the table. How many bottles are needed for 24 and 42 students? 4 bottles, 7 bottles

6 How do you use a table to show equivalent ratios? Possible answer: Write the given ratio in the table. Identify the relationship between the quantities in the ratio. Then use multiplication or division to find other quantities with the same relationship and write these number pairs in the table.

Try It

Use what you learned to solve these problems. Show your work on a separate sheet of paper.

7 Mikaela travels 15 blocks on her skateboard in 5 minutes. At this speed, how many blocks can she travel on her skateboard in 12 minutes? 36 blocks

8 A seamstress uses 12 yards of fabric to make 3 costumes for students in the chorus. How many yards will she need to make costumes for all 25 students in the chorus? 100 yards

L3: Equivalent Ratios 19
©Curriculum Associates, LLC Copying is not permitted.

ELL Support

- Remind students that a ratio compares two quantities. After reading the problem, help students focus on what two quantities are being compared.
- Before making a table or graph, write the ratio in words such as $\frac{\text{bottles}}{\text{students}}$, $\frac{\text{blocks}}{\text{minutes}}$, or $\frac{\text{yards}}{\text{costumes}}$. Make sure students understand what the terms mean. They may also want to develop and use symbols to further emphasize the quantities used.
- As students work through each problem, have them refer to the terms in their ratio so that they understand what the related numbers mean.

TRY IT SOLUTIONS

7 *Solution:* 36 blocks; Students may make a ratio table that shows the ratio of blocks per minute. All ratios shown should simplify to 3:1.

8 *Solution:* 100 yards; Students may make a ratio table that compares yards to costumes. All ratios shown should simplify to 4:1.

ERROR ALERT: Students who wrote 28 yards may have made a table starting with 4:1 and used addition (+4) instead of multiplication (×4) to fill it in and solve the problem. $\frac{28 \text{ yards}}{25 \text{ costumes}}$ is not equivalent to $\frac{12 \text{ yards}}{3 \text{ costumes}}$, or $\frac{4 \text{ yards}}{1 \text{ costume}}$.

AT A GLANCE

Students use a table and a graph that shows the proportional relationship needed to solve a problem.

STEP BY STEP

- Read the problem at the top of the page as a class.
- Read Model It. Note that the numbers in the row for ounces of yogurt do not increase by ones. Ask, "How can you find the ratios of yogurt to protein using the information given?" (Take half of each term of the ratio 4:8 to get the ratio 2:4 and take half of each term again to get the ratio 1:2. Double or triple any of the terms of the ratios. Add the ratios 4:8 and 8:16 to get the ratio 12:24.) Encourage a variety of answers.
- Study Graph It. Ask students to explain how to draw the graph from the information given. Have them identify the meaning of each point on the coordinate plane in the context of the problem.

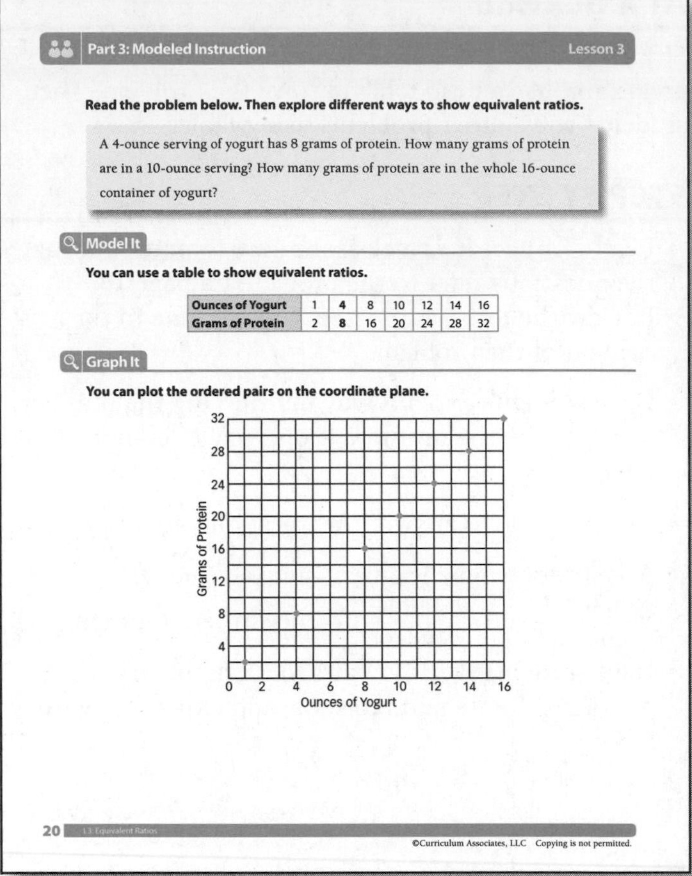

Part 3: Modeled Instruction Lesson 3

Read the problem below. Then explore different ways to show equivalent ratios.

A 4-ounce serving of yogurt has 8 grams of protein. How many grams of protein are in a 10-ounce serving? How many grams of protein are in the whole 16-ounce container of yogurt?

Model It

You can use a table to show equivalent ratios.

Ounces of Yogurt	1	4	8	10	12	14	16
Grams of Protein	2	8	16	20	24	28	32

Graph It

You can plot the ordered pairs on the coordinate plane.

20 L3: Equivalent Ratios ©Curriculum Associates, LLC Copying is not permitted.

Concept Extension

Illustrate the difference between adding fractions and adding ratios.

- Say, *Suppose you have $\frac{1}{4}$ pound of pecans and $\frac{2}{8}$ pound of cashews. How would you find the amount of nuts altogether?*
- Have students demonstrate how to find a common denominator and add the fractions to get a total of $\frac{1}{2}$ pound.
- Then say, *Suppose Amanda brought 1 bag of popcorn to a picnic to serve 4 people. Julie brought 2 bags of popcorn to serve 8 people. How much popcorn is there? How many people would it serve?*
- Make sure students understand that the total of 3 bags would serve 12 people.
- Model the problem by adding ratios.
  $\frac{\text{popcorn}}{\text{people}} = \frac{1+2}{4+8} = \frac{3}{12}$
- Compare the process with the addition of fractions. Discuss how adding fractions is different from adding ratios.

Mathematical Discourse

- *Suppose you only found two ratios of yogurt to protein. Could you use the two ratios to draw a line on the coordinate plane and answer the question? How? Would the line be the same if you used two different ratios from the table?*

  You only need 2 points to draw the line because all the points are on the same line. Any two points from the table would result in the same line. You would plot and connect the points. Then you would look to see how much protein corresponded with 16 ounces of yogurt.

- *What are the advantages of using a table? What are advantages of using a graph? Which format do you prefer?*

  Students' answers will vary.

AT A GLANCE

Students revisit the problem on page 20 to learn how to use the table and the graph to solve the problem. Then, they solve similar problems using ratios.

STEP BY STEP

- Read Connect It as a class. Be sure to point out that the questions refer to the problem on page 20.
- Have students read the labels on the coordinate plane. Make sure they understand that the first coordinate refers to the amount of yogurt and the second to the amount of protein.
- Call on volunteers to compare and contrast the table and the graph.

SMP Tip: Using both tables and graphs to represent proportional relationships shows students different ways to model with mathematics (*SMP 4*). Have students evaluate how effective each model is. Discuss whether they would rather solve the problems by using a table, creating a graph, or just thinking about the problem.

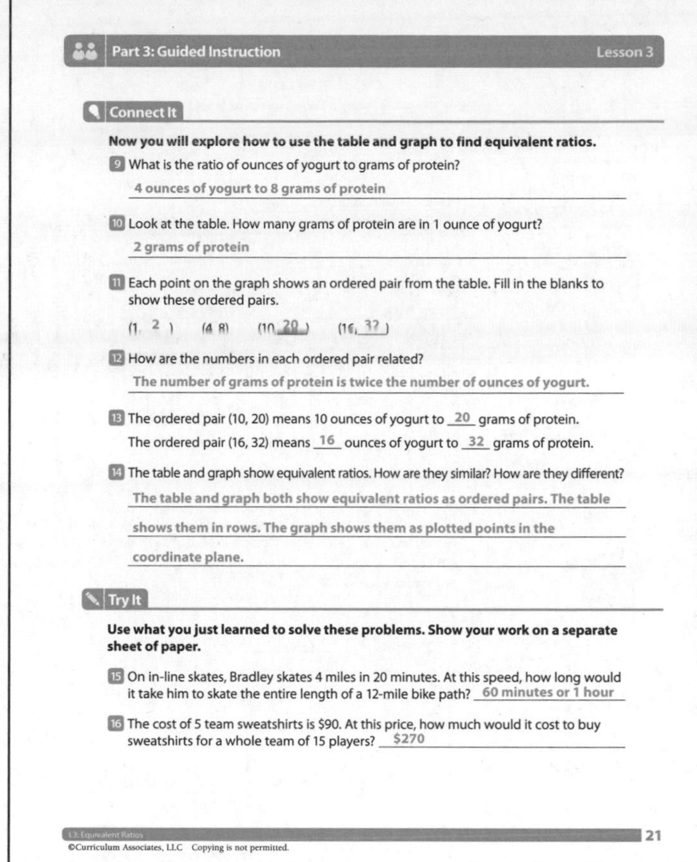

Part 3: Guided Instruction Lesson 3

Connect It

Now you will explore how to use the table and graph to find equivalent ratios.

9 What is the ratio of ounces of yogurt to grams of protein?
4 ounces of yogurt to 8 grams of protein

10 Look at the table. How many grams of protein are in 1 ounce of yogurt?
2 grams of protein

11 Each point on the graph shows an ordered pair from the table. Fill in the blanks to show these ordered pairs.
(1, 2) (4, 8) (10, 20) (16, 32)

12 How are the numbers in each ordered pair related?
The number of grams of protein is twice the number of ounces of yogurt.

13 The ordered pair (10, 20) means 10 ounces of yogurt to 20 grams of protein.
The ordered pair (16, 32) means 16 ounces of yogurt to 32 grams of protein.

14 The table and graph show equivalent ratios. How are they similar? How are they different?
The table and graph both show equivalent ratios as ordered pairs. The table shows them in rows. The graph shows them as plotted points in the coordinate plane.

Try It

Use what you just learned to solve these problems. Show your work on a separate sheet of paper.

15 On in-line skates, Bradley skates 4 miles in 20 minutes. At this speed, how long would it take him to skate the entire length of a 12-mile bike path? 60 minutes or 1 hour

16 The cost of 5 team sweatshirts is $90. At this price, how much would it cost to buy sweatshirts for a whole team of 15 players? $270

L3: Equivalent Ratios 21
©Curriculum Associates, LLC Copying is not permitted.

TRY IT SOLUTIONS

15 *Solution:* 60 minutes or 1 hour; Students may create a ratio table or a graph that shows various ratios of miles to minutes that all simplify to 1:5.

ERROR ALERT: Students who wrote 2.4 or $2\frac{2}{5}$ found the distance Bradley could skate in 12 minutes, not how long it would take him to skate 12 miles.

16 *Solution:* $270; Students may create a ratio table or a graph that shows various ratios of costs to players that all simplify to 18:1.

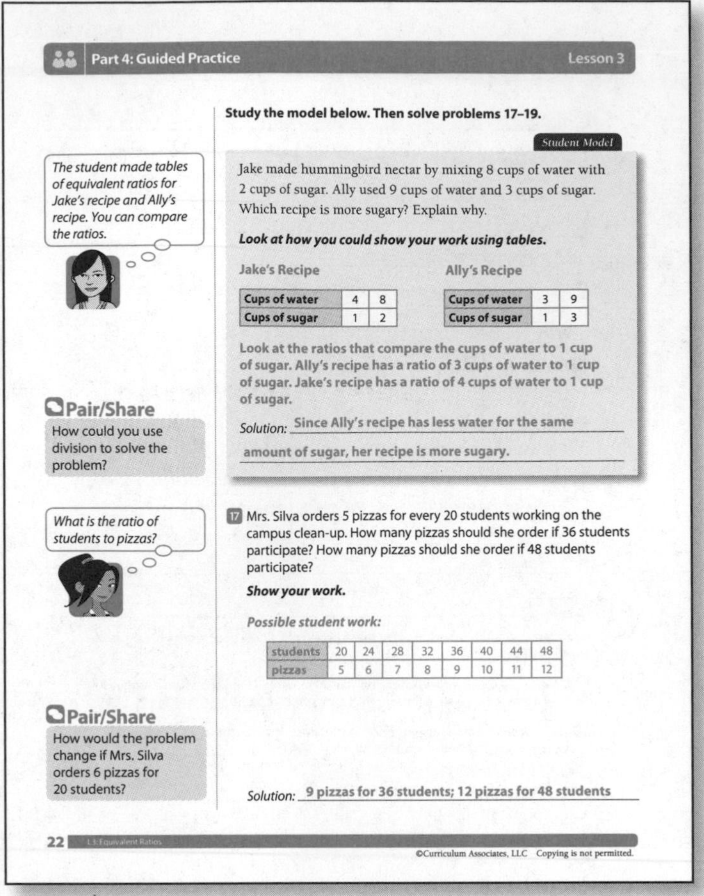

Part 4: Guided Practice Lesson 3

Study the model below. Then solve problems 17–19.

The student made tables of equivalent ratios for Jake's recipe and Ally's recipe. You can compare the ratios.

Student Model

Jake made hummingbird nectar by mixing 8 cups of water with 2 cups of sugar. Ally used 9 cups of water and 3 cups of sugar. Which recipe is more sugary? Explain why.

Look at how you could show your work using tables.

Jake's Recipe

Cups of water	4	8
Cups of sugar	1	2

Ally's Recipe

Cups of water	3	9
Cups of sugar	1	3

Look at the ratios that compare the cups of water to 1 cup of sugar. Ally's recipe has a ratio of 3 cups of water to 1 cup of sugar. Jake's recipe has a ratio of 4 cups of water to 1 cup of sugar.

Solution: Since Ally's recipe has less water for the same amount of sugar, her recipe is more sugary.

Pair/Share
How could you use division to solve the problem?

What is the ratio of students to pizzas?

17 Mrs. Silva orders 5 pizzas for every 20 students working on the campus clean-up. How many pizzas should she order if 36 students participate? How many pizzas should she order if 48 students participate?

Show your work.

Possible student work:

students	20	24	28	32	36	40	44	48
pizzas	5	6	7	8	9	10	11	12

Pair/Share
How would the problem change if Mrs. Silva orders 6 pizzas for 20 students?

Solution: 9 pizzas for 36 students; 12 pizzas for 48 students

22 L3: Equivalent Ratios
©Curriculum Associates, LLC Copying is not permitted.

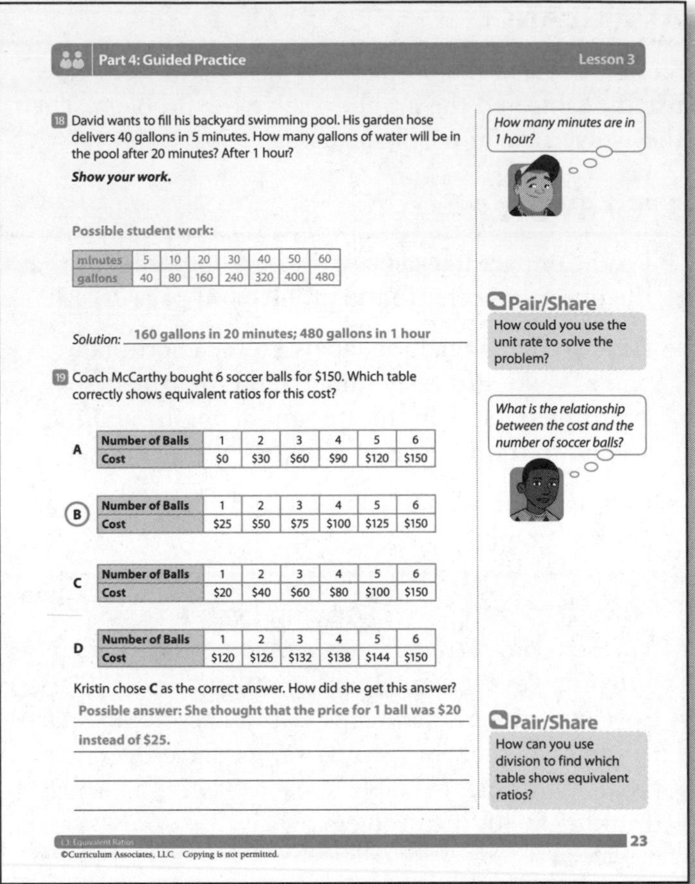

Part 4: Guided Practice Lesson 3

18 David wants to fill his backyard swimming pool. His garden hose delivers 40 gallons in 5 minutes. How many gallons of water will be in the pool after 20 minutes? After 1 hour?

Show your work.

How many minutes are in 1 hour?

Possible student work:

minutes	5	10	20	30	40	50	60
gallons	40	80	160	240	320	400	480

Solution: 160 gallons in 20 minutes; 480 gallons in 1 hour

Pair/Share
How could you use the unit rate to solve the problem?

19 Coach McCarthy bought 6 soccer balls for $150. Which table correctly shows equivalent ratios for this cost?

What is the relationship between the cost and the number of soccer balls?

A

Number of Balls	1	2	3	4	5	6
Cost	$0	$30	$60	$90	$120	$150

(B)

Number of Balls	1	2	3	4	5	6
Cost	$25	$50	$75	$100	$125	$150

C

Number of Balls	1	2	3	4	5	6
Cost	$20	$40	$60	$80	$100	$150

D

Number of Balls	1	2	3	4	5	6
Cost	$120	$126	$132	$138	$144	$150

Kristin chose **C** as the correct answer. How did she get this answer?

Possible answer: She thought that the price for 1 ball was $20 instead of $25.

Pair/Share
How can you use division to find which table shows equivalent ratios?

L3: Equivalent Ratios 23
©Curriculum Associates, LLC Copying is not permitted.

AT A GLANCE

Students use ratio tables, graphs, and proportional reasoning to solve problems involving ratios.

STEP BY STEP

- Ask students to solve the problems individually and explain their reasoning using tables, graphs, or a written explanation.
- When students have completed each problem, have them Pair/Share to discuss their solutions with a partner or in a group.

SOLUTIONS

Ex Creating and comparing two tables is one way to solve the problem. Students can also graph the data or find the unit rates and use proportional reasoning.

17 *Solution:* 9 pizzas for 36 students, 12 pizzas for 48 students; Students could solve the problem by using a table. ***(DOK 2)***

18 *Solution:* 160 gallons in 20 minutes, 480 gallons in 1 hour; Students can also solve the problem by using a table. ***(DOK 2)***

19 *Solution:* **B**; Kristin may have mistakenly thought the unit price was $20 instead of $25.

Explain to students why the other two answer choices are not correct:

A is not correct because the unit price cannot be $0.

D is not correct because the ratios may have been found by subtracting $6 from the cost and are not equivalent. ***(DOK 3)***

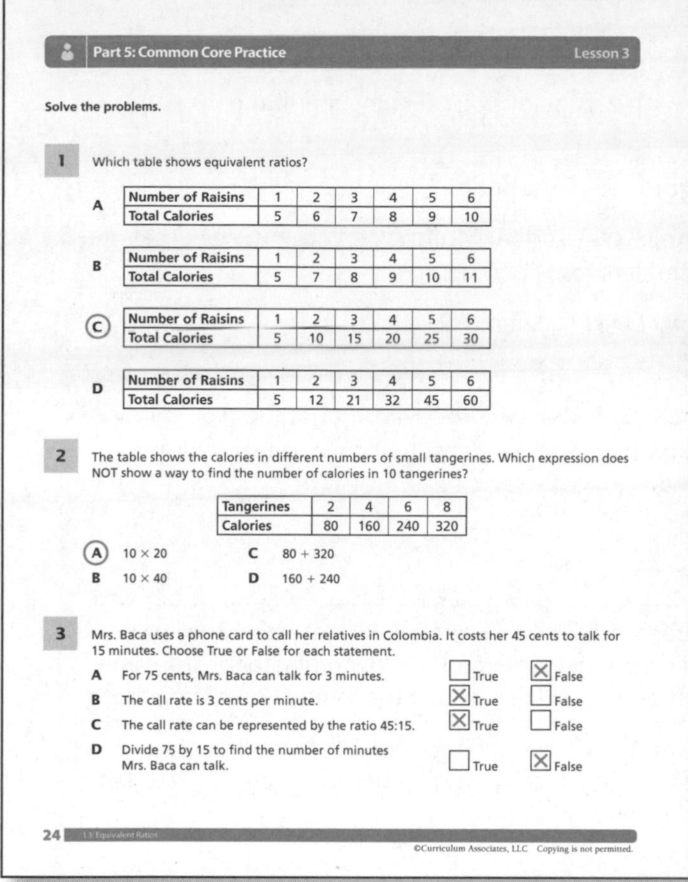

Part 5: Common Core Practice — Lesson 3

Solve the problems.

1 Which table shows equivalent ratios?

A

Number of Raisins	1	2	3	4	5	6
Total Calories	5	6	7	8	9	10

B

Number of Raisins	1	2	3	4	5	6
Total Calories	5	7	8	9	10	11

(C)

Number of Raisins	1	2	3	4	5	6
Total Calories	5	10	15	20	25	30

D

Number of Raisins	1	2	3	4	5	6
Total Calories	5	12	21	32	45	60

2 The table shows the calories in different numbers of small tangerines. Which expression does NOT show a way to find the number of calories in 10 tangerines?

Tangerines	2	4	6	8
Calories	80	160	240	320

(A) 10×20 C $80 + 320$

B 10×40 D $160 + 240$

3 Mrs. Baca uses a phone card to call her relatives in Colombia. It costs her 45 cents to talk for 15 minutes. Choose True or False for each statement.

A	For 75 cents, Mrs. Baca can talk for 3 minutes.	☐ True	☒ False
B	The call rate is 3 cents per minute.	☒ True	☐ False
C	The call rate can be represented by the ratio 45:15.	☒ True	☐ False
D	Divide 75 by 15 to find the number of minutes Mrs. Baca can talk.	☐ True	☒ False

24 L3: Equivalent Ratios ©Curriculum Associates, LLC Copying is not permitted.

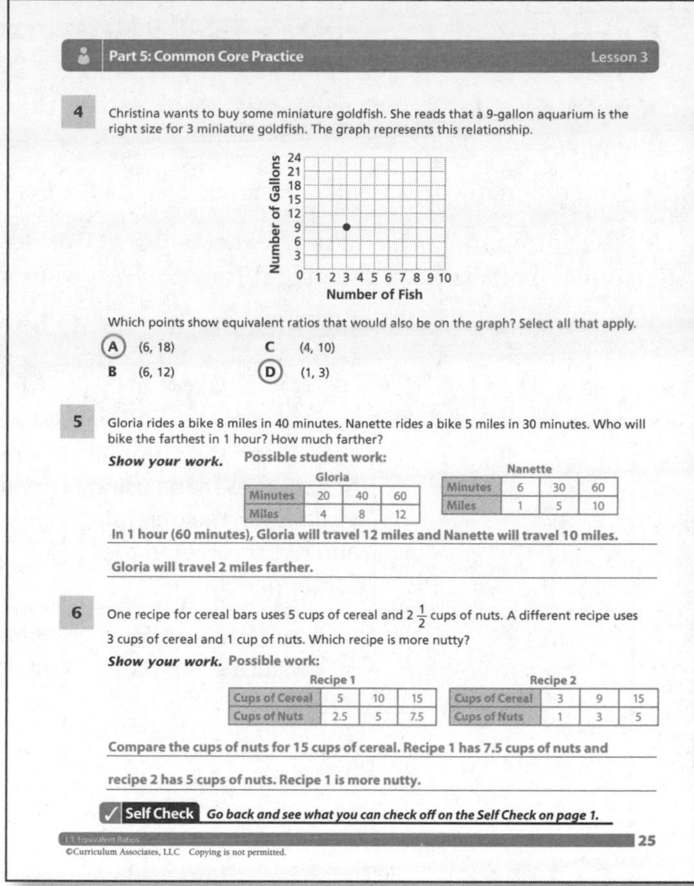

Part 5: Common Core Practice — Lesson 3

4 Christina wants to buy some miniature goldfish. She reads that a 9-gallon aquarium is the right size for 3 miniature goldfish. The graph represents this relationship.

Which points show equivalent ratios that would also be on the graph? Select all that apply.

(A) (6, 18) C (4, 10)

B (6, 12) (D) (1, 3)

5 Gloria rides a bike 8 miles in 40 minutes. Nanette rides a bike 5 miles in 30 minutes. Who will bike the farthest in 1 hour? How much farther?

Show your work. Possible student work:

Gloria

Minutes	20	40	60
Miles	4	8	12

Nanette

Minutes	6	30	60
Miles	1	5	10

In 1 hour (60 minutes), Gloria will travel 12 miles and Nanette will travel 10 miles.

Gloria will travel 2 miles farther.

6 One recipe for cereal bars uses 5 cups of cereal and $2\frac{1}{2}$ cups of nuts. A different recipe uses 3 cups of cereal and 1 cup of nuts. Which recipe is more nutty?

Show your work. Possible work:

Recipe 1

Cups of Cereal	5	10	15
Cups of Nuts	2.5	5	7.5

Recipe 2

Cups of Cereal	3	9	15
Cups of Nuts	1	3	5

Compare the cups of nuts for 15 cups of cereal. Recipe 1 has 7.5 cups of nuts and recipe 2 has 5 cups of nuts. Recipe 1 is more nutty.

✓ Self Check *Go back and see what you can check off on the Self Check on page 1.*

L3: Equivalent Ratios ©Curriculum Associates, LLC Copying is not permitted. 25

AT A GLANCE

Students find equivalent ratios to solve problems that might appear on a mathematics test.

SOLUTIONS

1 *Solution:* **C**; Find the table with equivalent ratios by simplifying. ***(DOK 1)***

2 *Solution:* **A**; See which method does not produce a ratio equivalent to 1:40. ***(DOK 2)***

3 *Solution:* A **False**; B **True**; C **True**; D **False** ***(DOK 2)***

4 *Solution:* **A**; Multiply 3 fish and 9 gallons by 2 to get 6 fish and 18 gallons, which is ordered pair (6, 18).

D; Divide 3 fish and 9 gallons by 3 to get 1 fish and 3 gallons, which is ordered pair (1, 3). ***(DOK 2)***

5 *Solution:* Gloria will travel 2 miles farther; Show that Gloria travels 12 miles in an hour and Nanette travels 10 miles in an hour. ***(DOK 2)***

6 *Solution:* Recipe 1 is more nutty; Show that the rate of cereal to nuts is 2 to 1 for Recipe 1, and 3 to 1 for Recipe 2. You could also show that for 15 cups of cereal, Recipe 1 uses 7.5 cups of nuts and Recipe 2 uses 5 cups. See possible student work above. ***(DOK 3)***

Assessment and Remediation

- Ask students to find how many pancakes they can make with 2 cups of flour if they can make 30 pancakes using 3 cups flour. (20)
- For students who are struggling, use the chart below to guide remediation.
- After providing remediation, check students' understanding. Ask students to find how many eggs they need to make omelets for 6 people if they use 6 eggs to make omelets for 4 people.
- If a student is still having difficulty, use ***Ready Instruction, Level 6,*** Lesson 2.

If the error is . . .	Students may . . .	To remediate . . .
10	have found the number of pancakes made using 1 cup flour, the unit rate, and not completed the solution.	Reread the problem with students to focus on what they are trying to find.
29	have subtracted 1 from 30 because 2 cups is 1 less than 3 cups.	Remind students that when using equivalent ratios, they can multiply or divide the numerator and denominator by the same number but cannot add or subtract the same number from both.
60	have doubled the number of pancakes.	Reread the problem with students. Point out that if they are using less flour, they should make fewer pancakes. Have students make a ratio table.

Hands-On Activity

Act out a situation involving ratios.

Materials: 6 pencils per student

Draw a ratio table on the board, labeling the rows *Pencils* and *Students*. Fill in the first column to show 12 pencils for 2 students. Place 12 pencils on a desk. Call up 2 students. Have them figure out how many pencils each would get in order to have the same number. Record *6 pencils* and *1 student* in the next column of the chart. Ask students to identify the unit rate.

Have all students get 6 pencils. Have them figure out different ratios of pencils to students they can demonstrate. Encourage them to find quick ways to count the number of pencils such as counting by 6s or multiplying by 6.

Once the table has been completed, have students simplify the ratios formed to demonstrate that they are equivalent.

Challenge Activity

Use ratios to find distances on a map.

Materials: maps with a scale of miles, rulers

Have students work in pairs. Give each pair a map and a ruler. Have them use the scale of miles to find out how many miles are represented by one inch or one centimeter, depending on the map.

Have students create a ratio table with 3 rows: cities, inches (or centimeters) on map, and miles. Have them locate two cities on the map and measure the distance between them to the nearest inch or centimeter. Have them record the names of the cities and distance on the map in the table. Then have them use proportional reasoning to figure out how far apart the cities are in miles. Have students repeat the exercise with other pairs of cities.

Lesson 4 (Student Book pages 26–37)
Solve Problems with Unit Rate

LESSON OBJECTIVES

- Solve unit rate problems about unit pricing.
- Solve unit rate problems involving constant speed.
- Use ratio reasoning to convert measurement units within the same system and between different systems.

PREREQUISITE SKILLS

- Understand ratio reasoning and relationships.
- Understand equivalent fractions.
- Use the four basic operations (+, −, ×, ÷).
- Represent equivalent ratios with ratio notation.

VOCABULARY

unit price: the price for 1 unit

THE LEARNING PROGRESSION

Ratios are used to compare measures of two different types. Students have worked with tables and graphs to find and use equivalent ratios. In this lesson, they apply the concepts to solve problems involving ratios and rates including those that require them to convert among units of measure. Students learn to use double number lines in addition to using ratio tables to model the relationship between the two quantities. They also begin to work with the concept more abstractly as they multiply and divide by unit rates to solve problems. Understanding ratios, rates, and unit rates prepares students to understand and use percents.

Ready *Teacher Toolbox* Teacher-Toolbox.com

	Prerequisite Skills	*6.RP.A.3b 6.RP.A.3d*
Ready Lessons	✓	✓
Tools for Instruction	✓	✓
Interactive Tutorials	✓	

CCSS Focus

6.RP.A.3: Use ratio and rate reasoning to solve real-world and mathematical problems, e.g., by reasoning about tables of equivalent ratios, tape diagrams, double number line diagrams, or equations.

b. Solve unit rate problems including those involving unit pricing and constant speed. *For example, if it took 7 hours to mow 4 lawns, then at that rate, how many lawns could be mowed in 35 hours? At what rate were lawns being mowed?*

d. Use ratio reasoning to convert measurement units; manipulate and transform units appropriately when multiplying or dividing quantities.

STANDARDS FOR MATHEMATICAL PRACTICE: ***SMP 2–4*** *(see page A9 for full text)*

AT A GLANCE

Students read a word problem and answer questions designed to review the use of a ratio table to solve problems involving ratios.

STEP BY STEP

- Tell students that this page models using a ratio table to find the equivalent ratios that will help them answer questions.
- Have students read the problem at the top of the page.
- Work through Explore It as a class.
- Have students explain their reasoning as they find the equivalent ratios. Emphasize that there is often more than one correct way to get some of the quantities. Encourage students to find more than one way when it is possible.
- Ask volunteers to explain their answers for each question.

SMP Tip: The variety of possible strategies for filling in the table allows students to construct viable arguments and critique the reasoning of others *(SMP3)*. As students suggest values for the table, challenge them to explain their reasoning clearly.

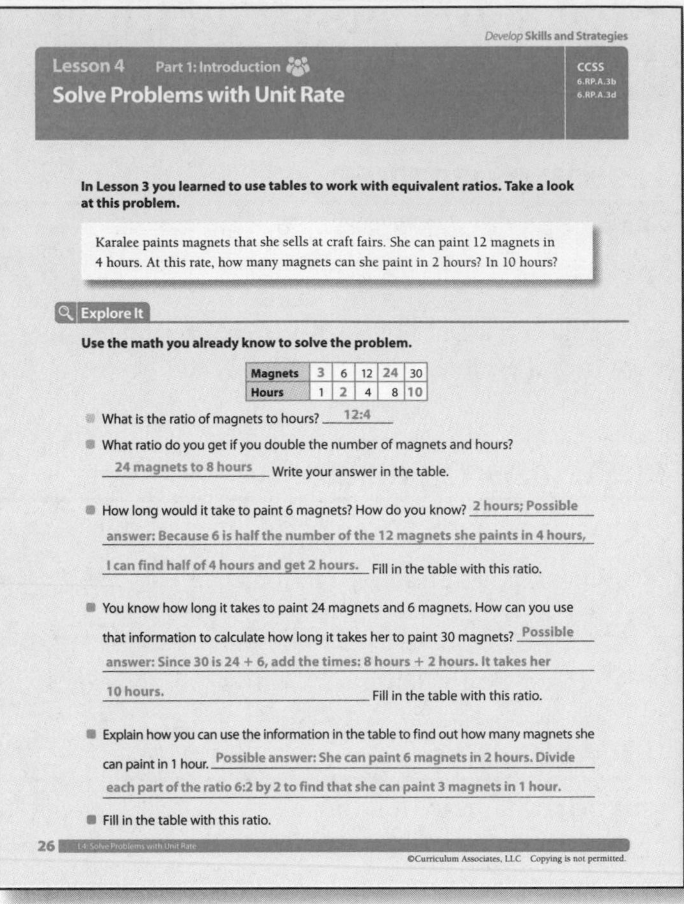

Develop **Skills and Strategies**

Lesson 4 Part 1: Introduction

Solve Problems with Unit Rate

CCSS 6.RP.A.3b 6.RP.A.3d

In Lesson 3 you learned to use tables to work with equivalent ratios. Take a look at this problem.

Karalee paints magnets that she sells at craft fairs. She can paint 12 magnets in 4 hours. At this rate, how many magnets can she paint in 2 hours? In 10 hours?

Explore It

Use the math you already know to solve the problem.

Magnets	3	6	12	24	30
Hours	1	2	4	8	10

- What is the ratio of magnets to hours? 12:4
- What ratio do you get if you double the number of magnets and hours? 24 magnets to 8 hours Write your answer in the table.
- How long would it take to paint 6 magnets? How do you know? 2 hours; Possible answer: Because 6 is half the number of the 12 magnets she paints in 4 hours, I can find half of 4 hours and get 2 hours. Fill in the table with this ratio.
- You know how long it takes to paint 24 magnets and 6 magnets. How can you use that information to calculate how long it takes her to paint 30 magnets? Possible answer: Since 30 is 24 + 6, add the times: 8 hours + 2 hours. It takes her 10 hours. Fill in the table with this ratio.
- Explain how you can use the information in the table to find out how many magnets she can paint in 1 hour. Possible answer: She can paint 6 magnets in 2 hours. Divide each part of the ratio 6:2 by 2 to find that she can paint 3 magnets in 1 hour.
- Fill in the table with this ratio.

26 L4: Solve Problems with Unit Rate

©Curriculum Associates, LLC Copying is not permitted.

Hands-On Activity

Create a model of magnets to hours.

Materials: sticky notes, drawing paper

- Ask students to divide a sheet of drawing paper in fourths and label each fourth *one hour.*
- Give each student 12 sticky notes. Have them place the sticky notes on the paper so that there are the same number of notes in each quarter. They should label each note *magnet.*
- Have students use their model to tell the number of magnets that Karalee can paint in 2 hours and in 1 hour.
- Discuss how they could extend or combine their models to find how many magnets could be painted in 10 hours.

Mathematical Discourse

- *How can you use multiplication or division to find equivalent ratios?*

  Multiply both terms of the ratio by the same number or divide both terms of the ratio by the same number.

- *Can you explain why it makes sense to use multiplication instead of addition to find equivalent ratios?*

  Responses should reflect the idea that multiplication is about combining equal groups and that ratios and rates are also about equal groups.

AT A GLANCE

Students visualize equivalent ratios using a double number line. They use the double number line to solve problems.

STEP BY STEP

- Read Find Out More as a class.
- Describe how the number line represents the problem. Ask, *What does the line that connects 21 and 7 mean?* [21 magnets completed in 7 hours)
- Discuss why finding halves is an effective way to find the number of magnets completed in 1 and 2 hours. Help students relate 3 magnets completed in 1 hour to the unit rate.
- As students answer the questions, have them confirm their answers by looking at the double number line.
- Have students complete Reflect on their own.

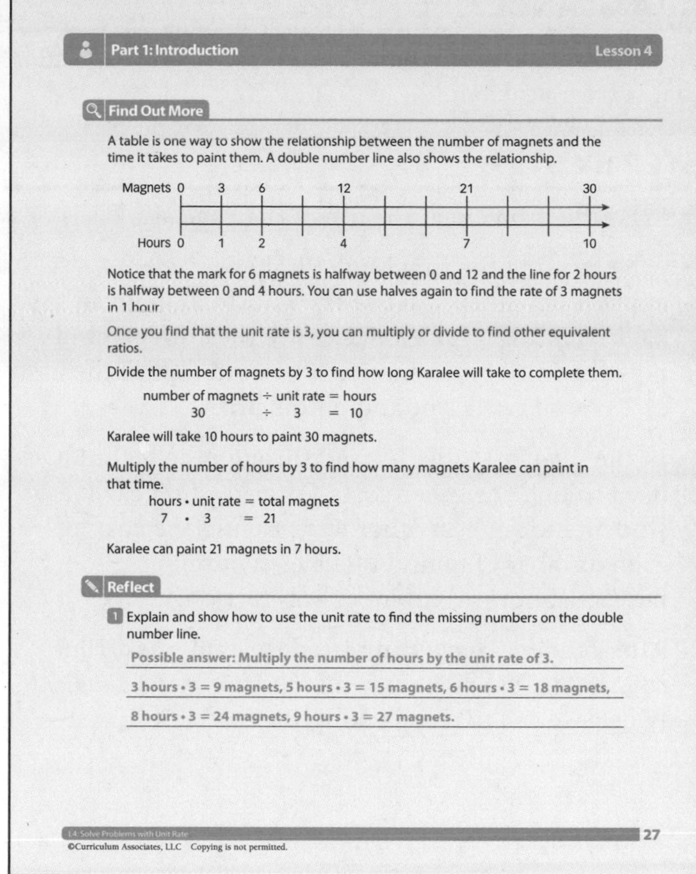

Find Out More

A table is one way to show the relationship between the number of magnets and the time it takes to paint them. A double number line also shows the relationship.

Notice that the mark for 6 magnets is halfway between 0 and 12 and the line for 2 hours is halfway between 0 and 4 hours. You can use halves again to find the rate of 3 magnets in 1 hour.

Once you find that the unit rate is 3, you can multiply or divide to find other equivalent ratios.

Divide the number of magnets by 3 to find how long Karalee will take to complete them.

number of magnets ÷ unit rate = hours
30 ÷ 3 = 10

Karalee will take 10 hours to paint 30 magnets.

Multiply the number of hours by 3 to find how many magnets Karalee can paint in that time.

hours • unit rate = total magnets
7 • 3 = 21

Karalee can paint 21 magnets in 7 hours.

Reflect

1 Explain and show how to use the unit rate to find the missing numbers on the double number line.

Possible answer: Multiply the number of hours by the unit rate of 3.

3 hours • 3 = 9 magnets, 5 hours • 3 = 15 magnets, 6 hours • 3 = 18 magnets,

8 hours • 3 = 24 magnets, 9 hours • 3 = 27 magnets.

Concept Extension

Use multiple strategies to find answers.

- Say that you want to use the double number line to find how long it would take Karalee to make 24 magnets.
- Ask, *How could you use multiplication with one of the known ratios to get the answer?* [Multiply both terms of 12 magnets completed in 4 hours by 2.]
- Ask, *How could you use addition with two of the known ratios to get the answer?* [Add 3 magnets completed in 1 hour to 21 magnets completed in 7 hours.]
- Ask, *How could you use subtraction with two of the known ratios to get the answer?* [Subtract 6 magnets completed in 2 hours from 30 magnets completed in 10 hours.]
- Stress that all the strategies are mathematically correct. Have students explain how they would decide which method is most efficient to use.

Real-World Connection

Encourage students to think about everyday situations in which they might want to estimate how long a task will take based on past experience with a similar task. Have volunteers share their ideas.

Examples: How long it takes to travel somewhere, to finish math problems, to read pages in a book, to mow lawns, to wrap presents.

AT A GLANCE

Students create a ratio table to find the equivalent ratios that solve a problem.

STEP BY STEP

- Read the problem at the top of the page as a class.
- After reading the first Model It, have students explain how they can use the information given to begin making a table. Make sure they understand how the initial information was used to find the cost of 2 pounds and 1 pound of tomatoes.
- In the second Model It, read through the techniques used to find the other costs. After reading each, ask students to suggest other ways to find the cost for each number of pounds. They may use multiplication, addition, or subtraction.
- After students have completed the table, ask, *How can we check to make sure all the ratios are equivalent?* [Check to see that each simplifies to $1.50:1.)

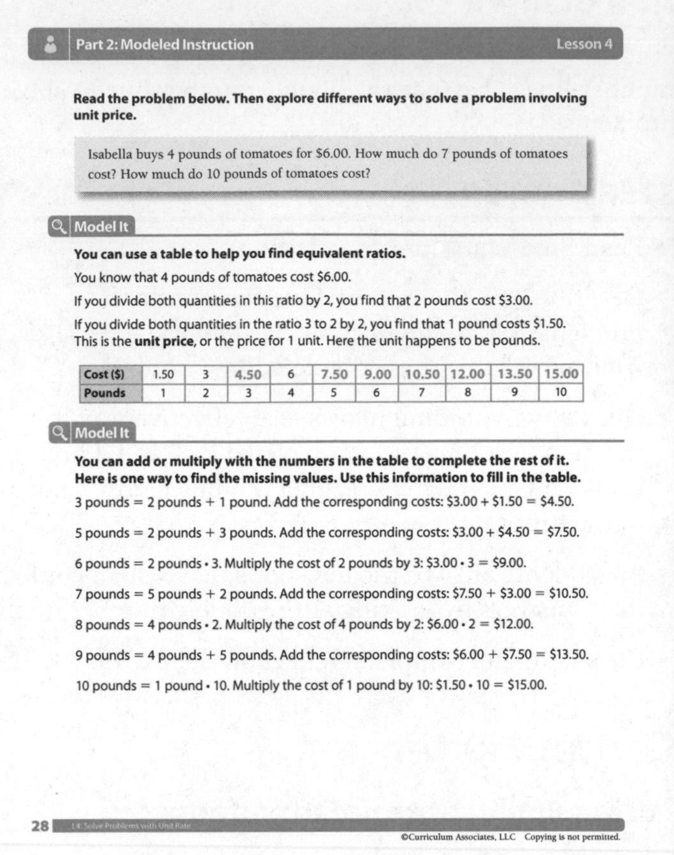

Part 2: Modeled Instruction Lesson 4

Read the problem below. Then explore different ways to solve a problem involving unit price.

Isabella buys 4 pounds of tomatoes for $6.00. How much do 7 pounds of tomatoes cost? How much do 10 pounds of tomatoes cost?

Model It

You can use a table to help you find equivalent ratios.

You know that 4 pounds of tomatoes cost $6.00.

If you divide both quantities in this ratio by 2, you find that 2 pounds cost $3.00.

If you divide both quantities in the ratio 3 to 2 by 2, you find that 1 pound costs $1.50. This is the **unit price**, or the price for 1 unit. Here the unit happens to be pounds.

Cost ($)	1.50	3	4.50	6	7.50	9.00	10.50	12.00	13.50	15.00
Pounds	1	2	3	4	5	6	7	8	9	10

Model It

You can add or multiply with the numbers in the table to complete the rest of it. Here is one way to find the missing values. Use this information to fill in the table.

3 pounds = 2 pounds + 1 pound. Add the corresponding costs: $3.00 + $1.50 = $4.50.

5 pounds = 2 pounds + 3 pounds. Add the corresponding costs: $3.00 + $4.50 = $7.50.

6 pounds = 2 pounds • 3. Multiply the cost of 2 pounds by 3: $3.00 • 3 = $9.00.

7 pounds = 5 pounds + 2 pounds. Add the corresponding costs: $7.50 + $3.00 = $10.50.

8 pounds = 4 pounds • 2. Multiply the cost of 4 pounds by 2: $6.00 • 2 = $12.00.

9 pounds = 4 pounds + 5 pounds. Add the corresponding costs: $6.00 + $7.50 = $13.50.

10 pounds = 1 pound • 10. Multiply the cost of 1 pound by 10: $1.50 • 10 = $15.00.

28 L4: Solve Problems with Unit Rate

©Curriculum Associates, LLC Copying is not permitted.

Mathematical Discourse

- *What are some of the ways you can find equivalent ratios using the ratios you already know?*

  Multiply both terms of a ratio by the same number; add the first terms and then the second terms of two equivalent ratios; or subtract the first terms and then the second terms of equivalent ratios.

- *When you fill in a ratio table, there may be more than one way to find a given ratio. If you use different ways, should you always get the same answer?*

  Yes, if you found the ratios correctly.

- *If you get two different answers, how can you decide which one is correct?*

  Simplify both of them. See which one is equivalent to the ratios that you already know.

AT A GLANCE

Students revisit the problem on page 28 to learn how to use the unit price to solve the problem.

STEP BY STEP

- Read Connect It as a class. Be sure to point out that Connect It refers to the problem on page 28.
- Emphasize how to use the given information to find the unit price. Have students explain why it is important to know the unit price.
- Ask students to explain why they would multiply the number of pounds by the unit price to get the total price.
- As students discuss when they would use a table of equivalent ratios and when they would find the unit rate and use multiplication to solve a problem, stress that there is no one correct response. Both methods are useful and will result in the right answer.
- Encourage a variety of responses as students explain how to find the amount of tomatoes they could buy with $18.00.
- Have students complete Try It. Discuss their answers.

SMP Tip: Students move outside of the problem context and think about the relationship between operations abstractly (*SMP 2*) when they figure how much they can buy for a given cost. Continue to help them connect operations and contexts by asking them why they chose the operations they did and how they know their solution methods will work.

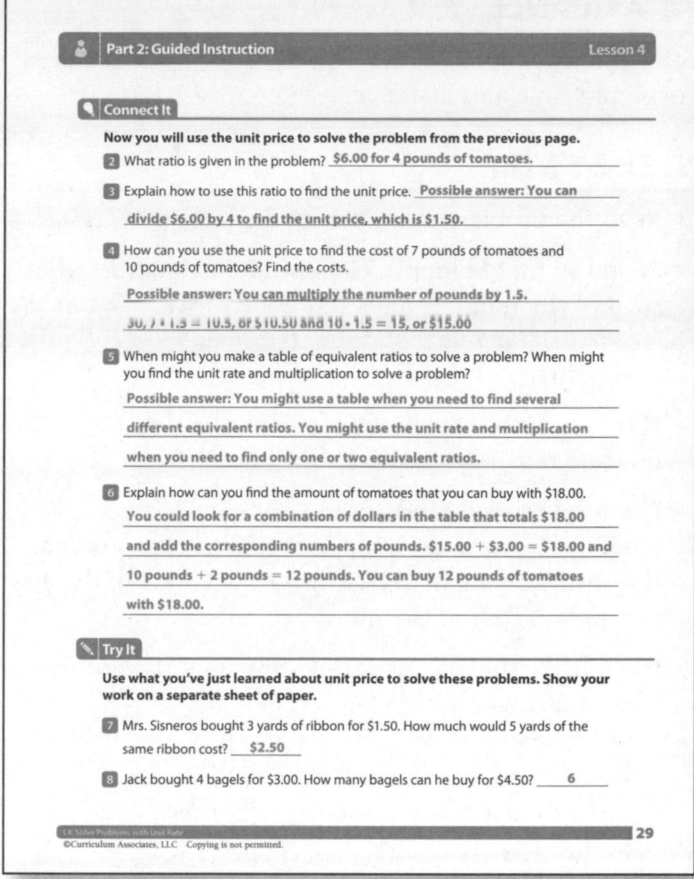

Part 2: Guided Instruction Lesson 4

Connect It

Now you will use the unit price to solve the problem from the previous page.

2 What ratio is given in the problem? **$6.00 for 4 pounds of tomatoes.**

3 Explain how to use this ratio to find the unit price. **Possible answer: You can divide $6.00 by 4 to find the unit price, which is $1.50.**

4 How can you use the unit price to find the cost of 7 pounds of tomatoes and 10 pounds of tomatoes? Find the costs.

Possible answer: You can multiply the number of pounds by 1.5. So, 7 • 1.5 = 10.5, or $10.50 and 10 • 1.5 = 15, or $15.00

5 When might you make a table of equivalent ratios to solve a problem? When might you find the unit rate and multiplication to solve a problem?

Possible answer: You might use a table when you need to find several different equivalent ratios. You might use the unit rate and multiplication when you need to find only one or two equivalent ratios.

6 Explain how can you find the amount of tomatoes that you can buy with $18.00.

You could look for a combination of dollars in the table that totals $18.00 and add the corresponding numbers of pounds. $15.00 + $3.00 = $18.00 and 10 pounds + 2 pounds = 12 pounds. You can buy 12 pounds of tomatoes with $18.00.

Try It

Use what you've just learned about unit price to solve these problems. Show your work on a separate sheet of paper.

7 Mrs. Sisneros bought 3 yards of ribbon for $1.50. How much would 5 yards of the same ribbon cost? **$2.50**

8 Jack bought 4 bagels for $3.00. How many bagels can he buy for $4.50? **6**

L4: Solve Problems with Unit Rate 29

©Curriculum Associates, LLC Copying is not permitted.

TRY IT SOLUTIONS

7 *Solution:* $2.50; Students may use a table of ratios. They may also find the unit rate and multiply it by 5.

ERROR ALERT: Students who wrote $0.90 found the unit rate for 5 yards for $1.50 and then the total amount for 3 yards.

8 *Solution:* 6; Students may use a table of ratios. They may also divide $4.50 by the unit rate.

AT A GLANCE

Students use double number lines to solve problems involving time and distance.

STEP BY STEP

- Read the problem at the top of the page as a class.
- Read the first Model It. Have students identify what each of the number lines represents. Ask, *What is the meaning of the line that connects 200 and 4?* [200 miles in 4 hours.]
- Have students explain how to find the unit rate in their own words.
- Read the second Model It to see how to finish labeling the number lines. If students are confident, use the Mathematical Discourse questions to discuss other ways to find the numbers.
- Emphasize that all the ratios shown by the number line simplify to 50:1.

SMP Tip: As students label the double number line, they are learning to model with mathematics *(SMP 4)*. Encourage them to connect the model with the context of the problem as they use it to answer questions.

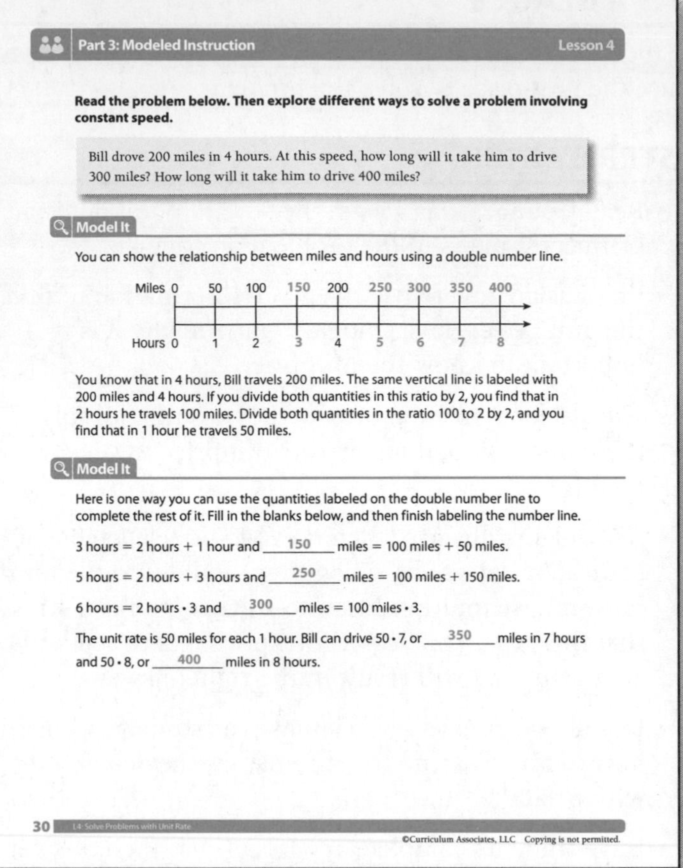

Part 3: Modeled Instruction Lesson 4

Read the problem below. Then explore different ways to solve a problem involving constant speed.

Bill drove 200 miles in 4 hours. At this speed, how long will it take him to drive 300 miles? How long will it take him to drive 400 miles?

Model It

You can show the relationship between miles and hours using a double number line.

You know that in 4 hours, Bill travels 200 miles. The same vertical line is labeled with 200 miles and 4 hours. If you divide both quantities in this ratio by 2, you find that in 2 hours he travels 100 miles. Divide both quantities in the ratio 100 to 2 by 2, and you find that in 1 hour he travels 50 miles.

Model It

Here is one way you can use the quantities labeled on the double number line to complete the rest of it. Fill in the blanks below, and then finish labeling the number line.

3 hours = 2 hours + 1 hour and __150__ miles = 100 miles + 50 miles.

5 hours = 2 hours + 3 hours and __250__ miles = 100 miles + 150 miles.

6 hours = 2 hours • 3 and __300__ miles = 100 miles • 3.

The unit rate is 50 miles for each 1 hour. Bill can drive 50 • 7, or __350__ miles in 7 hours and 50 • 8, or __400__ miles in 8 hours.

30 L4: Solve Problems with Unit Rate

©Curriculum Associates, LLC Copying is not permitted.

Mathematical Discourse

- *Can you find another way to figure out the equivalent ratios?*

  Students may explain using division or addition and subtraction. Allow some wait time and consider having students talk together before sharing ideas with the class.

AT A GLANCE

Students revisit the problem on page 30 to learn how to use the unit rate to solve time and distance problems.

STEP BY STEP

- Read page 31 as a class. Be sure to point out that Connect It refers to the problem on page 30.
- Ask, *Why can you divide the total distance by the unit rate to find how long it will take?* [The unit rate is 50 and you want to find out how many groups of 50 miles are in 300 miles and in 400 miles.]
- After students find the time to drive 325 miles using both the double number line and division, have them compare the answers and explain why they are the same.
- As students compare constant speed and unit price problems, emphasize that it is important to keep in mind the units of measure when solving such problems.
- After students have completed Try It on their own, discuss their answers and how they got them.

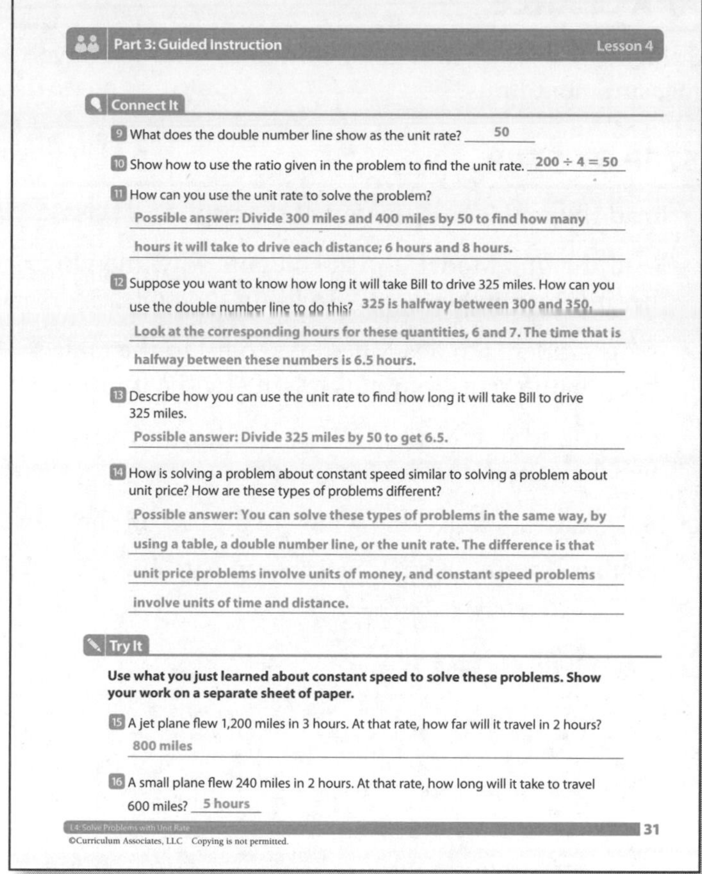
Part 3: Guided Instruction Lesson 4

Connect It

9 What does the double number line show as the unit rate? 50

10 Show how to use the ratio given in the problem to find the unit rate. $200 \div 4 = 50$

11 How can you use the unit rate to solve the problem?
Possible answer: Divide 300 miles and 400 miles by 50 to find how many hours it will take to drive each distance; 6 hours and 8 hours.

12 Suppose you want to know how long it will take Bill to drive 325 miles. How can you use the double number line to do this? 325 is halfway between 300 and 350. Look at the corresponding hours for these quantities, 6 and 7. The time that is halfway between these numbers is 6.5 hours.

13 Describe how you can use the unit rate to find how long it will take Bill to drive 325 miles.
Possible answer: Divide 325 miles by 50 to get 6.5.

14 How is solving a problem about constant speed similar to solving a problem about unit price? How are these types of problems different?
Possible answer: You can solve these types of problems in the same way, by using a table, a double number line, or the unit rate. The difference is that unit price problems involve units of money, and constant speed problems involve units of time and distance.

Try It

Use what you just learned about constant speed to solve these problems. Show your work on a separate sheet of paper.

15 A jet plane flew 1,200 miles in 3 hours. At that rate, how far will it travel in 2 hours?
800 miles

16 A small plane flew 240 miles in 2 hours. At that rate, how long will it take to travel 600 miles? 5 hours

L4: Solve Problems with Unit Rate 31
©Curriculum Associates, LLC Copying is not permitted.

TRY IT SOLUTIONS

15 *Solution:* 800 miles; Students may find the unit rate, 400, and multiply it by the number of hours, 2.

ERROR ALERT: Students who wrote 200 found the unit rate, 400, and divided instead of multiplied by 2 hours.

16 *Solution:* 5 hours; Students may find the unit rate, 120, and divide it into the total number of miles, 600.

AT A GLANCE

Students use tables and double number lines to convert measurement units.

STEP BY STEP

- Read the problem at the top of the page as a class.
- Read the first Model It. Ask students why knowing the unit rate makes it easy to fill in the table.
- Invite students to describe ways to fill in the table that are different from multiplying by the unit rate.
- Read the second Model It. Have students explain why the labels on the scales are important.
- Make sure students know how to find 10 on the number line and why $2\frac{1}{2}$ corresponds to 10.

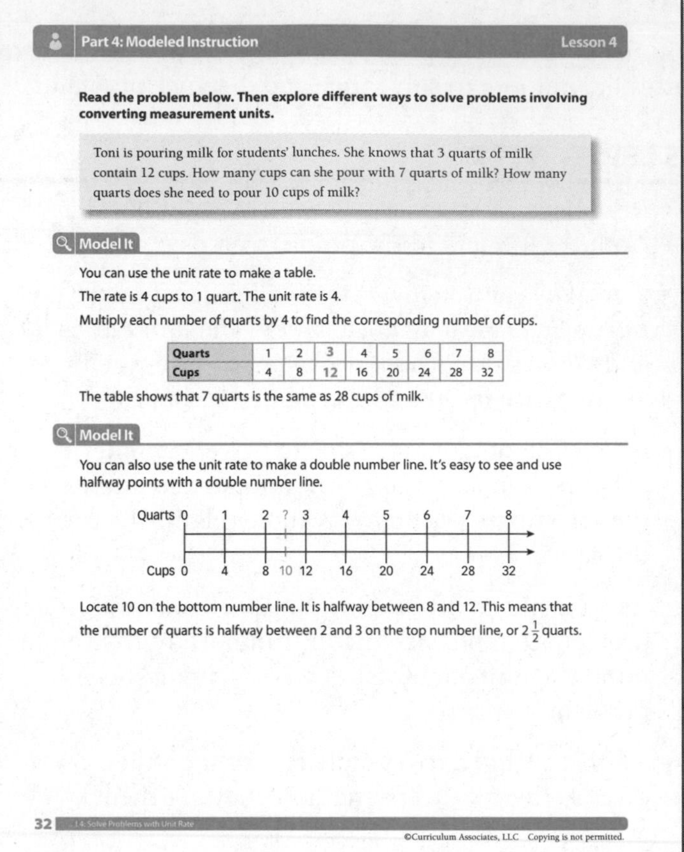

Part 4: Modeled Instruction Lesson 4

Read the problem below. Then explore different ways to solve problems involving converting measurement units.

Toni is pouring milk for students' lunches. She knows that 3 quarts of milk contain 12 cups. How many cups can she pour with 7 quarts of milk? How many quarts does she need to pour 10 cups of milk?

Model It

You can use the unit rate to make a table.

The rate is 4 cups to 1 quart. The unit rate is 4.

Multiply each number of quarts by 4 to find the corresponding number of cups.

Quarts	1	2	3	4	5	6	7	8
Cups	4	8	12	16	20	24	28	32

The table shows that 7 quarts is the same as 28 cups of milk.

Model It

You can also use the unit rate to make a double number line. It's easy to see and use halfway points with a double number line.

Locate 10 on the bottom number line. It is halfway between 8 and 12. This means that the number of quarts is halfway between 2 and 3 on the top number line, or $2\frac{1}{2}$ quarts.

32 L4: Solve Problems with Unit Rate ©Curriculum Associates, LLC Copying is not permitted.

Visual Model

Use a diagram to see equivalent ratios.

- Draw this diagram on the board.
- Tell students that the rate is 4 cups per 1 quart, so you will use this symbol for 1 quart.

1 cup	1 cup
1 cup	1 cup

1 quart

- Draw another quart symbol. Show why two symbols show that 8 cups are the same as 2 quarts.
- Continue to draw symbols, having students state the number of cups represented by each number of quarts. Once you reach 28 cups, count to see how many quarts you used.
- Discuss how you can use the quart symbol to show 10 cups. Note that 2 symbols are not enough but 3 symbols are too many. Help students see why $2\frac{1}{2}$ symbols represent 10 cups.

Mathematical Discourse

- *Let's say I want to know how many cups are equivalent to $2\frac{1}{2}$ quarts. How can I use the double number line to find the answer?*

  Listen for responses that $2\frac{1}{2}$ is halfway between 2 and 3 and that you draw a vertical line and then figure out the number that is halfway between the numbers on the bottom number line, 8 and 12.

- *How is the double number line model similar to a table of equivalent ratios?*

  Students' responses will vary but many will see that the labels for the number lines are the same as the equivalent ratios in a ratio table. Some students will prefer the double number line model because it feels more concrete than the ratio table.

AT A GLANCE

Students revisit the problem on page 32 to learn how to find the solution by multiplying or dividing by the unit rate.

STEP BY STEP

- Read Connect It as a class. Be sure to point out that the questions refer to the problem on page 32.
- Review how to find the unit rate using division. Remind students that the fraction bar in $\frac{12}{3}$ signifies division.
- Discuss why you multiply by the unit rate to convert quarts to cups but divide when converting cups to quarts.
- Have students describe a strategy for converting $4\frac{1}{2}$ pounds to ounces before they attempt problem 21. If they have trouble getting started, suggest that they first find the unit rate.
- Have students complete Try It on their own.

ELL SUPPORT

- Write *How Long or How Far* on the board. Discuss what it means to measure length or distance. Underneath, write units of length such as feet, inches, miles, meters, and kilometers. Give examples of each such as *The book is 10 inches long* or *It is 100 kilometers to his cousin's house.*
- Write *How Heavy* on the board. Discuss what it means to weigh an item. Underneath, write the units of weight: ounces, pounds, and tons. Give examples such as *His brother weighs 86 pounds* or *The box of crackers weighs 9 ounces.*
- Write *How Much* on the board. Discuss what it means to measure the volume of a liquid. Underneath, write units such as cups, gallons, and liters. Give examples of each such as *The bottle contains 2 liters of soda* or *The carton contains $\frac{1}{2}$ gallon of milk.*

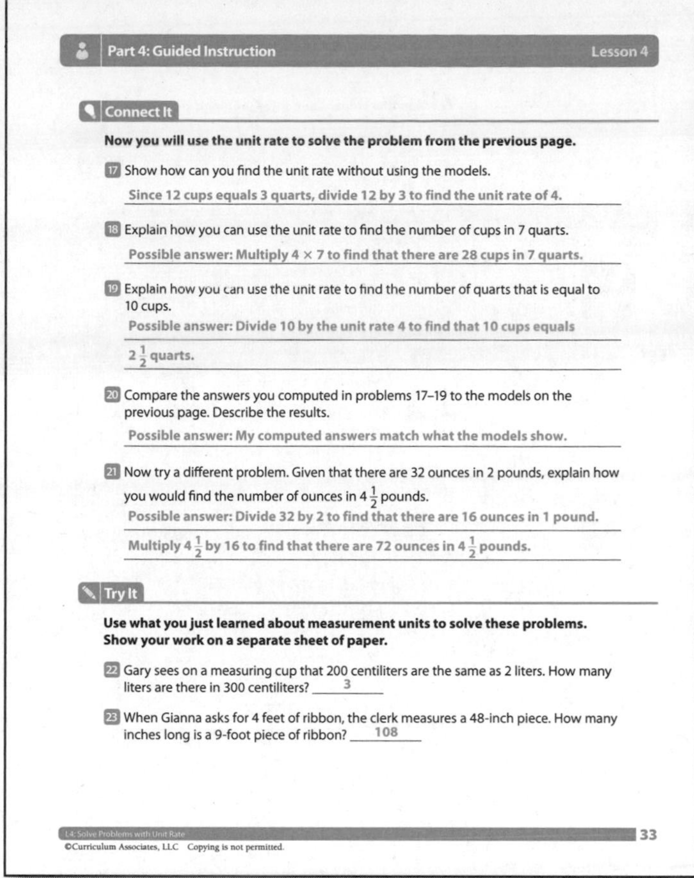

Part 4: Guided Instruction Lesson 4

Connect It

Now you will use the unit rate to solve the problem from the previous page.

17 Show how can you find the unit rate without using the models.
Since 12 cups equals 3 quarts, divide 12 by 3 to find the unit rate of 4.

18 Explain how you can use the unit rate to find the number of cups in 7 quarts.
Possible answer: Multiply 4 × 7 to find that there are 28 cups in 7 quarts.

19 Explain how you can use the unit rate to find the number of quarts that is equal to 10 cups.
Possible answer: Divide 10 by the unit rate 4 to find that 10 cups equals $2\frac{1}{2}$ quarts.

20 Compare the answers you computed in problems 17–19 to the models on the previous page. Describe the results.
Possible answer: My computed answers match what the models show.

21 Now try a different problem. Given that there are 32 ounces in 2 pounds, explain how you would find the number of ounces in $4\frac{1}{2}$ pounds.
Possible answer: Divide 32 by 2 to find that there are 16 ounces in 1 pound. Multiply $4\frac{1}{2}$ by 16 to find that there are 72 ounces in $4\frac{1}{2}$ pounds.

Try It

Use what you just learned about measurement units to solve these problems. Show your work on a separate sheet of paper.

22 Gary sees on a measuring cup that 200 centiliters are the same as 2 liters. How many liters are there in 300 centiliters? **3**

23 When Gianna asks for 4 feet of ribbon, the clerk measures a 48-inch piece. How many inches long is a 9-foot piece of ribbon? **108**

L4: Solve Problems with Unit Rate 33
©Curriculum Associates, LLC Copying is not permitted.

TRY IT SOLUTIONS

22 *Solution:* 3; Students may find the rate, 100 centiliters to 1 liter, and divide 300 by the rate. They may also use a table or double number line.

ERROR ALERT: Students who wrote 30,000 multiplied by the unit rate instead of dividing by it.

23 *Solution:* 108; Students may find the rate, 12 inches to 1 foot, and multiply 9 by the rate. They may also use a table or double number line.

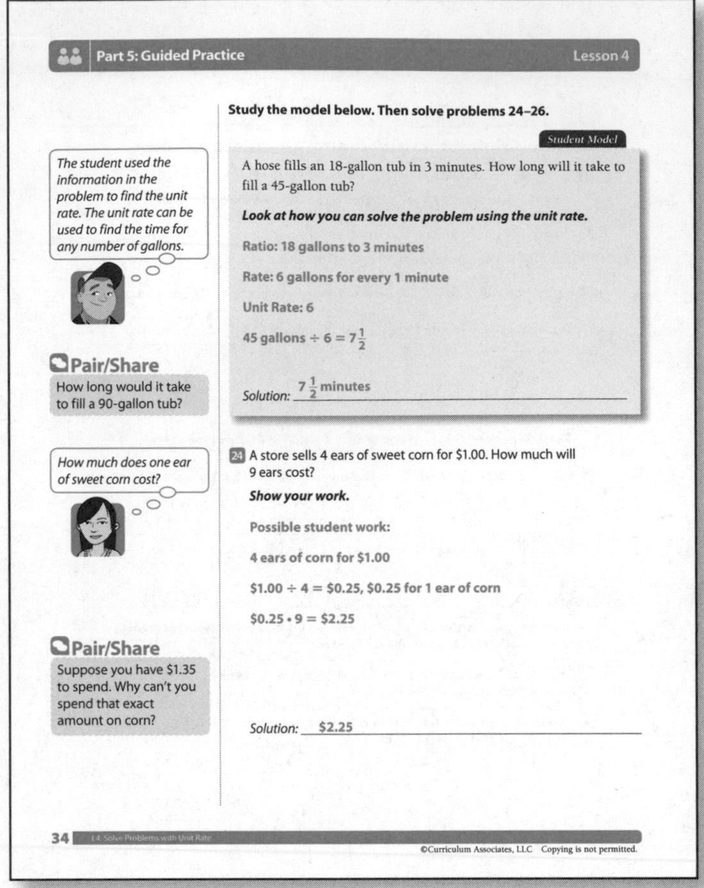

Part 5: Guided Practice Lesson 4

Study the model below. Then solve problems 24–26.

Student Model

The student used the information in the problem to find the unit rate. The unit rate can be used to find the time for any number of gallons.

A hose fills an 18-gallon tub in 3 minutes. How long will it take to fill a 45-gallon tub?

Look at how you can solve the problem using the unit rate.

Ratio: 18 gallons to 3 minutes

Rate: 6 gallons for every 1 minute

Unit Rate: 6

45 gallons ÷ 6 = $7\frac{1}{2}$

Solution: $7\frac{1}{2}$ minutes

Pair/Share
How long would it take to fill a 90-gallon tub?

How much does one ear of sweet corn cost?

24 A store sells 4 ears of sweet corn for $1.00. How much will 9 ears cost?

Show your work.

Possible student work:

4 ears of corn for $1.00

$1.00 ÷ 4 = $0.25, $0.25 for 1 ear of corn

$0.25 • 9 = $2.25

Solution: $2.25

Pair/Share
Suppose you have $1.35 to spend. Why can't you spend that exact amount on corn?

34 L4: Solve Problems with Unit Rate ©Curriculum Associates, LLC Copying is not permitted.

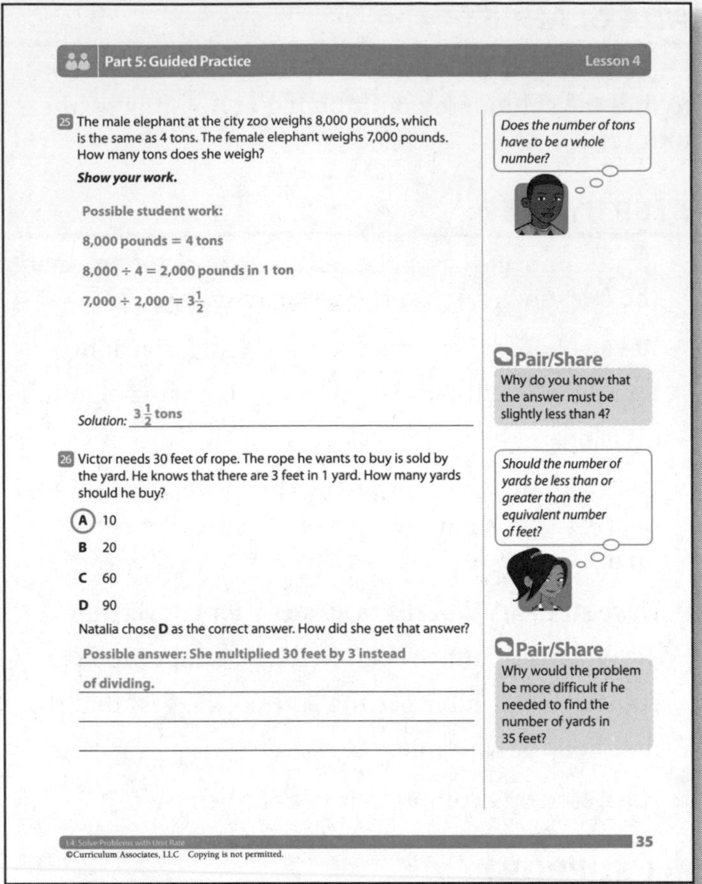

Part 5: Guided Practice Lesson 4

25 The male elephant at the city zoo weighs 8,000 pounds, which is the same as 4 tons. The female elephant weighs 7,000 pounds. How many tons does she weigh?

Show your work.

Does the number of tons have to be a whole number?

Possible student work:

8,000 pounds = 4 tons

8,000 ÷ 4 = 2,000 pounds in 1 ton

7,000 ÷ 2,000 = $3\frac{1}{2}$

Solution: $3\frac{1}{2}$ tons

Pair/Share
Why do you know that the answer must be slightly less than 4?

26 Victor needs 30 feet of rope. The rope he wants to buy is sold by the yard. He knows that there are 3 feet in 1 yard. How many yards should he buy?

Should the number of yards be less than or greater than the equivalent number of feet?

(A) 10

B 20

C 60

D 90

Natalia chose **D** as the correct answer. How did she get that answer?

Possible answer: She multiplied 30 feet by 3 instead of dividing.

Pair/Share
Why would the problem be more difficult if he needed to find the number of yards in 35 feet?

L4: Solve Problems with Unit Rate ©Curriculum Associates, LLC Copying is not permitted. 35

AT A GLANCE

Students use tables, double number lines, multiplication, and division to solve problems involving ratios.

STEP BY STEP

- Ask students to solve the problems individually. Remind them to show their work in the form of a table, a double number line, or a series of computations.
- When students have completed each problem, have them Pair/Share to discuss their solutions with a partner or in a group.

SOLUTIONS

Ex One way to solve the problem is find the unit rate and divide the number of gallons by that. Students could also compare gallons to minutes using a table or double number line.

24 *Solution:* $2.25; Students could solve the problem by multiplying by the unit rate. ***(DOK 1)***

25 *Solution:* $3\frac{1}{2}$ tons; Students could solve the problem by dividing by the unit rate. ***(DOK 1)***

26 *Solution:* **A**; Natalia found the number of feet in 30 yards instead of yards in 30 feet.

Explain to students why the other two answer choices are not correct:

B is not correct because there are 3 feet in 1 yard, not 3 feet in 2 yards.

C is not correct because doubling the number of feet has nothing to do with the solution. ***(DOK 3)***

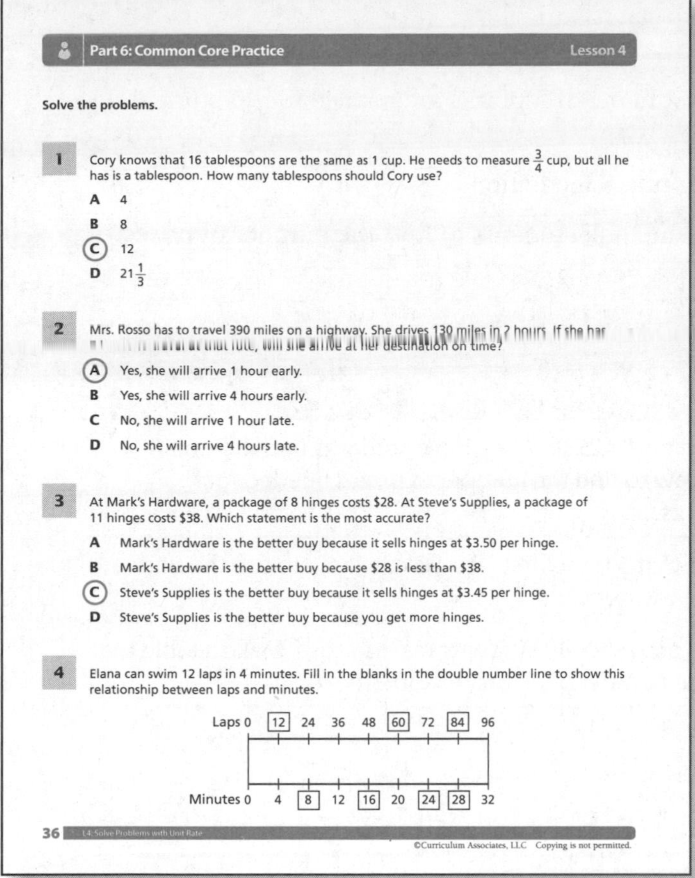

Part 6: Common Core Practice Lesson 4

Solve the problems.

1 Cory knows that 16 tablespoons are the same as 1 cup. He needs to measure $\frac{3}{4}$ cup, but all he has is a tablespoon. How many tablespoons should Cory use?

A 4
B 8
Ⓒ 12
D $21\frac{1}{3}$

2 Mrs. Rosso has to travel 390 miles on a highway. She drives 130 miles in 2 hours. If she ha[illegible] at that rate, will she arrive at her destination on time?

Ⓐ Yes, she will arrive 1 hour early.
B Yes, she will arrive 4 hours early.
C No, she will arrive 1 hour late.
D No, she will arrive 4 hours late.

3 At Mark's Hardware, a package of 8 hinges costs \$28. At Steve's Supplies, a package of 11 hinges costs \$38. Which statement is the most accurate?

A Mark's Hardware is the better buy because it sells hinges at \$3.50 per hinge.
B Mark's Hardware is the better buy because \$28 is less than \$38.
Ⓒ Steve's Supplies is the better buy because it sells hinges at \$3.45 per hinge.
D Steve's Supplies is the better buy because you get more hinges.

4 Elana can swim 12 laps in 4 minutes. Fill in the blanks in the double number line to show this relationship between laps and minutes.

Laps 0 [12] 24 36 48 [60] 72 [84] 96

Minutes 0 4 [8] 12 [16] 20 [24] [28] 32

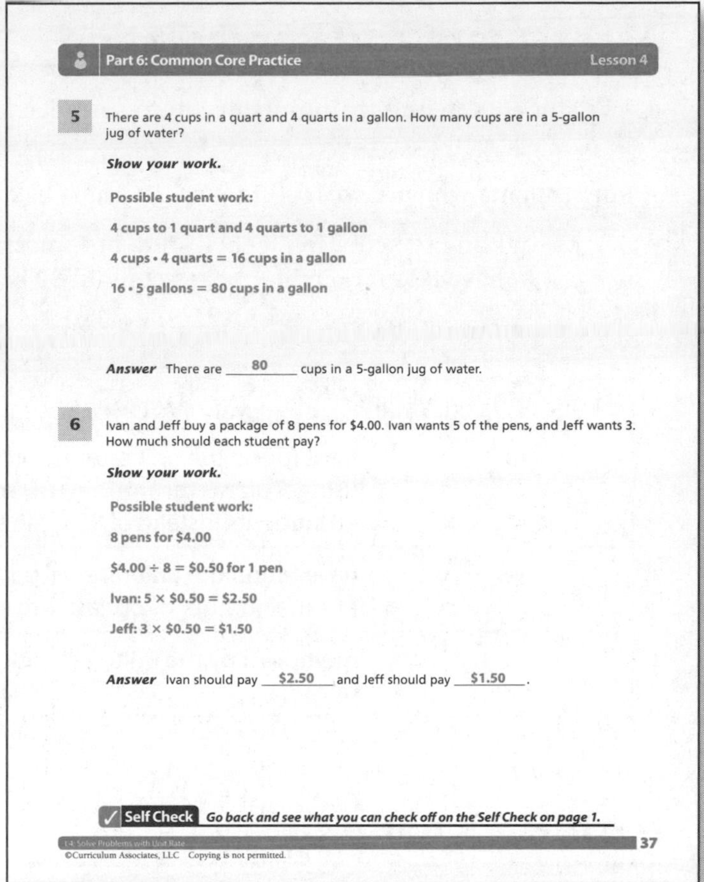

Part 6: Common Core Practice Lesson 4

5 There are 4 cups in a quart and 4 quarts in a gallon. How many cups are in a 5-gallon jug of water?

Show your work.

Possible student work:

4 cups to 1 quart and 4 quarts to 1 gallon

4 cups • 4 quarts = 16 cups in a gallon

16 • 5 gallons = 80 cups in a gallon

Answer There are __80__ cups in a 5-gallon jug of water.

6 Ivan and Jeff buy a package of 8 pens for \$4.00. Ivan wants 5 of the pens, and Jeff wants 3. How much should each student pay?

Show your work.

Possible student work:

8 pens for \$4.00

\$4.00 ÷ 8 = \$0.50 for 1 pen

Ivan: 5 × \$0.50 = \$2.50

Jeff: 3 × \$0.50 = \$1.50

Answer Ivan should pay __\$2.50__ and Jeff should pay __\$1.50__.

✓ Self Check *Go back and see what you can check off on the Self Check on page 1.*

AT A GLANCE

Students use unit rates to solve problems that might appear on a mathematics test.

SOLUTIONS

1 *Solution:* **C**; The unit rate is given. Multiply $\frac{3}{4}$ by the unit rate. ***(DOK 1)***

2 *Solution:* **A**; Find the unit rate. Divide the number of miles by 65 to find the number of hours. Compare the number of hours needed to the number she has. ***(DOK 2)***

3 *Solution:* **C**; Find the cost for one hinge at each store by dividing the total cost by the number of hinges bought. Compare the unit costs. ***(DOK 1)***

4 *Solution:* See student book page above for solution; Find the unit rate by dividing 12 laps by 4 minutes. Divide number of laps on number line by unit rate to find number of minutes, and multiply number of minutes on number line by unit rate to find number of laps. ***(DOK 1)***

5 *Solution:* 80; Multiply for the number of cups in 1 gallon and then in 5 gallons. See possible student work above. ***(DOK 2)***

6 *Solution:* Ivan: \$2.50 and Jeff \$1.50; Find the unit price and multiply to see how much each should pay. See possible student work above. ***(DOK 2)***

Assessment and Remediation

- Ask students to find the number of pizzas needed for 40 students if 5 pizzas are needed for 25 students. [8 pizzas]
- For students who are struggling, use the chart below to guide remediation.
- After providing remediation, check students' understanding. Ask students to find the number of boxes needed to have 80 markers if 4 boxes contain 32 markers. [10]
- If a student is still having difficulty, use ***Ready Instruction, Level 6,*** Lesson 2.

If the error is . . .	Students may . . .	To remediate . . .
$3\frac{1}{8}$	have found the unit rate using 5 pizzas for 40 students instead of 25.	circle *5 pizzas for 25 students*. Have students find the unit rate. Discuss how to find the number of pizzas needed for 40 students.
5	have found the unit rate, not the number of pizzas.	point out that 5 is the unit rate. Discuss how to use the unit rate to answer the question.
200	multiplied by the unit rate.	ask if 200 pizzas for 40 students makes sense. Make a table that relates the number of pizzas to students.

Hands-On Activity

Create and use a model of a proportional relationship.

Materials: 18" by 3" strips of paper, ruler, dried beans, glue

Distribute a strip of paper, a ruler, a handful of beans, and glue to each student. Instruct students to mark off their paper strip lengthwise in 1-inch portions.

Tell students that a gardener wants to plant 3 seeds every 6 inches in a garden and that the seeds should be spaced evenly. Have them glue beans to represent the situation. After students create their model, have them find the ratio of seeds to inches in simplest form. [1 seed to 2 inches] Have them use their work to figure out how many seeds are needed for 18 inches and for 60 inches. [9 and 30] Have them predict how long a row they would need to plant 5 seeds and 24 seeds. [10 and 48]

Challenge Activity

Work with unit prices.

Materials: index cards, graph paper

Prepare index cards with the cost of several items such as 4 bagels for $2.00, 3 pens for $0.75, and 6 pieces of gum for $1.20. In each case, the number of items should divide into the price without a remainder.

Have students work in groups of 2 or 3. Give each group a card. They should use the information on the card to do the following:

- Find the unit price.
- Write a problem that asks for the total price of a certain number of the item.
- Write a problem that asks how many of the item they could buy with a given amount of money.
- Provide solutions to their problems using tables, graphs, and computations.

Have each group present its work to the class.

Lesson 5 (Student Book pages 38–47)

Solve Problems with Percent

LESSON OBJECTIVES

- Understand percent as a rate per hundred.
- Find a percent of a quantity as a rate per hundred.
- Solve percent problems involving finding the whole.

PREREQUISITE SKILLS

- Understand the concept of rate as detailed in 6.RP.A.3b.
- Understand whole and parts in the context of a ratio.
- Use unit pricing and constant speed to solve problems.
- Use unit rates to solve problems.
- Represent unit rates with models.

VOCABULARY

percent: a rate "for every 100" or "per 100"

THE LEARNING PROGRESSION

Previously, students developed an understanding of ratios and rates and how to use them to solve problems.

In this lesson, students learn about percent, a special type of rate in which the second quantity is 100. They learn that percents are an efficient way to compare two ratios with different second quantities as they use tables and diagrams to compare them. They find the percent of a number using bar models as well as multiplication. They use tables and double number lines to find the whole when a part and a percent are known. They apply these concepts and skills as they solve problems.

In later grades, students will extend their knowledge of percent as they solve a variety of complex problems involving percent, e.g., percent increase or decrease. A strong understanding of percent as a special rate will give them a deeper understanding of the applications they encounter.

Ready *Teacher Toolbox* — Teacher-Toolbox.com

	Prerequisite Skills	*6.RP.A.3c*
Ready Lessons	✓	✓
Tools for Instruction		✓✓
Interactive Tutorials		✓✓

CCSS Focus

6.RP.A.3 Use ratio and rate reasoning to solve real-world and mathematical problems, e.g., by reasoning about tables of equivalent ratios, tape diagrams, double number line diagrams, or equations.

c. Find a percent of a quantity as a rate per 100 (e.g., 30% of a quantity means $\frac{30}{100}$ times the quantity); solve problems involving finding the whole, given a part and the percent.

ADDITIONAL STANDARDS: ***6.RP.A.3b, 6.RP.A.3a*** *(see page A42 for full text)*

STANDARDS FOR MATHEMATICAL PRACTICE: ***SMP 1, 2, 4, 5, 7*** *(see page A9 for full text)*

AT A GLANCE

Students read a word problem and answer a series of questions that help them solve the problem using ratios with 100 for the second quantities. The questions are designed to introduce them to the concept of percent.

STEP BY STEP

- Tell students that this page models comparing ratios with different denominators. It shows them how to find equivalent ratios which both have 100 for the second quantity.
- Have students read the problem at the top of the page.
- Work through Explore It as a class.
- Have students describe more than one way to find the values in the tables. Students may suggest using increments of 5% for either test table or 10% for the second test table.
- Ask, *Is it possible to find ratios with the second number greater than 100?* [Yes, you can extend the table to infinity.]
- Ask, *Why can you solve the problem without extending the tables past 100 for the second number?* [Once the second numbers are the same, you can compare the ratios.]
- Ask student pairs or groups to explain their answers for the remaining questions.

SMP Tip: Students look for and make use of structure in the table in order to recognize the relationship among numbers (*SMP 7*). Regularly ask students to look for relationships between numbers and any similarities, differences, or patterns in those relationships.

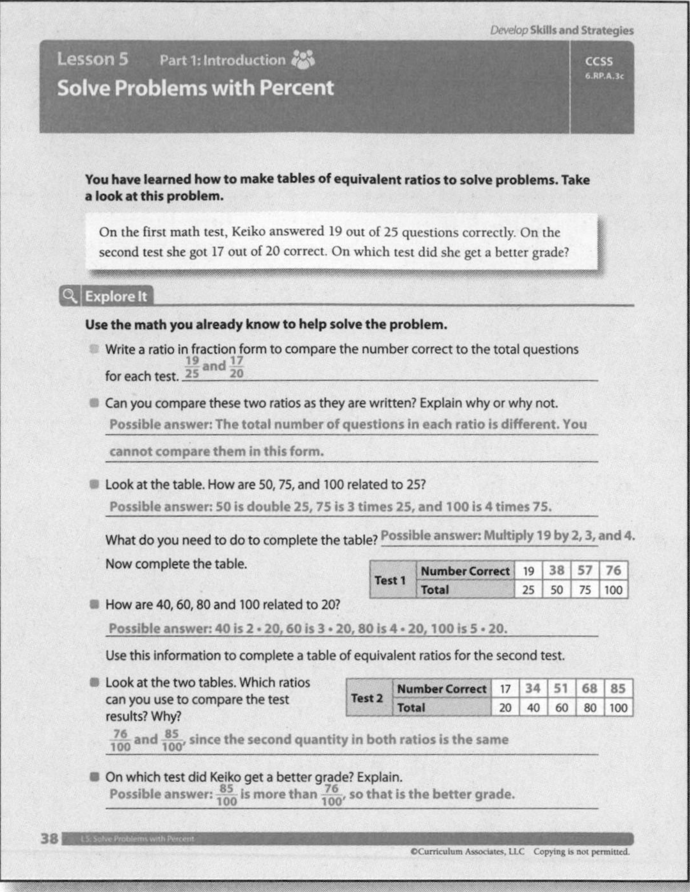

Develop Skills and Strategies

Lesson 5 Part 1: Introduction

Solve Problems with Percent

CCSS 6.RP.A.3c

You have learned how to make tables of equivalent ratios to solve problems. Take a look at this problem.

On the first math test, Keiko answered 19 out of 25 questions correctly. On the second test she got 17 out of 20 correct. On which test did she get a better grade?

Explore It

Use the math you already know to help solve the problem.

- Write a ratio in fraction form to compare the number correct to the total questions for each test. $\frac{19}{25}$ and $\frac{17}{20}$
- Can you compare these two ratios as they are written? Explain why or why not. **Possible answer: The total number of questions in each ratio is different. You cannot compare them in this form.**
- Look at the table. How are 50, 75, and 100 related to 25? **Possible answer: 50 is double 25, 75 is 3 times 25, and 100 is 4 times 75.**

What do you need to do to complete the table? **Possible answer: Multiply 19 by 2, 3, and 4.**

Now complete the table.

Test 1	Number Correct	19	38	57	76
	Total	25	50	75	100

- How are 40, 60, 80 and 100 related to 20? **Possible answer: 40 is 2 • 20, 60 is 3 • 20, 80 is 4 • 20, 100 is 5 • 20.**

Use this information to complete a table of equivalent ratios for the second test.

Test 2	Number Correct	17	34	51	68	85
	Total	20	40	60	80	100

- Look at the two tables. Which ratios can you use to compare the test results? Why? **$\frac{76}{100}$ and $\frac{85}{100}$, since the second quantity in both ratios is the same**
- On which test did Keiko get a better grade? Explain. **Possible answer: $\frac{85}{100}$ is more than $\frac{76}{100}$, so that is the better grade.**

38 L5: Solve Problems with Percent

©Curriculum Associates, LLC Copying is not permitted.

Mathematical Discourse

- *Suppose Keiko answered 36 out of 40 questions correctly on the third test. How could you use a table to find the percent for 36 out of 40 questions answered correctly?*

  Discussion should include that 100 is not a multiple of 40, so you cannot multiply by a whole number and get a ratio with 100 as the second number. Allow wait time or ask students to Pair/Share. Suggestions might include multiplying by a fraction. You might suggest simplifying the ratio to $\frac{18}{20}$ or $\frac{9}{10}$ and use a simplified ratio to build the table. Similarly, you could multiply each term by 5 to get $\frac{180}{200}$ and then simplify to $\frac{90}{100}$, or 90%.

AT A GLANCE

Students learn that ratios with 100 for the second number are called percents. Percents can be used to compare ratios that have different second numbers.

STEP BY STEP

- Read Find Out More as a class.
- Distinguish *per cent* from using *cent* for a penny. Because there are 100 pennies (cents) per dollar, 1 penny is 1% of \$1.
- Emphasize that percents are ratios in which the whole is 100.
- Study the base-ten models that compare 76% and 85%. Relate them to the problem and tables on the previous page.
- As students consider the table on this page, stress that the fraction, decimal, and percent are different ways of writing the same quantity.
- Discuss the Reflect question, calling attention to commonplace situations like scores on tests.

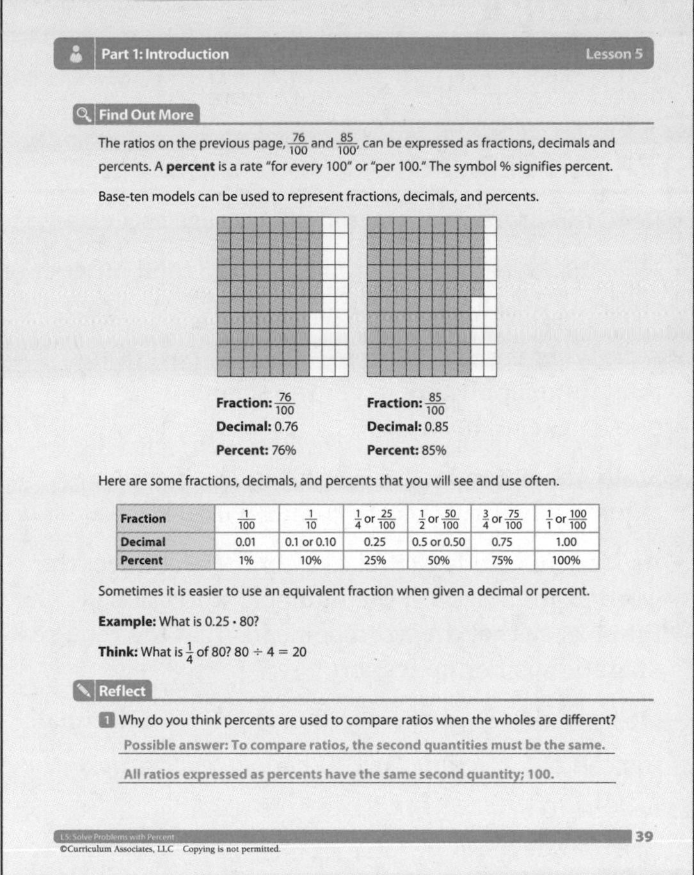

Part 1: Introduction Lesson 5

Find Out More

The ratios on the previous page, $\frac{76}{100}$ and $\frac{85}{100}$, can be expressed as fractions, decimals and percents. A **percent** is a rate "for every 100" or "per 100." The symbol % signifies percent.

Base-ten models can be used to represent fractions, decimals, and percents.

Fraction: $\frac{76}{100}$ **Decimal:** 0.76 **Percent:** 76%

Fraction: $\frac{85}{100}$ **Decimal:** 0.85 **Percent:** 85%

Here are some fractions, decimals, and percents that you will see and use often.

Fraction	$\frac{1}{100}$	$\frac{1}{10}$	$\frac{1}{4}$ or $\frac{25}{100}$	$\frac{1}{2}$ or $\frac{50}{100}$	$\frac{3}{4}$ or $\frac{75}{100}$	$\frac{1}{1}$ or $\frac{100}{100}$
Decimal	0.01	0.1 or 0.10	0.25	0.5 or 0.50	0.75	1.00
Percent	1%	10%	25%	50%	75%	100%

Sometimes it is easier to use an equivalent fraction when given a decimal or percent.

Example: What is $0.25 \cdot 80$?

Think: What is $\frac{1}{4}$ of 80? $80 \div 4 = 20$

Reflect

1 Why do you think percents are used to compare ratios when the wholes are different?

Possible answer: To compare ratios, the second quantities must be the same. All ratios expressed as percents have the same second quantity; 100.

L5: Solve Problems with Percent 39

©Curriculum Associates, LLC Copying is not permitted.

Visual Model

Use circle graphs to illustrate percents.

- Draw a circle on the board. Divide it in half. Ask students what percent is equivalent to $\frac{1}{2}$. Label the $\frac{1}{2}$ as 50%.
- Divide the remaining half into two fourths. Ask students what percent is equivalent to $\frac{1}{4}$. Label each of the fourths as 25%. Note that the percents add up to 100%, and that 100% is one whole.
- Draw another circle on the board. Tell students that you want to divide it into 50%, 20%, and 30%. Have them tell you how to show 50%. Label it.
- Draw a very light line dividing the other half into fourths. Discuss how to draw a line so that the portions are 20% and 30% instead of 25% and 25%. Draw the line and label the portions. Show that $50\% + 20\% + 30\% = 100\%$, which is 1 whole.

Real-World Connection

Ask students to list some situations in which they have heard people talk about percent.

Examples: grades on a test, sale prices, interest rates, how a candidate is rated in a poll, amount of a goal reached.

AT A GLANCE

Students use a bar model and a mathematical expression to find the percent of a number.

STEP BY STEP

- Read the problem at the top of the page as a class.
- Ask, *What does the 800 stand for?* [the total number of students in school]
- Ask, *What are you trying to find?* [the part of the total number of students in the school that participate in music]
- Study the bar model in Picture It. Have students explain why the 80 corresponds with 10%.
- As students study Model It, help them connect the word *expression* with the number expression. Emphasize that the word *of* means that the required operation is multiplication.
- Observe that students could multiply by a decimal instead of a fraction. Ask, *What decimal is equivalent to $\frac{60}{100}$?* [0.6].

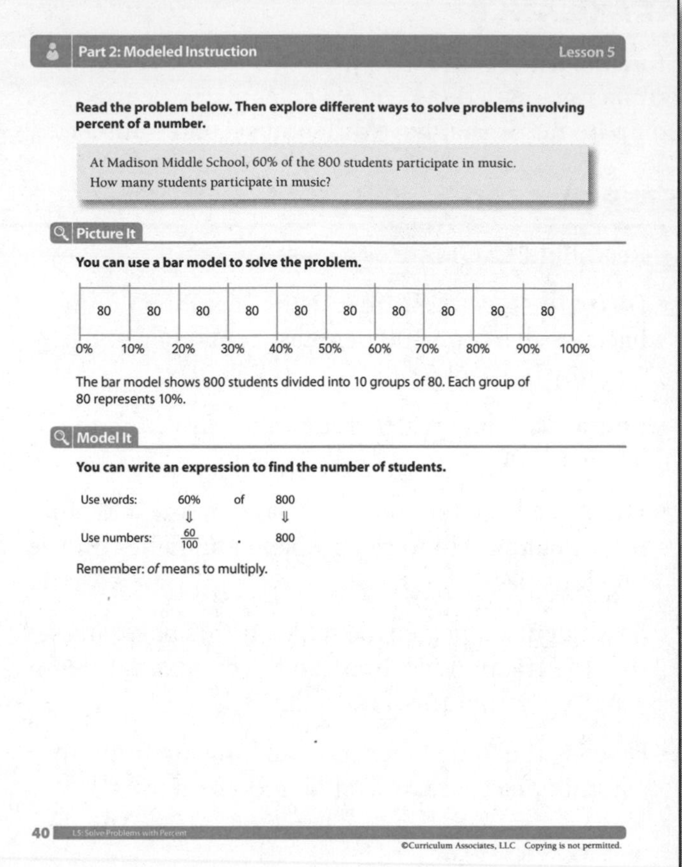

Part 2: Modeled Instruction Lesson 5

Read the problem below. Then explore different ways to solve problems involving percent of a number.

At Madison Middle School, 60% of the 800 students participate in music. How many students participate in music?

Picture It

You can use a bar model to solve the problem.

80	80	80	80	80	80	80	80	80	80

0% 10% 20% 30% 40% 50% 60% 70% 80% 90% 100%

The bar model shows 800 students divided into 10 groups of 80. Each group of 80 represents 10%.

Model It

You can write an expression to find the number of students.

Use words: 60% of 800

Use numbers: $\frac{60}{100} \cdot 800$

Remember: *of* means to multiply.

40 L5: Solve Problems with Percent

©Curriculum Associates, LLC Copying is not permitted.

Concept Extension

Use estimation to see if answers are reasonable.

- Ask, *Is 60% more or less than $\frac{1}{2}$?* [more]
- Ask, *What is $\frac{1}{2}$ of 800?* [400]
- Ask, *Should 60% of 800 be more or less than 400?* [more than] Have students explain their reasoning.
- Have students explain why the answer 480 = 60% of 800 is reasonable.
- Pose other problems, such as 40% of 300 or 70% of 80. Have students decide if the results should be less than $\frac{1}{2}$ or greater than $\frac{1}{2}$ of the number. Then have them find both the percent of the total and $\frac{1}{2}$ of the total and decide if their answers make sense.

Mathematical Discourse

- *Look at the bar model. How does showing 800 as 10 parts with 80 in each help you understand the problem?*

  Responses should include that using 10 parts makes it easy to figure 60% because the bar represents 100% and each part represents 10%, or 80 students.

- *What other bar models could you use to find 60% of 800 easily? How many parts would you use? How many students would each represent?*

  Students may suggest dividing the bar into 5 parts each representing 20%, or 20 parts each representing 5%. Work through each suggestion and ask students to discuss which they prefer and why.

AT A GLANCE

Students revisit the problem on page 40 to explore how to use a bar model or an expression to find the percent of a number.

STEP BY STEP

- Read Connect It as a class. Be sure to point out that the questions refer to the problem on page 40.
- Have students describe how to use the bar model to solve the problem.
- Review how to multiply by $\frac{60}{100}$ to find the answer. Have students explain why they could also multiply by $\frac{6}{10}$, $\frac{3}{5}$, or 0.6. Discuss which method is easiest for this problem.
- Have students share ideas for finding 55% of 800 using a bar model. Decide which suggestions are correct and which are the easiest.
- Have students complete Try It on their own. As a class, discuss different ways to solve the problems. In problem 7, some students may see that once they've found 25% ($10), they can subtract that amount from $40 to find the remaining part of the whole 100% ($30).

SMP Tip: Encourage students to find a variety of ways to solve the problem. Have them evaluate the possibilities to see which is most efficient. As they explain the reasons behind their choices, they learn to construct viable arguments and critique the reasoning of others (*SMP 3*). Remind students that sometimes a technique that is easier for one person may not be easier for another.

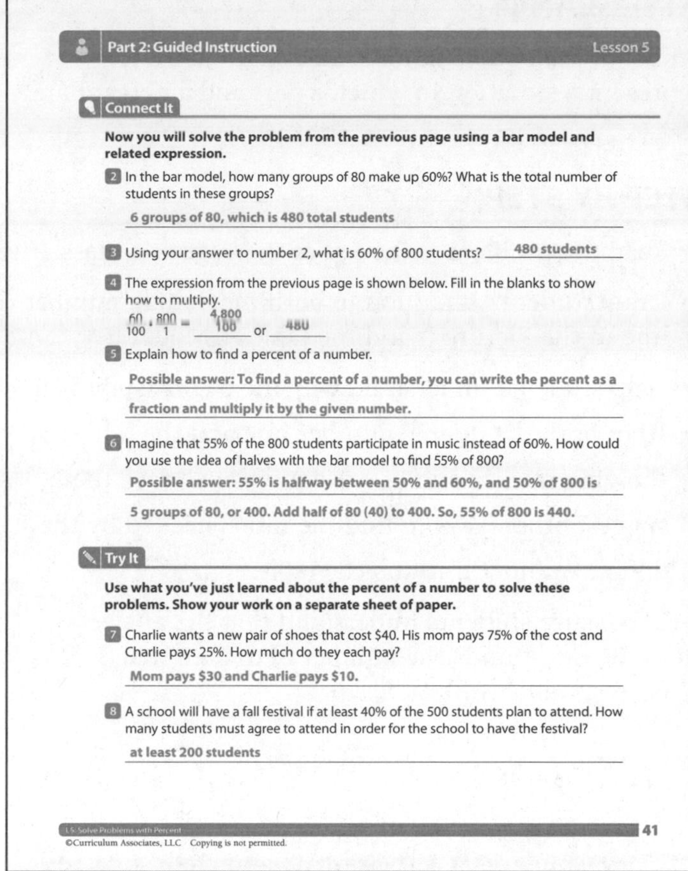

Part 2: Guided Instruction Lesson 5

Connect It

Now you will solve the problem from the previous page using a bar model and related expression.

2 In the bar model, how many groups of 80 make up 60%? What is the total number of students in these groups?

6 groups of 80, which is 480 total students

3 Using your answer to number 2, what is 60% of 800 students? **480 students**

4 The expression from the previous page is shown below. Fill in the blanks to show how to multiply.

$\frac{60}{100} \cdot \frac{800}{1} = \frac{4,800}{100}$ or 480

5 Explain how to find a percent of a number.

Possible answer: To find a percent of a number, you can write the percent as a fraction and multiply it by the given number.

6 Imagine that 55% of the 800 students participate in music instead of 60%. How could you use the idea of halves with the bar model to find 55% of 800?

Possible answer: 55% is halfway between 50% and 60%, and 50% of 800 is 5 groups of 80, or 400. Add half of 80 (40) to 400. So, 55% of 800 is 440.

Try It

Use what you've just learned about the percent of a number to solve these problems. Show your work on a separate sheet of paper.

7 Charlie wants a new pair of shoes that cost $40. His mom pays 75% of the cost and Charlie pays 25%. How much do they each pay?

Mom pays $30 and Charlie pays $10.

8 A school will have a fall festival if at least 40% of the 500 students plan to attend. How many students must agree to attend in order for the school to have the festival?

at least 200 students

L5: Solve Problems with Percent 41
©Curriculum Associates, LLC Copying is not permitted.

TRY IT SOLUTIONS

7 *Solution:* Mom, $30; Charlie $10; Students may multiply 0.75×40 and 0.25×40 or $\frac{3}{4} \times 40$ and $\frac{1}{4} \times 40$. Note that in this case the fraction may be more efficient than the decimal.

8 *Solution:* at least 200 students; Students may multiply 0.40×500, $\frac{40}{100} \times 500$, or $\frac{2}{5} \times 500$. Discuss which is the most efficient.

ERROR ALERT: Students who wrote at least 20 students may have multiplied by 0.04 and need to review how to find the decimal equivalent of 40%.

AT A GLANCE

Students use double number lines and tables to represent a situation in which a part and a percent are given.

STEP BY STEP

- Read the problem at the top of the page as a class.
- Draw students' attention to both the double number line in the Picture It and the table in Model It.
- Help students understand why the 6 corresponds to 10 in both the double number line and the table by showing that $\frac{24}{40}$ and $\frac{6}{10}$ are equivalent. Have them suggest other ways to find the ratios needed by the double number line and the table.
- Make sure students understand that the answer to the question is the number of dollars that corresponds to 100%.

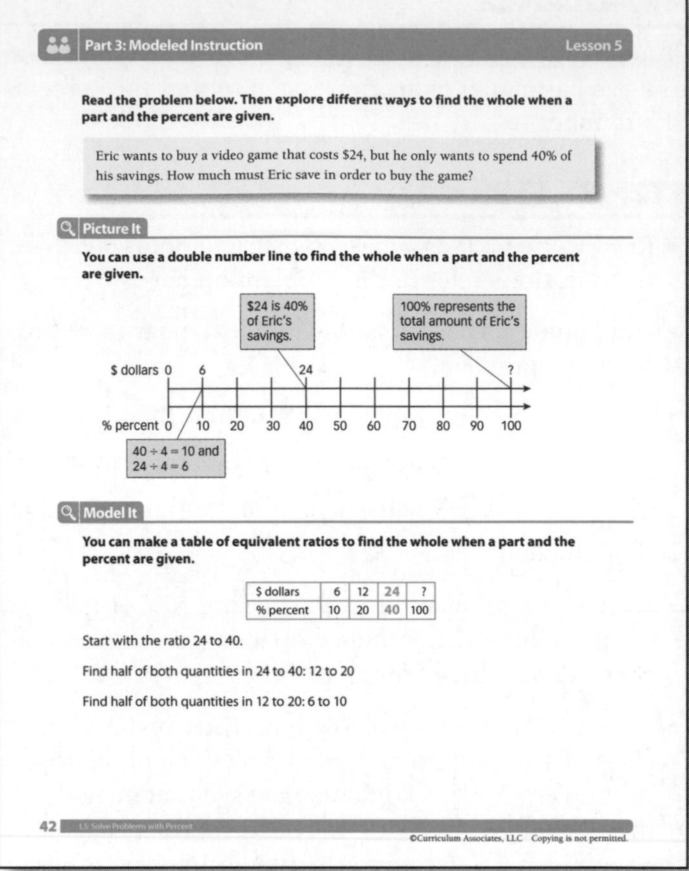

Part 3: Modeled Instruction Lesson 5

Read the problem below. Then explore different ways to find the whole when a part and the percent are given.

Eric wants to buy a video game that costs $24, but he only wants to spend 40% of his savings. How much must Eric save in order to buy the game?

Picture It

You can use a double number line to find the whole when a part and the percent are given.

Model It

You can make a table of equivalent ratios to find the whole when a part and the percent are given.

$ dollars	6	12	24	?
% percent	10	20	40	100

Start with the ratio 24 to 40.

Find half of both quantities in 24 to 40: 12 to 20

Find half of both quantities in 12 to 20: 6 to 10

42 L5: Solve Problems with Percent

©Curriculum Associates, LLC Copying is not permitted.

ELL Support

- Write the words *part* and *whole* on the board. Have students use their own words to describe each.
- Model examples of part and whole: *There are 28 students in the class and 17 ride the bus. The whole is 28 and the part is 17. Erin has 7 friends, and 3 live in houses and 4 live in apartments. The whole is 7 and the parts are 4 and 3.*
- Call on each student to describe a situation involving a part and a whole and to identify each.

SMP Tip: As students compare the two models with each other and with the problem, they model with mathematics (*SMP 4*). Have students describe carefully and completely what each part of the model represents in the problem.

Mathematical Discourse

- *Notice that the number line increases by increments of 10% and the table by different increments. Explain which is correct.*

  Both are. All the ratios shown will simplify to the same amount.

- *Why is it important for the scale number line to increase by the same amount from line to line, but it is not important for the table to do so as well?*

  The number line is visual. Because the vertical marks are the same distance apart, the numbers must also increase by the same amount. In the table, you just find equivalent ratios until you get one with the second quantity. You don't have to find all the ratios in between the ones you already know.

AT A GLANCE

Students revisit the problem on page 42 and use double number lines and tables to find the whole when a part and a percent are given.

STEP BY STEP

- Read Connect It as a class.
- Work through the reasoning that explains how to find the number that corresponds to 100%. Have volunteers describe other ways to find the number that is the whole or 100%.
- When students describe how to find the whole when they know the part and the percent, encourage them to be specific about how they would label the number line or how they would find the values for the table.
- Have students complete Try It on their own.

Hands-On Activity

Create a model to show the relationship between a part and the whole in a percent problem.

Materials: drawing paper, crayons, adhesive dots

- Display this to students: *15 is 30% of ____.*
- Give each student 15 adhesive dots. Say that the 15 dots are 30% of an entire page of dots. Say that their task is to show how many dots would be on an entire page.
- Have students divide the paper into 10 portions, labeling them 10%, 20%, and so on to 100%. They should shade 3 portions to show 30%.
- Have them distribute the dots in the shaded (30%) area, placing 5 dots on each 10% portion. Note that 10% of the total is 5.
- Have students draw 5 circles on each of the remaining 10% portions and find the total number of dots and circles.
- Complete the statement given above to say the following: *15 is 30% of* <u>50</u>.

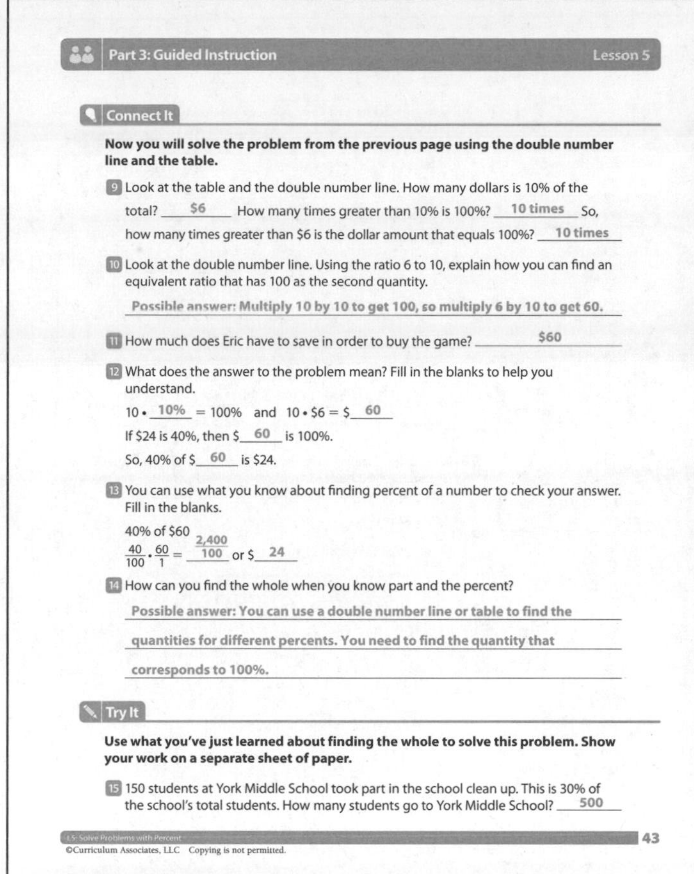

Part 3: Guided Instruction Lesson 5

Connect It

Now you will solve the problem from the previous page using the double number line and the table.

9 Look at the table and the double number line. How many dollars is 10% of the total? <u>$6</u> How many times greater than 10% is 100%? <u>10 times</u> So, how many times greater than $6 is the dollar amount that equals 100%? <u>10 times</u>

10 Look at the double number line. Using the ratio 6 to 10, explain how you can find an equivalent ratio that has 100 as the second quantity.

<u>Possible answer: Multiply 10 by 10 to get 100, so multiply 6 by 10 to get 60.</u>

11 How much does Eric have to save in order to buy the game? <u>$60</u>

12 What does the answer to the problem mean? Fill in the blanks to help you understand.

10 • <u>10%</u> = 100% and 10 • $6 = $<u>60</u>

If $24 is 40%, then $<u>60</u> is 100%.

So, 40% of $<u>60</u> is $24.

13 You can use what you know about finding percent of a number to check your answer. Fill in the blanks.

40% of $60

$\frac{40}{100} \cdot \frac{60}{1} = \frac{2,400}{100}$ or $<u>24</u>

14 How can you find the whole when you know part and the percent?

<u>Possible answer: You can use a double number line or table to find the quantities for different percents. You need to find the quantity that corresponds to 100%.</u>

Try It

Use what you've just learned about finding the whole to solve this problem. Show your work on a separate sheet of paper.

15 150 students at York Middle School took part in the school clean up. This is 30% of the school's total students. How many students go to York Middle School? <u>500</u>

L5: Solve Problems with Percent 43

©Curriculum Associates, LLC Copying is not permitted.

TRY IT SOLUTION

15 *Solution:* 500; Students may draw a double number line showing that 30% lines up with 150 and 100% lines up with 500. They may also use a table of equivalent ratios.

ERROR ALERT: Students who wrote 45 found 30% of 150; students who wrote 4,500 multiplied 150 and 30.

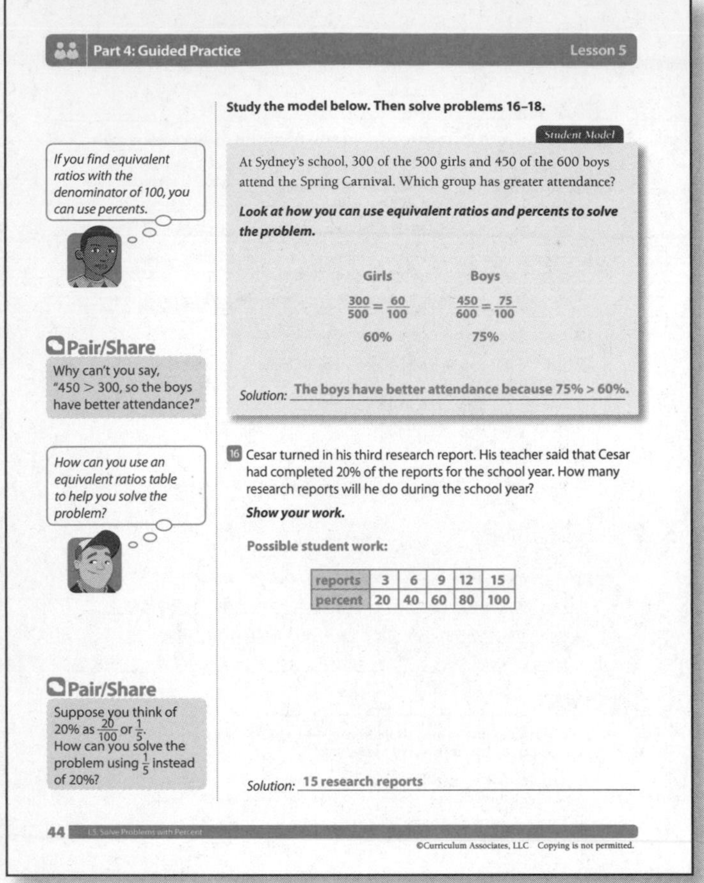

Part 4: Guided Practice Lesson 5

Study the model below. Then solve problems 16–18.

Student Model

At Sydney's school, 300 of the 500 girls and 450 of the 600 boys attend the Spring Carnival. Which group has greater attendance?

Look at how you can use equivalent ratios and percents to solve the problem.

Girls	Boys
$\frac{300}{500} = \frac{60}{100}$	$\frac{450}{600} = \frac{75}{100}$
60%	75%

Solution: The boys have better attendance because 75% > 60%.

If you find equivalent ratios with the denominator of 100, you can use percents.

Pair/Share

Why can't you say, "450 > 300, so the boys have better attendance?"

16 Cesar turned in his third research report. His teacher said that Cesar had completed 20% of the reports for the school year. How many research reports will he do during the school year?

Show your work.

Possible student work:

reports	3	6	9	12	15
percent	20	40	60	80	100

Solution: 15 research reports

How can you use an equivalent ratios table to help you solve the problem?

Pair/Share

Suppose you think of 20% as $\frac{20}{100}$ or $\frac{1}{5}$. How can you solve the problem using $\frac{1}{5}$ instead of 20%?

44 L5: Solve Problems with Percent ©Curriculum Associates, LLC Copying is not permitted.

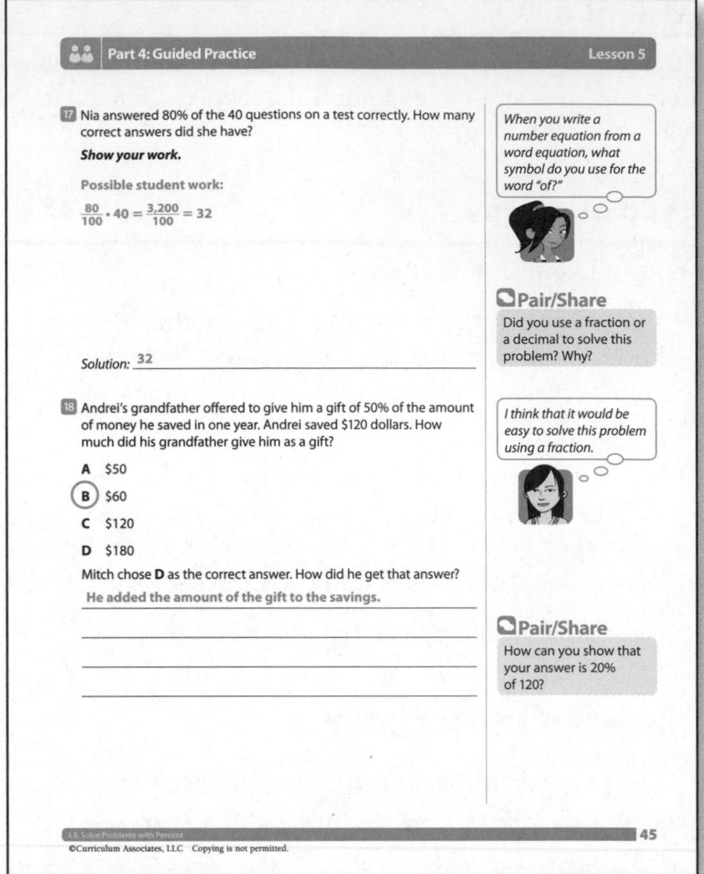

Part 4: Guided Practice Lesson 5

17 Nia answered 80% of the 40 questions on a test correctly. How many correct answers did she have?

Show your work.

Possible student work:

$\frac{80}{100} \cdot 40 = \frac{3{,}200}{100} = 32$

Solution: 32

When you write a number equation from a word equation, what symbol do you use for the word "of?"

Pair/Share

Did you use a fraction or a decimal to solve this problem? Why?

18 Andrei's grandfather offered to give him a gift of 50% of the amount of money he saved in one year. Andrei saved $120 dollars. How much did his grandfather give him as a gift?

A $50

B $60 (circled)

C $120

D $180

Mitch chose **D** as the correct answer. How did he get that answer?

He added the amount of the gift to the savings.

I think that it would be easy to solve this problem using a fraction.

Pair/Share

How can you show that your answer is 20% of 120?

L5: Solve Problems with Percent ©Curriculum Associates, LLC Copying is not permitted. 45

AT A GLANCE

Students use tables, double number lines, bar models, and computation to solve problems involving percent.

STEP BY STEP

- Ask students to solve the problems individually and to show their work using a table, a model, or computation.
- When students have completed each problem, have them Pair/Share to discuss their solutions with a partner or in a group.

SOLUTIONS

Ex Equivalent ratios with 100s for the second number are shown as one way to solve the problem. Students could also solve it using tables or two double number lines.

16 *Solution:* **15**; Students could solve the problem by making a table to find the number that corresponds to 100%. They could also use a double number line. ***(DOK 2)***

17 *Solution:* **32**; Students could solve the problem by writing an expression and multiplying. They could also use a table. ***(DOK 2)***

18 *Solution:* **B**; Mitch added the amount of the gift to the amount of savings.

Explain to students why the other two answer choices are not correct:

A is not correct because you find 50% of $120, not $100.

C is not correct because you find 50% of $120, not 50% of $120 plus $120. ***(DOK 3)***

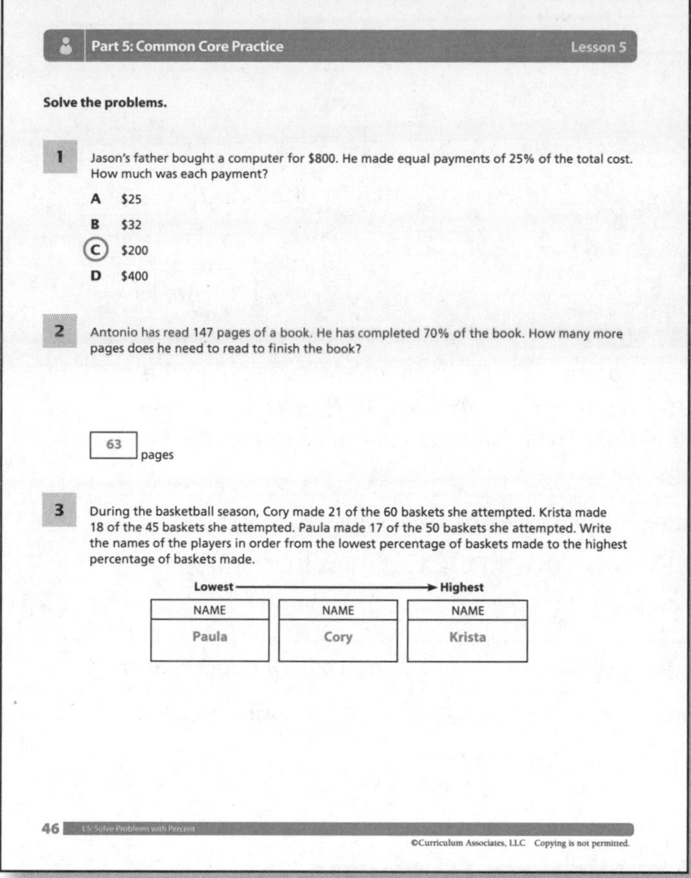

Part 5: Common Core Practice Lesson 5

Solve the problems.

1 Jason's father bought a computer for $800. He made equal payments of 25% of the total cost. How much was each payment?

A $25

B $32

Ⓒ $200

D $400

2 Antonio has read 147 pages of a book. He has completed 70% of the book. How many more pages does he need to read to finish the book?

63 pages

3 During the basketball season, Cory made 21 of the 60 baskets she attempted. Krista made 18 of the 45 baskets she attempted. Paula made 17 of the 50 baskets she attempted. Write the names of the players in order from the lowest percentage of baskets made to the highest percentage of baskets made.

Lowest ⟶ Highest

NAME	NAME	NAME
Paula	Cory	Krista

46 L5: Solve Problems with Percent

©Curriculum Associates, LLC Copying is not permitted.

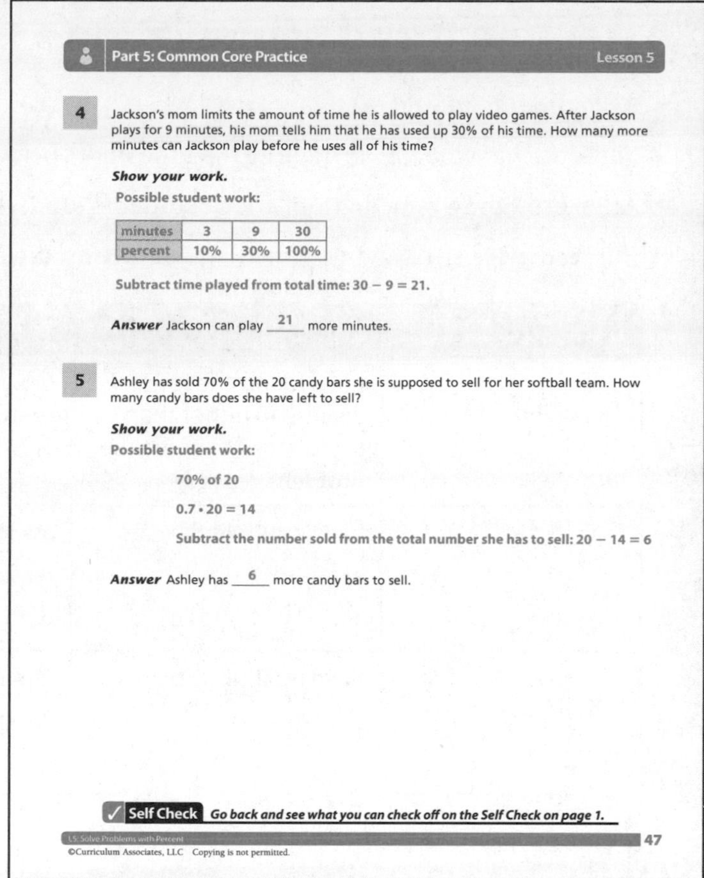

Part 5: Common Core Practice Lesson 5

4 Jackson's mom limits the amount of time he is allowed to play video games. After Jackson plays for 9 minutes, his mom tells him that he has used up 30% of his time. How many more minutes can Jackson play before he uses all of his time?

Show your work.

Possible student work:

minutes	3	9	30
percent	10%	30%	100%

Subtract time played from total time: 30 − 9 = 21.

Answer Jackson can play 21 more minutes.

5 Ashley has sold 70% of the 20 candy bars she is supposed to sell for her softball team. How many candy bars does she have left to sell?

Show your work.

Possible student work:

70% of 20

0.7 • 20 = 14

Subtract the number sold from the total number she has to sell: 20 − 14 = 6

Answer Ashley has 6 more candy bars to sell.

✓ Self Check *Go back and see what you can check off on the Self Check on page 1.*

L5: Solve Problems with Percent 47

©Curriculum Associates, LLC Copying is not permitted.

AT A GLANCE

Students use percents to solve problems that might appear on a mathematics test.

SOLUTIONS

1 *Solution:* **C**; Multiply $\frac{25}{100} \times 800$ or $\frac{1}{4} \times 800$, or use a table to find 25% of 800. ***(DOK 1)***

2 *Solution:* **63**; Use a proportion or division to find the total number of pages in the book. Subtract the number of pages read to find the number left to read. ***(DOK 2)***

3 *Solution:* **Paula, Cory, Krista**; Rewrite all 3 ratios as ratios with 100 in the denominator. ***(DOK 2)***

4 *Solution:* 21; Find the number of minutes that corresponds to 100% if 9 minutes corresponds to 30%; then subtract 9 from the total time. See possible student work above. ***(DOK 2)***

5 *Solution:* 6; Multiply or use a table to find 70% of 20, then subtract from 20 to find the number left. See possible student work above. ***(DOK 2)***

Assessment and Remediation

- Ask students to find 40% of 25. [10]
- For students who are struggling, use the chart below to guide remediation.
- After providing remediation, check students' understanding. Ask students to find 70% of 90. [63]
- If a student is still having difficulty, use ***Ready Instruction, Level 4,*** Lesson 21.

If the error is . . .	Students may . . .	To remediate . . .
$\frac{25}{40}$ or $\frac{5}{8}$	have found the ratio of 25 and 40 rather than using ratios to solve the problem.	draw a double number line. Divide it into fifths, labeling the bottom line 20%, 40%, 60%, 80%, and 100% and the top line 5, 10, 15, 20, and 25. Help students see how they are related.
1	have multiplied by .04 or $\frac{4}{100}$.	ask students to review their answer to see whether it is reasonable. Point out that 40% is a little less than 50%, or $\frac{1}{2}$, or that 40% means $\frac{40}{100}$, or 0.4.
1,000	have multiplied by 40.	remind students that 40% means $\frac{40}{100}$ or 0.4, so it is less than 1. When a number is multiplied by less than 1, the product will have to be less than the number.

Hands-On Activity

Create models of percents.

Materials: graph paper, colored pencils

- Have students multiply fractions to find $\frac{1}{2}$, $\frac{1}{4}$, $\frac{3}{4}$, $\frac{1}{10}$, $\frac{1}{5}$, $\frac{2}{5}$, $\frac{3}{5}$, and $\frac{4}{5}$ of 100.
- Give each student 2 sheets of graph paper. They should outline a 10-by-10 grid in each quarter of the graph paper.
- Ask, *What is half of 100?* [50] Direct students to shade 50 of the squares in the first 10-by-10 grid.
- Have them write $\frac{1}{2} = \frac{50}{100} = 0.50 = 50\%$ below the grid.
- Discuss why each is an accurate way to describe the shaded portion. Then, guide students through the process of illustrating $\frac{1}{4} = \frac{25}{100} = 0.25 = 25\%$.
- Have students illustrate the other fractions independently. Discuss how students can use their illustrations to compare fractions.

Challenge Activity

Write and solve problems in which a percent and a part are known but the total is not.

Materials: index cards

- Tell students that they should write three problems in which the percent and the part are known but the total is not.
- Discuss why it might be easier to write the problems by starting with the total, or answer, and a percent and then find the part.
- Students should record each problem on the front of the card and the solution on the back. They should exchange cards with classmates and solve one another's problems.

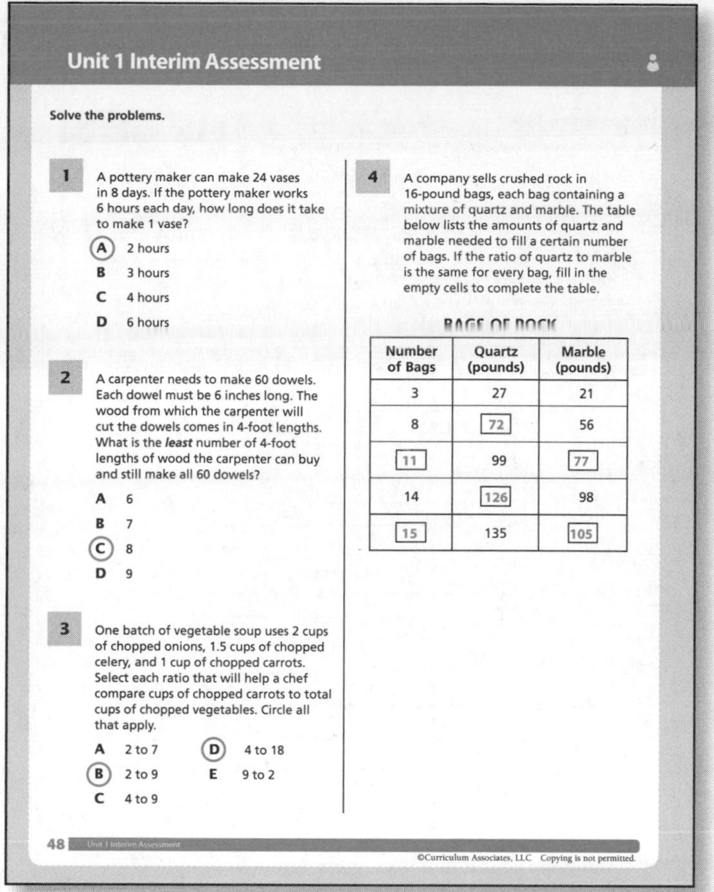

Unit 1 Interim Assessment

Solve the problems.

1 A pottery maker can make 24 vases in 8 days. If the pottery maker works 6 hours each day, how long does it take to make 1 vase?

(A) 2 hours
B 3 hours
C 4 hours
D 6 hours

2 A carpenter needs to make 60 dowels. Each dowel must be 6 inches long. The wood from which the carpenter will cut the dowels comes in 4-foot lengths. What is the ***least*** number of 4-foot lengths of wood the carpenter can buy and still make all 60 dowels?

A 6
B 7
(C) 8
D 9

3 One batch of vegetable soup uses 2 cups of chopped onions, 1.5 cups of chopped celery, and 1 cup of chopped carrots. Select each ratio that will help a chef compare cups of chopped carrots to total cups of chopped vegetables. Circle all that apply.

A 2 to 7
(B) 2 to 9
C 4 to 9
(D) 4 to 18
E 9 to 2

4 A company sells crushed rock in 16-pound bags, each bag containing a mixture of quartz and marble. The table below lists the amounts of quartz and marble needed to fill a certain number of bags. If the ratio of quartz to marble is the same for every bag, fill in the empty cells to complete the table.

BAGS OF ROCK

Number of Bags	Quartz (pounds)	Marble (pounds)
3	27	21
8	72	56
11	99	77
14	126	98
15	135	105

48 Unit 1 Interim Assessment ©Curriculum Associates, LLC Copying is not permitted.

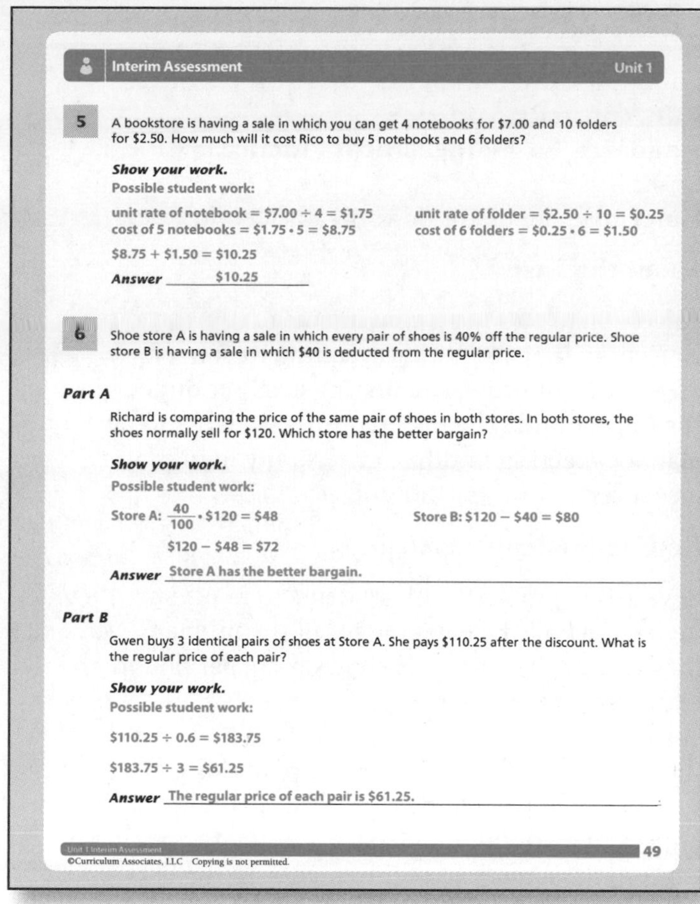

Interim Assessment Unit 1

5 A bookstore is having a sale in which you can get 4 notebooks for \$7.00 and 10 folders for \$2.50. How much will it cost Rico to buy 5 notebooks and 6 folders?

Show your work.
Possible student work:

unit rate of notebook = \$7.00 ÷ 4 = \$1.75
cost of 5 notebooks = \$1.75 • 5 = \$8.75

unit rate of folder = \$2.50 ÷ 10 = \$0.25
cost of 6 folders = \$0.25 • 6 = \$1.50

\$8.75 + \$1.50 = \$10.25

Answer \$10.25

6 Shoe store A is having a sale in which every pair of shoes is 40% off the regular price. Shoe store B is having a sale in which \$40 is deducted from the regular price.

Part A

Richard is comparing the price of the same pair of shoes in both stores. In both stores, the shoes normally sell for \$120. Which store has the better bargain?

Show your work.
Possible student work:

Store A: $\frac{40}{100}$ • \$120 = \$48
\$120 − \$48 = \$72

Store B: \$120 − \$40 = \$80

Answer Store A has the better bargain.

Part B

Gwen buys 3 identical pairs of shoes at Store A. She pays \$110.25 after the discount. What is the regular price of each pair?

Show your work.
Possible student work:

\$110.25 ÷ 0.6 = \$183.75

\$183.75 ÷ 3 = \$61.25

Answer The regular price of each pair is \$61.25.

Unit 1 Interim Assessment ©Curriculum Associates, LLC Copying is not permitted. 49

SCORING GUIDE AND ANSWER ANALYSIS

1 *Solution:* **A**; Set up a proportion to find how many vases are made in 1 day. Then set up a proportion to find out the hours it takes to make 1 vase. ***(DOK 2)***

2 *Solution:* **C**; Set up a proportion to find the length in inches of each piece of wood. Then divide to find how many dowels can be made from each piece of wood. Then divide to find out how many pieces of wood are needed. The carpenter cannot buy partial pieces of wood, so the least number the carpenter can buy is 8. ***(DOK 2)***

3 *Solution:* **B**; Add the cups of vegetables to find the total. Set up a ratio of cups of carrots to total cups of vegetables.

D; The ratio of cups of carrots to total cups of vegetables is 2:9. Multiply both parts of the ratio by 2 to find an equivalent ratio. ***(DOK 2)***

4 *Solution:* See student book page above for solution; Use unit rate to find out that each bag will have 9 pounds of quartz and 7 pounds of marble. Then use multiplication or division to find the missing numbers, or use proportions. ***(DOK 2)***

5 *Solution:* \$10.25; Divide to find the unit rate of a notebook and the unit cost of a folder. Then multiply to find the cost of 5 notebooks and 6 folders. Add the two costs to find the total. ***(DOK 2)***

6 *Part A Solution:* Store A; Find the sale price for \$120 shoes at both stores with their discounts.

Part B Solution: \$61.25; Use a proportion to find the original amount of the three pairs of shoes. Divide to find the original amount of each pair of shoes. See possible student work above. ***(DOK 2)***

PERFORMANCE TASK TEACHER NOTES

Common Core Standards: 6.RP.A.1, 6.RP.A.2, 6.RP.A.3b, 6.RP.A.3d
Standards for Mathematical Practice: SMP 1, 2, 4, 5, 6
DOK: 3
Materials: calculator or a spreadsheet program

About the Task

To complete this task, students use ratio and rate concepts. They use ratio reasoning to convert measurement units, calculating cost per ounce given cost per pound. The task requires students to develop a plan for meeting multiple criteria involving ratios, measurement units, and unit prices.

Getting Students Started

Review the problem with students to make sure they understand all the components of the problem. Make sure they realize that the table shows costs per pound and the requirements ask for price per ounce. For students who are struggling to get started, ask them how can they find the cost per ounce if the cost per pound is given. Some students may need to be reminded that there are 16 ounces in a pound. Emphasize that the recipe they develop must meet all requirements on the list.

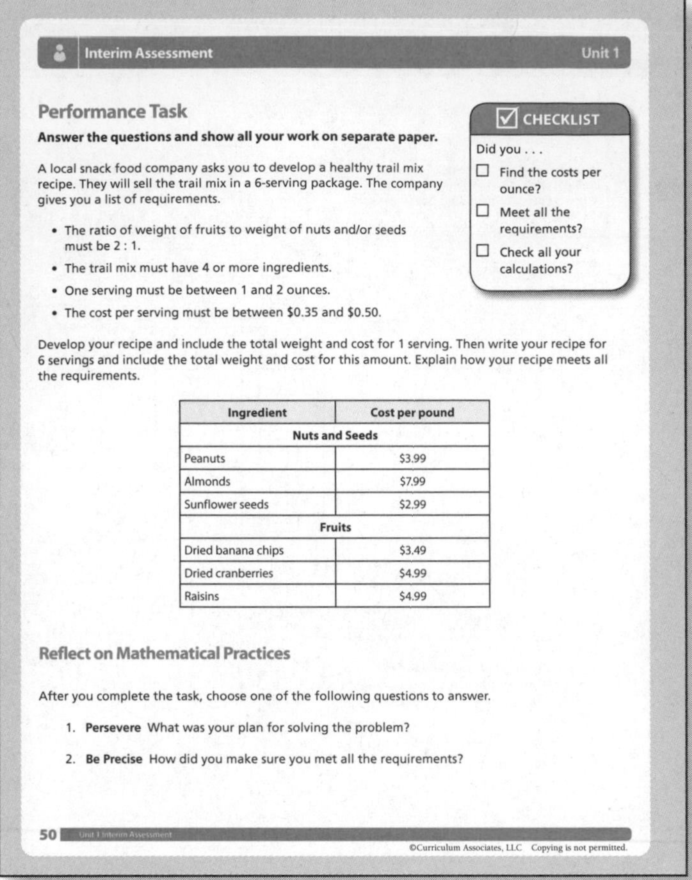
Interim Assessment Unit 1

Performance Task

Answer the questions and show all your work on separate paper.

A local snack food company asks you to develop a healthy trail mix recipe. They will sell the trail mix in a 6-serving package. The company gives you a list of requirements.

- The ratio of weight of fruits to weight of nuts and/or seeds must be 2 : 1.
- The trail mix must have 4 or more ingredients.
- One serving must be between 1 and 2 ounces.
- The cost per serving must be between $0.35 and $0.50.

CHECKLIST
Did you . . .
- Find the costs per ounce?
- Meet all the requirements?
- Check all your calculations?

Develop your recipe and include the total weight and cost for 1 serving. Then write your recipe for 6 servings and include the total weight and cost for this amount. Explain how your recipe meets all the requirements.

Ingredient	Cost per pound
Nuts and Seeds	
Peanuts	$3.99
Almonds	$7.99
Sunflower seeds	$2.99
Fruits	
Dried banana chips	$3.49
Dried cranberries	$4.99
Raisins	$4.99

Reflect on Mathematical Practices

After you complete the task, choose one of the following questions to answer.

1. **Persevere** What was your plan for solving the problem?
2. **Be Precise** How did you make sure you met all the requirements?

50 Unit 1 Interim Assessment ©Curriculum Associates, LLC Copying is not permitted.

Completing the Task

The first requirement is that the ratio of fruits to nuts and/or seeds needs to be 2 to 1. Ask students if 1 ounce of the trail mix is nuts and seeds, how many ounces are composed of dried fruit? Discuss whether the recipe could include 1 ounce or more of nuts and seeds. ***(SMP 2)***

Students need to realize that the costs of the ingredients listed are per pound. They will need to convert that information to a cost per ounce. Also, since the recipe must have 4 or more ingredients and the total weight is 1 to 2 ounces, they will need to use fractional parts of an ounce for at least some of the ingredients. ***(SMP 6)***

After students have chosen their ingredients and the amount of each one, they need to calculate the cost of 1 serving. Refer students back to the company's list of requirements to make sure all are met.

Next, students need to multiply the number of ounces for each ingredient in one serving to create a recipe and cost for 6 servings. Students may decide to organize this information in a table, with one column for one serving and columns for the number of ounces and costs for 6 servings. ***(SMP 4)***

Remind students to explain as thoroughly as possible how their recipe meets all the requirements. ***(SMP 1)***

Extension

If students have more time to spend on this problem, you can have them solve this extension:

An assembly line produces 2,020 packages of trail mix per week. If the line operates 5 days per week for 8 hours per day, what is the hourly unit rate?

PERFORMANCE TASK SAMPLE RESPONSES AND RUBRIC

4-Point Solution

Divide each cost per pound by 16 to find the cost per ounce. Then multiply each cost per ounce by the number of ounces in 1 serving to find the cost per serving.

Ingredient	Cost per pound	Cost per 1 ounce	Ounces in 1 serving	Cost per serving
Nuts and Seeds				
Almonds	$7.99	$0.50	0.25	$0.13
Sunflower seeds	$2.99	$0.19	0.25	$0.05
Fruits				
Dried banana chips	$3.49	$0.22	0.5	$0.11
Dried cranberries	$4.99	$0.31	0.5	$0.16
Total Weight/ Cost			**1.5**	**$0.45**

The chart shows that there are 4 ingredients. The total weight of the 4 ingredients is 1.5 ounces, which is between 1 and 2 ounces.

Ingredient	Recipe for 1 serving (1.5 ounces)	Recipe for 6 servings	Cost for 6 servings
Almonds	0.25 oz	$0.25 \times 6 = 1.5$ oz	$1.5 \times \$0.13 = \$0.20$
Sunflower seeds	0.25 oz	$0.25 \times 6 = 1.5$ oz	$1.5 \times \$0.05 = \$0.08$
Dried banana chips	0.5 oz	$0.5 \times 6 = 3$ oz	$3 \times \$0.11 = \$0.33$
Dried cranberries	0.5 oz	$0.5 \times 6 = 3$ oz	$3 \times \$0.16 = \$0.48$
Total Weight/ Cost		**9 oz**	**$1.09**

The total weight of the fruits is 1 ounce, and the total weight of the nuts and seeds is 0.5 ounce. So, the ratio of fruits to nuts and seeds is 1 : 0.5, which equals to 2 : 1.

The total cost per serving of all 4 ingredients is $0.45, which is between $0.35 and $0.50.

REFLECT ON MATHEMATICAL PRACTICES

1. Look for an understanding that the problem presented costs per pound and the requirements asked for price per ounce. Plans may also include creating a checklist to be sure that all requirements were met. ***(SMP 1)***
2. Look for explanations that include checking that the quantities are in the required ratios and that the total weight and cost match the requirements. ***(SMP 6)***

SCORING RUBRIC

4 points The student's response is accurate and complete. All calculations are correct and contain appropriate labels. The student clearly explains how all requirements have been met.

3 points The student has attempted all conversions and may have some minor errors in calculations. Units are labeled correctly, and all the requirements are addressed.

2 points The response contains several computation errors. The student may have attempted to address all the parts of the problem, but the response is incorrect and/or incomplete.

1 point The student's response is incorrect and incomplete. There may have been no attempt to convert the costs per pound to costs per ounce. The response does not address all requirements of the problem.

SOLUTION TO THE EXTENSION

Possible solution: 5 days per week $\times$ 8 hours per day = 40 hours per week; $2{,}020 \div 40 = 50.5$

The hourly unit rate is 50.5 packages.

Which lessons are students building upon?

Grade 5, Lesson 17
Understand Division With Unit Fractions
5.NF.B.7a, 5.NF.B.7b

Grade 5, Lesson 18
Divide Unit Fractions in Word Problems
5.NF.B.7c

Grade 5, Lesson 17
Understand Division With Unit Fractions
5.NF.B.7a, 5.NF.B.7b

Grade 5, Lesson 18
Divide Unit Fractions in Word Problems
5.NF.B.7c

Grade 5, Lesson 6
Divide Whole Numbers
5.NBT.B.6

Grade 5, Lesson 7
Add and Subtract Decimals
5.NBT.B.7

Grade 5, Lesson 8
Multiply Decimals
5.NBT.B.7

Grade 5, Lesson 9
Divide Decimals
5.NBT.B.7

Grade 4, Lesson 7
Multiples and Factors
4.OA.B.4

Grade 5, Lesson 5
Multiply Whole Numbers
5.NBT.B.5

Grade 5, Lesson 28
Understand the Coordinate Plane
5.G.A.1

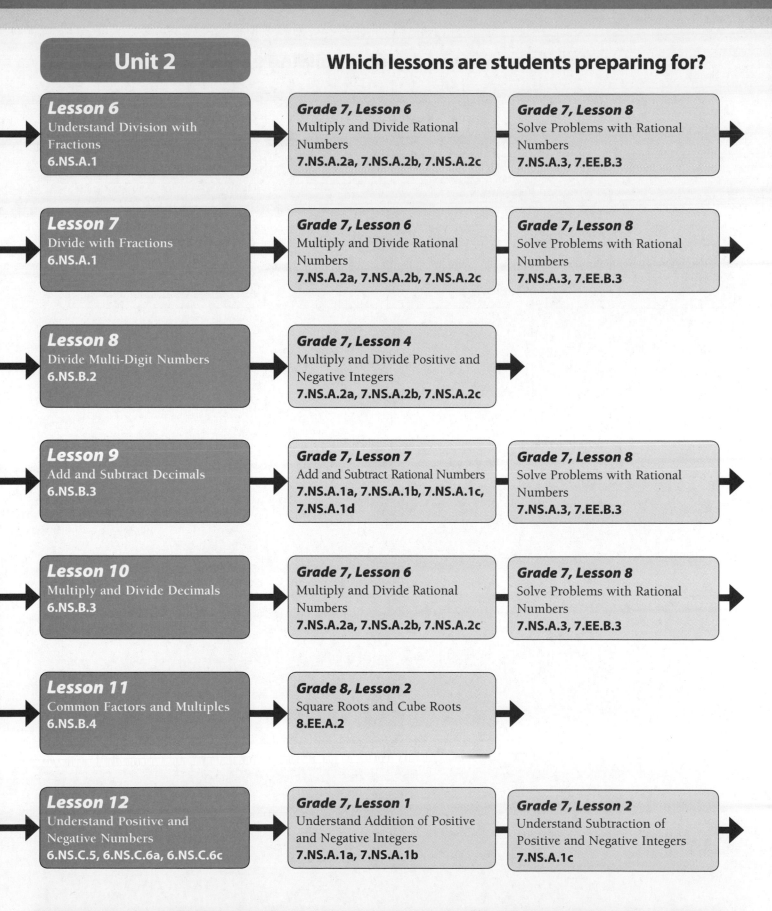

Unit 2

Which lessons are students preparing for?

Unit 2 Lesson	Prepares for	Then
Lesson 6 Understand Division with Fractions **6.NS.A.1**	***Grade 7, Lesson 6*** Multiply and Divide Rational Numbers **7.NS.A.2a, 7.NS.A.2b, 7.NS.A.2c**	***Grade 7, Lesson 8*** Solve Problems with Rational Numbers **7.NS.A.3, 7.EE.B.3**
Lesson 7 Divide with Fractions **6.NS.A.1**	***Grade 7, Lesson 6*** Multiply and Divide Rational Numbers **7.NS.A.2a, 7.NS.A.2b, 7.NS.A.2c**	***Grade 7, Lesson 8*** Solve Problems with Rational Numbers **7.NS.A.3, 7.EE.B.3**
Lesson 8 Divide Multi-Digit Numbers **6.NS.B.2**	***Grade 7, Lesson 4*** Multiply and Divide Positive and Negative Integers **7.NS.A.2a, 7.NS.A.2b, 7.NS.A.2c**	
Lesson 9 Add and Subtract Decimals **6.NS.B.3**	***Grade 7, Lesson 7*** Add and Subtract Rational Numbers **7.NS.A.1a, 7.NS.A.1b, 7.NS.A.1c, 7.NS.A.1d**	***Grade 7, Lesson 8*** Solve Problems with Rational Numbers **7.NS.A.3, 7.EE.B.3**
Lesson 10 Multiply and Divide Decimals **6.NS.B.3**	***Grade 7, Lesson 6*** Multiply and Divide Rational Numbers **7.NS.A.2a, 7.NS.A.2b, 7.NS.A.2c**	***Grade 7, Lesson 8*** Solve Problems with Rational Numbers **7.NS.A.3, 7.EE.B.3**
Lesson 11 Common Factors and Multiples **6.NS.B.4**	***Grade 8, Lesson 2*** Square Roots and Cube Roots **8.EE.A.2**	
Lesson 12 Understand Positive and Negative Numbers **6.NS.C.5, 6.NS.C.6a, 6.NS.C.6c**	***Grade 7, Lesson 1*** Understand Addition of Positive and Negative Integers **7.NS.A.1a, 7.NS.A.1b**	***Grade 7, Lesson 2*** Understand Subtraction of Positive and Negative Integers **7.NS.A.1c**

Which lessons are students building upon?

	Grade 5, Lesson 28 Understand the Coordinate Plane **5.G.A.1**	***Grade 6, Lesson 12*** Understand Positive and Negative Numbers **6.NS.C.5, 6.NS.C.6a, 6.NS.C.6c**
Grade 5, Lesson 28 Understand the Coordinate Plane **5.G.A.1**	***Grade 5, Lesson 29*** Graph Points in the Coordinate Plane **5.G.A.2**	***Grade 6, Lesson 12*** Understand Positive and Negative Numbers **6.NS.C.5, 6.NS.C.6a, 6.NS.C.6c**

Unit 2

Which lessons are students preparing for?

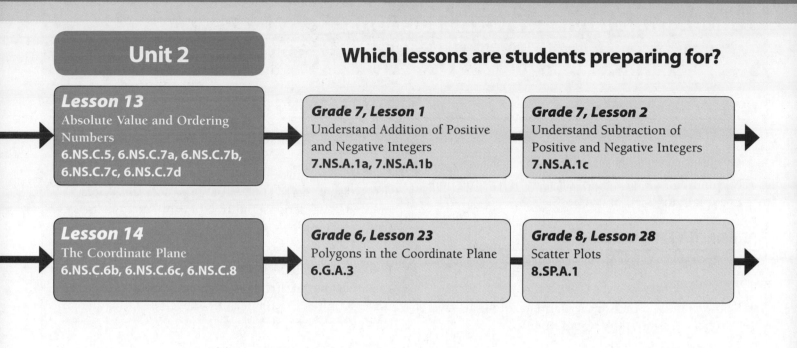

Lesson 13
Absolute Value and Ordering Numbers
6.NS.C.5, 6.NS.C.7a, 6.NS.C.7b, 6.NS.C.7c, 6.NS.C.7d

→ **Grade 7, Lesson 1**
Understand Addition of Positive and Negative Integers
7.NS.A.1a, 7.NS.A.1b

— **Grade 7, Lesson 2**
Understand Subtraction of Positive and Negative Integers
7.NS.A.1c

Lesson 14
The Coordinate Plane
6.NS.C.6b, 6.NS.C.6c, 6.NS.C.8

→ **Grade 6, Lesson 23**
Polygons in the Coordinate Plane
6.G.A.3

— **Grade 8, Lesson 28**
Scatter Plots
8.SP.A.1

Lesson 6 (Student Book pages 52–57)

Understand Division with Fractions

LESSON OBJECTIVES

- Understand the meanings of division.
- Use a model to show division of fractions.
- Use an understanding of multiplication of fractions to explain division of fractions.

PREREQUISITE SKILLS

- Know that multiplication and division are inverse operations.
- Know that division is either fair sharing (partitive) or repeated subtraction (quotative).
- Divide with whole numbers.
- Divide a whole number by a fraction.
- Model division with manipulatives, diagrams and story contexts.

VOCABULARY

There is no new vocabulary.

THE LEARNING PROGRESSION

In Grade 5, students divided whole numbers by unit fractions.

Students continue this understanding in Grade 6 by using visual models and equations to divide whole numbers by fractions and fractions by fractions to solve word problems.

In Grade 7, students will continue their work with fractions to include all rational number operations (positive and negative). Students will build on understanding of number lines developed in Grade 6.

Ready *Teacher Toolbox* Teacher-Toolbox.com

	Prerequisite Skills	*6.NS.A.1*
Ready Lessons	✓	✓
Tools for Instruction	✓	✓
Interactive Tutorials		✓

CCSS Focus

6.NS.A.1 Interpret . . . quotients of fractions, and solve word problems involving division of fractions by fractions, e.g., by using visual fraction models and equations to represent the problem. *For example, create a story context for* $\left(\frac{2}{3}\right) \div \left(\frac{3}{4}\right)$ *and use a visual fraction model to show the quotient; use the relationship between multiplication and division to explain that* $\left(\frac{2}{3}\right) \div \left(\frac{3}{4}\right) = \frac{8}{9}$ *because* $\frac{3}{4}$ of $\frac{8}{9}$ is $\frac{2}{3}$. *(In general,* $\left(\frac{a}{b}\right) \div \left(\frac{c}{d}\right) = \frac{ad}{bc}$.*) How much chocolate will each person get if 3 people share* $\frac{1}{2}$ *lb of chocolate equally? How many* $\frac{3}{4}$*-cup servings are in* $\frac{2}{3}$ *of a cup of yogurt? How wide is a rectangular strip of land with length* $\frac{3}{4}$ *mi and area* $\frac{1}{2}$ *square mi?*

STANDARDS FOR MATHEMATICAL PRACTICE: *SMP 1–4, 7, 8* *(see page A9 for full text)*

AT A GLANCE

Students explore dividing a fraction and a whole number by a fraction.

STEP BY STEP

- Introduce the Question at the top of the page.
- Read the description of how to divide a whole number by a unit fraction.
- Ask students to explain in their own words why $6 \div \frac{1}{4}$ is the same as 6×4. Ask them to use the number line illustration to make the explanation clear.
- Have students explain a reciprocal. Remind them that the reciprocal is the same as the multiplicative inverse.
- Discuss the number line in Think and ask a student to explain in his or her own words how the model shows $6 \div \frac{3}{4}$.

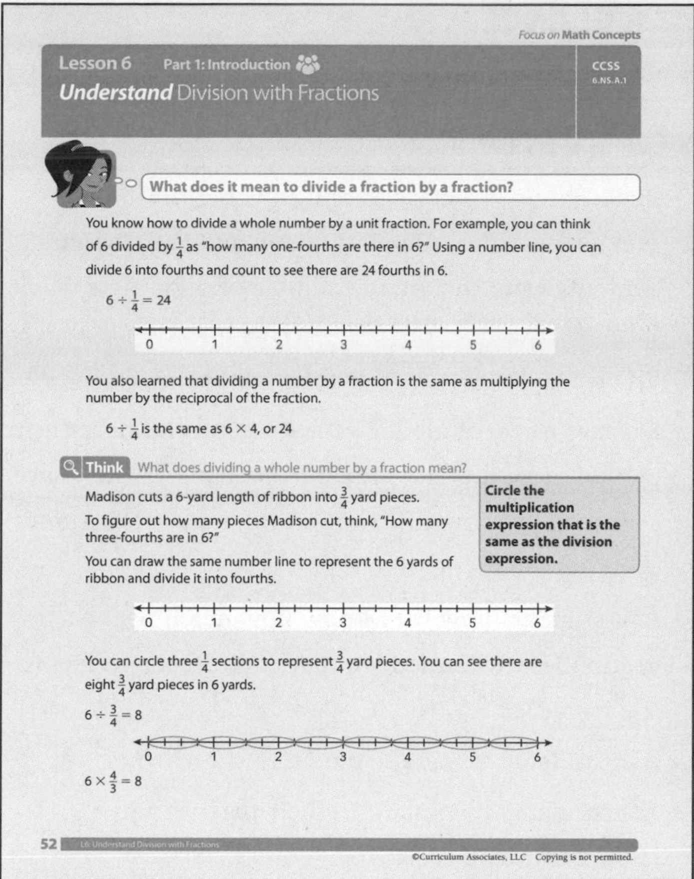

Focus on Math Concepts

Lesson 6 Part 1: Introduction CCSS 6.NS.A.1

Understand **Division with Fractions**

What does it mean to divide a fraction by a fraction?

You know how to divide a whole number by a unit fraction. For example, you can think of 6 divided by $\frac{1}{4}$ as "how many one-fourths are there in 6?" Using a number line, you can divide 6 into fourths and count to see there are 24 fourths in 6.

$6 \div \frac{1}{4} = 24$

You also learned that dividing a number by a fraction is the same as multiplying the number by the reciprocal of the fraction.

$6 \div \frac{1}{4}$ is the same as 6×4, or 24

Think What does dividing a whole number by a fraction mean?

Madison cuts a 6-yard length of ribbon into $\frac{3}{4}$ yard pieces.

To figure out how many pieces Madison cut, think, "How many three-fourths are in 6?"

You can draw the same number line to represent the 6 yards of ribbon and divide it into fourths.

Circle the multiplication expression that is the same as the division expression.

You can circle three $\frac{1}{4}$ sections to represent $\frac{3}{4}$ yard pieces. You can see there are eight $\frac{3}{4}$ yard pieces in 6 yards.

$6 \div \frac{3}{4} = 8$

$6 \times \frac{4}{3} = 8$

52 L6: Understand Division with Fractions

©Curriculum Associates, LLC Copying is not permitted.

ELL Support

Discuss the difference between the phrases "dividing by" and "dividing into." Dividing by $\frac{1}{4}$, for example, asks how many groups of $\frac{1}{4}$ are in a number, but dividing into fourths means to separate a number into four equal groups—i.e., multiplying by a unit fraction.

Mathematical Discourse

- *When you divide a whole number by a fraction less than 1, the quotient is larger than the dividend. Can you explain why?*

  Students might explain that since the fraction is less than 1, you would be able to take out more than one group from each whole in the dividend. Ask other students to add to the explanation and to use the same reasoning to solve $10 \div \frac{3}{5}$ and explain why the answer makes sense.

AT A GLANCE

Students explore dividing a fraction by a whole number.

STEP BY STEP

- Read Think as a class. Emphasize that in the previous problem about Madison and the ribbon, students were shown an example of dividing a whole number by a fraction: $6 \div \frac{3}{4}$. This question is about dividing a fraction by a whole number: $\frac{3}{4} \div 6$.
- Discuss the area model with students and have them explain how the first model represents $\frac{3}{4}$. Then have a student explain how the second model represents dividing the model into 6 parts.
- Ask students how they know how much is in each group. Be sure students understand that $\frac{3}{24}$ refers to the whole.
- Ask students to use the model to show why $\frac{3}{24} = \frac{1}{8}$.
- Ask students to explain to their partner why $\frac{3}{4} \div 6$ is the same as $\frac{3}{4} \times \frac{1}{6}$.
- Have students read and reply to the Reflect directive.

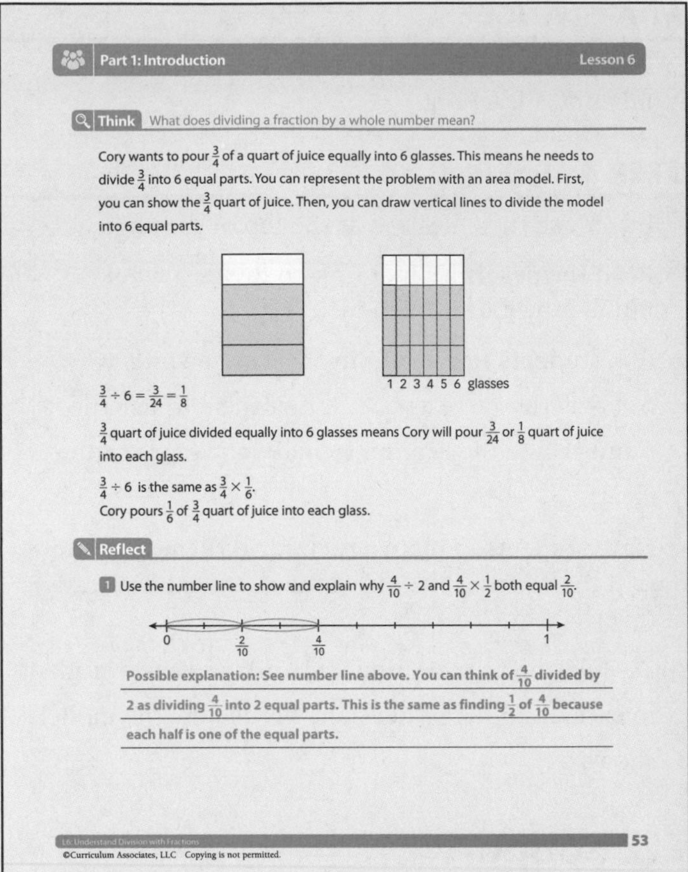

Part 1: Introduction Lesson 6

Think What does dividing a fraction by a whole number mean?

Cory wants to pour $\frac{3}{4}$ of a quart of juice equally into 6 glasses. This means he needs to divide $\frac{3}{4}$ into 6 equal parts. You can represent the problem with an area model. First, you can show the $\frac{3}{4}$ quart of juice. Then, you can draw vertical lines to divide the model into 6 equal parts.

$\frac{3}{4} \div 6 = \frac{3}{24} = \frac{1}{8}$

$\frac{3}{4}$ quart of juice divided equally into 6 glasses means Cory will pour $\frac{3}{24}$ or $\frac{1}{8}$ quart of juice into each glass.

$\frac{3}{4} \div 6$ is the same as $\frac{3}{4} \times \frac{1}{6}$.
Cory pours $\frac{1}{6}$ of $\frac{3}{4}$ quart of juice into each glass.

Reflect

1 Use the number line to show and explain why $\frac{4}{10} \div 2$ and $\frac{4}{10} \times \frac{1}{2}$ both equal $\frac{2}{10}$.

Possible explanation: See number line above. You can think of $\frac{4}{10}$ divided by 2 as dividing $\frac{4}{10}$ into 2 equal parts. This is the same as finding $\frac{1}{2}$ of $\frac{4}{10}$ because each half is one of the equal parts.

L6: Understand Division with Fractions 53
©Curriculum Associates, LLC Copying is not permitted.

Visual Model

Folding paper to divide a fraction by a whole number.

Materials: rectangular sheet of paper

- Paul uses $\frac{3}{4}$ of his back yard for gardening. He will divide this gardening section into 3 equal parts for vegetables. Model $\frac{3}{4} \div 3$ using paper.
- Start by folding the paper into fourths and shading $\frac{3}{4}$.
- Now fold the paper into thirds to show 3 sections for vegetables.
- Unfold. Ask, *How is the paper divided now?* [twelfths]
- Ask, *So how much of the gardening section of Paul's back yard is used for each vegetable?* [The shaded portion of each column represents $\frac{3}{12} = \frac{1}{4}$ of the whole.]

Real-World Connection

Ask students to describe real world situations in which they would have to divide a fraction by a whole number.

Ask students to think of a problem or situation that represents $\frac{3}{4} \div 6$. Share a situation in which $\frac{3}{4}$ of something is divided into 6 equal groups or shared equally by 6 people.

Example: Susan wants to create a picture frame in the shape of a regular hexagon. She has a strip of trim that is $\frac{3}{4}$ of a meter long. If she uses the entire strip, how long would each side be?

AT A GLANCE

Students use a number line to divide a fraction by a fraction.

STEP BY STEP

- Tell students that they will have time to work individually on the Explore It problems on this page and then share their responses in groups. You may choose to work through problem 2 together as a class.
- As students work individually, circulate among them. This is an opportunity to assess student understanding and address student misconceptions. Use the Mathematical Discourse questions to engage student thinking.
- Check to see that students label the number line correctly before they use it to answer questions.
- Take note of students who are still having difficulty and wait to see if their understanding progresses as they work in their groups during the next part of the lesson.

STUDENT MISCONCEPTION ALERT: Students may believe that *dividing by* $\frac{1}{2}$ is the same as dividing into half. *Dividing by* one half means how many $\frac{1}{2}$s are in a quantity, 7 *divided by* $\frac{1}{2} = 14$.

Dividing in half means "to take a quantity and split into two equal parts." 7 *divided in* half equals $3\frac{1}{2}$.

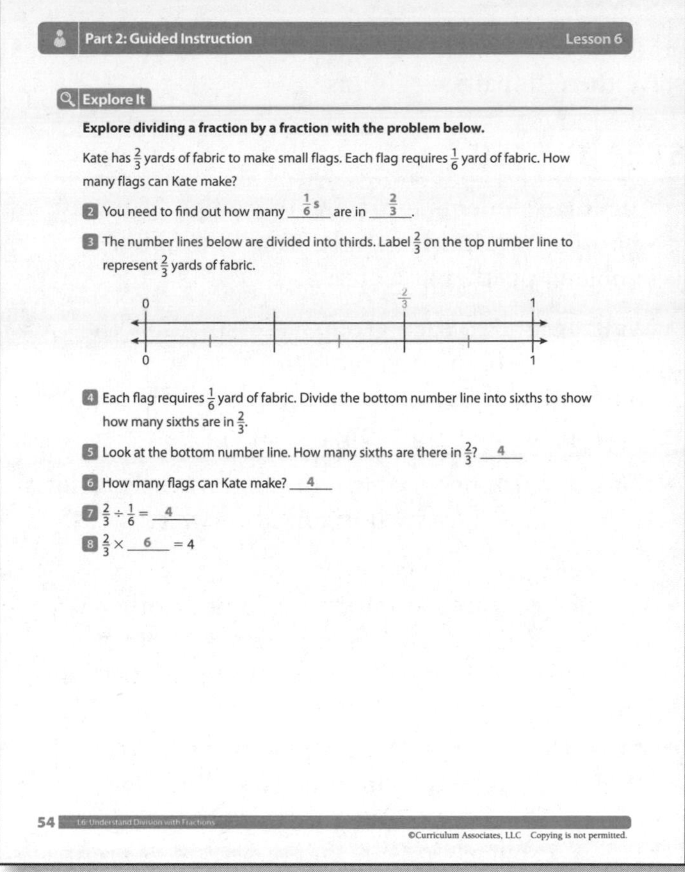

Part 2: Guided Instruction Lesson 6

Explore It

Explore dividing a fraction by a fraction with the problem below.

Kate has $\frac{2}{3}$ yards of fabric to make small flags. Each flag requires $\frac{1}{6}$ yard of fabric. How many flags can Kate make?

2 You need to find out how many $\frac{1}{6}$s are in $\frac{2}{3}$.

3 The number lines below are divided into thirds. Label $\frac{2}{3}$ on the top number line to represent $\frac{2}{3}$ yards of fabric.

4 Each flag requires $\frac{1}{6}$ yard of fabric. Divide the bottom number line into sixths to show how many sixths are in $\frac{2}{3}$.

5 Look at the bottom number line. How many sixths are there in $\frac{2}{3}$? 4

6 How many flags can Kate make? 4

7 $\frac{2}{3} \div \frac{1}{6} = $ 4

8 $\frac{2}{3} \times$ 6 $= 4$

54 L6: Understand Division with Fractions

©Curriculum Associates, LLC Copying is not permitted.

Mathematical Discourse

- *How would you explain dividing a fraction by a fraction using the number line model to a student who was absent from class?*

  Students should explain that you first draw and label the dividend on a number line. Then, draw another number line beneath it and divide it equally into the number of parts that are in the divisor. They should then count and circle how many groups of the divisor there are up to the dividend. Students should model the number lines on the board for the class to see.

- *What is another way you could model this problem?*

  Students might describe an area model or paper folding.

- *Which method for solving fraction division problems do you prefer and why?*

  Students may prefer multiplying by the reciprocal or modeling. Listen for and encourage correct usage of math vocabulary.

AT A GLANCE

Students read fraction division word problems and solve them in pairs or groups.

STEP BY STEP

- Organize students into pairs or groups. You may choose to work through the first Talk About It problem together as a class.
- Walk around to each group, assessing how the groups are solving the problem. Use the Mathematical Discourse questions to help support or extend students' thinking.
- Students may need to be reminded what direction horizontal is. Review horizontal and vertical as needed.
- Direct the group's attention to Try It Another Way. Have a volunteer from each group come to the board to explain the group's solutions to problems 15 and 16.

SMP Tip: Students construct arguments using verbal or written explanations accompanied by models. Provide students an opportunity to refine their mathematical communication skills through discussions in which they evaluate their own thinking and the thinking of other students (*SMP 3*).

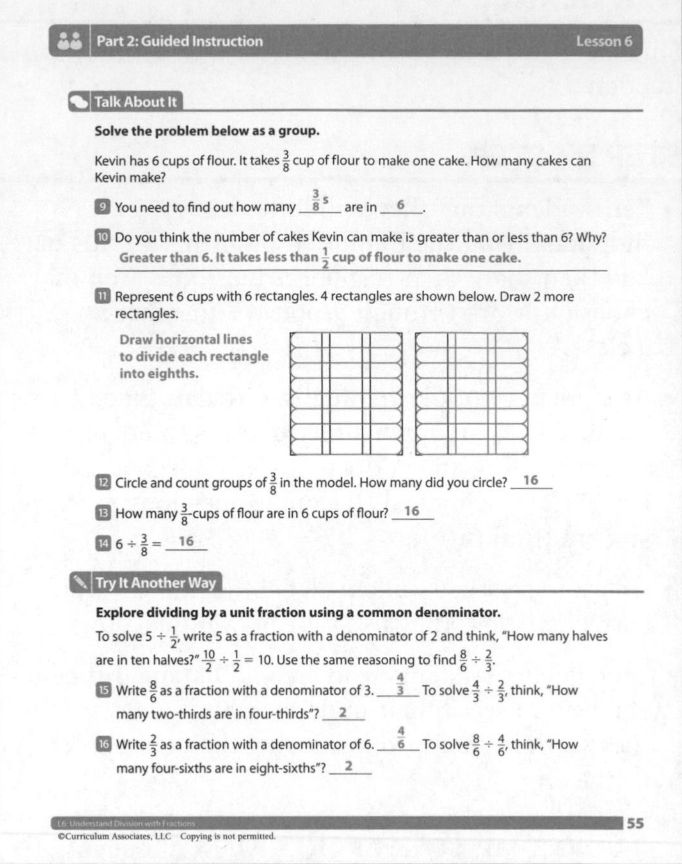

Part 2: Guided Instruction Lesson 6

Talk About It

Solve the problem below as a group.

Kevin has 6 cups of flour. It takes $\frac{3}{8}$ cup of flour to make one cake. How many cakes can Kevin make?

9 You need to find out how many $\frac{3}{8}$s are in 6.

10 Do you think the number of cakes Kevin can make is greater than or less than 6? Why?
Greater than 6. It takes less than $\frac{1}{2}$ cup of flour to make one cake.

11 Represent 6 cups with 6 rectangles. 4 rectangles are shown below. Draw 2 more rectangles.

Draw horizontal lines to divide each rectangle into eighths.

12 Circle and count groups of $\frac{3}{8}$ in the model. How many did you circle? 16

13 How many $\frac{3}{8}$-cups of flour are in 6 cups of flour? 16

14 $6 \div \frac{3}{8} =$ 16

Try It Another Way

Explore dividing by a unit fraction using a common denominator.

To solve $5 \div \frac{1}{2}$, write 5 as a fraction with a denominator of 2 and think, "How many halves are in ten halves?" $\frac{10}{2} \div \frac{1}{2} = 10$. Use the same reasoning to find $\frac{8}{6} \div \frac{2}{3}$.

15 Write $\frac{8}{6}$ as a fraction with a denominator of 3. $\frac{4}{3}$ To solve $\frac{4}{3} \div \frac{2}{3}$, think, "How many two-thirds are in four-thirds"? 2

16 Write $\frac{2}{3}$ as a fraction with a denominator of 6. $\frac{4}{6}$ To solve $\frac{8}{6} \div \frac{4}{6}$, think, "How many four-sixths are in eight-sixths"? 2

L6: Understand Division with Fractions 55

©Curriculum Associates, LLC Copying is not permitted.

Mathematical Discourse

- *Why would you use rectangles to model the problem?*

  Using an area model is a strategy for solving fraction division problems.

- *The problem is asking you to divide by* $\frac{3}{8}$*s. Why didn't you divide it into thirds?*

  To count by $\frac{3}{8}$s, you would need to start by dividing it into eighths.

- *How would you explain dividing a fraction by a fraction using a common denominator?*

  Students should realize that once they have a common denominator they know the parts are the same size, so they can simply divide numerators.

AT A GLANCE

Students demonstrate their understanding of dividing a fraction by a fraction.

STEP BY STEP

- Discuss each Connect It problem as a class using the discussion points outlined below.

Explain:

- Ask, *What does the top number line represent?* $\left[\frac{5}{6}\right]$
- Ask, *What does the bottom number line represent?* [twelfths]
- Ask, *What do the circled portions represent?* [Groups of $\frac{1}{12}$ in $\frac{5}{6}$. There are 10.]

Analyze:

- Students may draw an area model or a number line.
- Remind students that the problem is asking how many groups of $\frac{1}{4}$ s are in $\frac{3}{2}$. The quotient must be greater than one because there is more than one $\frac{1}{4}$ in $\frac{3}{2}$.

Justify:

- Read the problem as a class. Remind students that the problem is asking how many groups of $\frac{4}{6}$ are in 2.
- Students should draw a number line or area model to model the problem.

SMP Tip: Students need many opportunities to connect and explain the connections between different representations. Encourage students to compare the number line and area models and explain how they help to solve the problem (*SMP 4*).

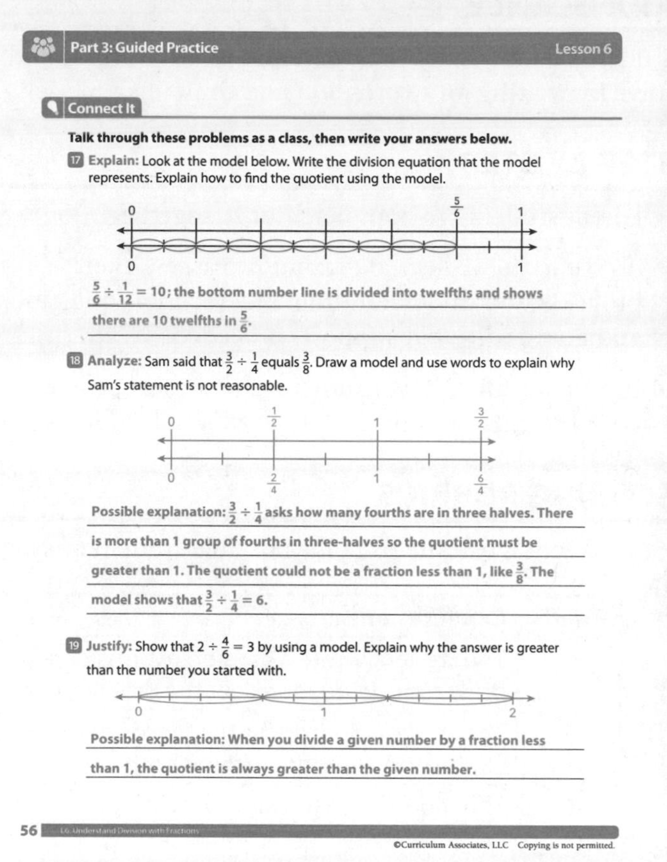
Part 3: Guided Practice Lesson 6

Connect It

Talk through these problems as a class, then write your answers below.

17 **Explain:** Look at the model below. Write the division equation that the model represents. Explain how to find the quotient using the model.

$\frac{5}{6} \div \frac{1}{12} = 10$; the bottom number line is divided into twelfths and shows there are 10 twelfths in $\frac{5}{6}$.

18 **Analyze:** Sam said that $\frac{3}{2} \div \frac{1}{4}$ equals $\frac{3}{8}$. Draw a model and use words to explain why Sam's statement is not reasonable.

Possible explanation: $\frac{3}{2} \div \frac{1}{4}$ asks how many fourths are in three halves. There is more than 1 group of fourths in three-halves so the quotient must be greater than 1. The quotient could not be a fraction less than 1, like $\frac{3}{8}$. The model shows that $\frac{3}{2} \div \frac{1}{4} = 6$.

19 **Justify:** Show that $2 \div \frac{4}{6} = 3$ by using a model. Explain why the answer is greater than the number you started with.

Possible explanation: When you divide a given number by a fraction less than 1, the quotient is always greater than the given number.

56 L6: Understand Division with Fractions ©Curriculum Associates, LLC Copying is not permitted.

AT A GLANCE

Students choose a fraction division word problem and solve by writing an expression and drawing a model.

STEP BY STEP

- Direct students to complete Put It Together.
- As students work, walk around to assess their progress and understanding, answer their questions, and give additional support, if needed.
- If time permits, have students share their problem with the class and discuss how they solved it.

SCORING RUBRICS

See student facsimile page for possible student answers.

A

Points	Expectations
2	The student wrote a division expression and drew a model to represent the problem.
1	The student only draws the model or the expression, does not include both.
0	The model or expression is incorrect.

B

Points	Expectations
2	Student uses the model to explain how to find the quotient and what the quotient means.
1	Student does not explain how to find the quotient or what the quotient means.
0	Student provides an incorrect explanation or response.

C

Points	Expectations
2	The student estimates what they think the quotient should be and proves if it will be greater than or less than the dividend.
1	The student does not explain why he/she thinks the quotient would be greater than or less than the dividend.
0	The student estimates incorrectly or gives an incorrect explanation.

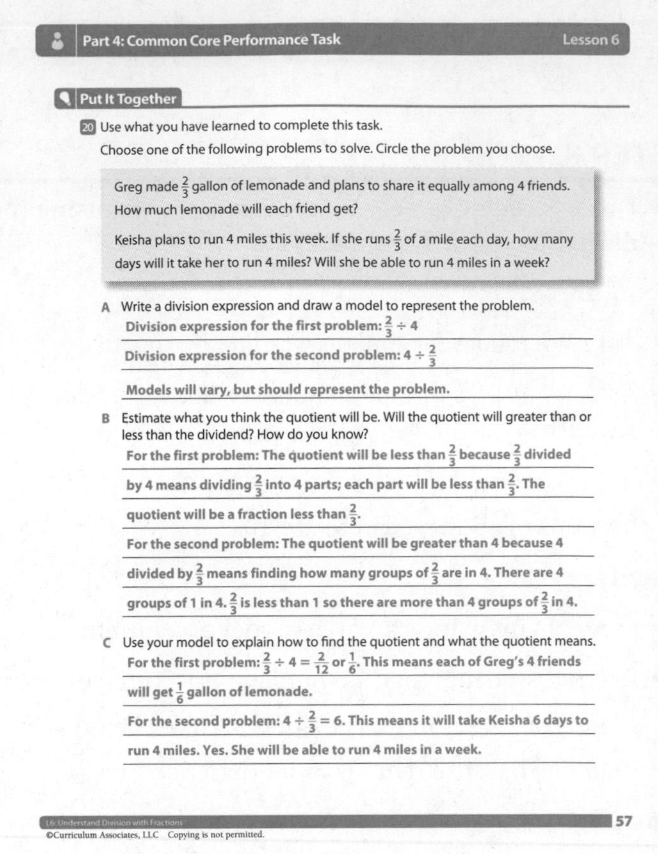

Part 4: Common Core Performance Task — Lesson 6

Put It Together

20 Use what you have learned to complete this task.

Choose one of the following problems to solve. Circle the problem you choose.

> Greg made $\frac{2}{3}$ gallon of lemonade and plans to share it equally among 4 friends. How much lemonade will each friend get?
>
> Keisha plans to run 4 miles this week. If she runs $\frac{2}{3}$ of a mile each day, how many days will it take her to run 4 miles? Will she be able to run 4 miles in a week?

A Write a division expression and draw a model to represent the problem.

Division expression for the first problem: $\frac{2}{3} \div 4$

Division expression for the second problem: $4 \div \frac{2}{3}$

Models will vary, but should represent the problem.

B Estimate what you think the quotient will be. Will the quotient will greater than or less than the dividend? How do you know?

For the first problem: The quotient will be less than $\frac{2}{3}$ because $\frac{2}{3}$ divided by 4 means dividing $\frac{2}{3}$ into 4 parts; each part will be less than $\frac{2}{3}$. The quotient will be a fraction less than $\frac{2}{3}$.

For the second problem: The quotient will be greater than 4 because 4 divided by $\frac{2}{3}$ means finding how many groups of $\frac{2}{3}$ are in 4. There are 4 groups of 1 in 4. $\frac{2}{3}$ is less than 1 so there are more than 4 groups of $\frac{2}{3}$ in 4.

C Use your model to explain how to find the quotient and what the quotient means.

For the first problem: $\frac{2}{3} \div 4 = \frac{2}{12}$ or $\frac{1}{6}$. This means each of Greg's 4 friends will get $\frac{1}{6}$ gallon of lemonade.

For the second problem: $4 \div \frac{2}{3} = 6$. This means it will take Keisha 6 days to run 4 miles. Yes. She will be able to run 4 miles in a week.

L6: Understand Division with Fractions 57

©Curriculum Associates, LLC Copying is not permitted.

Intervention Activity

Explore fraction division on a number line.

Materials: painter's tape, index cards, markers, string

Use painter's tape to create a number line on the floor across the classroom. Label the number line 1 through 5 with index cards spaced evenly apart on the number line. Write the problem $5 \div \frac{1}{3}$ on the board.

Ask students to explain how the number line can be used to solve the problem. Ask students to use painter's tape to divide the line into $\frac{1}{3}$s. Ask them to explain why $5 \div \frac{1}{3}$ is 15.

Next, ask students to model $5 \div \frac{2}{3}$. Students should use string to circle groups of $\frac{2}{3}$. There will be 7 groups of $\frac{2}{3}$ and $\frac{1}{3}$ left over. The quotient would be $7\frac{1}{2}$. Help students to realize that $\frac{1}{3}$ is half of $\frac{2}{3}$, so they have 7 and $\frac{1}{2}$ groups.

Continue to model using the number line for problems such as $10 \div \frac{1}{3}$, then $10 \div \frac{2}{3}$.

On-Level Activity

Make a fraction division handbook or poster.

Guide students to create a three-page "handbook" or three-part poster highlighting the steps to solving a fraction division problem.

Examples should include dividing a fraction by a whole number, dividing a whole number by a fraction, and dividing a fraction by a fraction. Each example should include an expression, a model, and an explanation for how to solve the problem.

Challenge Activity

Think about dividing whole numbers by fractions and dividing fractions by whole numbers.

Tell students, *Yolanda wants to cut $\frac{1}{2}$-foot pieces from a 4-foot rope.* Ask, *How would you record this number sentence?* [$4 \div \frac{1}{2} = 8$] *What do you know about the quotient?* [It will be larger than the dividend.] *How many pieces will she cut?* [8]

Tell students, *Now Yolanda wants to cut 4-foot pieces of rope from a $\frac{1}{2}$-foot piece of rope. How would you record this number sentence?* $\left(\frac{1}{2} \div 4 = \frac{1}{8}\right)$ *What do you know about this quotient?* [It is smaller than dividend.] *Is it possible to cut 4 feet pieces of rope from a $\frac{1}{2}$ foot piece of rope?* [No, so the real world answer is 0.]

Ask students to think of other real-world situations in which they would use division with fractions. Work with students to determine that their situations make sense.

Lesson 7 (Student Book pages 58–69)

Divide with Fractions

LESSON OBJECTIVES

- Solve word problems using division of fractions.
- Write an equation to solve a problem using division of fractions.
- Write a story problem that will use division of fractions.

PREREQUISITE SKILLS

- Know that multiplication and division are inverse operations.
- Know that division is either fair sharing (partitive) or repeated subtraction (quotative).
- Divide with whole numbers.
- Divide a whole number by a fraction.
- Model division with manipulatives, diagrams, and story contexts.

VOCABULARY

multiplicative inverse: a number which when multiplied by x yields the multiplicative identity, 1

reciprocal: the multiplicative inverse of a number; with fractions, the numerator and denominator are switched

THE LEARNING PROGRESSION

In Grade 5, students learn to understand fractions as division and to divide whole numbers by unit fractions.

In Lesson 6, students built upon the understanding from Grade 5 using models to show division of fractions. In this lesson, students continue to build upon their knowledge by using visual models and equations to divide whole numbers by fractions, fractions by fractions, and mixed numbers by fractions to solve word problems.

In Grade 7, students will continue their work with fractions to include all rational number operations.

Ready *Teacher Toolbox* Teacher-Toolbox.com

	Prerequisite Skills	*6.NS.A.1*
Ready Lessons	✓	✓
Tools for Instruction	✓	✓
Interactive Tutorials		✓✓

CCSS Focus

6.NS.A.1 Interpret and compute quotients of fractions, and solve word problems involving division of fractions by fractions, e.g., by using visual fraction models and equations to represent the problem. *For example, create a story context for $\frac{2}{3} \div \frac{3}{4}$ and use a visual fraction model to show the quotient; use the relationship between multiplication and division to explain that $\frac{2}{3} \div \frac{3}{4} = \frac{8}{9}$ because $\frac{3}{4}$ of $\frac{8}{9}$ is $\frac{2}{3}$. (In general, $\frac{a}{b} \div \frac{c}{d} = \frac{ad}{bc}$.) How much chocolate will each person get if 3 people share $\frac{1}{2}$ lb of chocolate equally? How many $\frac{3}{4}$-cup servings are in $\frac{2}{3}$ of a cup of yogurt? How wide is a rectangular strip of land with length $\frac{3}{4}$ mi and area $\frac{1}{2}$ square mi?*

STANDARDS FOR MATHEMATICAL PRACTICE: **SMP 1–4, 7, 8** *(see page A9 for full text)*

AT A GLANCE

Students read a word problem and explore dividing a whole number by a fraction using a model.

STEP BY STEP

- Tell students that this page models dividing whole numbers by fractions using a visual model.
- Have students read the problem at the top of the page.
- Work through Explore It as a class.
- Ask students how they determined whether the number of planters would be greater or less than 4.

ELL Support

Use the diagram on the page to review the words *divisor*, *dividend*, and *quotient*. Throughout the lesson, use models or manipulatives to demonstrate concepts and processes. Allow students to use the models to demonstrate their learning.

SMP Tip: Students map important quantities in the problem to the diagram as a way of understanding dividing with fractions (*SMP 4*). Students need many opportunities to explain the connections between different representations. Have students explain how the model helps them solve the problem.

Visual Model

Model dividing by a number less than 1.

- Draw 2 identical circles on the board. Write $2 \div \frac{1}{4}$.
- Ask, *Is the divisor,* $\frac{1}{4}$, greater than *or less than 1?* [less]
- *How many* $\frac{1}{4}$*s are in 2 circles?* Let a volunteer draw lines in the circles to show fourths. Ask, *Which is greater: the number of* $\frac{1}{4}$ *parts or the number of whole circles?* [The number of $\frac{1}{4}$ parts is more.]
- Write $\frac{1}{2} \div \frac{1}{4} =$ __. Ask, *Will the quotient be greater than or less than 1?* [greater than 1] Then let a volunteer draw a model to illustrate.

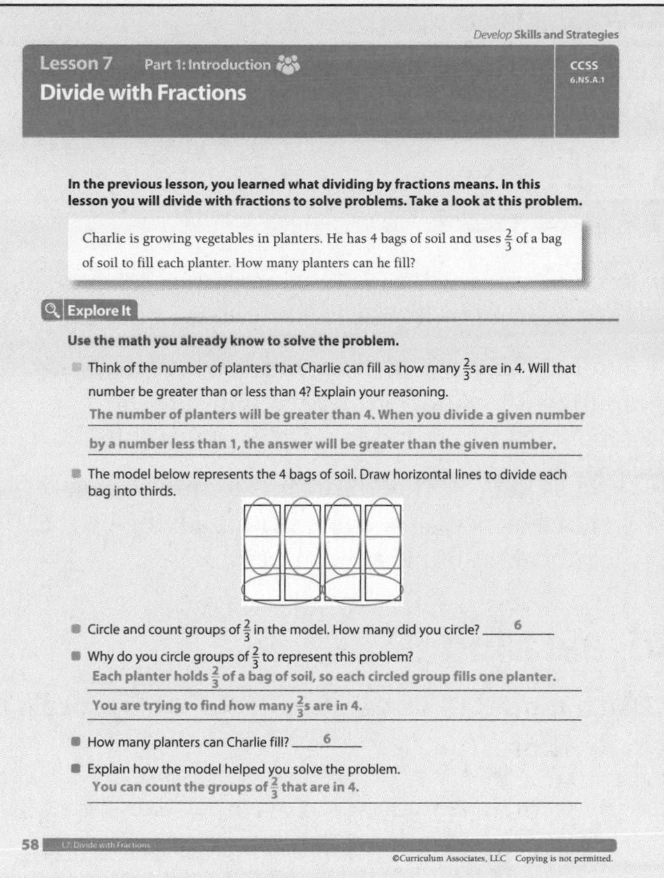

Develop Skills and Strategies

Lesson 7 Part 1: Introduction CCSS 6.NS.A.1

Divide with Fractions

In the previous lesson, you learned what dividing by fractions means. In this lesson you will divide with fractions to solve problems. Take a look at this problem.

Charlie is growing vegetables in planters. He has 4 bags of soil and uses $\frac{2}{3}$ of a bag of soil to fill each planter. How many planters can he fill?

Explore It

Use the math you already know to solve the problem.

- Think of the number of planters that Charlie can fill as how many $\frac{2}{3}$s are in 4. Will that number be greater than or less than 4? Explain your reasoning.
  The number of planters will be greater than 4. When you divide a given number by a number less than 1, the answer will be greater than the given number.
- The model below represents the 4 bags of soil. Draw horizontal lines to divide each bag into thirds.
- Circle and count groups of $\frac{2}{3}$ in the model. How many did you circle? 6
- Why do you circle groups of $\frac{2}{3}$ to represent this problem?
  Each planter holds $\frac{2}{3}$ of a bag of soil, so each circled group fills one planter. You are trying to find how many $\frac{2}{3}$s are in 4.
- How many planters can Charlie fill? 6
- Explain how the model helped you solve the problem.
  You can count the groups of $\frac{2}{3}$ that are in 4.

58 L7: Divide with Fractions ©Curriculum Associates, LLC Copying is not permitted.

Mathematical Discourse

- *How does using a model help you solve the problem?*

  Students may answer that drawing the model helps them to see and count the groups.

- *Explain, in your own words, dividing fractions with a model.*

  Responses should discuss drawing the dividend and dividing it into groups of the divisor.

- *Why does it make sense that the quotient is greater than the dividend when you divide with a fraction less than 1? If the divisor is a fraction greater than 1, will the quotient be greater or less than the dividend?*

  Responses should show understanding that taking out groups that are less than one whole will mean that there are more groups than the dividend. Dividing by a fraction greater than 1 will result in fewer groups than the dividend.

AT A GLANCE

Students explore solving a division problem using multiplication.

STEP BY STEP

- Read Find Out More as a class.
- Remind students that a fraction and its reciprocal must have a product of 1.
- Point out that when you multiply fractions you multiply the numerators, then multiply the denominators, and then simplify if possible.
- Discuss Reflect. Guide students to think about dividing as being the same as multiplying by the reciprocal (multiplicative inverse).

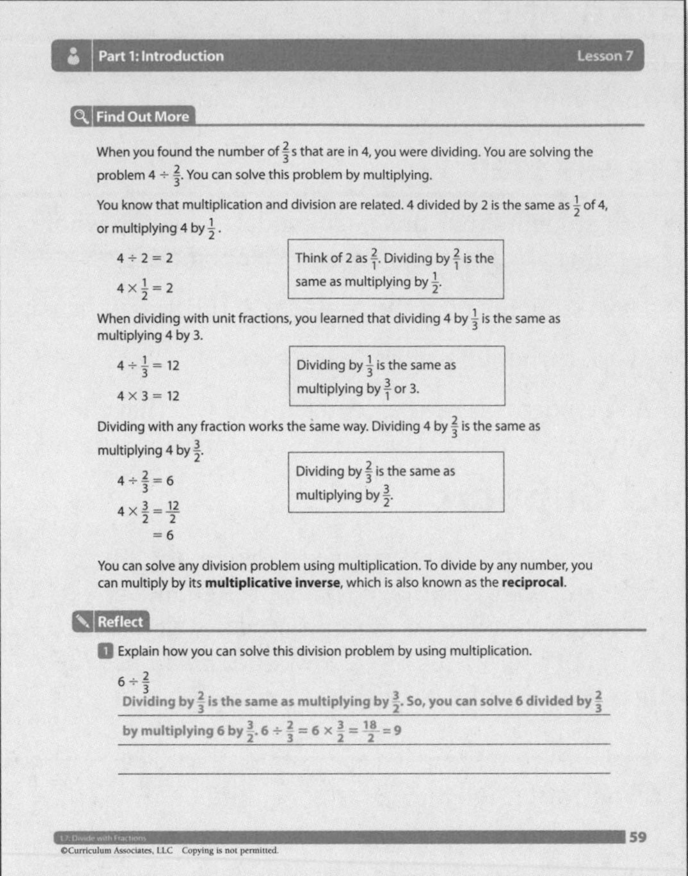

Part 1: Introduction Lesson 7

Find Out More

When you found the number of $\frac{2}{3}$s that are in 4, you were dividing. You are solving the problem $4 \div \frac{2}{3}$. You can solve this problem by multiplying.

You know that multiplication and division are related. 4 divided by 2 is the same as $\frac{1}{2}$ of 4, or multiplying 4 by $\frac{1}{2}$.

$4 \div 2 = 2$

$4 \times \frac{1}{2} = 2$

Think of 2 as $\frac{2}{1}$. Dividing by $\frac{2}{1}$ is the same as multiplying by $\frac{1}{2}$.

When dividing with unit fractions, you learned that dividing 4 by $\frac{1}{3}$ is the same as multiplying 4 by 3.

$4 \div \frac{1}{3} = 12$

$4 \times 3 = 12$

Dividing by $\frac{1}{3}$ is the same as multiplying by $\frac{3}{1}$ or 3.

Dividing with any fraction works the same way. Dividing 4 by $\frac{2}{3}$ is the same as multiplying 4 by $\frac{3}{2}$.

$4 \div \frac{2}{3} = 6$

$4 \times \frac{3}{2} = \frac{12}{2}$

$= 6$

Dividing by $\frac{2}{3}$ is the same as multiplying by $\frac{3}{2}$.

You can solve any division problem using multiplication. To divide by any number, you can multiply by its **multiplicative inverse**, which is also known as the **reciprocal**.

Reflect

1 Explain how you can solve this division problem by using multiplication.

$6 \div \frac{2}{3}$

Dividing by $\frac{2}{3}$ is the same as multiplying by $\frac{3}{2}$. So, you can solve 6 divided by $\frac{2}{3}$ by multiplying 6 by $\frac{3}{2}$. $6 \div \frac{2}{3} = 6 \times \frac{3}{2} = \frac{18}{2} = 9$

L7: Divide with Fractions 59

©Curriculum Associates, LLC Copying is not permitted.

Visual Model

Use a model to understand using reciprocals in division.

- Help students understand why they can solve any division problem by multiplying the dividend by the reciprocal of the divisor.
- Draw this model on the board for $5 \div \frac{1}{3}$:

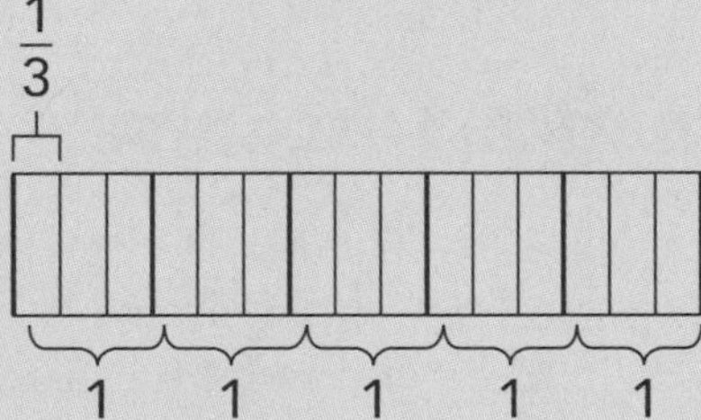

- Explain that the expression can be read as "how many groups of $\frac{1}{3}$ are in 5?" Show on the model that 1 contains 3 groups of $\frac{1}{3}$, and there are 5 groups of 1 in 5. The total number of groups of $\frac{1}{3}$ in 5 is simply $5 \times 3 = 15$.

Real-World Connection

Ask students to think of everyday places or situations where people might need to divide by fractions. Encourage them to share their ideas with the class.

Examples: cooking, making crafts, measuring, building structures

AT A GLANCE

Students read a word problem and explore how to divide a whole number by a fraction using a bar picture and by modeling the problem using words and an equation.

STEP BY STEP

- Read the problem at the top of the page as a class.
- Read and discuss Picture It. Ask, *What does the shaded part of the bar show?* [how much of the whole bottle Kelly drank, or two fifths]

SMP Tip: Students reason abstractly when they analyze a problem and represent it as an equation with a missing factor in order to find a solution (*SMP 2*). Ask students to explain how their equations or models represent the context of the problem.

- Read and discuss Model It. Walk through each step to be sure students understand how to use the inverse operation.

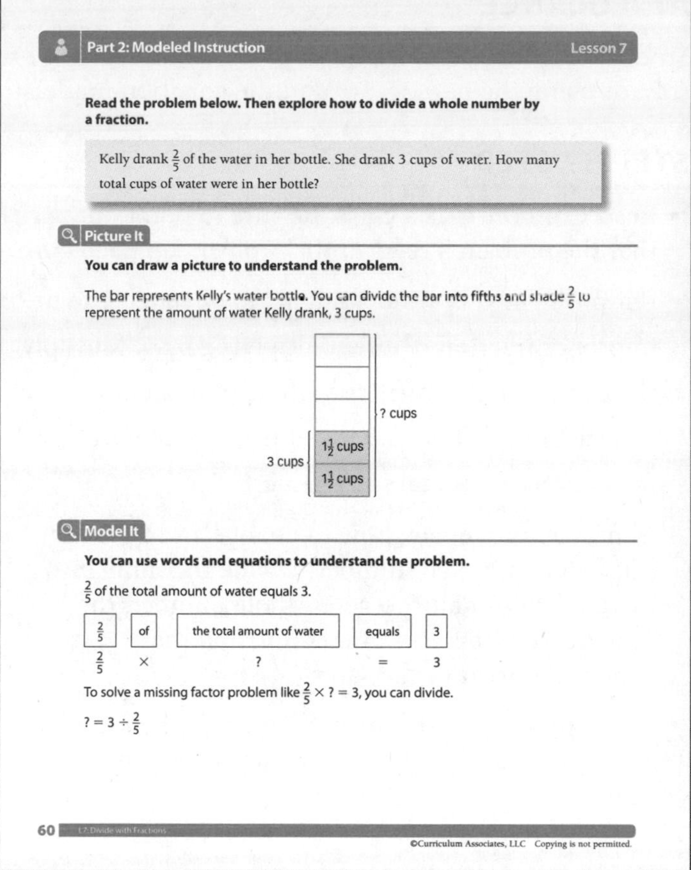

Part 2: Modeled Instruction Lesson 7

Read the problem below. Then explore how to divide a whole number by a fraction.

Kelly drank $\frac{2}{5}$ of the water in her bottle. She drank 3 cups of water. How many total cups of water were in her bottle?

Picture It

You can draw a picture to understand the problem.

The bar represents Kelly's water bottle. You can divide the bar into fifths and shade $\frac{2}{5}$ to represent the amount of water Kelly drank, 3 cups.

Model It

You can use words and equations to understand the problem.

$\frac{2}{5}$ of the total amount of water equals 3.

$\frac{2}{5}$	of	the total amount of water	equals	3
$\frac{2}{5}$	$\times$	?	=	3

To solve a missing factor problem like $\frac{2}{5} \times ? = 3$, you can divide.

$? = 3 \div \frac{2}{5}$

60 L7: Divide with Fractions

©Curriculum Associates, LLC Copying is not permitted.

Hands-On Activity

Make a model to show how many $\frac{2}{3}$s are in 4.

Materials: sheet of paper for each student, pencils

- Tell students they will make a model to show how many $\frac{2}{3}$s are in 4.
- Give each student a sheet of paper. Have them fold it into 4 equal parts and draw lines on the folds to show 4 equal sections. Tell them this will be a model for 4.
- Ask, *What is the first thing you could do to the model to start showing how many $\frac{2}{3}$s are in 4?* [Draw lines to divide each of the 4 whole sections into thirds.] *What might you do next?* [Circle each group of 2 of the thirds and count them.]
- Let students finish their models. Ask them what the solution is. Suggest they label their model with the equation solved: $4 \div \frac{2}{3} = 6$.

Mathematical Discourse

- *What is another way you could solve the problem regarding Kelly's water bottle on page 60?*

  Responses may include dividing 3 cups in half to find $\frac{1}{5}$ of the amount in the bottle, and then multiplying by 5 to find the total amount in the bottle.

- *How is dividing fractions similar to dividing whole numbers?*

  Listen for responses that indicate dividing a quantity into groups.

AT A GLANCE

Students revisit the problem on page 60 to learn how to solve it using the bar picture and the equation model.

STEP BY STEP

- Read Connect It as a class. Be sure to point out that the problems refer to the problem on page 60.
- For problem 4, remind students to change $1\frac{1}{2}$ to an improper fraction before multiplying by 5. Multiply the denominator times the whole number, and then add the numerator. The result is the numerator, and the denominator stays the same.
- In problem 5, review how to change an improper fraction to a mixed number: Divide the numerator by the denominator to get a whole number, the remainder is the new numerator, and the denominator stays the same.
- Have students work through Try It on their own. Then discuss with them how they solved the problems.

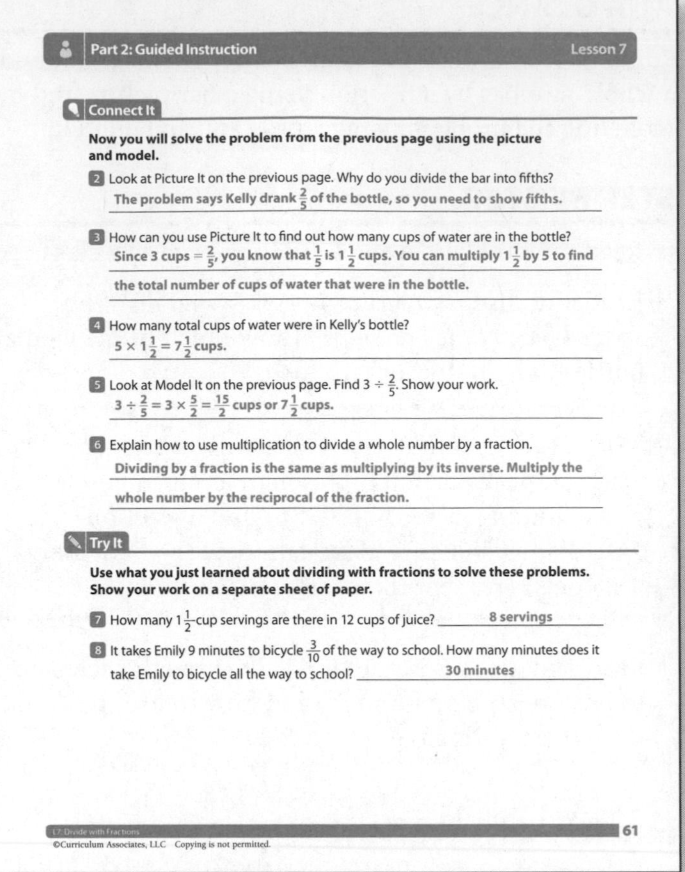

Part 2: Guided Instruction Lesson 7

Connect It

Now you will solve the problem from the previous page using the picture and model.

2 Look at Picture It on the previous page. Why do you divide the bar into fifths?
The problem says Kelly drank $\frac{2}{5}$ of the bottle, so you need to show fifths.

3 How can you use Picture It to find out how many cups of water are in the bottle?
Since 3 cups = $\frac{2}{5}$, you know that $\frac{1}{5}$ is $1\frac{1}{2}$ cups. You can multiply $1\frac{1}{2}$ by 5 to find the total number of cups of water that were in the bottle.

4 How many total cups of water were in Kelly's bottle?
$5 \times 1\frac{1}{2} = 7\frac{1}{2}$ cups.

5 Look at Model It on the previous page. Find $3 \div \frac{2}{5}$. Show your work.
$3 \div \frac{2}{5} = 3 \times \frac{5}{2} = \frac{15}{2}$ cups or $7\frac{1}{2}$ cups.

6 Explain how to use multiplication to divide a whole number by a fraction.
Dividing by a fraction is the same as multiplying by its inverse. Multiply the whole number by the reciprocal of the fraction.

Try It

Use what you just learned about dividing with fractions to solve these problems. Show your work on a separate sheet of paper.

7 How many $1\frac{1}{2}$-cup servings are there in 12 cups of juice? **8 servings**

8 It takes Emily 9 minutes to bicycle $\frac{3}{10}$ of the way to school. How many minutes does it take Emily to bicycle all the way to school? **30 minutes**

L7: Divide with Fractions 61
©Curriculum Associates, LLC Copying is not permitted.

TRY IT SOLUTIONS

7 *Solution:* 8 servings; Students solve the problem by using the equation $12 \div \frac{3}{2} = ?$ or a drawing such as 12 cups with lines dividing each cup into halves and circled groups of $1\frac{1}{2}$.

ERROR ALERT: Students who wrote 18 servings forgot to multiply by the reciprocal of the divisor. Remind them that they need to find the reciprocal of the divisor before multiplying.

8 *Solution:* 30 minutes; Students may use the equation $9 \div \frac{3}{10} = ?$ They may use a drawing such as a bar divided into tenths with $\frac{3}{10}$ shaded to model the distance she went in 9 minutes. This would show that $\frac{1}{10}$ is equal to 3 minutes; $3 \times 10 = 30$ minutes.

AT A GLANCE

Students read a word problem and explore how to divide a fraction by a fraction using a double number line and by modeling the problem using words and an equation.

STEP BY STEP

- Read the problem at the top of the page as a class.
- Discuss Picture It:

  Ask, *What does the top number line represent?* [the distance divided into fourths]

  Ask, *What does the bottom number line represent?* [the distance divided into eighths]
- Discuss Model It. Ask, *What does the question mark in the equation represent?* [the number of hurdles Eli jumped over during his $\frac{3}{4}$-mile run]

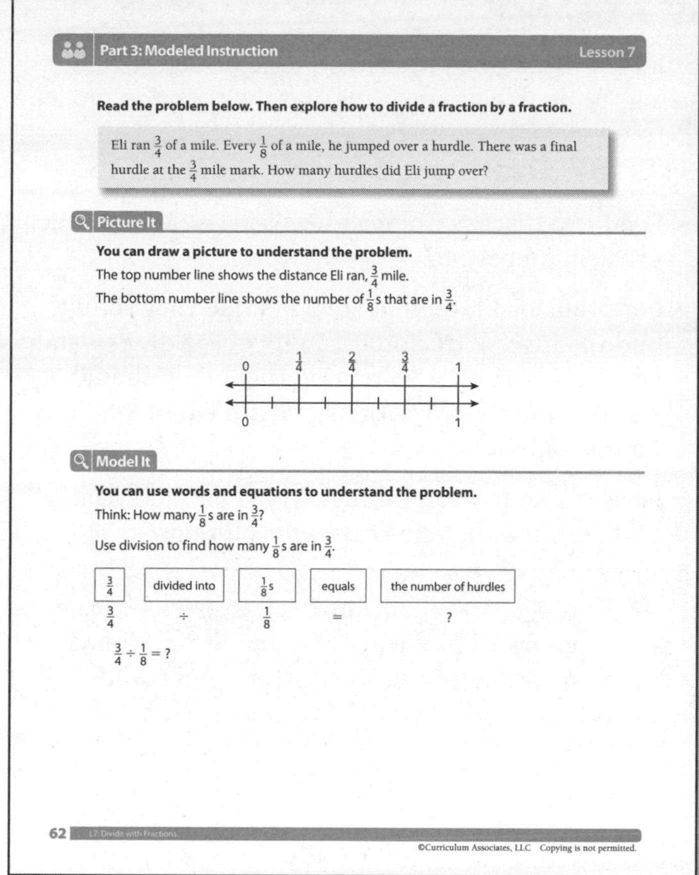

Read the problem below. Then explore how to divide a fraction by a fraction.

Eli ran $\frac{3}{4}$ of a mile. Every $\frac{1}{8}$ of a mile, he jumped over a hurdle. There was a final hurdle at the $\frac{3}{4}$ mile mark. How many hurdles did Eli jump over?

Picture It

You can draw a picture to understand the problem.

The top number line shows the distance Eli ran, $\frac{3}{4}$ mile.

The bottom number line shows the number of $\frac{1}{8}$s that are in $\frac{3}{4}$.

Model It

You can use words and equations to understand the problem.

Think: How many $\frac{1}{8}$s are in $\frac{3}{4}$?

Use division to find how many $\frac{1}{8}$s are in $\frac{3}{4}$.

$\frac{3}{4}$	divided into	$\frac{1}{8}$s	equals	the number of hurdles
$\frac{3}{4}$	$\div$	$\frac{1}{8}$	=	?

$\frac{3}{4} \div \frac{1}{8} = ?$

Mathematical Discourse

- *Which method for dividing fractions do you prefer? Why? Are there situations when one method may be easier to use than another?*

  Encourage students to support their opinions and to listen to the opinions of others. Point out that there is no correct answer, and that different students may have different preferences.
- *Can you think of another way to describe dividing fractions? Explain.*

  Encourage students to suggest ideas or knowledge on other ways to divide fractions.

AT A GLANCE

Students revisit the problem on page 62 and solve it using the double number line and the equation model.

STEP BY STEP

- Read and discuss Connect It as a class. Refer to the problem on page 62.
- For problem 13, remind students that they should find the inverse (reciprocal) only of the divisor and not the dividend. Also remind them they should simplify improper fractions to a mixed- or whole-number answer.
- Have students work through Try It on their own. Then discuss their answers and solutions.

SMP Tip: Give students multiple opportunities to solve and model problems. Students use repeated reasoning to understand algorithms and make generalizations about patterns (*SMP 8*).

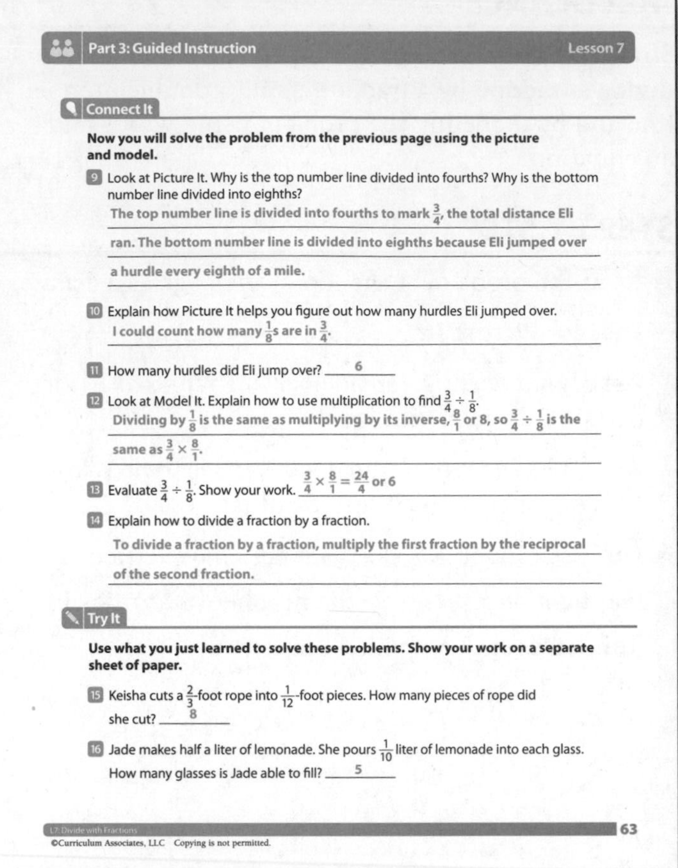

Part 3: Guided Instruction Lesson 7

Connect It

Now you will solve the problem from the previous page using the picture and model.

9 Look at Picture It. Why is the top number line divided into fourths? Why is the bottom number line divided into eighths?
The top number line is divided into fourths to mark $\frac{3}{4}$, the total distance Eli ran. The bottom number line is divided into eighths because Eli jumped over a hurdle every eighth of a mile.

10 Explain how Picture It helps you figure out how many hurdles Eli jumped over.
I could count how many $\frac{1}{8}$s are in $\frac{3}{4}$.

11 How many hurdles did Eli jump over? 6

12 Look at Model It. Explain how to use multiplication to find $\frac{3}{4} \div \frac{1}{8}$.
Dividing by $\frac{1}{8}$ is the same as multiplying by its inverse, $\frac{8}{1}$ or 8, so $\frac{3}{4} \div \frac{1}{8}$ is the same as $\frac{3}{4} \times \frac{8}{1}$.

13 Evaluate $\frac{3}{4} \div \frac{1}{8}$. Show your work. $\frac{3}{4} \times \frac{8}{1} = \frac{24}{4}$ or 6

14 Explain how to divide a fraction by a fraction.
To divide a fraction by a fraction, multiply the first fraction by the reciprocal of the second fraction.

Try It

Use what you just learned to solve these problems. Show your work on a separate sheet of paper.

15 Keisha cuts a $\frac{2}{3}$-foot rope into $\frac{1}{12}$-foot pieces. How many pieces of rope did she cut? 8

16 Jade makes half a liter of lemonade. She pours $\frac{1}{10}$ liter of lemonade into each glass. How many glasses is Jade able to fill? 5

L7: Divide with Fractions 63

©Curriculum Associates, LLC Copying is not permitted.

TRY IT SOLUTIONS

15 *Solution:* 8; Students may draw a double number line or may use the standard algorithm to solve the problem.

$$\frac{2}{3} \div \frac{1}{12} = \frac{2}{3} \times \frac{12}{1} = \frac{24}{3} = 8$$

ERROR ALERT: Students who wrote 18 pieces of rope may have multiplied the inverse of both the dividend and the divisor. Remind students that they should only multiply by the inverse (reciprocal) of the divisor. Review Find Out More on page 59 of this lesson to help students understand why multiplying by the reciprocal is mathematically valid.

16 *Solution:* 5; Students may draw a bar picture and shade half of the figure, then draw lines to divide the figure into tenths. 5 parts would be shaded. Or, they may use the standard algorithm.

$$\frac{1}{2} \div \frac{1}{10} = \frac{1}{2} \times \frac{10}{1} = 5$$

AT A GLANCE

Students explore how to divide a mixed number by a fraction using bar pictures and by modeling the problem using words and an equation.

STEP BY STEP

- Read the problem at the top of the page as a class.
- Discuss Picture It:

  Ask, *How do the shaded bars in the first picture represent $1\frac{4}{5}$ pounds of granola?* [One whole and 4 more parts are shaded.]

  Ask, *What does each circle in the second picture represent?* [Each circle represents one $\frac{2}{5}$-pound bag of granola.]

- In Picture It, some students might be confused by the circle that contains part of the whole bar and part of the partial bar. Suggest to students that they think of the entire 1 bar plus $\frac{4}{5}$ bar as one entity.
- Discuss Model It. Remind students that they must write the mixed number in the dividend as an improper fraction before dividing.

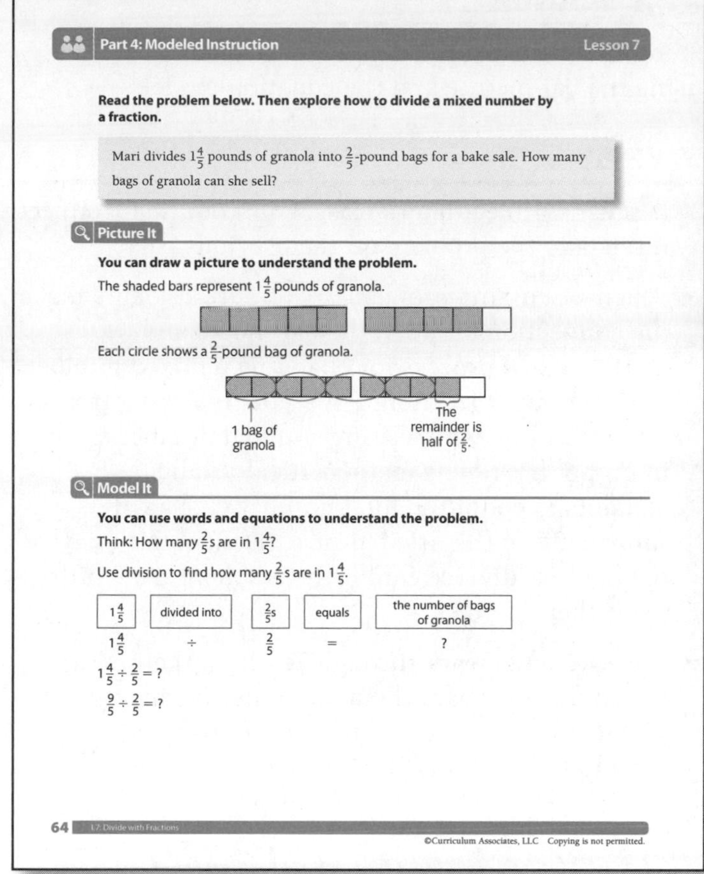

Part 4: Modeled Instruction Lesson 7

Read the problem below. Then explore how to divide a mixed number by a fraction.

Mari divides $1\frac{4}{5}$ pounds of granola into $\frac{2}{5}$-pound bags for a bake sale. How many bags of granola can she sell?

Picture It

You can draw a picture to understand the problem.

The shaded bars represent $1\frac{4}{5}$ pounds of granola.

Each circle shows a $\frac{2}{5}$-pound bag of granola.

Model It

You can use words and equations to understand the problem.

Think: How many $\frac{2}{5}$s are in $1\frac{4}{5}$?

Use division to find how many $\frac{2}{5}$s are in $1\frac{4}{5}$.

$1\frac{4}{5}$	divided into	$\frac{2}{5}$s	equals	the number of bags of granola
$1\frac{4}{5}$	÷	$\frac{2}{5}$	=	?

$1\frac{4}{5} \div \frac{2}{5} = ?$

$\frac{9}{5} \div \frac{2}{5} = ?$

64 L7: Divide with Fractions

©Curriculum Associates, LLC Copying is not permitted.

Mathematical Discourse

- *Mari is selling bags of granola to raise money, so she wants to have as many bags as possible to sell. What else might she think about when dividing up the granola?*

  Listen for responses that show students making connections to personal experiences to make sense of the problem. They might discuss how the size of each bag might make a difference to buyers: Customers might not buy if they think there is not enough granola in a bag. Students might also mention cost to customers or the amount left over after filling the bags.

AT A GLANCE

Students revisit the problem on page 64 and solve it using the bar picture and the equation model.

STEP BY STEP

- Discuss Connect It as a class. Point out that Connect It refers to the problem on the previous page.
- When discussing problem 20, be sure students make the connection between the bar model and the mathematical process for changing a mixed number to an improper fraction. For students having trouble understanding why writing a mixed number as an improper fraction is mathematically valid, ask students to count the total number of shaded squares (9) in the first bar picture and point out that the bars are divided into fifths, so there are 9 fifths altogether.
- Have students work through Try It on their own. Let volunteers share their solutions and answers with the class. Clear up misconceptions and discuss any questions students may have.

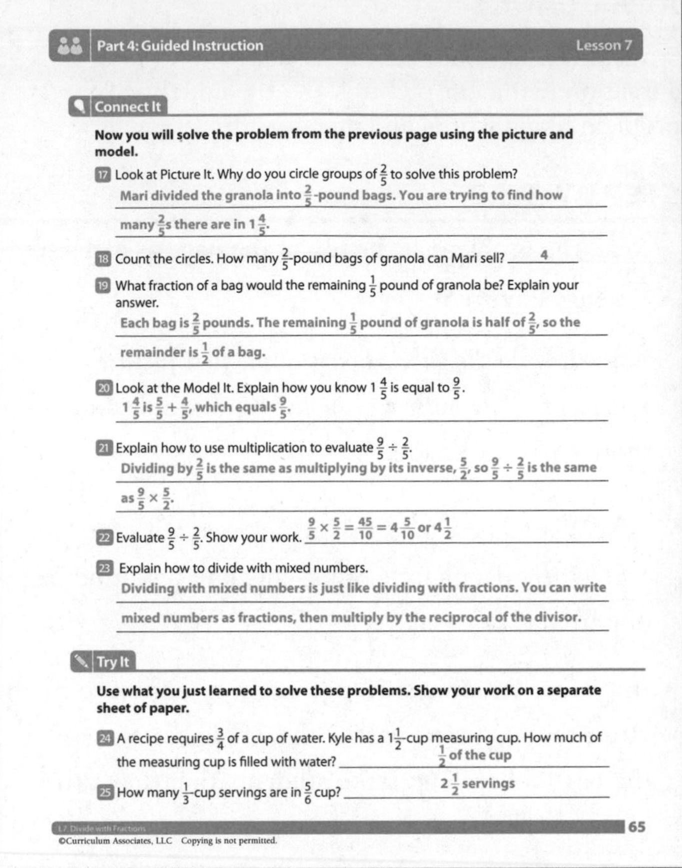

Part 4: Guided Instruction Lesson 7

Connect It

Now you will solve the problem from the previous page using the picture and model.

17 Look at Picture It. Why do you circle groups of $\frac{2}{5}$ to solve this problem?
Mari divided the granola into $\frac{2}{5}$-pound bags. You are trying to find how many $\frac{2}{5}$s there are in $1\frac{4}{5}$.

18 Count the circles. How many $\frac{2}{5}$-pound bags of granola can Mari sell? 4

19 What fraction of a bag would the remaining $\frac{1}{5}$ pound of granola be? Explain your answer.
Each bag is $\frac{2}{5}$ pounds. The remaining $\frac{1}{5}$ pound of granola is half of $\frac{2}{5}$, so the remainder is $\frac{1}{2}$ of a bag.

20 Look at the Model It. Explain how you know $1\frac{4}{5}$ is equal to $\frac{9}{5}$.
$1\frac{4}{5}$ is $\frac{5}{5} + \frac{4}{5}$, which equals $\frac{9}{5}$.

21 Explain how to use multiplication to evaluate $\frac{9}{5} \div \frac{2}{5}$.
Dividing by $\frac{2}{5}$ is the same as multiplying by its inverse, $\frac{5}{2}$, so $\frac{9}{5} \div \frac{2}{5}$ is the same as $\frac{9}{5} \times \frac{5}{2}$.

22 Evaluate $\frac{9}{5} \div \frac{2}{5}$. Show your work. $\frac{9}{5} \times \frac{5}{2} = \frac{45}{10} = 4\frac{5}{10}$ or $4\frac{1}{2}$

23 Explain how to divide with mixed numbers.
Dividing with mixed numbers is just like dividing with fractions. You can write mixed numbers as fractions, then multiply by the reciprocal of the divisor.

Try It

Use what you just learned to solve these problems. Show your work on a separate sheet of paper.

24 A recipe requires $\frac{3}{4}$ of a cup of water. Kyle has a $1\frac{1}{2}$-cup measuring cup. How much of the measuring cup is filled with water? $\frac{1}{2}$ of the cup

25 How many $\frac{1}{3}$-cup servings are in $\frac{5}{6}$ cup? $2\frac{1}{2}$ servings

L7: Divide with Fractions 65
©Curriculum Associates, LLC Copying is not permitted.

TRY IT SOLUTIONS

24 *Solution:* $\frac{1}{2}$ of the cup; Students may draw a model that shows $1\frac{1}{2}$ and divide it into fourths. $\frac{3}{4}$ of a cup would be half of the model.

25 *Solution:* $2\frac{1}{2}$; Students may write an equation.
$\frac{5}{6} \div \frac{1}{3} = \frac{5}{6} \times \frac{3}{1} = \frac{15}{6} = 2\frac{1}{2}$

ERROR ALERT: Students who wrote $\frac{2}{5}$ transposed the fractions and found $\frac{1}{3} \div \frac{5}{6}$. Encourage students who made this error to draw a model to help them visualize the problem.

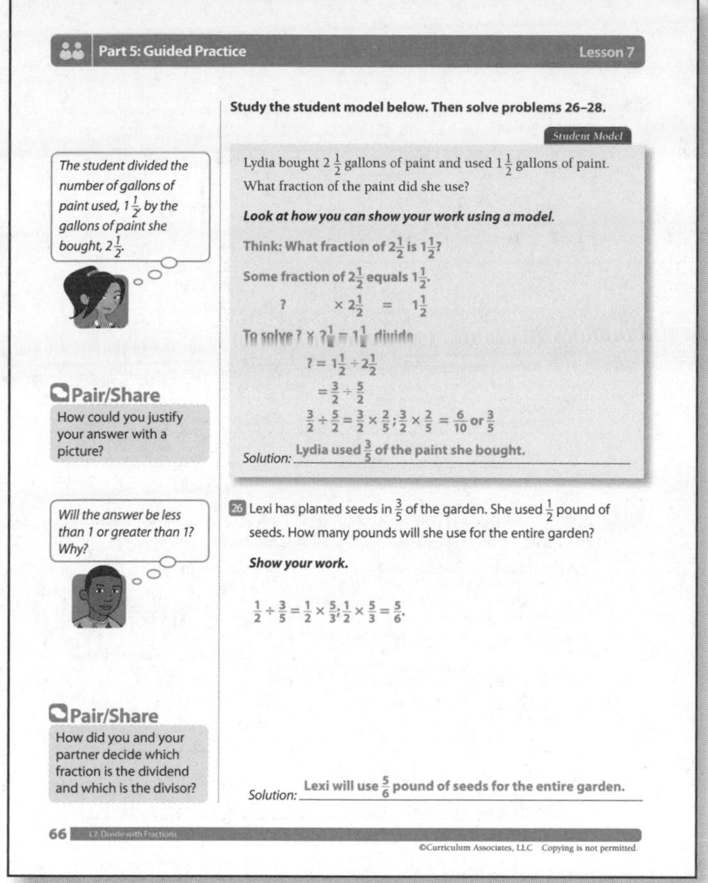

Part 5: Guided Practice Lesson 7

Study the student model below. Then solve problems 26–28.

Student Model

Lydia bought $2\frac{1}{2}$ gallons of paint and used $1\frac{1}{2}$ gallons of paint. What fraction of the paint did she use?

Look at how you can show your work using a model.

Think: What fraction of $2\frac{1}{2}$ is $1\frac{1}{2}$?

Some fraction of $2\frac{1}{2}$ equals $1\frac{1}{2}$.

$? \times 2\frac{1}{2} = 1\frac{1}{2}$

To solve $? \times 2\frac{1}{2} = 1\frac{1}{2}$, divide.

$? = 1\frac{1}{2} \div 2\frac{1}{2}$

$= \frac{3}{2} \div \frac{5}{2}$

$\frac{3}{2} \div \frac{5}{2} = \frac{3}{2} \times \frac{2}{5}; \frac{3}{2} \times \frac{2}{5} = \frac{6}{10}$ or $\frac{3}{5}$

Solution: Lydia used $\frac{3}{5}$ of the paint she bought.

The student divided the number of gallons of paint used, $1\frac{1}{2}$, by the gallons of paint she bought, $2\frac{1}{2}$.

Pair/Share How could you justify your answer with a picture?

26 Lexi has planted seeds in $\frac{3}{5}$ of the garden. She used $\frac{1}{2}$ pound of seeds. How many pounds will she use for the entire garden?

Show your work.

$\frac{1}{2} \div \frac{3}{5} = \frac{1}{2} \times \frac{5}{3}; \frac{1}{2} \times \frac{5}{3} = \frac{5}{6}$.

Solution: Lexi will use $\frac{5}{6}$ pound of seeds for the entire garden.

Will the answer be less than 1 or greater than 1? Why?

Pair/Share How did you and your partner decide which fraction is the dividend and which is the divisor?

66 L7: Divide with Fractions ©Curriculum Associates, LLC Copying is not permitted.

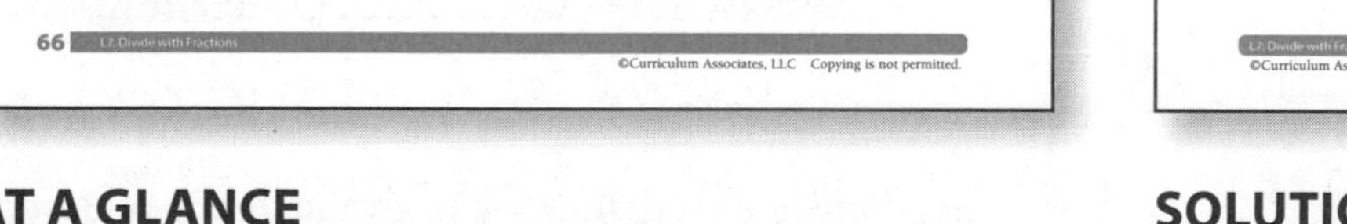

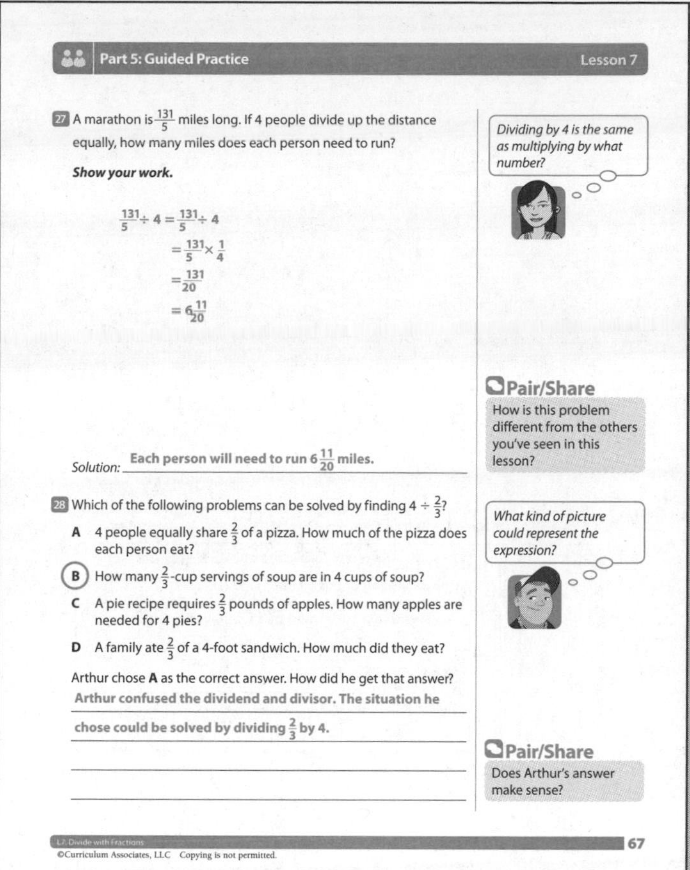

Part 5: Guided Practice Lesson 7

27 A marathon is $\frac{131}{5}$ miles long. If 4 people divide up the distance equally, how many miles does each person need to run?

Show your work.

$\frac{131}{5} \div 4 = \frac{131}{5} \div 4$

$= \frac{131}{5} \times \frac{1}{4}$

$= \frac{131}{20}$

$= 6\frac{11}{20}$

Solution: Each person will need to run $6\frac{11}{20}$ miles.

Dividing by 4 is the same as multiplying by what number?

Pair/Share How is this problem different from the others you've seen in this lesson?

28 Which of the following problems can be solved by finding $4 \div \frac{2}{3}$?

A 4 people equally share $\frac{2}{3}$ of a pizza. How much of the pizza does each person eat?

(B) How many $\frac{2}{3}$-cup servings of soup are in 4 cups of soup?

C A pie recipe requires $\frac{2}{3}$ pounds of apples. How many apples are needed for 4 pies?

D A family ate $\frac{2}{3}$ of a 4-foot sandwich. How much did they eat?

Arthur chose **A** as the correct answer. How did he get that answer?

Arthur confused the dividend and divisor. The situation he chose could be solved by dividing $\frac{2}{3}$ by 4.

What kind of picture could represent the expression?

Pair/Share Does Arthur's answer make sense?

L7: Divide with Fractions ©Curriculum Associates, LLC Copying is not permitted. 67

AT A GLANCE

Students practice solving problems that require dividing a whole number by a fraction, dividing a fraction by a fraction, and dividing a mixed number by a fraction.

STEP BY STEP

- Ask students to solve the problems individually on pages 66 and 67.
- In the student model at the top of the page, call attention to writing each mixed number as an improper fraction before multiplying.
- When students have completed each problem, have them Pair/Share to discuss their solutions with a partner or in a group.

SOLUTIONS

Ex Using a model of words and an equation is one way for students to show their solution to the problem.

26 *Solution:* Lexi will use $\frac{5}{6}$ pound of seeds for the entire garden; Students could solve the problem by using an equation. $\frac{1}{2} \div \frac{3}{5} = \frac{1}{2} \times \frac{5}{3} = \frac{5}{6}$ ***(DOK 1)***

27 *Solution:* Each person will need to run $6\frac{11}{20}$ miles; Students could solve the problem by using an equation.
$\frac{131}{5} \div 4 = \frac{131}{5} \times \frac{1}{4} = \frac{131}{20} = 6\frac{11}{20}$ ***(DOK 1)***

28 *Solution:* **B**; Students must recognize the language as a division problem "how many __ are in __?" Explain to students why the other two answer choices are not correct:

C is not correct because the problem asks "how many are needed for," which is a multiplication problem. $\frac{2}{3} \times 4$

D is not correct because the problem states $\frac{2}{3}$ "of" 4, which is a multiplication problem. $\frac{2}{3} \times 4$ ***(DOK 3)***

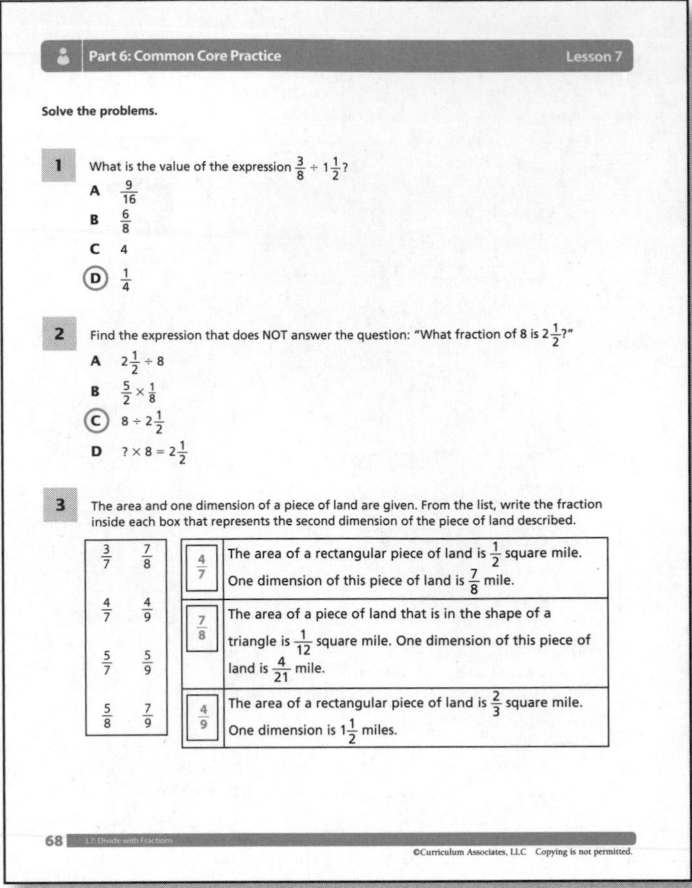

Solve the problems.

1 What is the value of the expression $\frac{3}{8} \div 1\frac{1}{2}$?

A $\frac{9}{16}$

B $\frac{6}{8}$

C 4

(D) $\frac{1}{4}$

2 Find the expression that does NOT answer the question: "What fraction of 8 is $2\frac{1}{2}$?"

A $2\frac{1}{2} \div 8$

B $\frac{5}{2} \times \frac{1}{8}$

(C) $8 \div 2\frac{1}{2}$

D $? \times 8 = 2\frac{1}{2}$

3 The area and one dimension of a piece of land are given. From the list, write the fraction inside each box that represents the second dimension of the piece of land described.

$\frac{3}{7}$	$\frac{7}{8}$
$\frac{4}{7}$	$\frac{4}{9}$
$\frac{5}{7}$	$\frac{5}{9}$
$\frac{5}{8}$	$\frac{7}{9}$

$\frac{4}{7}$	The area of a rectangular piece of land is $\frac{1}{2}$ square mile. One dimension of this piece of land is $\frac{7}{8}$ mile.
$\frac{7}{8}$	The area of a piece of land that is in the shape of a triangle is $\frac{1}{12}$ square mile. One dimension of this piece of land is $\frac{4}{21}$ mile.
$\frac{4}{9}$	The area of a rectangular piece of land is $\frac{2}{3}$ square mile. One dimension is $1\frac{1}{2}$ miles.

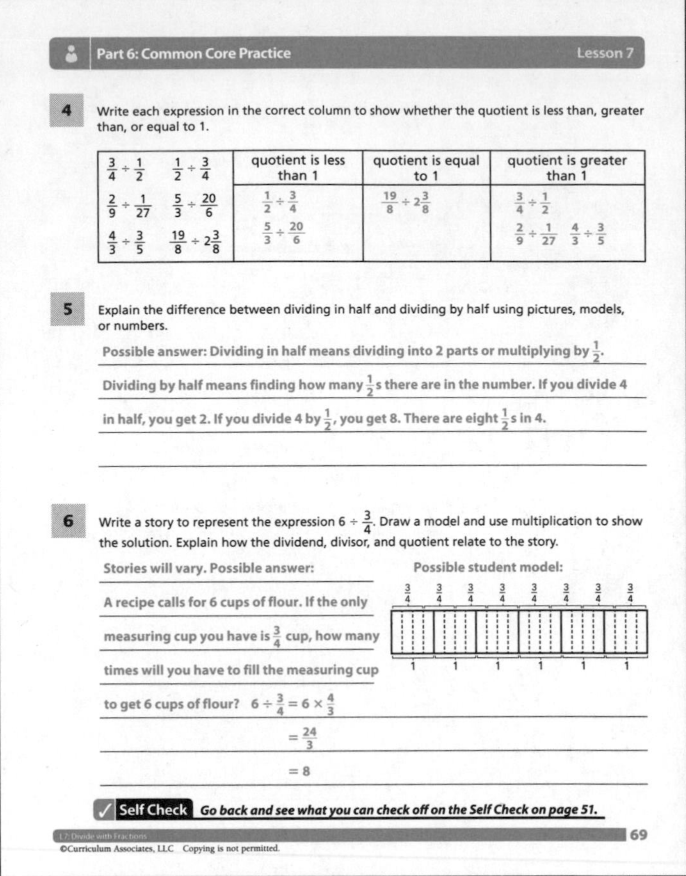

4 Write each expression in the correct column to show whether the quotient is less than, greater than, or equal to 1.

		quotient is less than 1	quotient is equal to 1	quotient is greater than 1
$\frac{3}{4} \div \frac{1}{2}$	$\frac{1}{2} \div \frac{3}{4}$	$\frac{1}{2} \div \frac{3}{4}$	$\frac{19}{8} \div 2\frac{3}{8}$	$\frac{3}{4} \div \frac{1}{2}$
$\frac{2}{9} \div \frac{1}{27}$	$\frac{5}{3} \div \frac{20}{6}$	$\frac{5}{3} \div \frac{20}{6}$		$\frac{2}{9} \div \frac{1}{27}$ $\frac{4}{3} \div \frac{3}{5}$
$\frac{4}{3} \div \frac{3}{5}$	$\frac{19}{8} \div 2\frac{3}{8}$			

5 Explain the difference between dividing in half and dividing by half using pictures, models, or numbers.

Possible answer: Dividing in half means dividing into 2 parts or multiplying by $\frac{1}{2}$. Dividing by half means finding how many $\frac{1}{2}$s there are in the number. If you divide 4 in half, you get 2. If you divide 4 by $\frac{1}{2}$, you get 8. There are eight $\frac{1}{2}$s in 4.

6 Write a story to represent the expression $6 \div \frac{3}{4}$. Draw a model and use multiplication to show the solution. Explain how the dividend, divisor, and quotient relate to the story.

Stories will vary. Possible answer:

A recipe calls for 6 cups of flour. If the only measuring cup you have is $\frac{3}{4}$ cup, how many times will you have to fill the measuring cup to get 6 cups of flour? $6 \div \frac{3}{4} = 6 \times \frac{4}{3}$

$= \frac{24}{3}$

$= 8$

Possible student model:

$\frac{3}{4}$ $\frac{3}{4}$ $\frac{3}{4}$ $\frac{3}{4}$ $\frac{3}{4}$ $\frac{3}{4}$ $\frac{3}{4}$ $\frac{3}{4}$

1 1 1 1 1 1

✓ Self Check *Go back and see what you can check off on the Self Check on page 51.*

AT A GLANCE

Students divide by fractions to solve word problems that might appear on a mathematics test.

SOLUTIONS

1 *Solution:* **D**; $\frac{3}{8} \div \frac{3}{2} = \frac{3}{8} \times \frac{2}{3} = \frac{6}{24} = \frac{1}{4}$ ***(DOK 1)***

2 *Solution:* **C**; transposed the dividend and divisor. Correct reasoning should be ? of 8 = $2\frac{1}{2}$, or ? = $2\frac{1}{2} \div 8$. ***(DOK 2)***

3 *Solution:* See student book page above for solution; Use the area formula for either a rectangle or triangle to find the unknown dimension. ***(DOK 2)***

4 *Solution:* See student book page above for solution; To divide fractions, multiply the first fraction by the reciprocal of the second fraction. ***(DOK 2)***

5 See student book page above for possible student explanation. ***(DOK 3)***

6 See student book page above for possible student model and explanation. ***(DOK 3)***

Assessment and Remediation

- Ask students to evaluate the expression $1\frac{1}{2} \div \frac{2}{3}\left[2\frac{1}{4}\right]$.
- For students who are struggling, use the chart below to guide remediation.
- After providing remediation, check students' understanding. Ask students to explain their thinking while evaluating $2\frac{1}{3} \div \frac{3}{4}\left[3\frac{1}{9}\right]$.
- If a student is still having difficulty, use ***Ready Instruction*, *Level 6*,** Lesson 6.

If the error is . . .	Students may . . .	To remediate . . .
1	have failed to find the multiplicative inverse (reciprocal) of the divisor before multiplying. $\frac{3}{2} \times \frac{2}{3} = \frac{6}{6} = 1$	Remind students that they must multiply by the multiplicative inverse of the divisor. For students not understanding why this works, write $6 \div \frac{1}{4}$. Draw 6 circles. Ask how to divide each circle by 1 fourth. Ask how many fourths altogether. Point out that 6 wholes are each split into 4 parts, so 6 wholes are multiplied by 4 parts to get 24. 6×4 is the same as $\frac{6}{1} \div \frac{1}{4}$.
$\frac{3}{4}$	have forgotten to include the whole number. $\frac{1}{2} \div \frac{2}{3} = \frac{1}{2} \times \frac{3}{2} = \frac{3}{4}$	Encourage students to write all mixed numbers as improper fractions as the first step in setting up their computation so they won't forget.

Hands-On Activity

Make a number line to model division.

Materials: half or whole sheets of paper, pencils

Tell students they will draw a model to solve a problem. Display this problem: "Mari has $1\frac{1}{2}$ hours left to prepare for the bake sale. It takes her $\frac{1}{4}$ hour to prepare each item. How many items can she prepare?" Tell students to draw a number line on their paper and use tic marks to divide the line into halves from 0 to 2. They should label each whole and half number mark (0, $\frac{1}{2}$, 1, $1\frac{1}{2}$, 2). Point out that the problem asks how many fourths are in one and a half. Tell students to divide each half on their number line with a tic mark to create a fourth. Then tell them to circle each fourth between 0 and $1\frac{1}{2}$. Ask students what each circled part represents $\left[\frac{1}{4}\text{ hour}\right]$ and how many circled parts there are [6]. Ask how many fourths are in one and a half [6]. Ask how many items Mari can prepare in the time she has left. [6 items]

Challenge Activity

Write problems involving division of fractions.

Materials: index cards or sheets of paper, pencils

Give each student 1–3 index cards or sheets of paper. Tell them to make up a word problem involving division of fractions and mixed numbers for each card. Have students write the word problem on one side of the card and the solution on the other side. Tell them their solution needs to be complete enough so that someone who doesn't know how to solve the problem can figure it out and why it works. The solution can include such things as a drawing, words explaining the process, or an equation. Have students exchange cards with another student. The other student is to solve the problem and then look at the solution and offer suggestions for changes if the student sees any. Alternatively, let students verbally show and tell how to solve the problems they've made up.

Lesson 8 (Student Book pages 70–79)

Divide Multi-Digit Numbers

LESSON OBJECTIVES

- Fluently divide multi-digit numbers using the standard algorithm. (4-digit by 2-digit)
- Understand how to set up a problem based on the context of the problem.
- Be able to interpret what the quotient represents.
- Recognize that what is known or not known is based on the type of division needed (partitive: $\frac{\text{Total}}{\text{number of groups}}$ = size of groups; quotative or measurement: $\frac{\text{Total}}{\text{size of group}}$ = number of groups).

PREREQUISITE SKILLS

- Know that multiplication and division are inverse operations.
- Know that division is either fair sharing (partitive) or repeated subtraction (quotative).
- Divide with whole numbers.
- Model division with manipulatives, diagrams, and story contexts.

VOCABULARY

There is no new vocabulary.

THE LEARNING PROGRESSION

In earlier grades, students were introduced to division through concrete models and various strategies to develop an understanding of the operation. In Grade 6, students become fluent in the use of the standard division algorithm. This understanding is foundational for work with fractions and decimals in Grade 7.

Ready ***Teacher Toolbox*** Teacher-Toolbox.com

	Prerequisite Skills	6.NS.B.2
Ready Lessons	✓	✓
Tools for Instruction		✓
Interactive Tutorials		✓✓

CCSS Focus

6.NS.B.2 Fluently divide multi-digit numbers using the standard algorithm.

STANDARDS FOR MATHEMATICAL PRACTICE: ***SMP 1, 2, 7, 8*** *(see page A9 for full text)*

AT A GLANCE

Students read a division word problem and use a bar model to solve.

STEP BY STEP

- Tell students that this page models dividing a three-digit number by a one-digit number.
- Have students read the problem at the top of the page.
- Work through Explore It as a class. Point out that the students are dividing 288 into 3 equal parts. A good estimate uses the basic fact 9×3 to get $90 \times 3 = 270$. Another estimate is 100×3. Emphasize that you can break a number into any number of parts to divide and that we choose the parts that are most convenient for the particular problem.
- Ask student pairs or groups to explain their answers for finding the total number of bags of popcorn each class can sell.

Develop Skills and Strategies

Lesson 8 Part 1: Introduction

Divide Multi-Digit Numbers

CCSS 6.NS.B.2

In 5th grade, you learned how to divide using models and partial quotients. Take a look at this problem.

For a fundraiser, the sixth graders have 288 bags of popcorn to sell. There are 3 sixth-grade classes. If each class sells an equal number of bags, how many bags of popcorn does each class sell?

Explore It

Use the math you already know to solve the problem.

- Use a bar model to represent the problem. Fill in the whole and the number of groups.

288

3

- What division expression represents this problem? $288 \div 3$
- Estimate the quotient. The quotient is around 90. Explain your thinking. I can use friendly numbers; $270 \div 3 = 90$.
- Use your estimate. At least how many bags of popcorn should each class sell? 90
- How many bags are left to sell altogether? 18 By each class? 6
- How many more bags can each class sell? How do you know? 6 bags, because $6 \times 3 = 18$
- Explain how to find the total number of bags of popcorn each class can sell. Add 90 and 6 because each class can sell at least 90 bags. Then, 18 bags are left. Each class can sell 6 more. $90 + 6 = 96$ bags

70 L8: Divide Multi-Digit Numbers ©Curriculum Associates, LLC Copying is not permitted.

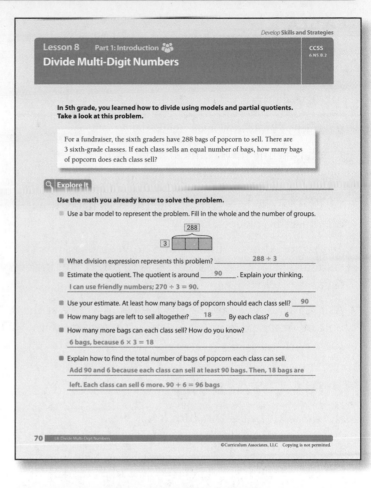

Hands-On Activity

Snack Division

Materials: crackers or some other type of treat that can be divided easily among the class.

Bring in a treat and have students figure out how many items there are in all. Ask students to divide to find out how many each student in the class should receive. When the division is done correctly, pass out the items and enjoy!

Mathematical Discourse

- Why would you want to estimate before solving a division problem?

  Estimating helps you to check for reasonableness.

- Can you think of another way to solve the problem?

  Students may have previous experience with using partial quotients or may choose to explain the standard division algorithm.

AT A GLANCE

Students use partial quotients and the division algorithm to solve a problem.

STEP BY STEP

- Read Find Out More as a class.
- Emphasize the place values of the digits in 288.
- Ask students to identify the divisor and dividend.
- Walk through each step of the division algorithm, emphasizing place value.
- To ensure students understand and can use the standard algorithm, ask students to direct you in dividing 199 ÷ 6.
- Ask students to complete the Reflect directive at the bottom of the page independently, then share with their partner.

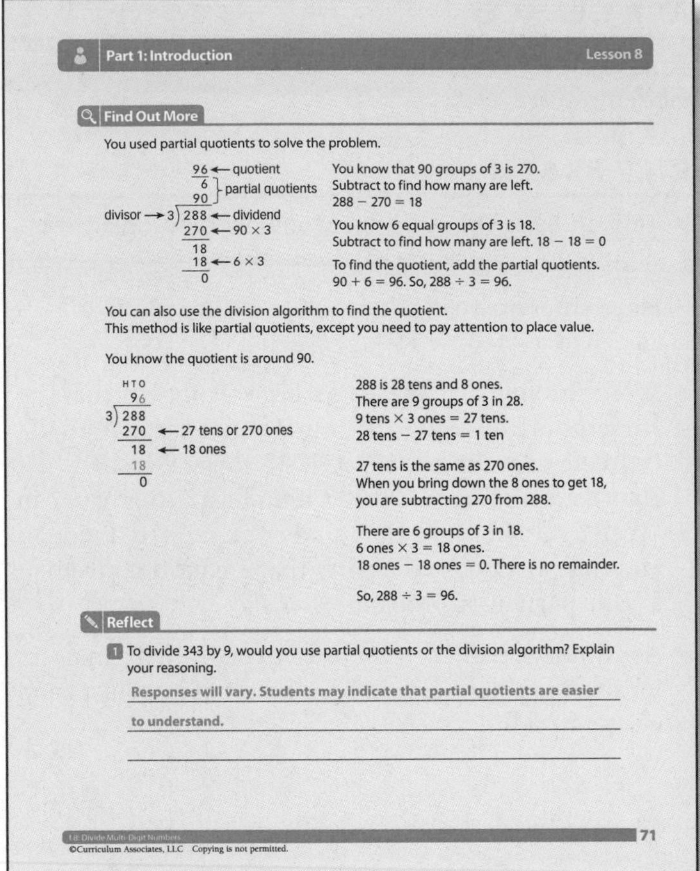

Part 1: Introduction Lesson 8

Find Out More

You used partial quotients to solve the problem.

96 ← quotient
6 } partial quotients
90
divisor → 3) 288 ← dividend
270 ← 90 × 3
18
18 ← 6 × 3
0

You know that 90 groups of 3 is 270. Subtract to find how many are left. 288 − 270 = 18

You know 6 equal groups of 3 is 18. Subtract to find how many are left. 18 − 18 = 0

To find the quotient, add the partial quotients. 90 + 6 = 96. So, 288 ÷ 3 = 96.

You can also use the division algorithm to find the quotient. This method is like partial quotients, except you need to pay attention to place value.

You know the quotient is around 90.

H T O
96
3) 288
270 ← 27 tens or 270 ones
18 ← 18 ones
18
0

288 is 28 tens and 8 ones. There are 9 groups of 3 in 28. 9 tens × 3 ones = 27 tens. 28 tens − 27 tens = 1 ten

27 tens is the same as 270 ones. When you bring down the 8 ones to get 18, you are subtracting 270 from 288.

There are 6 groups of 3 in 18. 6 ones × 3 = 18 ones. 18 ones − 18 ones = 0. There is no remainder.

So, 288 ÷ 3 = 96.

Reflect

1 To divide 343 by 9, would you use partial quotients or the division algorithm? Explain your reasoning.

Responses will vary. Students may indicate that partial quotients are easier to understand.

L8: Divide Multi-Digit Numbers 71

©Curriculum Associates, LLC Copying is not permitted.

Hands-On Activity

Divide with base-ten blocks.

Materials: base-ten blocks

Learners without strong place value knowledge will benefit from using base ten blocks. Model the problem 288 ÷ 3 using base ten blocks.

- Students start with 2 hundreds blocks, 8 ten rods, and 8 unit cubes.
- Ask students to start the division with the hundreds blocks because they have the largest value.
- Direct students to divide the hundreds blocks into 3 groups. Students should recognize that they cannot put 2 hundreds blocks into 3 groups.
- They must trade the 2 hundreds blocks for 20 tens rods.
- Now they have 28 tens rods to divide into 3 groups. They should have 9 tens in each group with 1 ten left over.
- The remaining ten rod should be traded for 10 unit cubes resulting in 18 unit cubes.

Hands-On Activity *(continued)*

- Students should divide the 18 unit cubes into 3 groups. There should be 6 in each group with no remainder.
- Each group has 9 tens and 6 units, so the value is 96. 288 ÷ 3 = 96.

Real-World Connection

Encourage students to think of everyday places or situations where people might need to divide multi-digit numbers.

Examples: buying items at the store in bulk and then dividing them among friends or buying a bag of pretzels and dividing it evenly among the students in the class.

AT A GLANCE

Students read a word problem and then use partial quotients and the division algorithm to solve.

STEP BY STEP

- Read the problem at the top of the page as a class.
- Read Estimate It. Ask students to explain why it is helpful to estimate first. Remind them that compatible numbers are numbers that are close to the dividend and divisor that can be easily divided mentally. Help them to see that their estimate should be less than the dividend so they can use partial quotients to find the final quotient.
- Direct students to look at the problem in the first Model It. Ask students if the modeled problem is the only correct way to solve using partial quotients. Students may recognize that they can use any combination of partial quotients which should all add up to the same result. Multiples of 10 are useful when dividing with partial quotients.
- Direct students to look at the problem in the second Model It.
- Students often have trouble remembering where to line up the product after the first step to subtract. Emphasize that they are dividing 56 into 67 tens. 1 ten $\times$ 56 = 56 tens. You may want to have students write 560 to ensure proper placement: 672 − 560 = 112.

SMP Tip: Students use repeated reasoning to understand algorithms and make generalizations about patterns. Give students multiple opportunities to solve and model problems, focusing on place value (SMP 8).

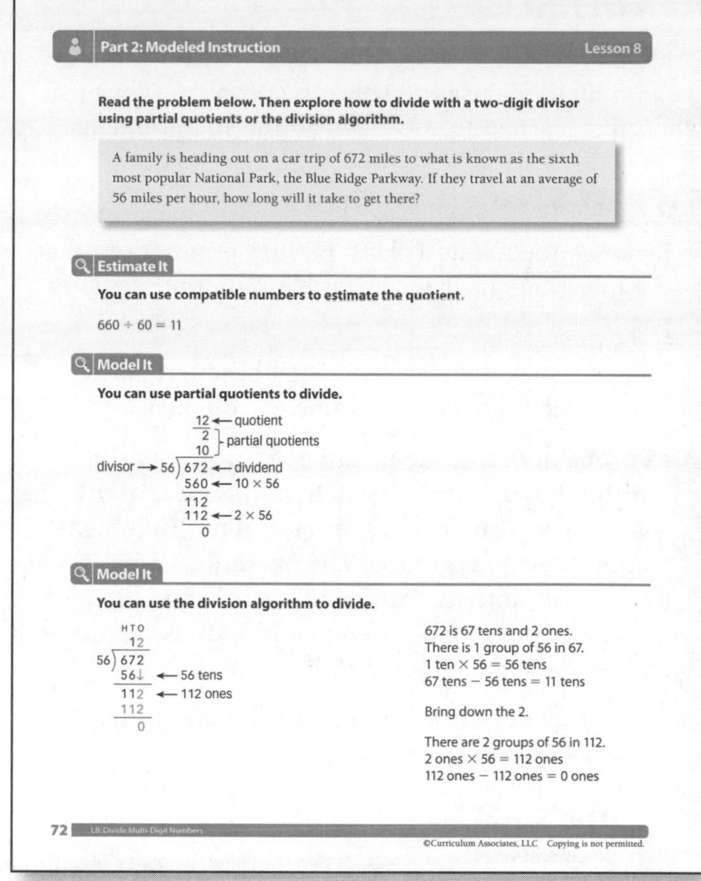
Part 2: Modeled Instruction Lesson 8

Read the problem below. Then explore how to divide with a two-digit divisor using partial quotients or the division algorithm.

A family is heading out on a car trip of 672 miles to what is known as the sixth most popular National Park, the Blue Ridge Parkway. If they travel at an average of 56 miles per hour, how long will it take to get there?

Estimate It

You can use compatible numbers to estimate the quotient.

660 ÷ 60 = 11

Model It

You can use partial quotients to divide.

Model It

You can use the division algorithm to divide.

672 is 67 tens and 2 ones.
There is 1 group of 56 in 67.
1 ten × 56 = 56 tens
67 tens − 56 tens = 11 tens

Bring down the 2.

There are 2 groups of 56 in 112.
2 ones × 56 = 112 ones
112 ones − 112 ones = 0 ones

72 L8: Divide Multi-Digit Numbers
©Curriculum Associates, LLC Copying is not permitted.

Mathematical Discourse

- *You have solved this problem using two different methods. Which do you prefer and why?*

  Students will have varied responses. Listen for correct use of math vocabulary such as dividend, quotient, divisor, and partial quotient.

- *How would you explain how to solve this division problem to a student who was absent?*

  Students should explain both methods and use correct vocabulary detailing the process.

AT A GLANCE

Students revisit the problem on page 72 and compare the two methods used to solve the problem. They use what they learned to solve two additional problems.

STEP BY STEP

- Read Connect It as a class. Be sure to point out that the questions refer to the problem on the previous page.
- Students may benefit from using base-ten blocks to model that 56 tens is the same as 560 ones.
- In problem 6, if students are not familiar with multiplying to check division, point out that dividing is separating into equal groups and multiplying is combining equal groups. The operations are inverse operations, and one "undoes" the other, so multiplication can be used to check division, division can be used to check multiplication.
- Have students work through Try It and discuss their answers with their group.

ELL Support

Review key vocabulary such as *divisor, dividend*, and *quotient*. Note the placement of the divisor, depending on the problem. For example, 56 is the divisor in both 672 ÷ 56 and $56\overline{)672}$.

SMP Tip: Students use the structure of the place value system to estimate and to use the standard division algorithm accurately with understanding (SMP 7). Occasionally ask students to talk about the value of the numbers they are working with in different steps of the algorithm, for example, *Does the 56 mean 56 tens or 56 ones?*

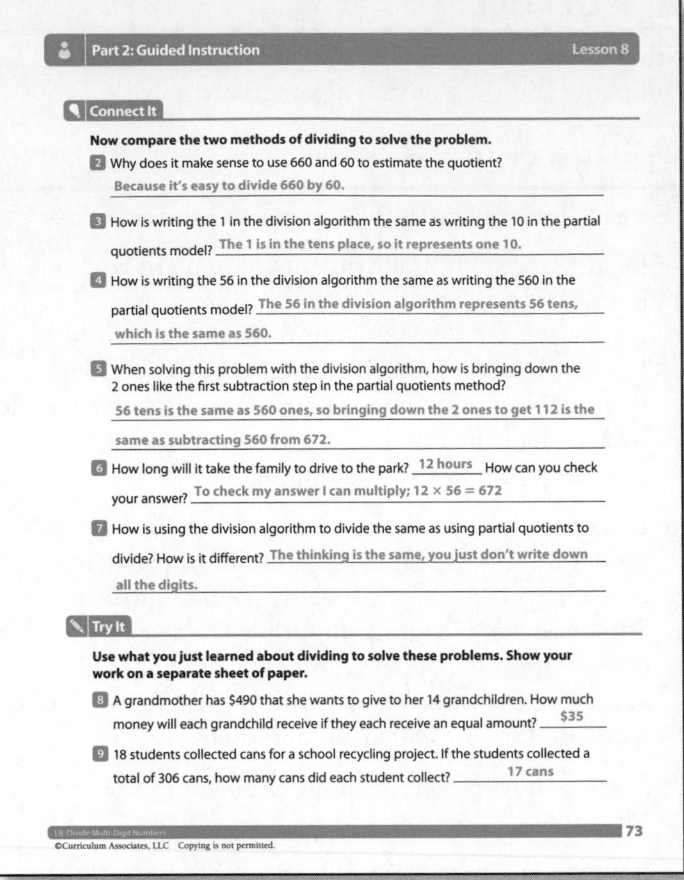

Part 2: Guided Instruction Lesson 8

Connect It

Now compare the two methods of dividing to solve the problem.

2 Why does it make sense to use 660 and 60 to estimate the quotient? **Because it's easy to divide 660 by 60.**

3 How is writing the 1 in the division algorithm the same as writing the 10 in the partial quotients model? **The 1 is in the tens place, so it represents one 10.**

4 How is writing the 56 in the division algorithm the same as writing the 560 in the partial quotients model? **The 56 in the division algorithm represents 56 tens, which is the same as 560.**

5 When solving this problem with the division algorithm, how is bringing down the 2 ones like the first subtraction step in the partial quotients method? **56 tens is the same as 560 ones, so bringing down the 2 ones to get 112 is the same as subtracting 560 from 672.**

6 How long will it take the family to drive to the park? **12 hours** How can you check your answer? **To check my answer I can multiply; 12 × 56 = 672**

7 How is using the division algorithm to divide the same as using partial quotients to divide? How is it different? **The thinking is the same, you just don't write down all the digits.**

Try It

Use what you just learned about dividing to solve these problems. Show your work on a separate sheet of paper.

8 A grandmother has $490 that she wants to give to her 14 grandchildren. How much money will each grandchild receive if they each receive an equal amount? **$35**

9 18 students collected cans for a school recycling project. If the students collected a total of 306 cans, how many cans did each student collect? **17 cans**

L8: Divide Multi-Digit Numbers 73

©Curriculum Associates, LLC Copying is not permitted.

TRY IT SOLUTIONS

8 *Solution:* $35; Students may use partial quotients to solve the problem.

ERROR ALERT: Students who wrote $350 did not record the quotient in the proper place. The 3 should be recorded above the 9 tens to represent 30, not above the 4 hundreds to represent 300. The 5 should be written above the 0 ones for a quotient of $35.

9 *Solution:* 17 cans; Students may use the standard algorithm to solve the problem.

AT A GLANCE

Students read a word problem and explore dividing a 5-digit dividend by a 2-digit divisor.

STEP BY STEP

- Read the problem at the top of the page as a class.
- Discuss Estimate It. Ask students to explain why you should first estimate a problem.
- Remind students that compatible numbers are numbers that can be easily multiplied or divided using mental math.
- Discuss Model It. Emphasize place value and proper placement of the quotient as you solve.
- Point out that the same methods used previously for division, partial products or the standard algorithm, are used to divide greater dividends, but with more steps.

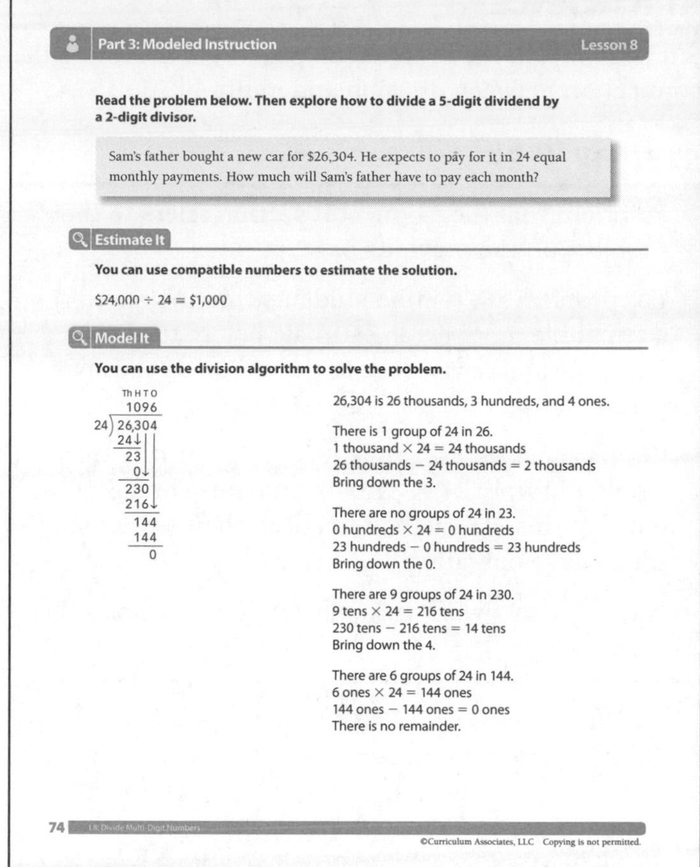

Part 3: Modeled Instruction Lesson 8

Read the problem below. Then explore how to divide a 5-digit dividend by a 2-digit divisor.

Sam's father bought a new car for $26,304. He expects to pay for it in 24 equal monthly payments. How much will Sam's father have to pay each month?

Estimate It

You can use compatible numbers to estimate the solution.

$24,000 ÷ 24 = $1,000

Model It

You can use the division algorithm to solve the problem.

```
     Th H T O
      1 0 9 6
24 ) 26,304
     24↓
      23
       0↓
      230
      216↓
       144
       144
         0
```

26,304 is 26 thousands, 3 hundreds, and 4 ones.

There is 1 group of 24 in 26.
1 thousand × 24 = 24 thousands
26 thousands − 24 thousands = 2 thousands
Bring down the 3.

There are no groups of 24 in 23.
0 hundreds × 24 = 0 hundreds
23 hundreds − 0 hundreds = 23 hundreds
Bring down the 0.

There are 9 groups of 24 in 230.
9 tens × 24 = 216 tens
230 tens − 216 tens = 14 tens
Bring down the 4.

There are 6 groups of 24 in 144.
6 ones × 24 = 144 ones
144 ones − 144 ones = 0 ones
There is no remainder.

74 L8: Divide Multi-Digit Numbers ©Curriculum Associates, LLC Copying is not permitted.

Mathematical Discourse

- *Can you think of any other ways to solve the problem?*

  Students may describe partial quotients or may have experience using short division. Students may also have experience with "bringing up" rather than "bringing down."

- *How do you know where to record your first digits in the quotient when solving?*

  Students should be able to explain how they use place value to decide where to record the digits.

- *How could you use your answer to $26,304 ÷ 24 to find $26,304 ÷ 48?*

  Listen for responses that recognize that since 48 is 24 × 2, you can divide by 2 to get the new quotient. If students have trouble with the question, use an example with smaller numbers, for example using 24 ÷ 2 = 12 to figure out 24 ÷ 4.

AT A GLANCE

Students revisit the problem on page 74 and explore the connection between division and multiplication.

STEP BY STEP

- Point out that the Connect It section refers to the problem on the previous page.
- For problem 10, remind students that they used compatible numbers to estimate before they solved. Since the answer is close to the estimate, the answer is reasonable.
- For problem 11, ask students to tell you why they would multiply 24 × \$1,096. Students should point out that this is a method to check their work using the inverse operation.
- Have students work through Try It and discuss their answers.

SMP Tip: Mathematically proficient students check answers to problems using a different method and try to think of different ways to solve a problem. Remind students that there is more than one right way to solve the problems (SMP 1).

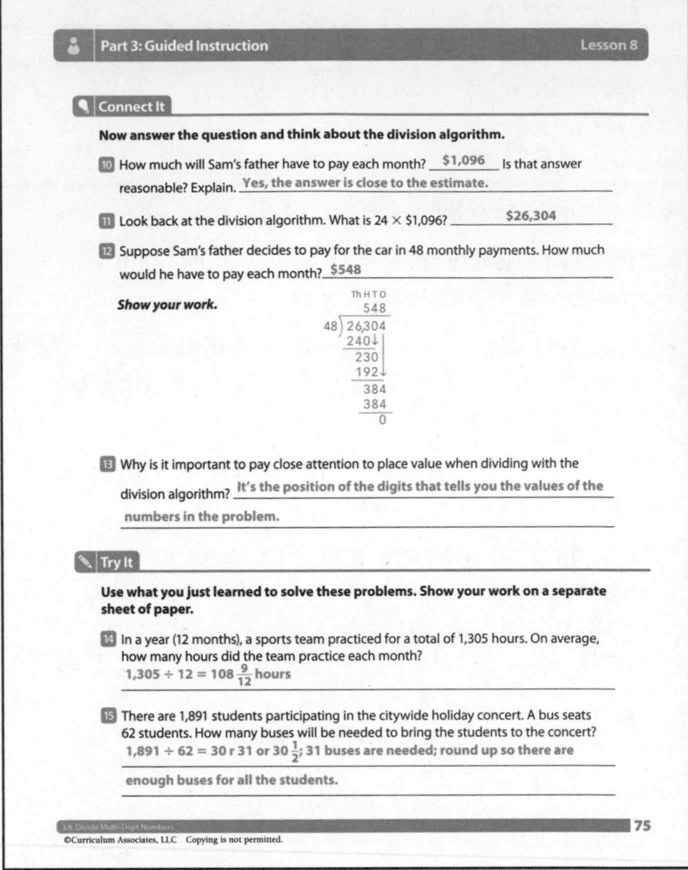

Part 3: Guided Instruction Lesson 8

Connect It

Now answer the question and think about the division algorithm.

10 How much will Sam's father have to pay each month? **\$1,096** Is that answer reasonable? Explain. **Yes, the answer is close to the estimate.**

11 Look back at the division algorithm. What is 24 × \$1,096? **\$26,304**

12 Suppose Sam's father decides to pay for the car in 48 monthly payments. How much would he have to pay each month? **\$548**

Show your work.

```
Th H T O
     548
48)26,304
   240↓
    230
    192↓
     384
     384
       0
```

13 Why is it important to pay close attention to place value when dividing with the division algorithm? **It's the position of the digits that tells you the values of the numbers in the problem.**

Try It

Use what you just learned to solve these problems. Show your work on a separate sheet of paper.

14 In a year (12 months), a sports team practiced for a total of 1,305 hours. On average, how many hours did the team practice each month?
$1{,}305 \div 12 = 108\frac{9}{12}$ hours

15 There are 1,891 students participating in the citywide holiday concert. A bus seats 62 students. How many buses will be needed to bring the students to the concert?
$1{,}891 \div 62 = 30$ r 31 or $30\frac{1}{2}$; 31 buses are needed; round up so there are enough buses for all the students.

L8: Divide Multi-Digit Numbers 75

©Curriculum Associates, LLC Copying is not permitted.

TRY IT SOLUTIONS

14 *Solution:* $108\frac{9}{12}$ hours; Students may use the standard algorithm or partial quotients to solve.

15 *Solution:* 30 r31 or $30\frac{1}{2}$; 31 buses are needed.

ERROR ALERT: Students who wrote 30 did not recognize that the remainder in this problem means to round up so there are enough buses for all the students.

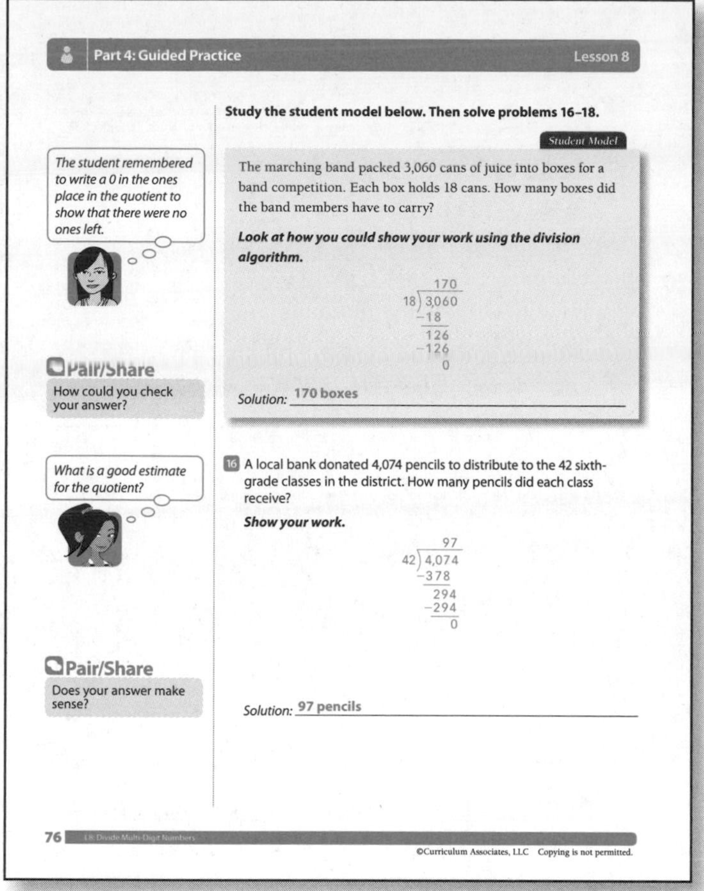

Part 4: Guided Practice Lesson 8

Study the student model below. Then solve problems 16–18.

The student remembered to write a 0 in the ones place in the quotient to show that there were no ones left.

Student Model

The marching band packed 3,060 cans of juice into boxes for a band competition. Each box holds 18 cans. How many boxes did the band members have to carry?

Look at how you could show your work using the division algorithm.

$$\begin{array}{r} 170 \\ 18\overline{)3{,}060} \\ -18 \\ \hline 126 \\ -126 \\ \hline 0 \end{array}$$

Solution: **170 boxes**

Pair/Share

How could you check your answer?

What is a good estimate for the quotient?

16 A local bank donated 4,074 pencils to distribute to the 42 sixth-grade classes in the district. How many pencils did each class receive?

Show your work.

$$\begin{array}{r} 97 \\ 42\overline{)4{,}074} \\ -378 \\ \hline 294 \\ -294 \\ \hline 0 \end{array}$$

Solution: **97 pencils**

Pair/Share

Does your answer make sense?

76 L8: Divide Multi-Digit Numbers ©Curriculum Associates, LLC Copying is not permitted.

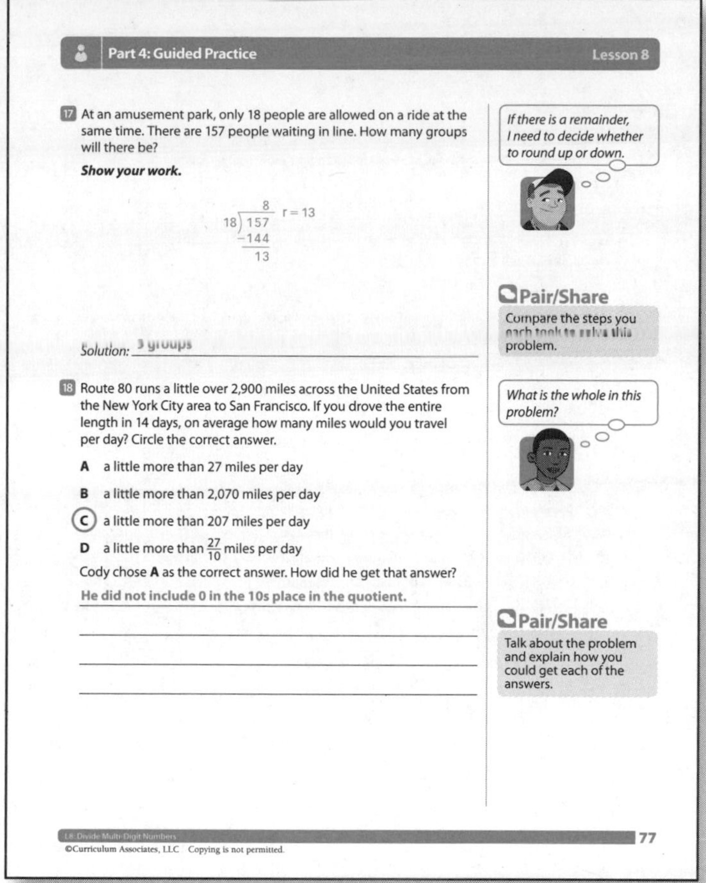

Part 4: Guided Practice Lesson 8

17 At an amusement park, only 18 people are allowed on a ride at the same time. There are 157 people waiting in line. How many groups will there be?

Show your work.

$$\begin{array}{r} 8 \; r = 13 \\ 18\overline{)157} \\ -144 \\ \hline 13 \end{array}$$

Solution: **9 groups**

If there is a remainder, I need to decide whether to round up or down.

Pair/Share

Compare the steps you each took to solve this problem.

18 Route 80 runs a little over 2,900 miles across the United States from the New York City area to San Francisco. If you drove the entire length in 14 days, on average how many miles would you travel per day? Circle the correct answer.

A a little more than 27 miles per day

B a little more than 2,070 miles per day

(C) a little more than 207 miles per day

D a little more than $\frac{27}{10}$ miles per day

Cody chose **A** as the correct answer. How did he get that answer?

He did not include 0 in the 10s place in the quotient.

What is the whole in this problem?

Pair/Share

Talk about the problem and explain how you could get each of the answers.

L8: Divide Multi-Digit Numbers 77 ©Curriculum Associates, LLC Copying is not permitted.

AT A GLANCE

Students use the standard division algorithm or partial quotients to solve word problems.

STEP BY STEP

- Ask students to solve the problems individually.
- When students have completed each problem, have them Pair/Share to discuss their solutions with a partner or in a group.

SOLUTIONS

Ex The division algorithm is used to divide 3,060 by 18. Students could also use partial quotients to find the answer.

16 *Solution:* 97 pencils; Students could solve the problem by dividing 4,074 by 42 using the standard division algorithm. ***(DOK 1)***

17 *Solution:* 9 groups; Students could solve the problem by dividing 157 by 18. The answer is 8 r13 but students should recognize the remaining 13 would also make up a group. ***(DOK 1)***

18 *Solution:* **C**; Cody did not include the 0 in the 10s place in the quotient.

Explain to students why the other two answer choices are not correct:

B is not correct because an extra digit is added to the quotient. The 2 may have been put in the thousands place rather than the hundreds place.

D is not correct because the place value was not used correctly. ***(DOK 3)***

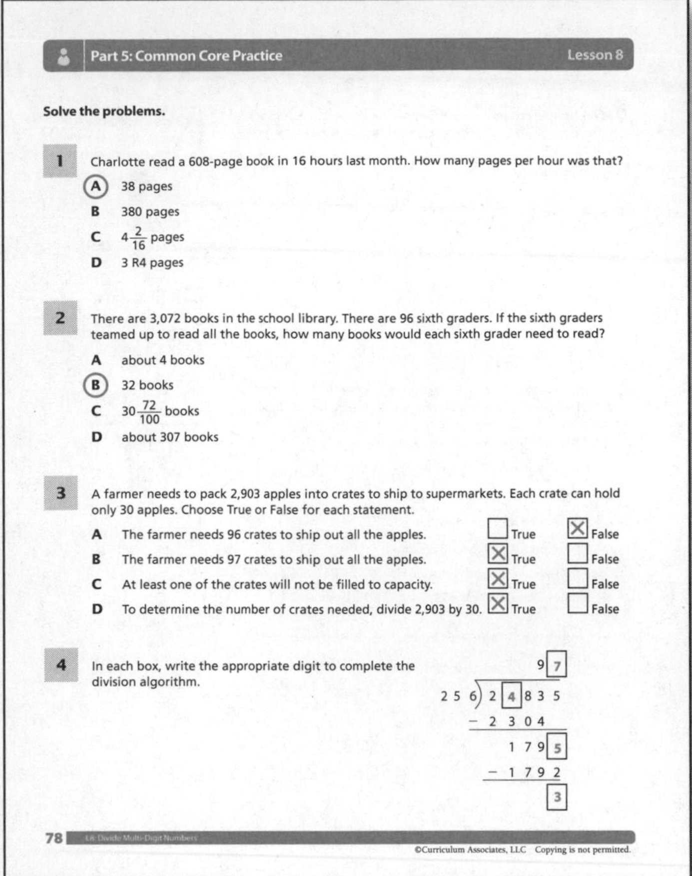

Part 5: Common Core Practice Lesson 8

Solve the problems.

1 Charlotte read a 608-page book in 16 hours last month. How many pages per hour was that?

- (A) 38 pages
- B 380 pages
- C $4\frac{2}{16}$ pages
- D 3 R4 pages

2 There are 3,072 books in the school library. There are 96 sixth graders. If the sixth graders teamed up to read all the books, how many books would each sixth grader need to read?

- A about 4 books
- (B) 32 books
- C $30\frac{72}{100}$ books
- D about 307 books

3 A farmer needs to pack 2,903 apples into crates to ship to supermarkets. Each crate can hold only 30 apples. Choose True or False for each statement.

A	The farmer needs 96 crates to ship out all the apples.	☐ True	☒ False
B	The farmer needs 97 crates to ship out all the apples.	☒ True	☐ False
C	At least one of the crates will not be filled to capacity.	☒ True	☐ False
D	To determine the number of crates needed, divide 2,903 by 30.	☒ True	☐ False

4 In each box, write the appropriate digit to complete the division algorithm.

```
          9[7]
256)2[4]835
  − 2 3 0 4
      1 7 9[5]
    − 1 7 9 2
            [3]
```

78 L8: Divide Multi-Digit Numbers ©Curriculum Associates, LLC Copying is not permitted.

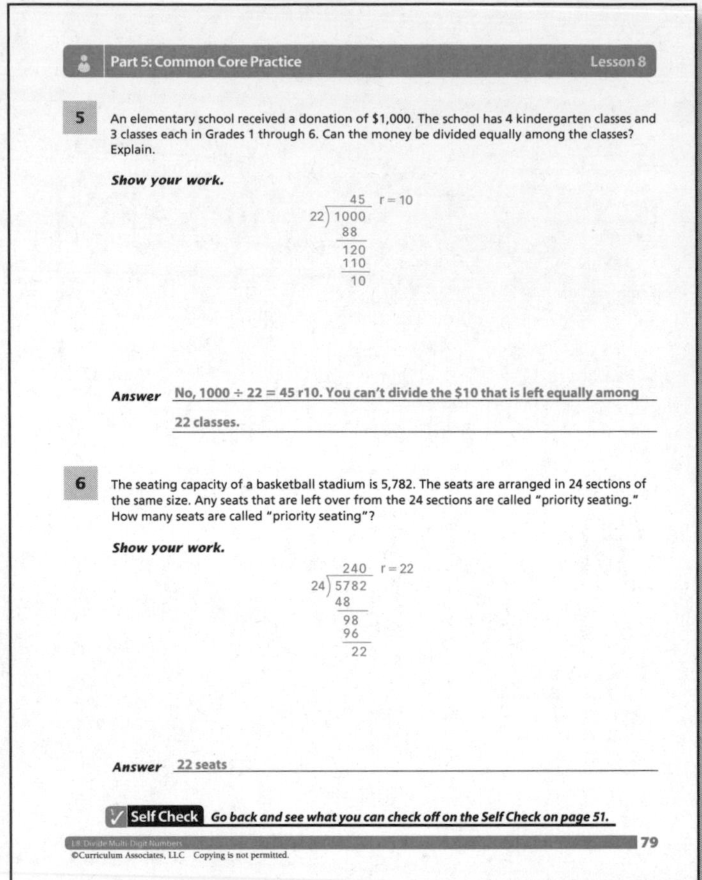

Part 5: Common Core Practice Lesson 8

5 An elementary school received a donation of $1,000. The school has 4 kindergarten classes and 3 classes each in Grades 1 through 6. Can the money be divided equally among the classes? Explain.

Show your work.

```
     45  r=10
22)1000
    88
    120
    110
     10
```

Answer No, 1000 ÷ 22 = 45 r10. You can't divide the $10 that is left equally among 22 classes.

6 The seating capacity of a basketball stadium is 5,782. The seats are arranged in 24 sections of the same size. Any seats that are left over from the 24 sections are called "priority seating." How many seats are called "priority seating"?

Show your work.

```
     240  r=22
24)5782
   48
    98
    96
     22
```

Answer 22 seats

✓ Self Check Go back and see what you can check off on the Self Check on page 51.

L8: Divide Multi-Digit Numbers 79 ©Curriculum Associates, LLC Copying is not permitted.

AT A GLANCE

Students divide multi-digit numbers to solve word problems that might appear on a mathematics test.

SOLUTIONS

1 *Solution:* **A**; Divide 608 by 16 to find the number of pages per hour. ***(DOK 2)***

2 *Solution:* **B**; Divide 3,072 by 96 to find the number of books per sixth grader. ***(DOK 1)***

3 *Solution:* A **False**; B **True**; C **True**; D **True** ***(DOK 2)***

4 *Solution:* See student book page above for solution. ***(DOK 1)***

5 *Solution:* No, 1,000 ÷ 22 = 45 R10. The $10 that is left cannot be equally divided among the 22 classes; See student book page above for possible student work. ***(DOK 2)***

6 *Solution:* 22 seats; See student book page above for possible student work. ***(DOK 3)***

Assessment and Remediation

- Ask students to divide 56,315 by 35. [1,609]
- For students who are struggling, use the chart below to guide remediation.
- After providing remediation, check students' understanding. Ask students to divide 79,695 by 63. [1,265]
- If a student is still having difficulty, use ***Ready Instruction, Level 5,*** Lesson 6.

If the error is . . .	Students may . . .	To remediate . . .
1,407 r35	have rounded the divisor to 40 to estimate, then forgotten to use the real divisor to compute.	Ask students to compare the answer to their estimate. Remind students that they can round to estimate a problem, but should use the actual numbers to solve.
169	have forgotten to record a zero in the tens place	Ask students if it is reasonable that there are 169 groups of 35 in 56,315. Have students show you their work, step by step. Ask them to think aloud and to describe the numbers in terms of place value. Remind them that they must place zeros in the quotient if in a step there are not enough for one group of the divisor.
any other number	made a calculation error.	Ask them to review their solution to see where they may have made an error. Consider allowing them to refer to a multiplication table.

Hands-On Activity

Play a division game.

Materials: two 1–6 number cubes, base-ten blocks

- Base-ten blocks represent the initial dividend. Players roll a number cube. The player with the higher number goes first.
- Player 1 rolls both number cubes and finds the sum. Divide the dividend by the sum of the cubes. If there is a remainder the player gets to keep the base-ten blocks that make up the remainder as points.
- Player 2 will only have the remaining base-ten blocks. Player 2 rolls the number cubes and divides the value of the base ten blocks by the sum of the cubes.
- Player 2 keeps the base ten blocks representing the remainder.
- Play continues until a player rolls a sum larger than the number of blocks left to divide.
- The winner is the player who has the most base-ten blocks in their pile.

Challenge Activity

Students who become proficient with the standard division algorithm may enjoy trying short division. Instead of writing out the multiplication and subtraction, it is done mentally and the remainder is written down before the next digit to be divided.

For example:

$$3\overline{)28^{1}8}\quad \text{quotient: } 9\ 6$$

Lesson 9 (Student Book pages 80–89)

Add and Subtract Decimals

LESSON OBJECTIVES

- Understand role of place value in the operations of addition and subtraction.
- Identify when it is appropriate to use the standard algorithm.
- Estimate sums and differences before using the standard algorithm, and use these sums and differences to check reasonableness of answers.
- Add and subtract multi-digit decimals.
- Model the operations of addition and subtraction with manipulatives, diagrams, and story contexts for multi-digit decimals.

PREREQUISITE SKILLS

- Understand decimal place values.
- Know basic facts for addition, subtraction, multiplication, and division.
- Add, subtract, multiply, and divide single-digit decimals.
- Model the operations of addition, subtraction, multiplication, and division with manipulatives, diagrams, and story contexts for single-digit decimals.

VOCABULARY

There is no new vocabulary.

THE LEARNING PROGRESSION

In earlier grades, students learned to add and subtract decimals. They have also learned the meaning of decimals and worked with decimal place value.

In Grade 6, students review how to add and subtract decimals with an emphasis on place value when they align the decimal points. By the end of this year, students should be fluent in the use of the standard algorithms of each of these operations. They use adding and subtracting decimals to solve real-world problems. They also practice estimating to see if their answers are reasonable.

In later grades, students will add and subtract decimals as they solve problems from algebra, geometry, and real-world contexts. By being fluent with the algorithms, they will be able to concentrate on the problems, not only how to add and subtract decimals.

Ready *Teacher Toolbox* Teacher-Toolbox.com

	Prerequisite Skills	6.NS.B.3
Ready Lessons	✓	✓
Tools for Instruction		
Interactive Tutorials		✓ ✓

CCSS Focus

6.NS.B.3 Fluently add, subtract, multiply, and divide multi-digit decimals using the standard algorithm for each operation.

STANDARDS FOR MATHEMATICAL PRACTICE: ***SMP 3, 6, 7*** *(see page A9 for full text)*

AT A GLANCE

Students read a word problem and answer a series of questions designed to help them add decimals. They use estimation to see if their answers are reasonable.

STEP BY STEP

- Tell students that this page models how to add and subtract decimals.
- Have students read the problem at the top of the page.
- Mention that beverages are often measured in liters because a liter is the metric unit of volume that is slightly more than a quart.
- Work through Explore It as a class.
- Have students find the numbers they are to add. Discuss how writing all the quantities as thousandths helps them line up the decimal points.
- Ask student pairs or groups to explain how they subtracted the total of the lemonade from 2 liters.

SMP Tip: When you use the correct place-value names, such as *375 thousandths* instead of *point three-seven-five,* you model to students that it is important to attend to precision (*SMP 6*).

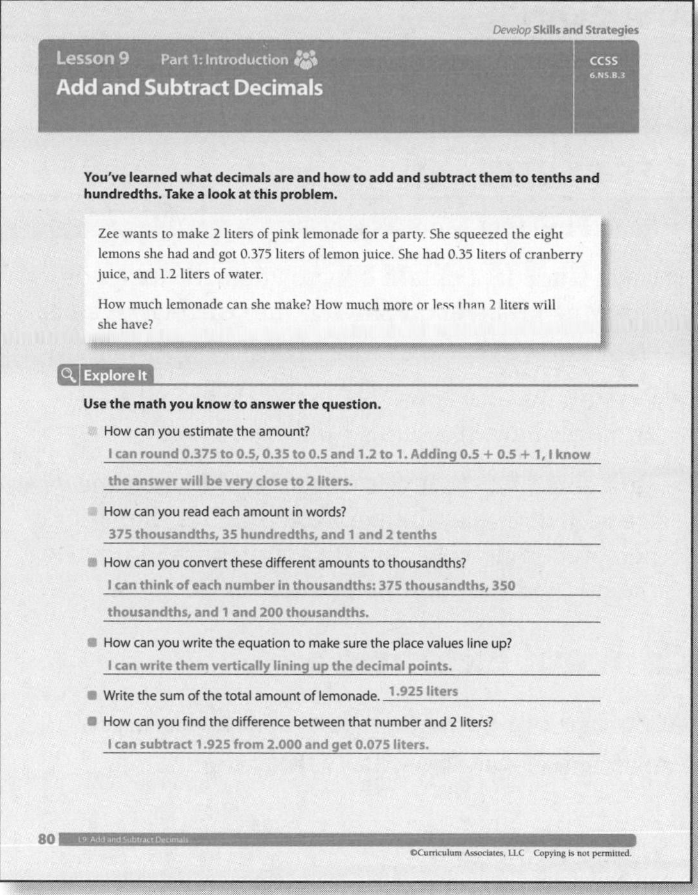

Develop Skills and Strategies

Lesson 9 Part 1: Introduction CCSS 6.NS.B.3

Add and Subtract Decimals

You've learned what decimals are and how to add and subtract them to tenths and hundredths. Take a look at this problem.

Zee wants to make 2 liters of pink lemonade for a party. She squeezed the eight lemons she had and got 0.375 liters of lemon juice. She had 0.35 liters of cranberry juice, and 1.2 liters of water.

How much lemonade can she make? How much more or less than 2 liters will she have?

Explore It

Use the math you know to answer the question.

- How can you estimate the amount?
  I can round 0.375 to 0.5, 0.35 to 0.5 and 1.2 to 1. Adding 0.5 + 0.5 + 1, I know the answer will be very close to 2 liters.
- How can you read each amount in words?
  375 thousandths, 35 hundredths, and 1 and 2 tenths
- How can you convert these different amounts to thousandths?
  I can think of each number in thousandths: 375 thousandths, 350 thousandths, and 1 and 200 thousandths.
- How can you write the equation to make sure the place values line up?
  I can write them vertically lining up the decimal points.
- Write the sum of the total amount of lemonade. 1.925 liters
- How can you find the difference between that number and 2 liters?
  I can subtract 1.925 from 2.000 and get 0.075 liters.

80 L9: Add and Subtract Decimals

©Curriculum Associates, LLC Copying is not permitted.

ELL Support

- Write *ten*, *hundred*, and *thousand* on the board. Read each word aloud as you write it.
- Have volunteers come to the board and write the correct numeral under each word. Point to each numeral and have students say the correct word.
- Write $\frac{1}{10}$, $\frac{1}{100}$, and $\frac{1}{1,000}$ on the board. Point to each and have volunteers tell how to read it. Write *tenth*, *hundredth*, and *thousandth* above the corresponding fraction. Point out that the addition of a "*th*" changes each word to a fraction.
- Write 0.1, 0.01, and 0.001 under the corresponding fraction. Say that decimals are another way to write *tenth*, *hundredth*, and *thousandth*.
- Point to the different numerals written on the board and have students read each aloud correctly.

Mathematical Discourse

- *For the problem on this page, why is it helpful to write all the addends as thousandths?*

  Students' responses should get to the concept that it makes it easier to line up the numbers and decimal point correctly.
- *Where would you put a decimal point on the 2, and how could you write it to show digits through the thousandths' place? Explain.*

  The decimal point goes to the right of the 2 because 2 is in the ones place. After you place the point, you would add 3 zeros to show that there are no tenths, hundredths, or thousandths.
- *How do you read 2.000?*

  Students should take into account each of the places and read "two and zero thousandths."

AT A GLANCE

Students use place-value charts to review the addition of decimals.

STEP BY STEP

- Read Find Out More as a class.
- Have students explain how to enter the addends from the problem on page 80 into the place-value chart.
- Discuss why it is possible to use 0s to make all numbers have the same number of places.
- Talk about whether it is easier to add when the 0s are added to the problem. Note that it is a matter of personal preference, but that students should use the method that best helps them be accurate.

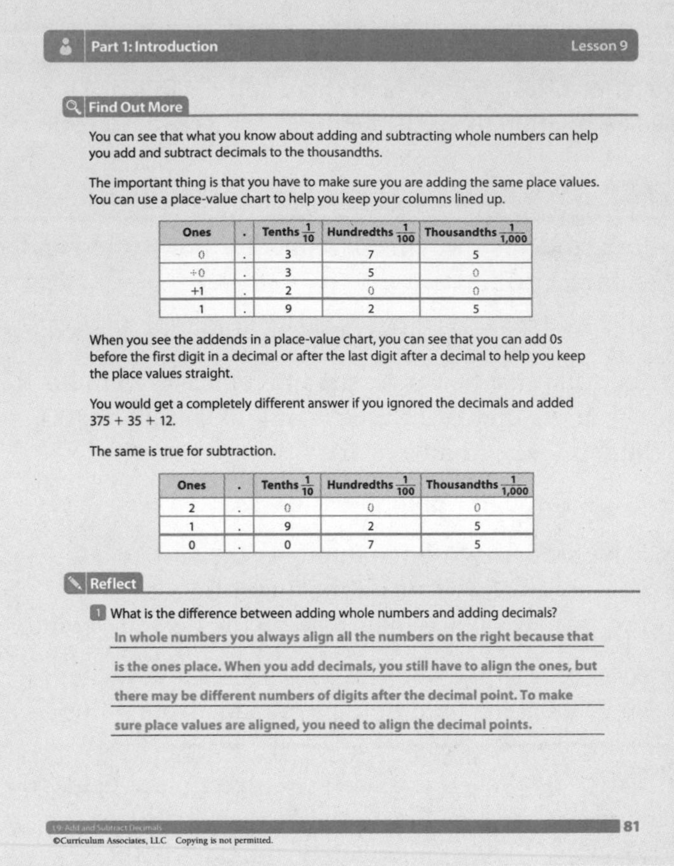

Part 1: Introduction Lesson 9

Find Out More

You can see that what you know about adding and subtracting whole numbers can help you add and subtract decimals to the thousandths.

The important thing is that you have to make sure you are adding the same place values. You can use a place-value chart to help you keep your columns lined up.

Ones	.	Tenths $\frac{1}{10}$	Hundredths $\frac{1}{100}$	Thousandths $\frac{1}{1,000}$
0	.	3	7	5
+0	.	3	5	0
+1	.	2	0	0
1	.	9	2	5

When you see the addends in a place-value chart, you can see that you can add 0s before the first digit in a decimal or after the last digit after a decimal to help you keep the place values straight.

You would get a completely different answer if you ignored the decimals and added 375 + 35 + 12.

The same is true for subtraction.

Ones	.	Tenths $\frac{1}{10}$	Hundredths $\frac{1}{100}$	Thousandths $\frac{1}{1,000}$
2	.	0	0	0
1	.	9	2	5
0	.	0	7	5

Reflect

1 What is the difference between adding whole numbers and adding decimals?

In whole numbers you always align all the numbers on the right because that is the ones place. When you add decimals, you still have to align the ones, but there may be different numbers of digits after the decimal point. To make sure place values are aligned, you need to align the decimal points.

L9: Add and Subtract Decimals 81

©Curriculum Associates, LLC Copying is not permitted.

Concept Extension

Explore the commutative and associative properties for the addition of decimals.

- Ask students to describe the commutative property of addition. Ask if they think it holds true for the addition of decimals.
- Divide the class into thirds. Have a third of the students add 0.35 + 0.375 + 1.2, another third add 0.375 + 1.2 + 0.35, and the last third add 1.2 + 0.375 + 0.35. Have them compare answers. Discuss whether the addition of decimals seems to be commutative.
- Ask students to describe the associative property of addition. Ask if they think it holds true for the addition of decimals.
- Divide the class into halves. Have half of the students add (0.375 + 0.35) + 1.2 and the other half add 0.375 + (0.35 + 1.2). Have them compare answers. Discuss whether the addition of decimals seems to be associative.

Real-World Connection

Ask students to think of real-world situations in which they have seen decimals.

Examples: money, amounts in packages, weights, distances

Now ask students to think of why they would add and subtract the decimals in the situations named.

Examples: They would add if they wanted to know how much altogether, and they would subtract if they wanted to know how much more one is than another or how much of something is left if some of it is taken away.

AT A GLANCE

Students explore a problem involving the addition of decimals by estimating, using a place-value chart, and lining up the decimal points.

STEP BY STEP

- Read the problem at the top of the page as a class. Make sure students understand which numbers they are to add.
- Before reading Estimate It, discuss why it is always a good idea to estimate the sum before adding. Go through the explanation of how to estimate the sum.
- As you examine Picture It, review how to write the addends in the place-value chart correctly. Discuss whether students would like to put 0s in some of the places.
- After students read Model It, have them explain their reasoning as they write the problem vertically without using extra 0s.

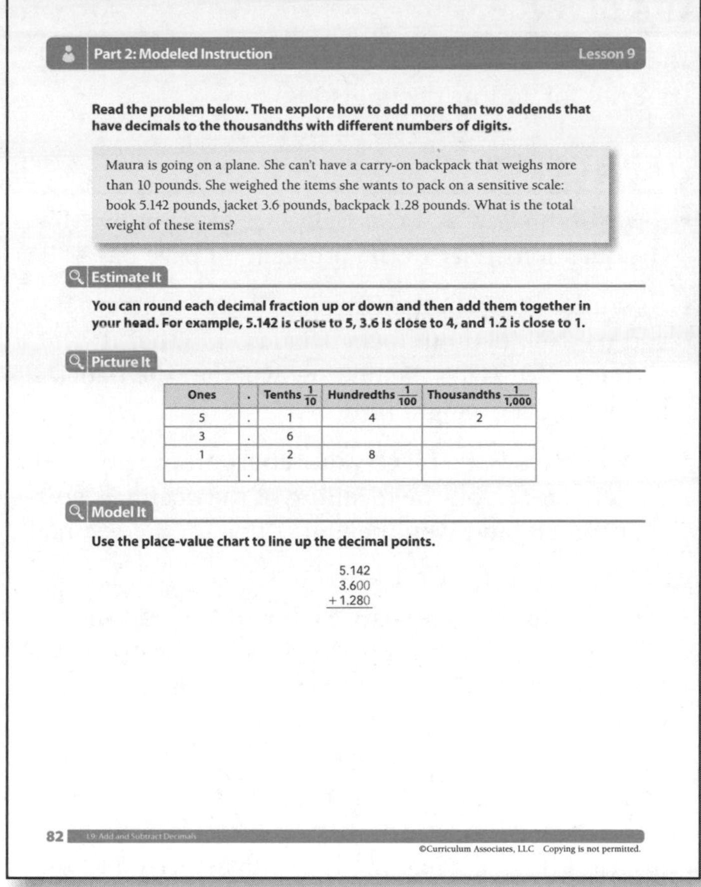

Part 2: Modeled Instruction Lesson 9

Read the problem below. Then explore how to add more than two addends that have decimals to the thousandths with different numbers of digits.

Maura is going on a plane. She can't have a carry-on backpack that weighs more than 10 pounds. She weighed the items she wants to pack on a sensitive scale: book 5.142 pounds, jacket 3.6 pounds, backpack 1.28 pounds. What is the total weight of these items?

Estimate It

You can round each decimal fraction up or down and then add them together in your head. For example, 5.142 is close to 5, 3.6 is close to 4, and 1.2 is close to 1.

Picture It

Ones	.	Tenths $\frac{1}{10}$	Hundredths $\frac{1}{100}$	Thousandths $\frac{1}{1,000}$
5	.	1	4	2
3	.	6		
1	.	2	8	
	.			

Model It

Use the place-value chart to line up the decimal points.

$$\begin{array}{r} 5.142 \\ 3.600 \\ +\,1.280 \\ \hline \end{array}$$

82 L9: Add and Subtract Decimals

©Curriculum Associates, LLC Copying is not permitted.

Visual Model

Align addends by place value.

- Tell students that the phrase *line up the decimal points* means that the decimal points must be in a straight line. Say that the points should look like the buttons on a shirt.
- On the board, write 4.5 + 0.215 + 0.31 in a vertical format with the points lined up correctly. Ask students if the problem is written correctly. Emphasize the alignment of the points by drawing a faint line through them.
- On the board, write 0.65 + 12.3 + 0.005 *incorrectly* in a vertical format with the right-hand digits aligned. Ask students if the problem is written correctly. Emphasize the misalignment of the points by showing that you cannot draw a straight line through them.
- Have a volunteer describe how to write the problem correctly. Check to make sure it is correct by drawing a faint straight line through the points.

Mathematical Discourse

- *Why is it a good idea to always estimate before you actually add?*

  If your answer is quite different from the estimate, it tells you that either the calculation or the estimate is incorrect.

- *If the answer and estimate are close, does that guarantee that your answer is correct?*

  No, you could have made a small error, making your answer merely close to the correct answer. Estimation helps you find large errors such as mistakes in place value.

AT A GLANCE

Students revisit the problem on page 82 to review strategies for adding decimals.

STEP BY STEP

- Read Connect It as a class. Be sure to point out that the questions refer to the problem on page 82.
- As students revisit the Estimate It, have them add the rounded numbers. Discuss whether the estimate, 10, helps them know whether the items are within the weight limit.
- As you review the place-value chart on page 82, help students focus on the meaning of the decimals so they understand why they must line up the decimal points.
- Have a volunteer come to the board and add the three numbers. Compare the result to the estimate. Discuss whether the items are within the weight limit.

SMP Tip: When students use place value to align the decimal points in addition or subtraction problems, they are making use of structure (*SMP 7*) rather than just applying a rule they learned by rote.

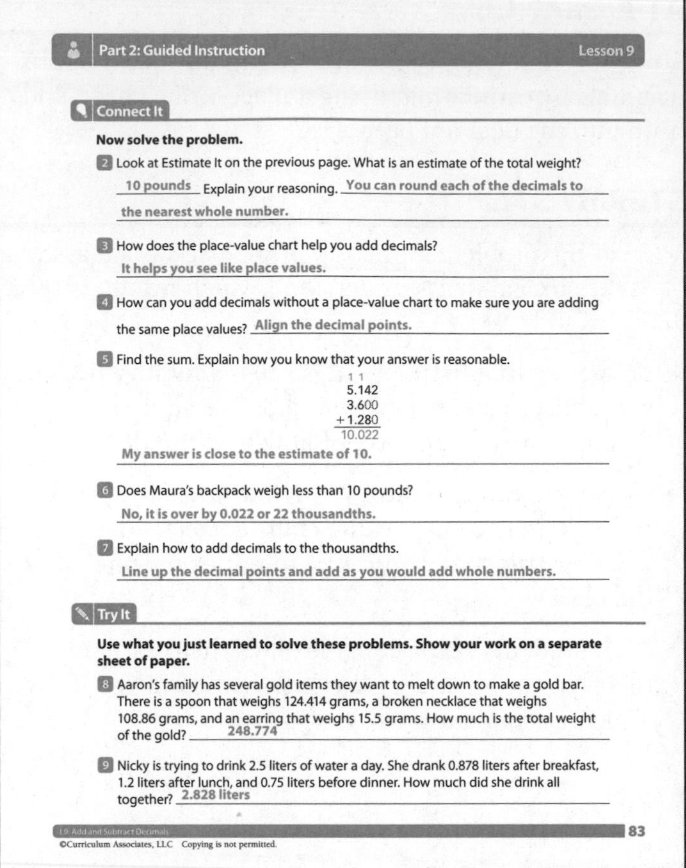
Part 2: Guided Instruction Lesson 9

Connect It

Now solve the problem.

2 Look at Estimate It on the previous page. What is an estimate of the total weight? 10 pounds Explain your reasoning. You can round each of the decimals to the nearest whole number.

3 How does the place-value chart help you add decimals? It helps you see like place values.

4 How can you add decimals without a place-value chart to make sure you are adding the same place values? Align the decimal points.

5 Find the sum. Explain how you know that your answer is reasonable.

$$\begin{array}{r} \overset{1\,1}{5.142} \\ 3.600 \\ +\,1.280 \\ \hline 10.022 \end{array}$$

My answer is close to the estimate of 10.

6 Does Maura's backpack weigh less than 10 pounds? No, it is over by 0.022 or 22 thousandths.

7 Explain how to add decimals to the thousandths. Line up the decimal points and add as you would add whole numbers.

Try It

Use what you just learned to solve these problems. Show your work on a separate sheet of paper.

8 Aaron's family has several gold items they want to melt down to make a gold bar. There is a spoon that weighs 124.414 grams, a broken necklace that weighs 108.86 grams, and an earring that weighs 15.5 grams. How much is the total weight of the gold? 248.774

9 Nicky is trying to drink 2.5 liters of water a day. She drank 0.878 liters after breakfast, 1.2 liters after lunch, and 0.75 liters before dinner. How much did she drink all together? 2.828 liters

L9: Add and Subtract Decimals 83
©Curriculum Associates, LLC Copying is not permitted.

TRY IT SOLUTIONS

8 *Solution:* 248.774; Students may use a place-value chart to align the decimals when adding. They may also estimate first to make sure their answer is reasonable.

9 *Solution:* 2.828 liters; Students may use a place-value chart to align the decimals when adding. They may also estimate first to make sure their answer is reasonable.

ERROR ALERT: Students who wrote 5.328 included Nicky's goal in the amount she drank.

AT A GLANCE

Students explore a problem involving the subtraction of decimals by estimating, using a place-value chart, and lining up the decimal points.

STEP BY STEP

- Read the problem at the top of the page as a class.
- As you read Estimate It, discuss why they rounded each number to the nearest tenth instead of the nearest hundredth or nearest whole number.
- Make sure students understand how the place-value chart in Picture It models the numbers in the problem. Talk about using a 0 so that the first number also has three decimal places. Have students explain why 2 and 760 thousandths is equivalent to 2 and 76 hundredths.
- As students consider Model It, say: *When subtracting decimals, the points must be lined up just as they are when adding decimals.*

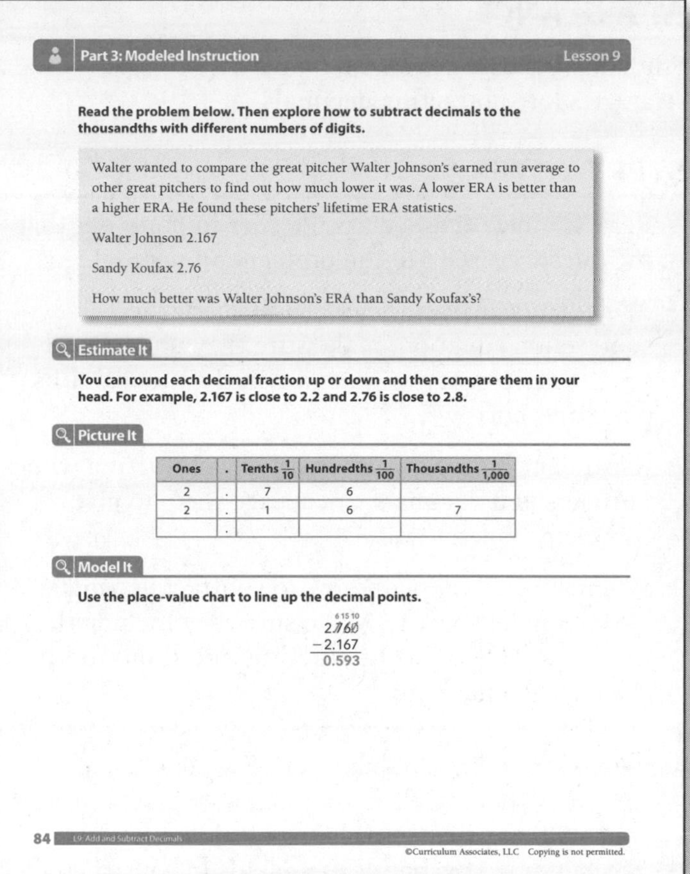

Part 3: Modeled Instruction Lesson 9

Read the problem below. Then explore how to subtract decimals to the thousandths with different numbers of digits.

Walter wanted to compare the great pitcher Walter Johnson's earned run average to other great pitchers to find out how much lower it was. A lower ERA is better than a higher ERA. He found these pitchers' lifetime ERA statistics.

Walter Johnson 2.167

Sandy Koufax 2.76

How much better was Walter Johnson's ERA than Sandy Koufax's?

Estimate It

You can round each decimal fraction up or down and then compare them in your head. For example, 2.167 is close to 2.2 and 2.76 is close to 2.8.

Picture It

Ones	.	Tenths $\frac{1}{10}$	Hundredths $\frac{1}{100}$	Thousandths $\frac{1}{1,000}$
2	.	7	6	
2	.	1	6	7
	.			

Model It

Use the place-value chart to line up the decimal points.

$$\begin{array}{r} \scriptstyle 6\,15\,10 \\ 2.\not{7}\not{6}\not{0} \\ -\,2.167 \\ \hline 0.593 \end{array}$$

84 L9: Add and Subtract Decimals

©Curriculum Associates, LLC Copying is not permitted.

Mathematical Discourse

- *When you add 2.76 + 2.167, can you just bring down the 7, or do you need to write in a 0 and then add? Explain.*

  It doesn't matter. The answer is the same either way.

  $$\begin{array}{r} 2.76 \\ +\,2.167 \\ \hline \end{array}$$

- *When you subtract 2.76 − 2.167, can you just bring down the 7, or do you need to write in a 0 and then subtract? Explain.*

  You must write in a 0 and regroup to subtract 7 hundredths from 10 hundredths.

  $$\begin{array}{r} 2.76 \\ -\,2.167 \\ \hline \end{array}$$

AT A GLANCE

Students revisit the problem on page 84 to review strategies for subtracting decimals.

STEP BY STEP

- Read Connect It as a class. Be sure to point out that the questions refer to the problem on page 84.
- As students answer the question about the subtraction equation, make sure they understand that it is necessary to write a 0 in the thousandths place and borrow.
- As students compare and contrast subtracting whole numbers and decimals, encourage them to give complete explanations.
- When students explain how to subtract decimals, have them be specific. Make sure they include the need to add 0s in the hundredths and thousandths places when necessary.

SMP Tip: When students compare, contrast, and explain methods used to subtract, they practice using mathematical terminology and giving clear explanations. This builds their skills in constructing viable arguments and critiquing the reasoning of others (*SMP 3*).

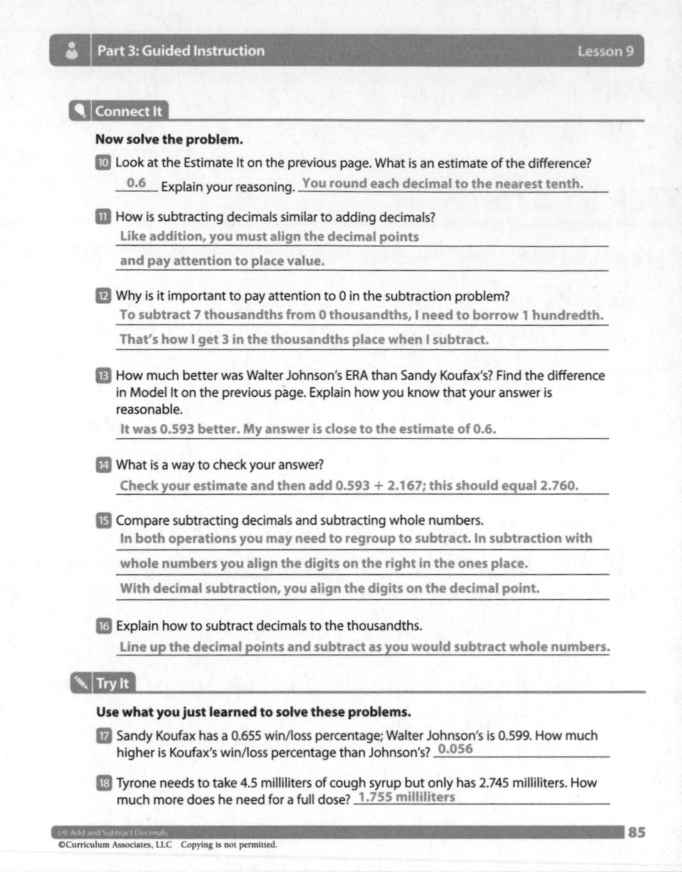

Part 3: Guided Instruction Lesson 9

Connect It

Now solve the problem.

10 Look at the Estimate It on the previous page. What is an estimate of the difference? 0.6 Explain your reasoning. You round each decimal to the nearest tenth.

11 How is subtracting decimals similar to adding decimals? Like addition, you must align the decimal points and pay attention to place value.

12 Why is it important to pay attention to 0 in the subtraction problem? To subtract 7 thousandths from 0 thousandths, I need to borrow 1 hundredth. That's how I get 3 in the thousandths place when I subtract.

13 How much better was Walter Johnson's ERA than Sandy Koufax's? Find the difference in Model It on the previous page. Explain how you know that your answer is reasonable. It was 0.593 better. My answer is close to the estimate of 0.6.

14 What is a way to check your answer? Check your estimate and then add 0.593 + 2.167; this should equal 2.760.

15 Compare subtracting decimals and subtracting whole numbers. In both operations you may need to regroup to subtract. In subtraction with whole numbers you align the digits on the right in the ones place. With decimal subtraction, you align the digits on the decimal point.

16 Explain how to subtract decimals to the thousandths. Line up the decimal points and subtract as you would subtract whole numbers.

Try It

Use what you just learned to solve these problems.

17 Sandy Koufax has a 0.655 win/loss percentage; Walter Johnson's is 0.599. How much higher is Koufax's win/loss percentage than Johnson's? 0.056

18 Tyrone needs to take 4.5 milliliters of cough syrup but only has 2.745 milliliters. How much more does he need for a full dose? 1.755 milliliters

L9: Add and Subtract Decimals 85

©Curriculum Associates, LLC Copying is not permitted.

TRY IT SOLUTIONS

17 *Solution:* 0.056; Students may use an equation to subtract. They may also use a place-value chart to line up the decimal points and estimation to make sure their answer is reasonable.

18 *Solution:* 1.755 millimeters; Students may use an equation to subtract. They may also use a place-value chart to line up the decimal points and estimation to make sure their answer is reasonable.

ERROR ALERT: Students who wrote 1.845 did not write 0s in the hundredths and thousandths places and borrow. Instead, they brought down the 45 and then subtracted 4.5 − 2.7.

Hands-On Activity

Use base ten blocks to model subtracting decimals.

Materials: base ten blocks

- Write 2.76 − 2.167 on the board.
- Ask students to model 2.76 using base ten blocks.
- Ask students why they cannot just remove 7 thousandths. Have them explain how to regroup by exchanging a hundredths rod for 10 thousandths blocks.
- Once students have regrouped the blocks, have them complete the problem. [0.593]
- Have students use base ten blocks to model other subtraction problems such as 1.45 − 0.98 and 3 − 1.45. [0.47; 1.55]

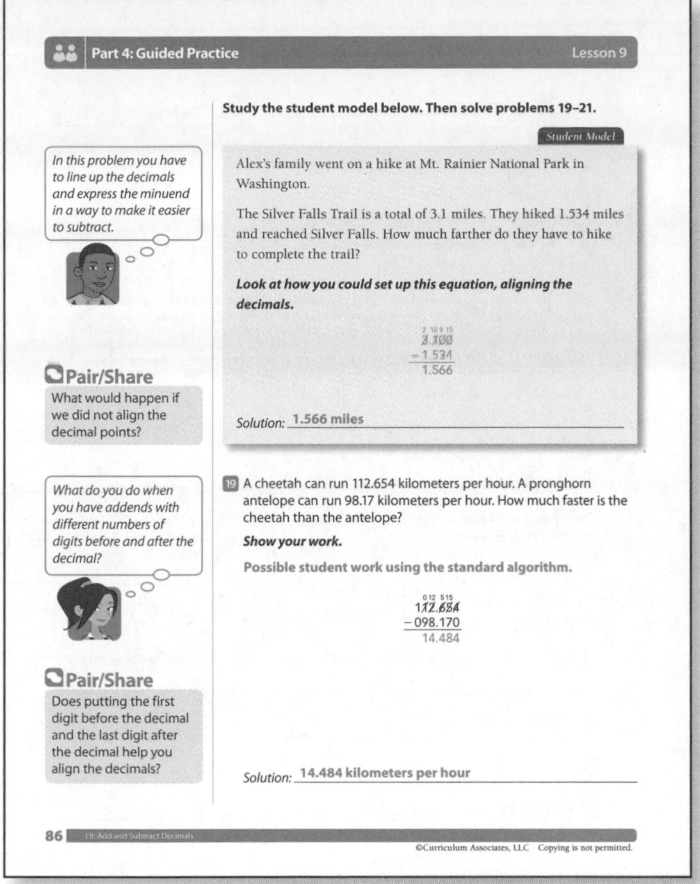

Part 4: Guided Practice Lesson 9

Study the student model below. Then solve problems 19–21.

Student Model

Alex's family went on a hike at Mt. Rainier National Park in Washington.

The Silver Falls Trail is a total of 3.1 miles. They hiked 1.534 miles and reached Silver Falls. How much farther do they have to hike to complete the trail?

Look at how you could set up this equation, aligning the decimals.

$$\begin{array}{r} 3.100 \\ -\,1.534 \\ \hline 1.566 \end{array}$$

Solution: 1.566 miles

In this problem you have to line up the decimals and express the minuend in a way to make it easier to subtract.

Pair/Share
What would happen if we did not align the decimal points?

19 A cheetah can run 112.654 kilometers per hour. A pronghorn antelope can run 98.17 kilometers per hour. How much faster is the cheetah than the antelope?

Show your work.

Possible student work using the standard algorithm.

$$\begin{array}{r} 112.654 \\ -\,098.170 \\ \hline 14.484 \end{array}$$

Solution: 14.484 kilometers per hour

What do you do when you have addends with different numbers of digits before and after the decimal?

Pair/Share
Does putting the first digit before the decimal and the last digit after the decimal help you align the decimals?

86 L9: Add and Subtract Decimals
©Curriculum Associates, LLC Copying is not permitted.

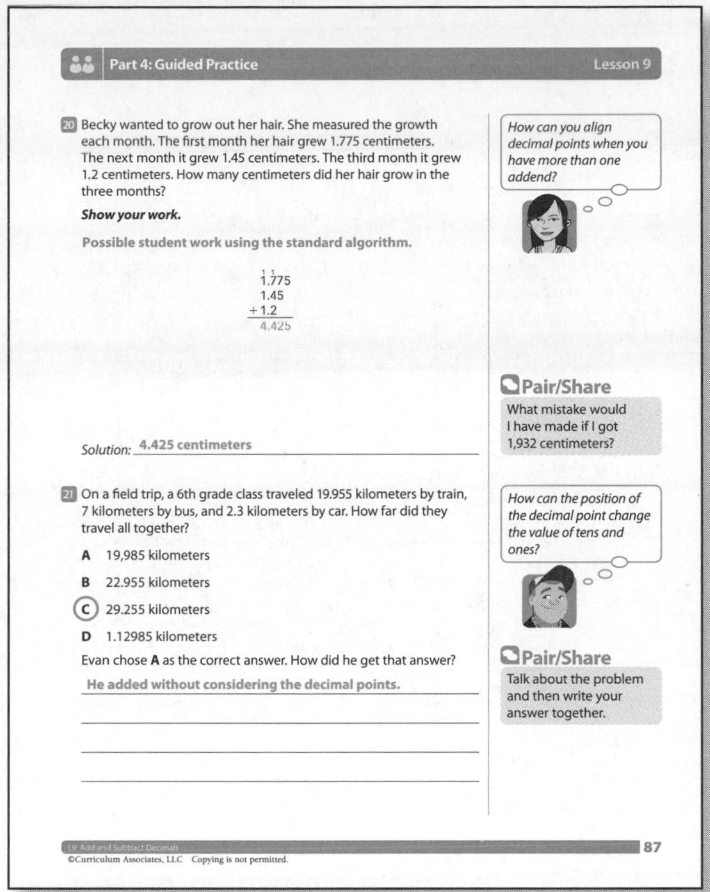

Part 4: Guided Practice Lesson 9

20 Becky wanted to grow out her hair. She measured the growth each month. The first month her hair grew 1.775 centimeters. The next month it grew 1.45 centimeters. The third month it grew 1.2 centimeters. How many centimeters did her hair grow in the three months?

Show your work.

Possible student work using the standard algorithm.

$$\begin{array}{r} 1.775 \\ 1.45 \\ +\,1.2 \\ \hline 4.425 \end{array}$$

Solution: 4.425 centimeters

How can you align decimal points when you have more than one addend?

Pair/Share
What mistake would I have made if I got 1,932 centimeters?

21 On a field trip, a 6th grade class traveled 19.955 kilometers by train, 7 kilometers by bus, and 2.3 kilometers by car. How far did they travel all together?

A 19,985 kilometers
B 22.955 kilometers
Ⓒ 29.255 kilometers
D 1.12985 kilometers

Evan chose **A** as the correct answer. How did he get that answer?

He added without considering the decimal points.

How can the position of the decimal point change the value of tens and ones?

Pair/Share
Talk about the problem and then write your answer together.

L9: Add and Subtract Decimals 87
©Curriculum Associates, LLC Copying is not permitted.

AT A GLANCE

Students use estimation, place-value charts, and equations to add and subtract decimals.

STEP BY STEP

- Ask students to solve the problems individually and show how they found each answer.
- When students have completed each problem, have them Pair/Share to discuss their solutions with a partner or in a group.

SOLUTIONS

Ex An equation with the decimals aligned properly is shown as one way to solve the problem. If students do not understand how to align the decimals, encourage them to use a place-value chart.

19 *Solution:* 14.484 kilometers per hour; Students could solve the problem by using the equation $112.654 - 98.17 = 14.484$. ***(DOK 1)***

20 *Solution:* 4.425 centimeters; Students could solve the problem by using the equation $1.775 + 1.45 + 1.2 = 4.425$. ***(DOK 1)***

21 *Solution:* **C**; Evan incorrectly aligned all the digits after the decimal.

Explain to students why the other two answer choices are not correct:

A is not correct because the numbers should be aligned by the decimal points, not by their right-hand digits.

B is not correct because the 7 is 7 ones, not 7 tenths. ***(DOK 3)***

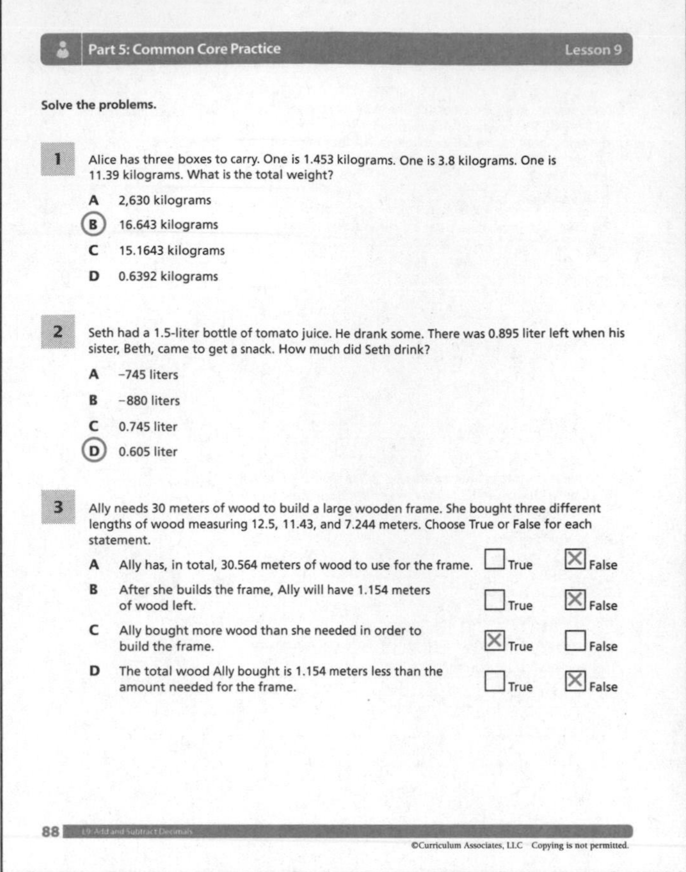

Part 5: Common Core Practice Lesson 9

Solve the problems.

1 Alice has three boxes to carry. One is 1.453 kilograms. One is 3.8 kilograms. One is 11.39 kilograms. What is the total weight?

A 2,630 kilograms

(B) 16.643 kilograms

C 15.1643 kilograms

D 0.6392 kilograms

2 Seth had a 1.5-liter bottle of tomato juice. He drank some. There was 0.895 liter left when his sister, Beth, came to get a snack. How much did Seth drink?

A −745 liters

B −880 liters

C 0.745 liter

(D) 0.605 liter

3 Ally needs 30 meters of wood to build a large wooden frame. She bought three different lengths of wood measuring 12.5, 11.43, and 7.244 meters. Choose True or False for each statement.

		True	False
A	Ally has, in total, 30.564 meters of wood to use for the frame.	☐	☒
B	After she builds the frame, Ally will have 1.154 meters of wood left.	☐	☒
C	Ally bought more wood than she needed in order to build the frame.	☒	☐
D	The total wood Ally bought is 1.154 meters less than the amount needed for the frame.	☐	☒

88 L9: Add and Subtract Decimals

©Curriculum Associates, LLC Copying is not permitted.

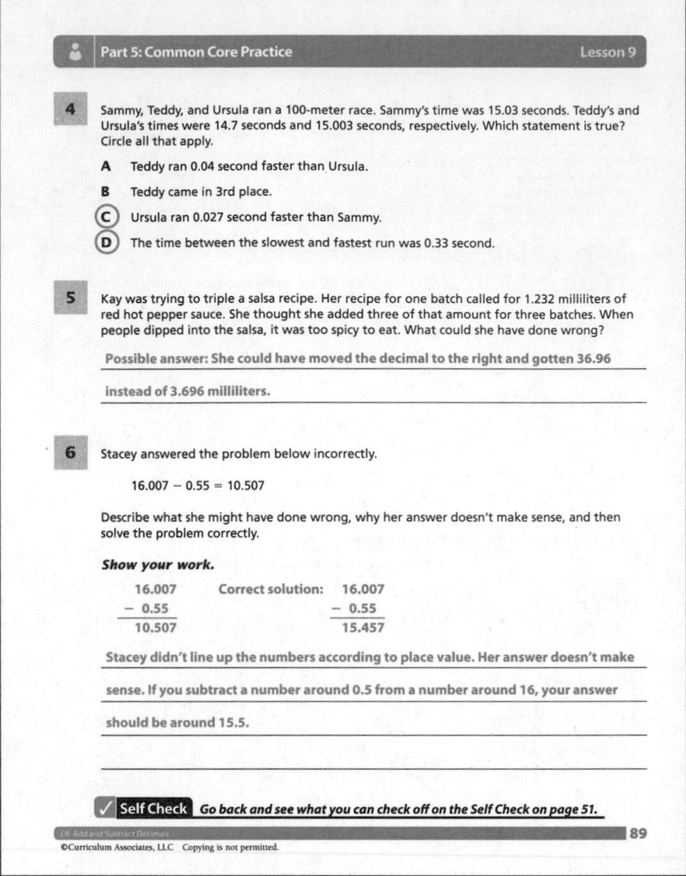

Part 5: Common Core Practice Lesson 9

4 Sammy, Teddy, and Ursula ran a 100-meter race. Sammy's time was 15.03 seconds. Teddy's and Ursula's times were 14.7 seconds and 15.003 seconds, respectively. Which statement is true? Circle all that apply.

A Teddy ran 0.04 second faster than Ursula.

B Teddy came in 3rd place.

(C) Ursula ran 0.027 second faster than Sammy.

(D) The time between the slowest and fastest run was 0.33 second.

5 Kay was trying to triple a salsa recipe. Her recipe for one batch called for 1.232 milliliters of red hot pepper sauce. She thought she added three of that amount for three batches. When people dipped into the salsa, it was too spicy to eat. What could she have done wrong?

Possible answer: She could have moved the decimal to the right and gotten 36.96 instead of 3.696 milliliters.

6 Stacey answered the problem below incorrectly.

16.007 − 0.55 = 10.507

Describe what she might have done wrong, why her answer doesn't make sense, and then solve the problem correctly.

Show your work.

$$\begin{array}{r} 16.007 \\ -\ 0.55 \\ \hline 10.507 \end{array} \qquad \text{Correct solution: } \begin{array}{r} 16.007 \\ -\ 0.55 \\ \hline 15.457 \end{array}$$

Stacey didn't line up the numbers according to place value. Her answer doesn't make sense. If you subtract a number around 0.5 from a number around 16, your answer should be around 15.5.

✓ Self Check *Go back and see what you can check off on the Self Check on page 51.*

L9: Add and Subtract Decimals 89

©Curriculum Associates, LLC Copying is not permitted.

AT A GLANCE

Students add and subtract decimals to solve word problems that might appear on a mathematics test.

SOLUTIONS

1 *Solution:* **B**; Find the sum of the weights by adding 1.453 + 3.8 + 11.39. ***(DOK 1)***

2 *Solution:* **D**; Find the difference in the volumes by subtracting 1.5 − 0.895. ***(DOK 2)***

3 *Solution:* A **False**; B **False**; C **True**; D **False** ***(DOK 2)***

4 *Solution:* **C**; Subtract Sammy's time, 14.7 seconds, from Ursula's time, 15.003 seconds.

D; Compare the times to find the slowest and fastest times. Subtract the slowest time, 14.7 seconds, from the fastest time, 15.03 seconds. ***(DOK 2)***

5 *Solution:* See student book page above for possible student answer. ***(DOK 3)***

6 *Solution:* Correct answer: 15.457; Possible explanation: Stacey incorrectly aligned the decimal points and subtracted 16.007 − 5.5. See student book page above for possible student answer. ***(DOK 3)***

Assessment and Remediation

- Ask students to find the difference of 4 and 1.456. [2.544]
- For students who are struggling, use the chart below to guide remediation.
- After providing remediation, check students' understanding. Ask students to find the difference of 6 and 2.295. [3.705]
- If a student is still having difficulty, use ***Ready Instruction, Level 5,*** Lesson 7.

If the error is . . .	Students may . . .	To remediate . . .
3.456	have brought down the .456 instead of rewriting 4 as 4.000.	Have students write the problem in a place-value chart and use 0s to show 4 as 4.000.
1.452	have set up the problem as 1.456 − 4	Remind students that the 4 is 4 ones, not 4 thousandths. Discuss how to write the 4 with a decimal point and 0s.
Any other answer	have regrouped incorrectly.	Review the process of regrouping when there are multiple 0s in the minuend.

Hands-On Activity

Use base-ten blocks to model subtracting decimals.

Materials: base-ten blocks

- Have students work in pairs using a set of base-ten blocks.
- Display the expression 4.12 − 2.143.
- Have one student model the problem with base-ten blocks and find the difference. [1.977]
- Have the other student model the related addition sentence, 1.977 + 2.143, to show that the subtraction was done correctly.
- Continue the activity with one student in each pair posing and modeling a decimal addition or subtraction problem and the other student checking the result by using a related problem.

Challenge Activity

Find numbers with the least difference and the greatest difference.

Materials: 6 number cubes for each group

- Divide students into groups of 3 or 4. Have one student roll 6 number cubes.
- Have students use the numbers rolled to fill in the digits in the following subtraction problem: ____ . ____ ____ − ____ . ____ ____ . Their goal is to find the least difference possible. Once students have arranged the digits, have them subtract and see who has the least difference.
- Students will then rearrange the digits, trying to get the greatest difference possible. When they have written their problems, have them subtract to see who has the greatest difference.
- Repeat the activity with problems in the form ____ . ____ − ____ . ____ ____ ____ and ____ . ____ ____ ____ − ____ . ____ .

Lesson 10 (Student Book pages 90–101)

Multiply and Divide Decimals

LESSON OBJECTIVES

- Fluently multiply and divide multi-digit decimals using the standard algorithm for each operation.
- Understand the role of place value in the operations of multiplication and division.
- Identify when it is appropriate to use the standard algorithm.
- Use estimation to approximate products and quotients to check for reasonableness of answers.
- Model the operations of multiplication and division with manipulatives, diagrams, and story contexts for multi-digit decimals.

PREREQUISITE SKILLS

- Understand decimal place values.
- Multiply and divide single-digit decimals.
- Model the operations of addition and subtraction with manipulatives, diagrams, and story contexts for single digit decimals.

VOCABULARY

There is no new vocabulary.

THE LEARNING PROGRESSION

In Grade 5, students learned to multiply and divide decimals to the hundredth place. These operations were based on concrete models or drawings, place value, and properties of operations. In Grade 6, students review how to multiply and divide decimals. They learn how to place the decimal point by relating decimal problems to equivalent fraction problems. By the end of this year, students should be fluent in the use of the standard algorithms to multiply and divide decimals. They use multiplication and division of decimals to solve real-world problems. They also use estimation to see if their answers are reasonable.

In later grades, students will multiply and divide decimals as they solve problems from algebra, geometry, and real-world contexts. By being fluent with the algorithms, they will be able to concentrate on the problems and not on the process of multiplying and dividing decimals.

Ready *Teacher Toolbox* Teacher-Toolbox.com

	Prerequisite Skills	*6.NS.B.3*
Ready Lessons	✓	✓
Tools for Instruction		✓
Interactive Tutorials		✓✓

CCSS Focus

6.NS.B.3 Fluently add, subtract, multiply, and divide multi-digit decimals using the standard algorithm for each operation.

STANDARDS FOR MATHEMATICAL PRACTICE: *SMP 2, 3, 6–8* *(see page A9 for full text)*

AT A GLANCE

Students read a word problem involving multiplying decimals and answer a series of questions that lead them to the solution. The questions are designed to have them apply previously learned skills and concepts about fractions and decimals to find the solution.

STEP BY STEP

- Tell students that this page models multiplication of decimals.
- Have students read the problem at the top of the page.
- Work through Explore It as a class.
- When discussing the estimation process, make sure students understand how the numbers 0.1 and 25 were obtained.
- Ask student pairs or groups to explain their answers for rewriting decimals as fractions, multiplying fractions, and rewriting the product as a decimal.
- Compare the product with the estimate.
- Review the concept that multiplication by a number less than one results in a smaller number.

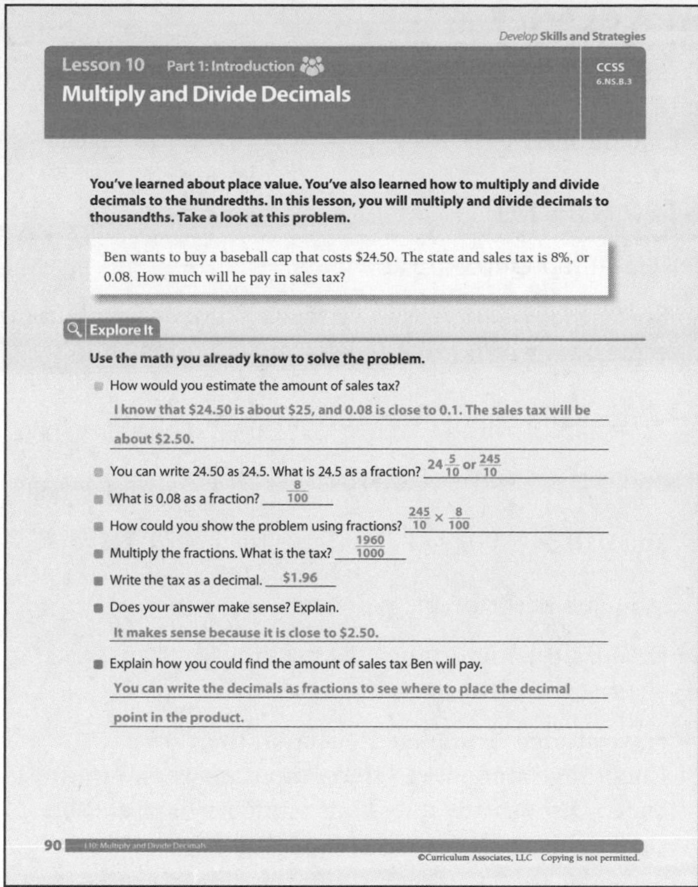

Develop Skills and Strategies

Lesson 10 Part 1: Introduction

Multiply and Divide Decimals

CCSS 6.NS.B.3

You've learned about place value. You've also learned how to multiply and divide decimals to the hundredths. In this lesson, you will multiply and divide decimals to thousandths. Take a look at this problem.

Ben wants to buy a baseball cap that costs $24.50. The state and sales tax is 8%, or 0.08. How much will he pay in sales tax?

Explore It

Use the math you already know to solve the problem.

- How would you estimate the amount of sales tax?
  I know that $24.50 is about $25, and 0.08 is close to 0.1. The sales tax will be about $2.50.
- You can write 24.50 as 24.5. What is 24.5 as a fraction? $24\frac{5}{10}$ or $\frac{245}{10}$
- What is 0.08 as a fraction? $\frac{8}{100}$
- How could you show the problem using fractions? $\frac{245}{10} \times \frac{8}{100}$
- Multiply the fractions. What is the tax? $\frac{1960}{1000}$
- Write the tax as a decimal. $1.96
- Does your answer make sense? Explain.
  It makes sense because it is close to $2.50.
- Explain how you could find the amount of sales tax Ben will pay.
  You can write the decimals as fractions to see where to place the decimal point in the product.

90 L10: Multiply and Divide Decimals ©Curriculum Associates, LLC Copying is not permitted.

Mathematical Discourse

- *When we multiply 24 and 8, the product is greater than 24, but when we multiply 24 and $\frac{8}{10}$, the product is less than 24. Why is that true?*

  Listen for responses that indicate that $\frac{8}{10}$ is less than 1, so the product will be less than 24 multiplied by 1, or 24. Some students may see that 24 can be considered a set, and $\frac{8}{10}$ of a set will be less than the whole set.

- *Can you give a rule, or general statement, about when a product will be less than one of the factors and when it will be more?*

  Responses should include that when one factor is less than 1, the product will be less than the other factor. Some students may reason that if both factors are less than 1, the product will be less than either factor.

AT A GLANCE

Students use their knowledge of fractions to learn to multiply decimals in the same way as they multiply whole numbers.

STEP BY STEP

- Read Find Out More as a class.
- Study the equations shown. Have students explain in their own words what the second equation shows.
- Write pairs of problems such as $\frac{1}{10} \times \frac{1}{1{,}000} = \frac{1}{10{,}000}$ and $0.1 \times 0.001 = 0.0001$ or $\frac{1}{100} \times \frac{1}{1{,}000} = \frac{1}{100{,}000}$ and $0.01 \times 0.001 = 0.00001$ on the board. Have students describe the pattern.
- Discuss the importance of checking your answer against the estimate.
- Have student complete Reflect on their own. Encourage students to share their answers with the class. Discuss any questions students have and be sure to clear up misunderstandings.

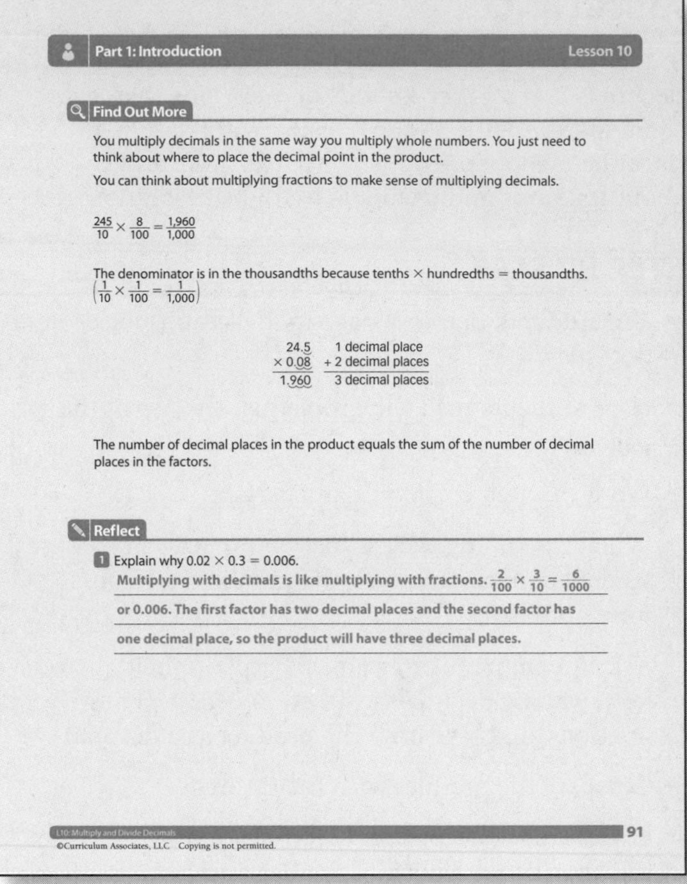

Part 1: Introduction Lesson 10

Find Out More

You multiply decimals in the same way you multiply whole numbers. You just need to think about where to place the decimal point in the product.

You can think about multiplying fractions to make sense of multiplying decimals.

$\frac{245}{10} \times \frac{8}{100} = \frac{1{,}960}{1{,}000}$

The denominator is in the thousandths because tenths × hundredths = thousandths. $\left(\frac{1}{10} \times \frac{1}{100} = \frac{1}{1{,}000}\right)$

24.5	1 decimal place
× 0.08	+ 2 decimal places
1.960	3 decimal places

The number of decimal places in the product equals the sum of the number of decimal places in the factors.

Reflect

1 Explain why $0.02 \times 0.3 = 0.006$.
Multiplying with decimals is like multiplying with fractions. $\frac{2}{100} \times \frac{3}{10} = \frac{6}{1000}$ or 0.006. The first factor has two decimal places and the second factor has one decimal place, so the product will have three decimal places.

L10: Multiply and Divide Decimals 91
©Curriculum Associates, LLC Copying is not permitted.

SMP Tip: Students use repeated reasoning to generalize a rule about placing the decimal point from the series of calculations with fractions and decimals (*SMP 8*). Where appropriate in the lesson, remind students of these calculations and how they can use them to understand where to place the decimal point instead of just applying the rule learned by rote.

Real-World Connection

Have students discuss everyday situations that involve the multiplication of decimals.

Examples: finding the cost of 3.2 ounces of cheese or 4.5 yards of fabric; finding the area of a figure with decimal dimensions

Another way that decimals are used in real life is how gas and electricity usage is billed to customers. Because students might not be familiar with this, you may want to suggest it.

Examples: 12.375 therms at \$1.047 per therm, 171.187 Kwh at \$0.128 per Kwh

AT A GLANCE

Students consider a problem involving multiplication of decimals and explore different ways to solve it, including using fractions and the standard multiplication algorithm.

STEP BY STEP

- Read the problem at the top of the page as a class.
- Have students explain why they would multiply to find the answer.
- Read Estimate It. Have students focus on the rounding process. Ask: *Will the estimate be greater or less than the actual answer? Why?* [It will be greater than because both factors were rounded down.]
- In the first Model It, focus on the fractional value of each decimal place as you study the factors: $3.05 = 3\frac{5}{100}$ and $3.658 = 3\frac{658}{1,000}$. Discuss how to show hundred thousandths in decimal form.
- In the second Model It, study the problem. Point out that when multiplying, it is not necessary to line up the decimal points as it is when adding or subtracting.

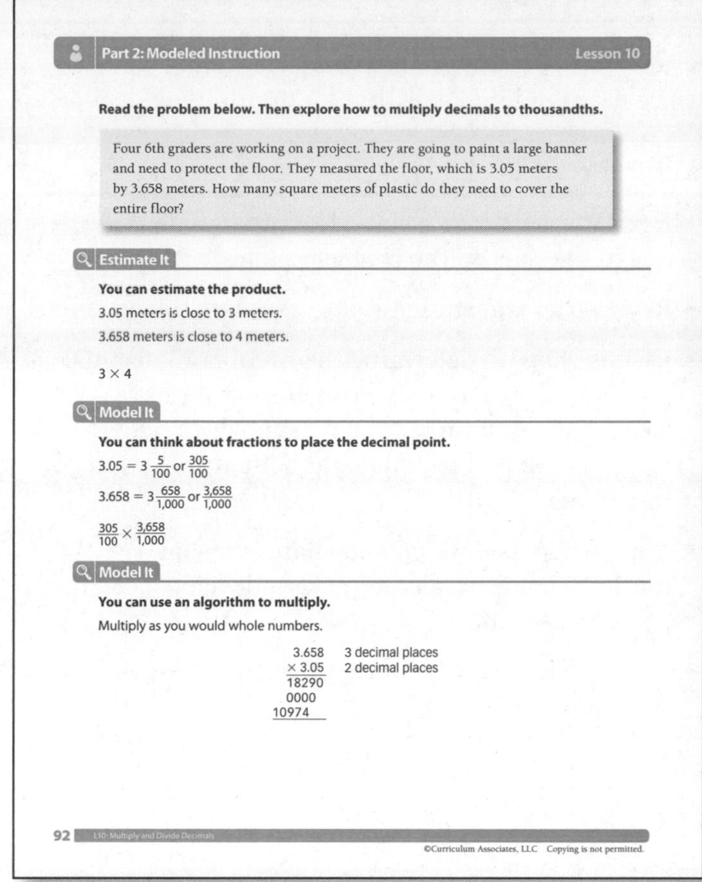

Part 2: Modeled Instruction Lesson 10

Read the problem below. Then explore how to multiply decimals to thousandths.

Four 6th graders are working on a project. They are going to paint a large banner and need to protect the floor. They measured the floor, which is 3.05 meters by 3.658 meters. How many square meters of plastic do they need to cover the entire floor?

Estimate It

You can estimate the product.

3.05 meters is close to 3 meters.

3.658 meters is close to 4 meters.

3×4

Model It

You can think about fractions to place the decimal point.

$3.05 = 3\frac{5}{100}$ or $\frac{305}{100}$

$3.658 = 3\frac{658}{1,000}$ or $\frac{3,658}{1,000}$

$\frac{305}{100} \times \frac{3,658}{1,000}$

Model It

You can use an algorithm to multiply.

Multiply as you would whole numbers.

```
   3.658   3 decimal places
 × 3.05    2 decimal places
  18290
  0000
 10974
```

92 L10: Multiply and Divide Decimals

©Curriculum Associates, LLC Copying is not permitted.

Visual Model

Use an area model to estimate a product.

- Lightly draw a 4 by 4 grid on the board. Ask: *How can you approximate a rectangle that is 3.05 units wide?* [Just a tiny bit past the 3.] Draw a horizontal line to approximate a width of 3.05.
- Ask: *How can you approximate a rectangle that is 3.658 units long?* $\left[\text{A little more than } 3\frac{1}{2}.\right]$ Draw a vertical line to approximate a length of 3.658.
- Outline the rectangle that is approximately 3.05 units × 3.658 units. Count the 9 full squares. Count the 3 approximate half squares.
- Have students find an approximate total. $\left[10\frac{1}{2}\right]$ Ask if the actual total is slightly more or less than $10\frac{1}{2}$.

Mathematical Discourse

- *Do you think the commutative property of multiplication holds true with decimals? Use examples to demonstrate your answer.*

  Responses may show that students understand that the properties of operations apply to all types of numbers—fractions, decimals, and negative numbers as well as whole numbers. Other students may not be sure.

  If students need more structure to use examples, have half of the students multiply 1.2×1.5 and the other half multiply 1.5×1.2. Have them compare answers.

  Point out that showing one example helps us understand another person's thinking, but it is not enough to prove that the generalization applies to all numbers.

AT A GLANCE

Students revisit the problem on page 92 and solve it using the standard algorithm for multiplying decimals.

STEP BY STEP

- Read Connect It as a class. Be sure to note that the questions refer to the problem on page 92.
- Review the reasoning used to estimate the product.
- Discuss how to determine the number of decimal places in the product. If students do not have a clear understanding of the reason why, relate the multiplication of decimals to the multiplication of fractions.
- Have students develop and share rules for multiplying decimals. As a class, develop a clear and concise rule.
- Have students do Try It on their own. Discuss their solutions.

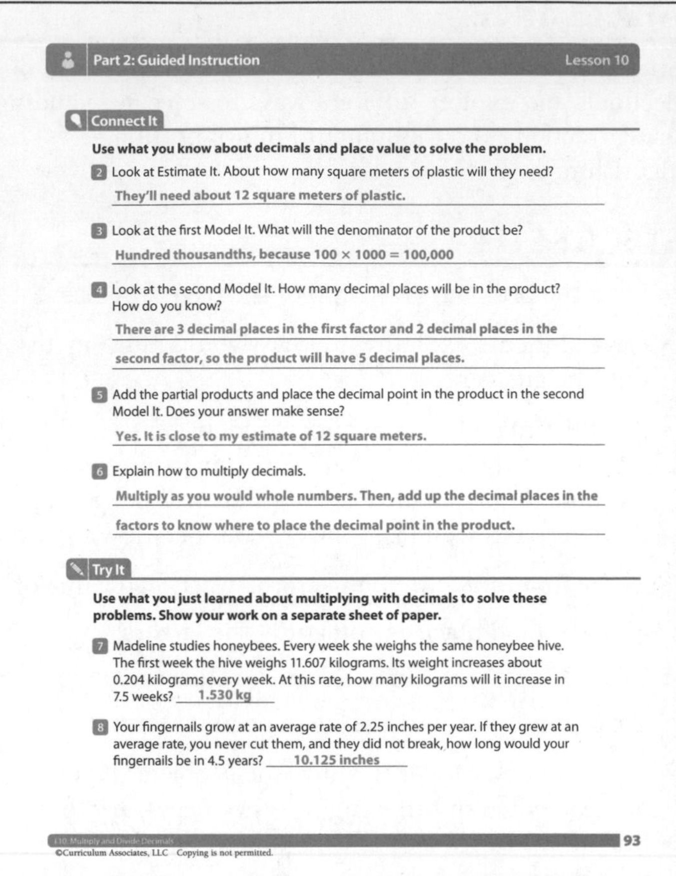

Part 2: Guided Instruction Lesson 10

Connect It

Use what you know about decimals and place value to solve the problem.

2 Look at Estimate It. About how many square meters of plastic will they need?

They'll need about 12 square meters of plastic.

3 Look at the first Model It. What will the denominator of the product be?

Hundred thousandths, because 100 × 1000 = 100,000

4 Look at the second Model It. How many decimal places will be in the product? How do you know?

There are 3 decimal places in the first factor and 2 decimal places in the second factor, so the product will have 5 decimal places.

5 Add the partial products and place the decimal point in the product in the second Model It. Does your answer make sense?

Yes. It is close to my estimate of 12 square meters.

6 Explain how to multiply decimals.

Multiply as you would whole numbers. Then, add up the decimal places in the factors to know where to place the decimal point in the product.

Try It

Use what you just learned about multiplying with decimals to solve these problems. Show your work on a separate sheet of paper.

7 Madeline studies honeybees. Every week she weighs the same honeybee hive. The first week the hive weighs 11.607 kilograms. Its weight increases about 0.204 kilograms every week. At this rate, how many kilograms will it increase in 7.5 weeks? **1.530 kg**

8 Your fingernails grow at an average rate of 2.25 inches per year. If they grew at an average rate, you never cut them, and they did not break, how long would your fingernails be in 4.5 years? **10.125 inches**

L10: Multiply and Divide Decimals 93

©Curriculum Associates, LLC Copying is not permitted.

Hands-On Activity

Use concrete objects to count decimal places.

Materials: paper clips

- Give each student 6 paper clips.
- Write a problem such as 1.23 × 4.3 = 5289 [5.289] on the board. Have students copy it in large numerals on a sheet of paper.
- Direct students to place a paper clip over each digit to the right of the decimal in the problem. Ask, *How many clips did you use?* [3]
- Have the students move the paper clips over the three right-hand digits in the product. Have them place the decimal point to the left of the paper clips.
- Have students estimate to show that the product 5.289 is reasonable.
- Repeat with other problems such as 2.064 × 0.182 = 375648 [0.375648] and 1.62 × 0.844 = 136728 [1.36728].

TRY IT SOLUTIONS

7 *Solution:* 1.530 kg. Students may use the standard algorithm to multiply 0.204 × 7.5.

ERROR ALERT: Students who wrote 13.137 found the total weight of the hive instead of the amount of increase.

8 *Solution:* 10.125 inches. Students may use the standard algorithm to multiply 2.25 × 4.5.

AT A GLANCE

Students consider a problem involving the division of decimals and explore different ways to solve it, including using equivalent fractions and the standard division algorithm.

STEP BY STEP

- Read the problem at the top of the page as a class.
- Read Estimate It and reinforce the importance of estimating the quotient before actually dividing. An estimate will help you see whether you have placed the decimal point in the right place in your quotient.
- After reading the first Model It, write $\frac{28.5}{0.75}$ and $\frac{2850}{75}$. Ask students which would be simplest to divide. Then have a volunteer explain why they are equivalent problems.
- When reading the second Model It, ask why moving the decimal point two places to the right is the same as multiplying by 100. Relate the process to writing an equivalent fraction, as in the previous model.

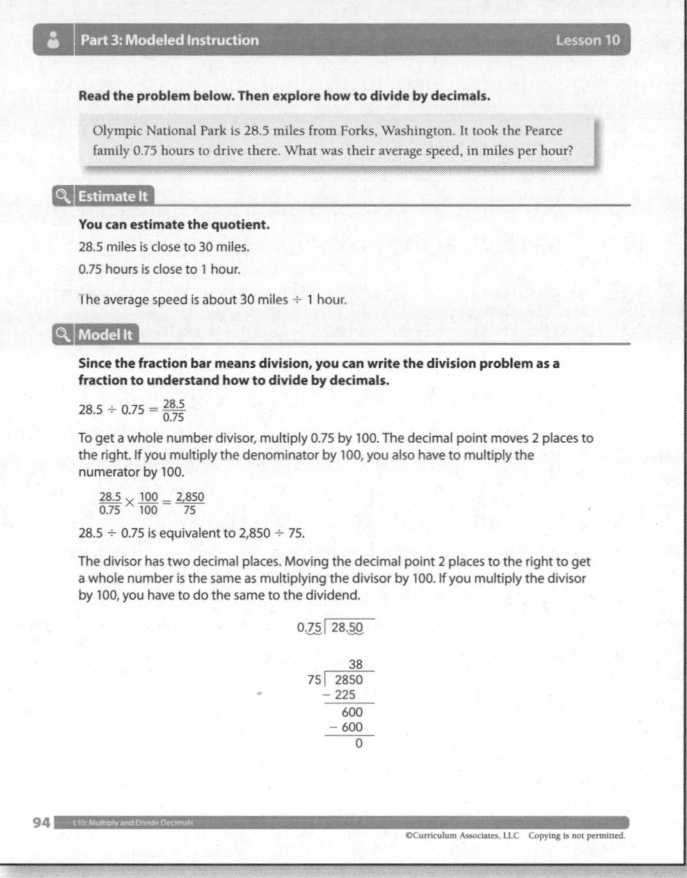

Part 3: Modeled Instruction Lesson 10

Read the problem below. Then explore how to divide by decimals.

Olympic National Park is 28.5 miles from Forks, Washington. It took the Pearce family 0.75 hours to drive there. What was their average speed, in miles per hour?

Estimate It

You can estimate the quotient.

28.5 miles is close to 30 miles.

0.75 hours is close to 1 hour.

The average speed is about 30 miles ÷ 1 hour.

Model It

Since the fraction bar means division, you can write the division problem as a fraction to understand how to divide by decimals.

$28.5 \div 0.75 = \frac{28.5}{0.75}$

To get a whole number divisor, multiply 0.75 by 100. The decimal point moves 2 places to the right. If you multiply the denominator by 100, you also have to multiply the numerator by 100.

$\frac{28.5}{0.75} \times \frac{100}{100} = \frac{2{,}850}{75}$

28.5 ÷ 0.75 is equivalent to 2,850 ÷ 75.

The divisor has two decimal places. Moving the decimal point 2 places to the right to get a whole number is the same as multiplying the divisor by 100. If you multiply the divisor by 100, you have to do the same to the dividend.

$0.75\overline{)28.50}$

$$\begin{array}{r} 38 \\ 75\overline{)2850} \\ -\,225 \\ \hline 600 \\ -\,600 \\ \hline 0 \end{array}$$

94 L10: Multiply and Divide Decimals ©Curriculum Associates, LLC Copying is not permitted.

ELL Support

- Write *left* and *right* on the board. Tell students the words can indicate directions. Illustrate this by drawing an arrow under each word. (Note that *left* can also mean *went* and right can also mean *correct*, but in this lesson the words will indicate directions.)
- Reinforce the words by asking students to follow directions such as: *Raise your right hand, turn your head to the left*, and *tap your right foot 3 times*.
- Write a decimal such as 4,390.1245 on the board. Ask students to move the decimal point 3 places to the right. Have a volunteer show it on the board.
- Repeat with other instructions for moving the point such as: *Move the decimal point 2 places to the left* and *Move the decimal point 4 places to the right.*

Mathematical Discourse

- *Can you explain in your own words how you can use equivalent fractions to help you divide 28.5 by 0.75?*

  Responses will include that 28.5 divided by 0.75 can be written as a fraction, and you can multiply 28.5 and 0.75 by 100 to get 2,850 and 75. Then you can divide 2850 by 75. It is easier to divide with whole numbers than it is with decimals.

- *Why does it make sense that the quotient stays the same when you multiply both the dividend and divisor by 100?*

  Students should explain that the dividend can be written as a numerator and the divisor as a denominator of a fraction. Multiplying the numerator and denominator by the same number produces an equivalent fraction.

AT A GLANCE

Students revisit the problem on page 94 and solve it using the standard algorithm for dividing decimals.

STEP BY STEP

- Read Connect It as a class. Be sure to note that the questions refer to the problem on page 94.
- As you discuss the process of moving the decimal points to divide, stress the concepts that make the moves possible. Write examples such as 16.5 ÷ 3.3, 1.65 ÷ 0.11, and 0.165 ÷ 0.003 on the board. Have volunteers explain how to move the decimals in their own words.
- Discuss the answer in relation to both the number of miles traveled and to the estimate. Have students explain why both make sense.

SMP Tip: Have students work individually to write a set of instructions for dividing decimals. Have students share them with the class. Help the class develop a clear and concise set of instructions they agree upon. Write the instructions on the board or on a poster. As students work together to develop a consensus about a set of instructions for the division of decimals, they must construct viable arguments and critique the reasoning of others (*SMP 3*).

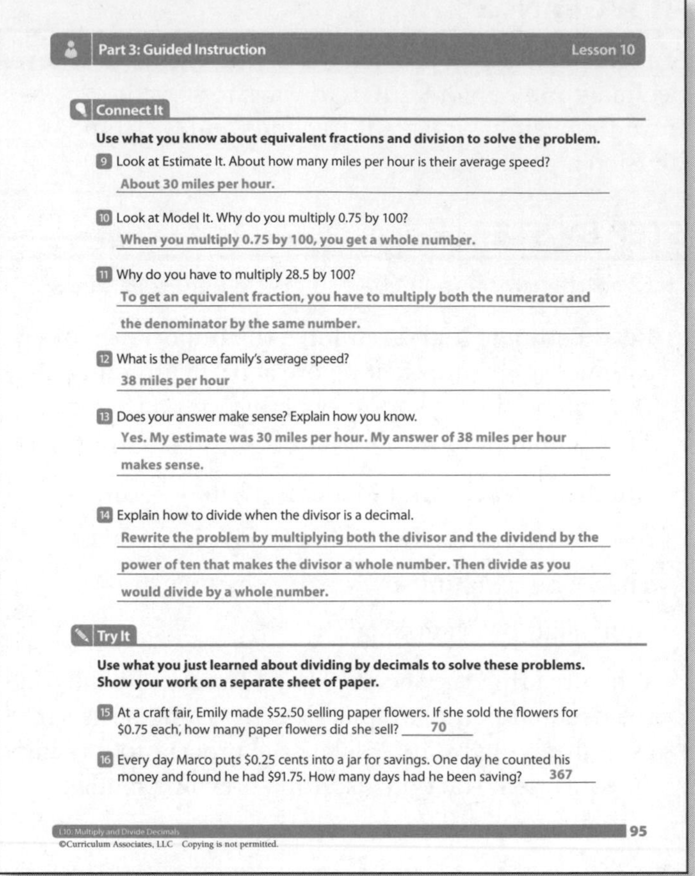
Part 3: Guided Instruction Lesson 10

Connect It

Use what you know about equivalent fractions and division to solve the problem.

9 Look at Estimate It. About how many miles per hour is their average speed?
About 30 miles per hour.

10 Look at Model It. Why do you multiply 0.75 by 100?
When you multiply 0.75 by 100, you get a whole number.

11 Why do you have to multiply 28.5 by 100?
To get an equivalent fraction, you have to multiply both the numerator and the denominator by the same number.

12 What is the Pearce family's average speed?
38 miles per hour

13 Does your answer make sense? Explain how you know.
Yes. My estimate was 30 miles per hour. My answer of 38 miles per hour makes sense.

14 Explain how to divide when the divisor is a decimal.
Rewrite the problem by multiplying both the divisor and the dividend by the power of ten that makes the divisor a whole number. Then divide as you would divide by a whole number.

Try It

Use what you just learned about dividing by decimals to solve these problems. Show your work on a separate sheet of paper.

15 At a craft fair, Emily made $52.50 selling paper flowers. If she sold the flowers for $0.75 each, how many paper flowers did she sell? **70**

16 Every day Marco puts $0.25 cents into a jar for savings. One day he counted his money and found he had $91.75. How many days had he been saving? **367**

L10: Multiply and Divide Decimals 95
©Curriculum Associates, LLC Copying is not permitted.

TRY IT SOLUTIONS

15 *Solution:* 70. Students may use the standard algorithm to divide $52.50 ÷ 0.75.

ERROR ALERT: Students who wrote 7 or 700 moved the decimal point the wrong number of places.

16 *Solution:* 367. Students may have used the standard algorithm to divide $91.75 ÷ 0.25.

AT A GLANCE

Students explore different ways to model a problem involving the division of decimals when the quotient is not a whole number.

STEP BY STEP

- Read the problem at the top of the page as a class.
- Review the estimation process as you read Estimate It. Discuss why the answer will be a little less than 1,000 instead of a little more.
- After reading the first Model It, ask: *Why would you multiply the fraction by* $\frac{10}{10}$ *and get* $\frac{30202.2}{34}$? [If the denominator were a whole number, you would be dividing by a whole number.]
- Ask students to explain the process described in the second Model It in their own words. Discuss why multiplying by powers of 10 can be done by moving the decimal point.

SMP Tip: Encourage students to explain why moving the decimal point in both the divisor and dividend by the same number of places is the same as multiplying the numerator and denominator of a fraction by the same power of 10. Students reason abstractly and quantitatively (*SMP 2*) as they make connections such as these.

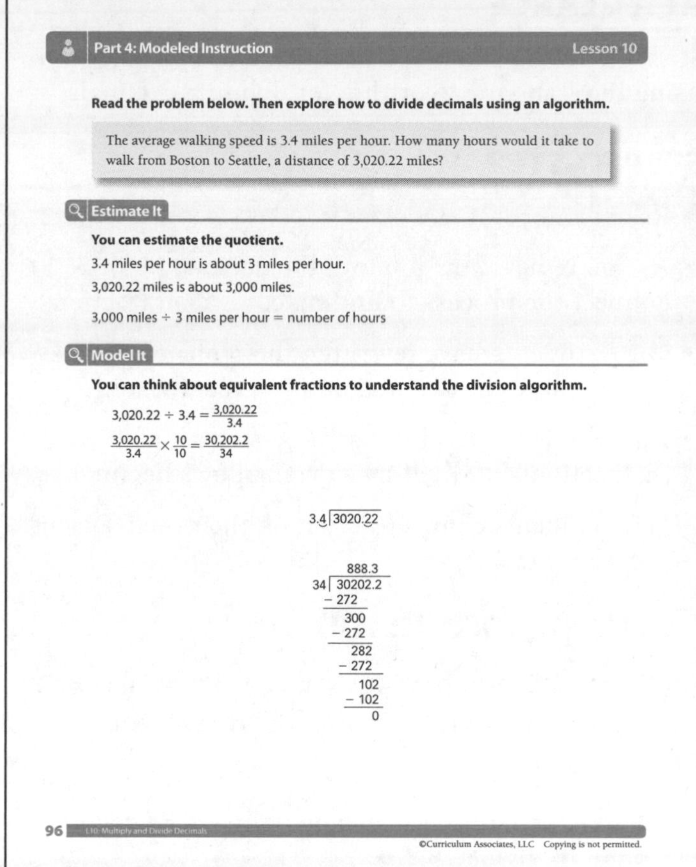

Part 4: Modeled Instruction
Lesson 10
Read the problem below. Then explore how to divide decimals using an algorithm.
The average walking speed is 3.4 miles per hour. How many hours would it take to walk from Boston to Seattle, a distance of 3,020.22 miles?
Estimate It
You can estimate the quotient.
3.4 miles per hour is about 3 miles per hour.
3,020.22 miles is about 3,000 miles.
3,000 miles ÷ 3 miles per hour = number of hours
Model It
You can think about equivalent fractions to understand the division algorithm.
3,020.22 ÷ 3.4 = 3,020.22/3.4
3,020.22/3.4 × 10/10 = 30,202.2/34
3.4⟌3020.22
888.3
34⟌30202.2
− 272
300
− 272
282
− 272
102
− 102
0
96
L10: Multiply and Divide Decimals
©Curriculum Associates, LLC Copying is not permitted.

Mathematical Discourse

- *Suppose you want to solve the problem on this page without using decimals. How would you do it? Why would it work?*

  Students should respond that they would multiply both 3.4 and 3020.22 by 100 to get 340 and 302,022. Then they would divide as with whole numbers. This would work because both factors are multiplied by the same number (power of 10) to get the equivalent fraction $\frac{302{,}022}{340}$.
- *Would the quotient be the same as if you multiplied both 3.4 and 3020.22 by 10? Why?*

  Yes, because the problem is still equivalent.
- *Which would be easier for you to divide:* $34\overline{)30{,}202.2}$ *or* $340\overline{)302{,}022}$? *Explain.*

  Students' preferences will vary.

AT A GLANCE

Students revisit the problem on page 96 and solve it using the standard algorithm for dividing decimals.

STEP BY STEP

- Read Connect It as a class.
- As you review how to move the decimal points, connect the process to finding equivalent fractions.
- Once students have rewritten the problem, discuss how to place the decimal point in the divisor.
- Have students develop a step-by-step set of instructions for dividing a decimal by a decimal.
- Have students complete Try It on their own. Discuss their answers.

Concept Extension

Extend the rule for moving the decimal point when there are not enough places in the dividend.

- Have students describe how to move the decimal point to divide 18.3 ÷ 6.1.
- Present the problem 18.3 ÷ 0.61. Ask how they could move the decimal point in 18.3 twice if there is only one place.
- Show that $\frac{18.3}{0.61} \times \frac{100}{100} = \frac{1830}{61}$. Then write 18.3 ÷ 0.61 is equivalent to 1830 ÷ 61. Have students note the 0 in 1830.
- Discuss a rule for moving the point when there are not enough places in the dividend.
- Repeat the discussion with 183 ÷ 0.61, relating the problem to the equivalent fractions $\frac{183}{0.61} = \frac{18300}{61}$.
- Help students formulate a rule for dividing a whole number by a decimal. It could be something such as: *Write a point and zeros to the right of the whole number and then move the points the needed number of places to have a whole number for the divisor.*

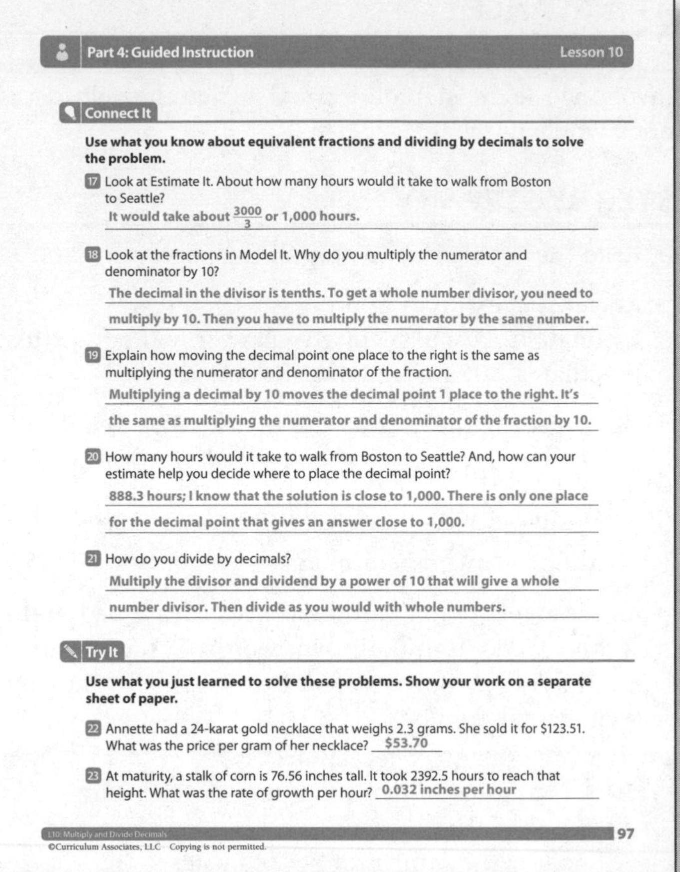
Part 4: Guided Instruction Lesson 10

Connect It

Use what you know about equivalent fractions and dividing by decimals to solve the problem.

17 Look at Estimate It. About how many hours would it take to walk from Boston to Seattle?
It would take about $\frac{3000}{3}$ or 1,000 hours.

18 Look at the fractions in Model It. Why do you multiply the numerator and denominator by 10?
The decimal in the divisor is tenths. To get a whole number divisor, you need to multiply by 10. Then you have to multiply the numerator by the same number.

19 Explain how moving the decimal point one place to the right is the same as multiplying the numerator and denominator of the fraction.
Multiplying a decimal by 10 moves the decimal point 1 place to the right. It's the same as multiplying the numerator and denominator of the fraction by 10.

20 How many hours would it take to walk from Boston to Seattle? And, how can your estimate help you decide where to place the decimal point?
888.3 hours; I know that the solution is close to 1,000. There is only one place for the decimal point that gives an answer close to 1,000.

21 How do you divide by decimals?
Multiply the divisor and dividend by a power of 10 that will give a whole number divisor. Then divide as you would with whole numbers.

Try It

Use what you just learned to solve these problems. Show your work on a separate sheet of paper.

22 Annette had a 24-karat gold necklace that weighs 2.3 grams. She sold it for $123.51. What was the price per gram of her necklace? **$53.70**

23 At maturity, a stalk of corn is 76.56 inches tall. It took 2392.5 hours to reach that height. What was the rate of growth per hour? **0.032 inches per hour**

L10: Multiply and Divide Decimals 97
©Curriculum Associates, LLC Copying is not permitted.

TRY IT SOLUTIONS

22 *Solution:* $53.70. Students may use the standard algorithm to divide $123.51 ÷ 2.3.

ERROR ALERT: Students who wrote $5.37 moved the decimal point in the divisor 1 place to the right but did not move the point in the dividend.

23 *Solution:* 0.032 inches per hour. Student may use the standard algorithm to divide 76.56 ÷ 2392.5.

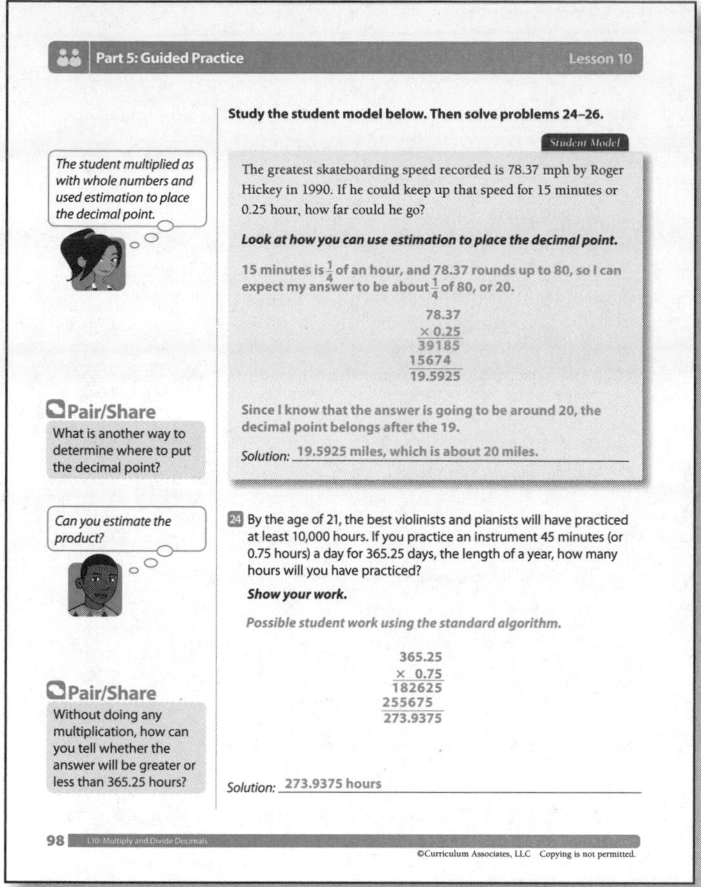

Part 5: Guided Practice Lesson 10

Study the student model below. Then solve problems 24–26.

Student Model

The greatest skateboarding speed recorded is 78.37 mph by Roger Hickey in 1990. If he could keep up that speed for 15 minutes or 0.25 hour, how far could he go?

Look at how you can use estimation to place the decimal point.

15 minutes is $\frac{1}{4}$ of an hour, and 78.37 rounds up to 80, so I can expect my answer to be about $\frac{1}{4}$ of 80, or 20.

$$\begin{array}{r} 78.37 \\ \times\ 0.25 \\ \hline 39185 \\ 15674 \\ \hline 19.5925 \end{array}$$

Since I know that the answer is going to be around 20, the decimal point belongs after the 19.

Solution: 19.5925 miles, which is about 20 miles.

Pair/Share What is another way to determine where to put the decimal point?

24 By the age of 21, the best violinists and pianists will have practiced at least 10,000 hours. If you practice an instrument 45 minutes (or 0.75 hours) a day for 365.25 days, the length of a year, how many hours will you have practiced?

Show your work.

Possible student work using the standard algorithm.

$$\begin{array}{r} 365.25 \\ \times\ 0.75 \\ \hline 182625 \\ 255675 \\ \hline 273.9375 \end{array}$$

Solution: 273.9375 hours

Pair/Share Without doing any multiplication, how can you tell whether the answer will be greater or less than 365.25 hours?

98 L10: Multiply and Divide Decimals ©Curriculum Associates, LLC Copying is not permitted.

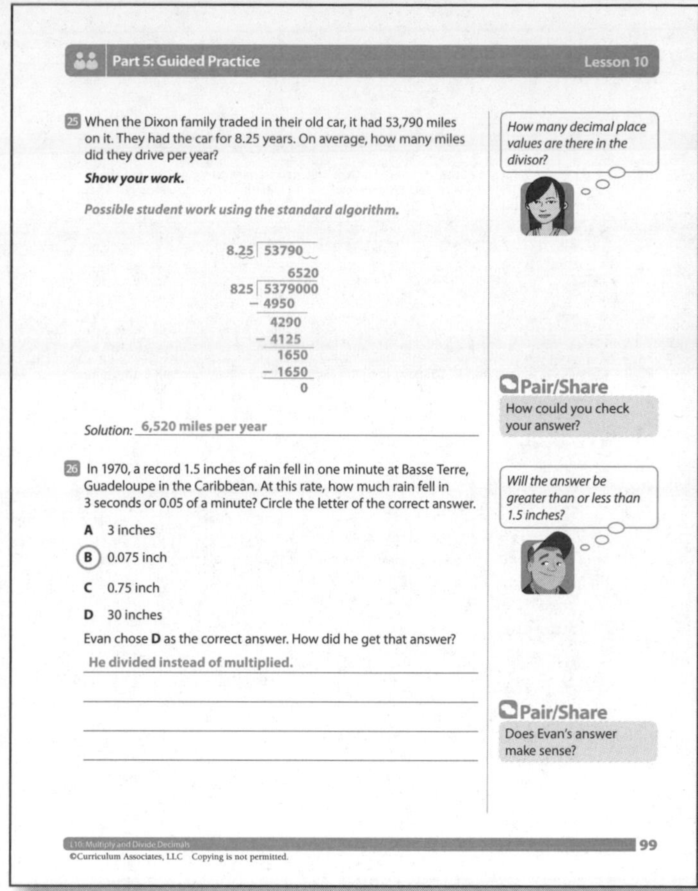

Part 5: Guided Practice Lesson 10

25 When the Dixon family traded in their old car, it had 53,790 miles on it. They had the car for 8.25 years. On average, how many miles did they drive per year?

Show your work.

Possible student work using the standard algorithm.

$$\begin{array}{r} 6520 \\ 825 \overline{)\,5379000} \\ -\,4950 \\ \hline 4290 \\ -\,4125 \\ \hline 1650 \\ -\,1650 \\ \hline 0 \end{array}$$

Solution: 6,520 miles per year

Pair/Share How could you check your answer?

26 In 1970, a record 1.5 inches of rain fell in one minute at Basse Terre, Guadeloupe in the Caribbean. At this rate, how much rain fell in 3 seconds or 0.05 of a minute? Circle the letter of the correct answer.

A 3 inches

(B) 0.075 inch

C 0.75 inch

D 30 inches

Evan chose **D** as the correct answer. How did he get that answer?

He divided instead of multiplied.

Pair/Share Does Evan's answer make sense?

L10: Multiply and Divide Decimals ©Curriculum Associates, LLC Copying is not permitted. 99

AT A GLANCE

Students use estimation and the standard algorithms to solve word problems involving multiplying and dividing decimals.

STEP BY STEP

- Ask students to solve the problems individually and show their work.
- When students have completed each problem, have them Pair/Share to discuss their solutions with a partner or in a group.

SOLUTIONS

Ex First, an estimate of the answer is given. Then, a solution using the standard algorithm is shown.

24 *Solution:* 273.9375 hours. Students could solve the problem using the standard algorithm to multiply 0.75 hours × 365.25 days. They could check the answer using estimation. ***(DOK 1)***

25 *Solution:* 6,520 miles per year. Students could solve the problem using the standard algorithm to divide 53,790 ÷ 8.25. They could check the answer using estimation. ***(DOK 1)***

26 *Solution:* **B;** Evan divided instead of multiplied to find the answer.

Explain to students why the other two answer choices are not correct:

A is not correct because 1.5 was divided by 0.5 instead of multiplied by 0.05.

C is not correct because the decimal point was not placed correctly. ***(DOK 3)***

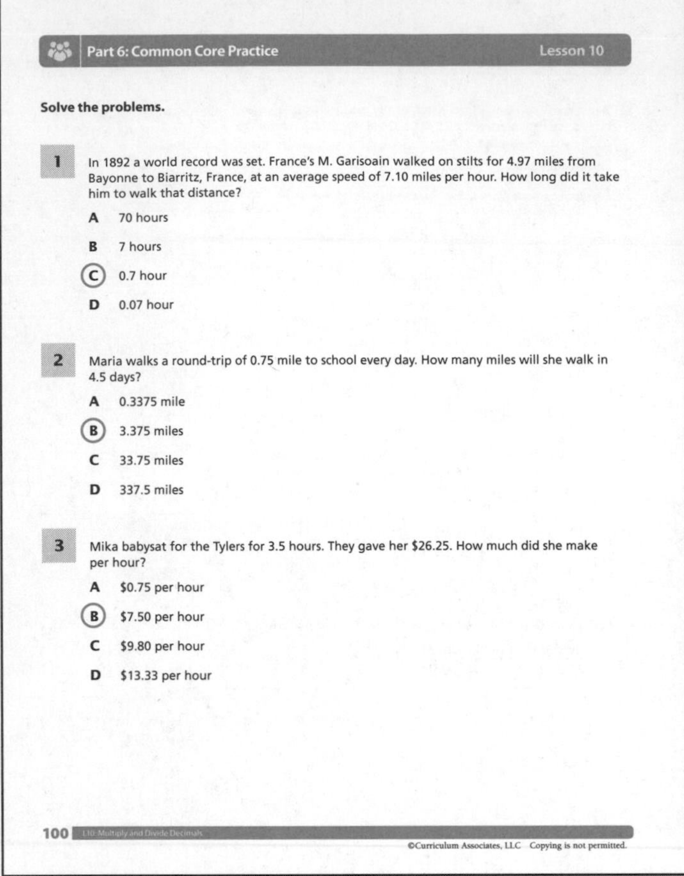

Part 6: Common Core Practice Lesson 10

Solve the problems.

1 In 1892 a world record was set. France's M. Garisoain walked on stilts for 4.97 miles from Bayonne to Biarritz, France, at an average speed of 7.10 miles per hour. How long did it take him to walk that distance?

A 70 hours

B 7 hours

(C) 0.7 hour

D 0.07 hour

2 Maria walks a round-trip of 0.75 mile to school every day. How many miles will she walk in 4.5 days?

A 0.3375 mile

(B) 3.375 miles

C 33.75 miles

D 337.5 miles

3 Mika babysat for the Tylers for 3.5 hours. They gave her $26.25. How much did she make per hour?

A $0.75 per hour

(B) $7.50 per hour

C $9.80 per hour

D $13.33 per hour

100 L10: Multiply and Divide Decimals

©Curriculum Associates, LLC Copying is not permitted.

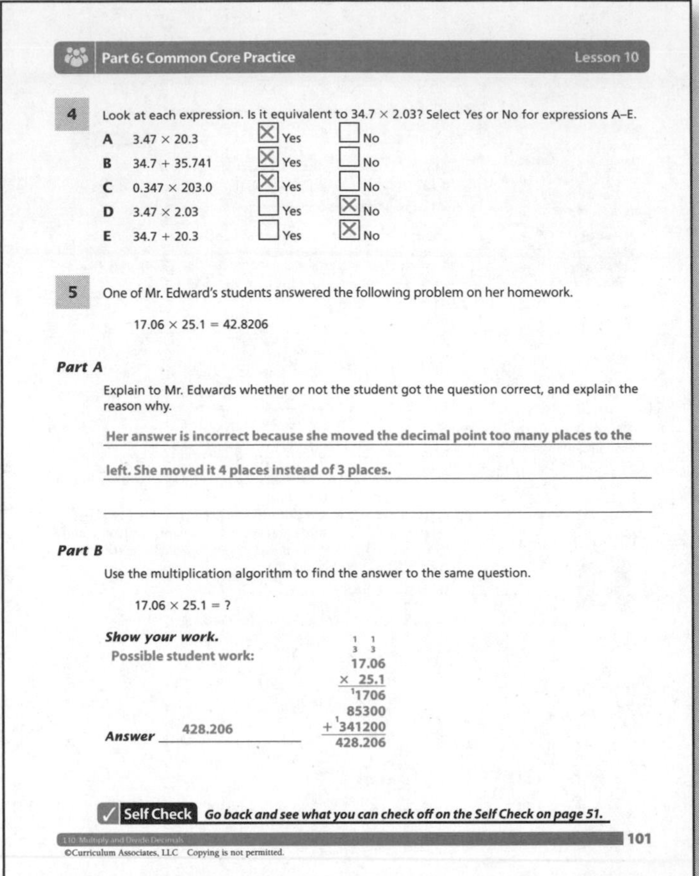

Part 6: Common Core Practice Lesson 10

4 Look at each expression. Is it equivalent to 34.7 × 2.03? Select Yes or No for expressions A–E.

A	3.47 × 20.3	☒ Yes	☐ No
B	34.7 + 35.741	☒ Yes	☐ No
C	0.347 × 203.0	☒ Yes	☐ No
D	3.47 × 2.03	☐ Yes	☒ No
E	34.7 + 20.3	☐ Yes	☒ No

5 One of Mr. Edward's students answered the following problem on her homework.

17.06 × 25.1 = 42.8206

Part A

Explain to Mr. Edwards whether or not the student got the question correct, and explain the reason why.

Her answer is incorrect because she moved the decimal point too many places to the left. She moved it 4 places instead of 3 places.

Part B

Use the multiplication algorithm to find the answer to the same question.

17.06 × 25.1 = ?

Show your work.

Possible student work:

```
    17.06
  ×  25.1
     1706
    85300
 + 341200
  428.206
```

Answer 428.206

✓ Self Check *Go back and see what you can check off on the Self Check on page 51.*

L10: Multiply and Divide Decimals 101

©Curriculum Associates, LLC Copying is not permitted.

AT A GLANCE

Students multiply and divide decimals to solve problems that might appear on a mathematics test.

SOLUTIONS

1 *Solution:* **C;** Divide the distance walked, 4.97 miles, by the average speed, 7.10 miles per hour. ***(DOK 2)***

2 *Solution:* **B;** Multiply the distance walked, 0.75 miles, by the time she will walk, 4.5 days. ***(DOK 2)***

3 *Solution:* **B;** Divide the amount made, $26.25, by the time worked, 3.5 hours. ***(DOK 1)***

4 *Solution:* A **Yes**; B **Yes**; C **Yes**; D **No**; E **No** ***(DOK 2)***

5 *Part A Solution:* See student book page above for possible explanation.

Part B Solution: 428.206; See student book page above for possible student work. ***(DOK 3)***

Assessment and Remediation

- Ask students to estimate and then divide 18.08 ÷ 1.6. [18 ÷ 2 = 9, so the quotient should be about 9; 11.3]
- For students who are struggling, use the chart below to guide remediation.
- After providing remediation, check students' understanding. Ask students to divide 3.886 ÷ 1.34. [2.9]
- If a student is still having difficulty, use ***Ready Instruction, Level 5,*** Lessons 8 and 9.

If the error is . . .	Students may . . .	To remediate . . .
1.13	not have moved the decimal point in the divisor or dividend.	Ask students to compare the quotient to the estimate to see whether the quotient is reasonable. Have students write out all the steps of the division process: write the division expression as a fraction; multiply numerator and denominator by the same power of 10 to get a whole number divisor; divide. Explain that moving the decimal point is a shortcut for the process and that they have to move the decimal point the same number of places in both the divisor and dividend.
113	have ignored the decimal point.	Ask students to compare the quotient to the estimate to see whether the quotient is reasonable. Remind students that the decimal point is important and then have them write out the division process as described above.
any other answer	have divided incorrectly.	Have students go over each step of the division problem to see if they made a computational mistake.

Hands-On Activity

Move the decimal point to make a whole number divisor.

Materials: paper clips

- Give each student 2 paper clips.
- Display the problem $0.12\overline{)3.732}$ with 311 written above. Have students copy it in large numerals on a piece of paper.
- Have students place a paper clip on each point. Have them move the clip to the right of the 0.12. Have them move the other clip the same number of places in the dividend. Have them put the point in the quotient above the second paper clip.
- Have students repeat the activity with other division problems: $0.61\overline{)1.159}$ (19 above), $5.5\overline{)15.455}$ (281 above), $4.56\overline{)15.048}$ (33 above), and $0.09\overline{)0.108}$ (12 above). [1.9, 2.81, 3.3, 1.2]

Challenge Activity

Convert fractions to decimals using division.

- Remind students that the fraction bar indicates division.
- Show how to find the decimal equivalent to $\frac{3}{8}$ by finding the quotient of 3 ÷ 8. [0.375]
- Have students multiply both $\frac{3}{8} \times 8$ and 0.375×8 to show that the two forms are equivalent.
- Have students make a table that shows the fractional and decimal forms of the following: $\frac{1}{2}, \frac{1}{4}, \frac{3}{4}, \frac{1}{5}, \frac{2}{5}, \frac{3}{5}, \frac{4}{5}, \frac{1}{8}, \frac{3}{8}, \frac{5}{8}$, and $\frac{7}{8}$.

Lesson 11 (Student Book pages 102–111)

Common Factors and Multiples

LESSON OBJECTIVES

- Understand that greatest common factor (GCF) and least common multiple (LCM) are ways to discuss number relationships in multiplication and division.
- Use the distributive property to express a sum of two numbers with a common factor as a multiple of a sum of two whole numbers with no common factor.
- Find the GCF of two whole numbers less than or equal to 100 and the LCM of two whole numbers less than or equal to 12.
- Model factorization of whole numbers 1–100.

PREREQUISITE SKILLS

- Understand that a factor is a whole number that divides without a remainder into another number.
- Understand that a multiple is a whole number that is a product of the number and any other factor.
- Find factors and multiples of a given number.
- Compute using the distributive property.

VOCABULARY

greatest common factor (GCF): the greatest factor two numbers have in common

least common multiple (LCM): the lowest multiple shared by two or more numbers

THE LEARNING PROGRESSION

In past grades, students have learned about factors, prime factors, and multiples. This year, they learn to solve problems using the greatest common factor (GCF) and the least common multiple (LCM). They also learn to rewrite sums using the greatest common factor of the addends and the distributive property. For example, $18 + 27$ can be written as $9(2 + 3)$.

The ability to find and use factors and multiples will be important to students in algebra as they factor algebraic expressions to solve problems.

Ready ***Teacher Toolbox*** Teacher-Toolbox.com

	Prerequisite Skills	*6.NS.B.4*
Ready Lessons	✓	✓
Tools for Instruction		✓✓
Interactive Tutorials		✓✓

CCSS Focus

6.NS.B.4 Find the greatest common factor of two whole numbers less than or equal to 100 and the least common multiple of two whole numbers less than or equal to 12. Use the distributive property to express a sum of two whole numbers 1–100 with a common factor as a multiple of a sum of two whole numbers with no common factor. *For example, express $36 + 8$ as $4 (9 + 2)$.*

STANDARDS FOR MATHEMATICAL PRACTICE: ***SMP 2, 3, 7*** *(see page A9 for full text)*

AT A GLANCE

Students read a word problem and answer a series of questions that guide students to use factors to find the solution.

STEP BY STEP

- Tell students that this page models how to use factors to answer a question.
- Have students read the problem at the top of the page.
- Work through Explore It as a class.
- Review the meaning of the term *factor pairs*. Ask students to explain how they know that all factor pairs are listed.
- Ask student pairs or groups to explain their answers for the remaining questions.

Develop Skills and Strategies

Lesson 11 Part 1: Introduction

Common Factors and Multiples

CCSS 6.NS.B.4

In earlier grades, you learned about factors. In this lesson you will learn about common factors and multiples. Take a look at this problem.

Matt is running for student council. His friends are going to help him give out 15 posters and 6 banners. Matthew plans to pack all of the posters and banners in boxes. He wants to put the same number of posters and the same number of banners in each box. What is the greatest number of boxes Matthew can pack?

Explore It

Use the math you already know to solve this problem.

- You know that Matt wants to pack the same number of posters in each box. There are four ways he can pack the 15 posters.

  If he uses 1 box, he will pack it with 15 posters.

  If he uses 3 boxes, he will pack it with 5 posters.

  If he uses 5 boxes, he will pack it with 3 posters.

  If he uses 15 boxes, he will pack it with 1 poster.
- Matt also wants to pack the same number of banners in each box. There are four ways to pack the 6 banners.

  If he uses 1 box, he will pack it with 6 banners.

  If he uses 2 boxes, he will pack it with 3 banners.

  If he uses 3 boxes, he will pack it with 2 banners.

  If he uses 6 boxes, he will pack it with 1 banner.
- Explain how you could find the greatest number of boxes Matthew can pack that have the same number of posters and the same number of banners.

  You could list all of the possibilities for how he could pack posters and how he could pack banners and see if there are any number of boxes in common. Matt could pack 3 boxes with 5 posters and 2 banners in each box.

102 L11: Common Factors and Multiples

Visual Model

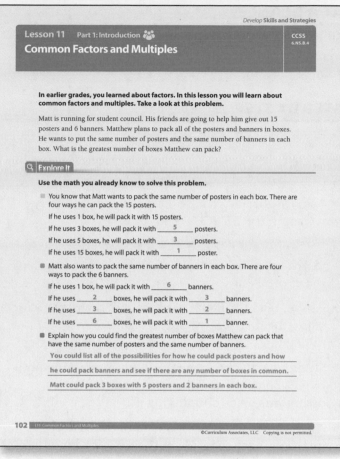

Model the distributive property.

- Use one color to draw a square on the board. In that square, write 15 and say that it shows 15 posters in a single box.
- Next, draw 2 squares. Ask: *Can you distribute the 15 posters between two boxes so the same number of posters are in each box?* [no]
- Draw a third square. Ask: *Can you distribute the 15 posters among three boxes so the same number of posters are in each box?* [yes] Write 5 in each of the 3 squares showing that there are 3 boxes of 5 posters.
- Continue the process until you show all possible ways to distribute the posters evenly among boxes.
- Use another color to show the possible distribution of 6 banners among boxes.
- Have students examine the diagram to find a common number of boxes for the posters and the banners. Of the two numbers, 1 and 3, have them identify the greatest.

Mathematical Discourse

- *How can you find the factor pairs for 15?*

  Ask students to think about different strategies for finding all factor pairs. Have students name multiplication facts and list whole numbers from 1 to 15. Encourage discussion about divisibility rules.
- *Suppose a student says 2 and $7\frac{1}{2}$ are factors of 15 because $2 \times 7\frac{1}{2} = 15$. Do you agree? Why or why not?*

  No, because $7\frac{1}{2}$ is not a whole number. Students should recall that factors by definition must be whole numbers.
- *Because factors must be whole numbers, is it possible to have an unlimited number of factor pairs? Why or why not?*

  No, the only numbers in factor pairs are less than or equal to that number. Not all numbers can be factors of a given number.

AT A GLANCE

Students learn how to use the distributive property to rewrite the sum of a number using the greatest common factor.

STEP BY STEP

- Read Find Out More as a class.
- Review the steps used to find the greatest common factor (GCF) of two numbers.
- Ask: *How would you use the distributive property to rewrite* $3(2 + 5)$*?* [$(3 \times 2) + (3 \times 5)$]
- Point out that if $3(2 + 5) = (3 \times 2) + (3 \times 5)$, then $(3 \times 2) + (3 \times 5) = 3(2 + 5)$. Underline the 3s in the expression.
- As you read through the process of rewriting $15 + 6$ using the distributive property, check for understanding before continuing to the next step.
- Study how to check the result by simplifying both expressions. Point out the use of the order of operations when simplifying $4(5 + 2)$.
- After students have responded to the Reflect question, have them share their explanations.

SMP Tip: Rewriting the sum of two numbers using the distributive property requires students to look for and make use of structure (*SMP 7*). As students rewrite the sums, make sure they can explain the process as well as show that the two expressions are equal.

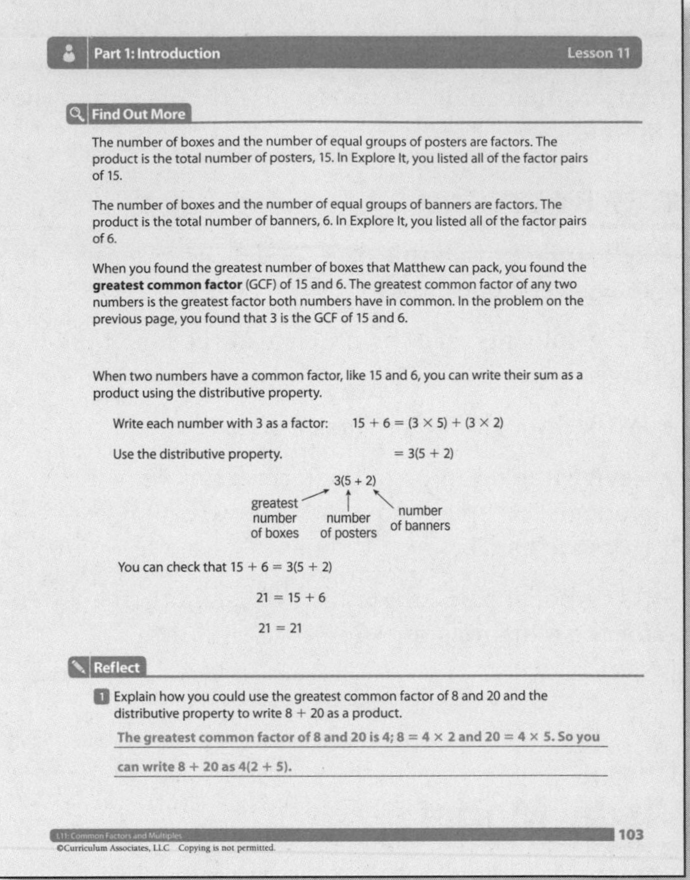

Part 1: Introduction Lesson 11

Find Out More

The number of boxes and the number of equal groups of posters are factors. The product is the total number of posters, 15. In Explore It, you listed all of the factor pairs of 15.

The number of boxes and the number of equal groups of banners are factors. The product is the total number of banners, 6. In Explore It, you listed all of the factor pairs of 6.

When you found the greatest number of boxes that Matthew can pack, you found the **greatest common factor** (GCF) of 15 and 6. The greatest common factor of any two numbers is the greatest factor both numbers have in common. In the problem on the previous page, you found that 3 is the GCF of 15 and 6.

When two numbers have a common factor, like 15 and 6, you can write their sum as a product using the distributive property.

Write each number with 3 as a factor: $15 + 6 = (3 \times 5) + (3 \times 2)$

Use the distributive property. $= 3(5 + 2)$

$3(5 + 2)$

You can check that $15 + 6 = 3(5 + 2)$

$21 = 15 + 6$

$21 = 21$

Reflect

1 Explain how you could use the greatest common factor of 8 and 20 and the distributive property to write $8 + 20$ as a product.

The greatest common factor of 8 and 20 is 4; $8 = 4 \times 2$ and $20 = 4 \times 5$. So you can write $8 + 20$ as $4(2 + 5)$.

L11: Common Factors and Multiples 103

©Curriculum Associates, LLC Copying is not permitted.

Real-World Connection

Encourage students to think of situations in which we divide objects or people into groups with the same number in each.

Examples: food items into packages with the same number in each, treats for a group of children, items for gift baskets, students into teams for a relay race

AT A GLANCE

Students use the greatest common factor (GCF) to model a problem situation.

STEP BY STEP

- Read the problem at the top of the page as a class.
- Ask: *Why do you find the factors to find the number of identical plates Alisha can prepare?* [You must divide the cheese into equal portions and the crackers into equal portions.]
- Circle the common factors of 24 and 40. Note the common factors in the table as the number of plates.
- Have students explain how the numbers in the table relate to the context of the problem.

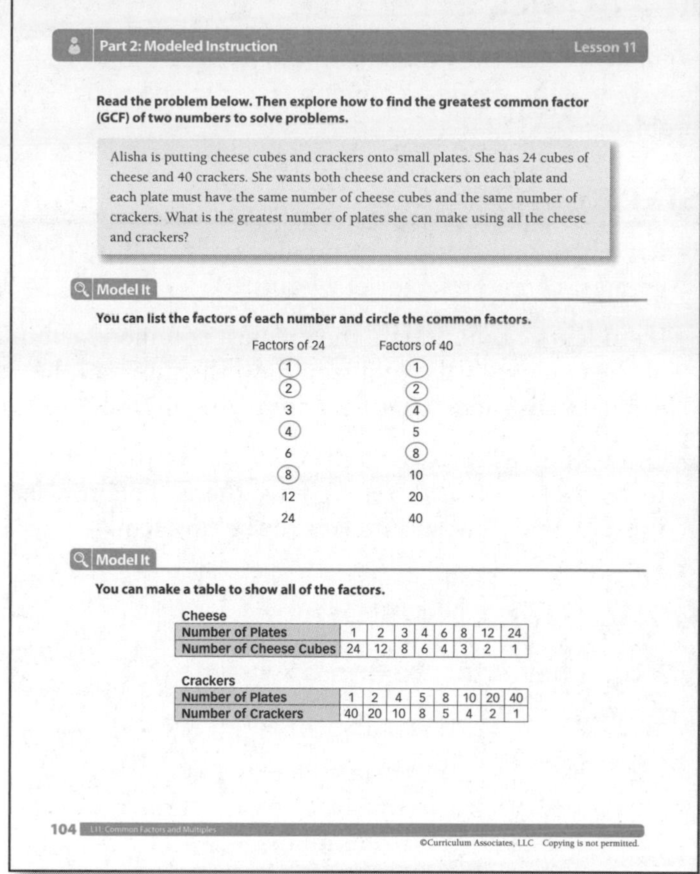

Part 2: Modeled Instruction Lesson 11

Read the problem below. Then explore how to find the greatest common factor (GCF) of two numbers to solve problems.

Alisha is putting cheese cubes and crackers onto small plates. She has 24 cubes of cheese and 40 crackers. She wants both cheese and crackers on each plate and each plate must have the same number of cheese cubes and the same number of crackers. What is the greatest number of plates she can make using all the cheese and crackers?

Model It

You can list the factors of each number and circle the common factors.

Factors of 24	Factors of 40
(1)	(1)
(2)	(2)
3	(4)
(4)	5
6	(8)
(8)	10
12	20
24	40

Model It

You can make a table to show all of the factors.

Cheese

Number of Plates	1	2	3	4	6	8	12	24
Number of Cheese Cubes	24	12	8	6	4	3	2	1

Crackers

Number of Plates	1	2	4	5	8	10	20	40
Number of Crackers	40	20	10	8	5	4	2	1

104 L11: Common Factors and Multiples

©Curriculum Associates, LLC Copying is not permitted.

ELL Support

- Write the word *common* on the board. Explain if two people have something in common, it is the same for both of them.
- Identify two students who have white shoes. Say, *They have white shoes in common.* Repeat with other characteristics.
- Have volunteers identify a characteristic they have that is the same as another student and model the term *in common*.

SMP Tip: Students identify important quantities in a situation and analyze their relationships mathematically (*SMP 4*) as they see how common factors can be used to solve a practical problem. Occasionally ask students to explain how the numbers they are working with relate to the problem situation or why the operation is appropriate to the situation.

Mathematical Discourse

- *How is the problem about cheese and crackers like the problem on page 102 about packing banners and posters?*

  Listen for responses that the problems have the same structure—dividing quantities of different things evenly to create groups (plates or boxes) that have some of both.

- *Is the table or the list of common factors more helpful for finding the answer? Why?*

  Students may have different opinions, but all should recognize that the table shows all possible solutions to dividing both cheese and crackers evenly. The list of factors helps figure out what should be in the table but is less specific.

AT A GLANCE

Students revisit the problem on the page 104 to learn how to use the greatest common factor to solve the problem.

STEP BY STEP

- Review the models on the previous page to find the greatest common factor of 24 and 40.
- If students cannot relate the greatest common factor to the context of the problem, have them reread the problem and state what they are trying to find.
- Once students have used the distributive property to rewrite 24 + 40 as 8(3 + 5), have them explain what the 8, 3, and 5 mean in terms of the problem.

Concept Extension

Use prime factors to find the greatest common factor.

- Review how to find prime factors. State that students can use prime factors to find the greatest common factor of two numbers.
- Ask students to find the prime factors of 18 and 30. List their factors, circling the ones they have in common.

  $18 = 2 \times 3 \times 3$

  $30 = 2 \times 3 \times 5$
- Multiply the numbers in the circles, one number per circle. $2 \times 3 = 6$
- Say that the greatest common factor of 18 and 30 is 6.

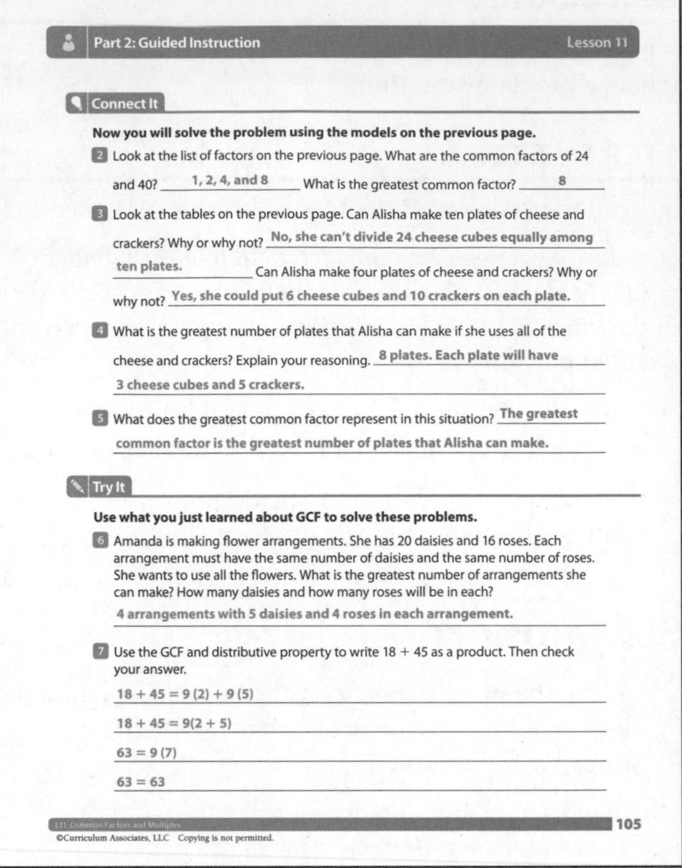

Part 2: Guided Instruction Lesson 11

Connect It

Now you will solve the problem using the models on the previous page.

2 Look at the list of factors on the previous page. What are the common factors of 24 and 40? 1, 2, 4, and 8 What is the greatest common factor? 8

3 Look at the tables on the previous page. Can Alisha make ten plates of cheese and crackers? Why or why not? No, she can't divide 24 cheese cubes equally among ten plates. Can Alisha make four plates of cheese and crackers? Why or why not? Yes, she could put 6 cheese cubes and 10 crackers on each plate.

4 What is the greatest number of plates that Alisha can make if she uses all of the cheese and crackers? Explain your reasoning. 8 plates. Each plate will have 3 cheese cubes and 5 crackers.

5 What does the greatest common factor represent in this situation? The greatest common factor is the greatest number of plates that Alisha can make.

Try It

Use what you just learned about GCF to solve these problems.

6 Amanda is making flower arrangements. She has 20 daisies and 16 roses. Each arrangement must have the same number of daisies and the same number of roses. She wants to use all the flowers. What is the greatest number of arrangements she can make? How many daisies and how many roses will be in each?
4 arrangements with 5 daisies and 4 roses in each arrangement.

7 Use the GCF and distributive property to write 18 + 45 as a product. Then check your answer.
18 + 45 = 9 (2) + 9 (5)
18 + 45 = 9(2 + 5)
63 = 9 (7)
63 = 63

L11: Common Factors and Multiples 105
©Curriculum Associates, LLC Copying is not permitted.

TRY IT SOLUTIONS

6 *Solution:* 4 arrangements each with 5 daisies and 4 roses; Students may list the factors of 16 and 20 and find the greatest common factor.

7 *Solution:* 18 + 45 = 9(2 + 5); 63 = 63; Students may find 9, the greatest common factor of 18 and 45, and use the distributive property to rewrite the sum.

ERROR ALERT: Students who wrote 18 + 45 = 3(6 + 15) used a common factor, 3, instead of the greatest common factor, 9.

AT A GLANCE

Students explore a model using the concept of the least common multiple (LCM).

STEP BY STEP

- Read the problem at the top of the page as a class.
- Review the meaning of the term *multiple*. Have a volunteer explain how to use a number line to find the multiples of a number.
- Have students describe different ways to list multiples without using a number line. Listen for ideas such as skip counting or multiplying the number by 1, then 2, then 3, and so on.
- Discuss how the least common multiple is different from other multiples.
- Ask students to explain how the models relate to the problem.

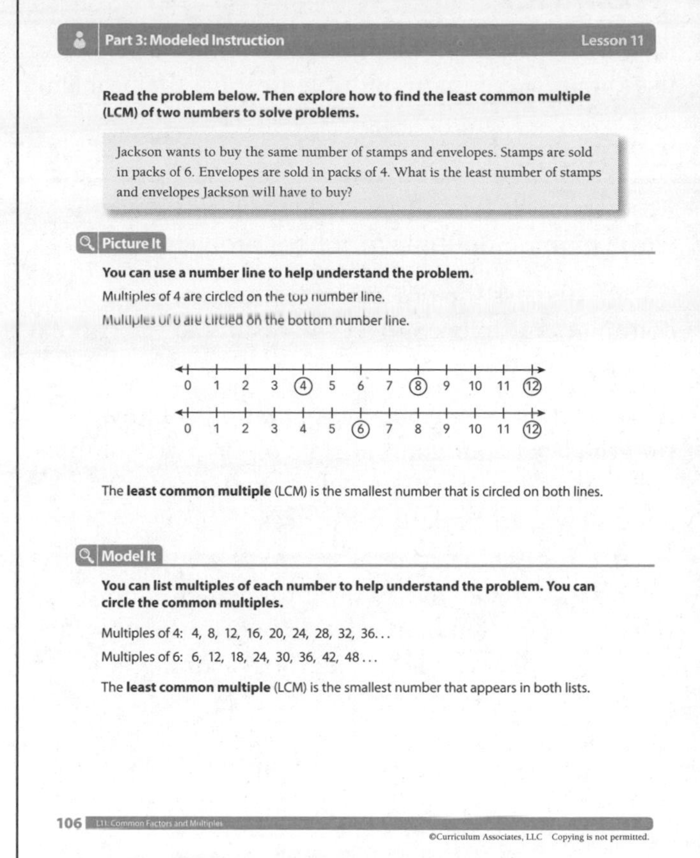

Part 3: Modeled Instruction Lesson 11

Read the problem below. Then explore how to find the least common multiple (LCM) of two numbers to solve problems.

Jackson wants to buy the same number of stamps and envelopes. Stamps are sold in packs of 6. Envelopes are sold in packs of 4. What is the least number of stamps and envelopes Jackson will have to buy?

Picture It

You can use a number line to help understand the problem.

Multiples of 4 are circled on the top number line.

Multiples of 6 are circled on the bottom number line.

The **least common multiple** (LCM) is the smallest number that is circled on both lines.

Model It

You can list multiples of each number to help understand the problem. You can circle the common multiples.

Multiples of 4: 4, 8, 12, 16, 20, 24, 28, 32, 36...

Multiples of 6: 6, 12, 18, 24, 30, 36, 42, 48...

The **least common multiple** (LCM) is the smallest number that appears in both lists.

106 L11: Common Factors and Multiples

©Curriculum Associates, LLC Copying is not permitted.

Hands-On Activity

Use physical representations of multiples to find the least common multiple.

Materials: index cards, crayons or markers

- Have students work in pairs. Give each student three sets of 10 index cards and 3 numbers from this list: 4, 6, 8, 9, 10, 12.
- Students should create 3 sets of cards showing the first 10 multiples of each of their numbers. Remind students that the multiplication facts are lists of multiples.
- The students will each choose a set of cards. Both students will try to find the least common multiple of the two numbers.
- To check their answers, the students will lay out the cards in order until both sets show the same multiple.
- Students should repeat the activity with other pairs of numbers.

Mathematical Discourse

- *A student claims that she has an easy way to find the least common multiple. She says that she lists the multiples of the greatest number. Then she finds the first multiple that the other number divides into evenly. Does her method work? Explain.*

  Yes, she finds the multiples of one number. If the second number divides into it evenly, it is also a multiple of the second number.

- *Do you like her method better than listing the multiples of both numbers? Explain.*

  Students' opinions will vary.

AT A GLANCE

Students revisit the problem on page 106 to learn how to use the least common multiple to solve the problem.

STEP BY STEP

- Read Connect It as a class to learn how to use the least common multiple to solve a problem.
- As you discuss the process of finding the least common multiple, connect the results to the context of the problem.
- After students share their explanations of how to find the least common multiple of any two numbers, come to an agreement as a class on a clear and concise way to explain the process.

SMP Tip: When students work together to develop a clear explanation of a process, they must construct viable arguments and critique the reasoning of others (*SMP 2*). Encourage students to interact in a respectful way to make sure their explanation is accurate, clear, and simple enough for other students in their grade to apply to any two numbers.

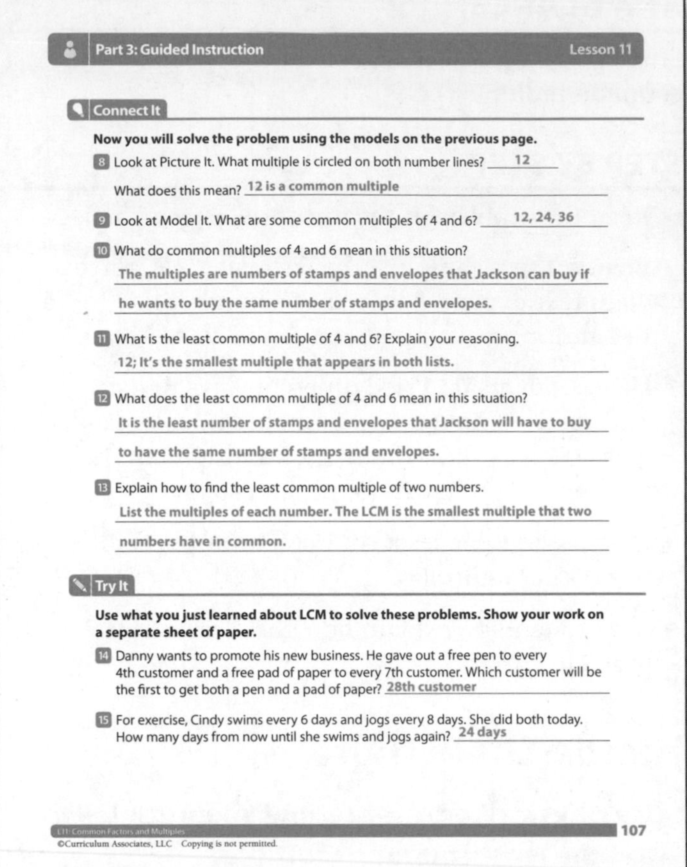

Part 3: Guided Instruction Lesson 11

Connect It

Now you will solve the problem using the models on the previous page.

8 Look at Picture It. What multiple is circled on both number lines? 12

What does this mean? 12 is a common multiple

9 Look at Model It. What are some common multiples of 4 and 6? 12, 24, 36

10 What do common multiples of 4 and 6 mean in this situation?
The multiples are numbers of stamps and envelopes that Jackson can buy if he wants to buy the same number of stamps and envelopes.

11 What is the least common multiple of 4 and 6? Explain your reasoning.
12; It's the smallest multiple that appears in both lists.

12 What does the least common multiple of 4 and 6 mean in this situation?
It is the least number of stamps and envelopes that Jackson will have to buy to have the same number of stamps and envelopes.

13 Explain how to find the least common multiple of two numbers.
List the multiples of each number. The LCM is the smallest multiple that two numbers have in common.

Try It

Use what you just learned about LCM to solve these problems. Show your work on a separate sheet of paper.

14 Danny wants to promote his new business. He gave out a free pen to every 4th customer and a free pad of paper to every 7th customer. Which customer will be the first to get both a pen and a pad of paper? 28th customer

15 For exercise, Cindy swims every 6 days and jogs every 8 days. She did both today. How many days from now until she swims and jogs again? 24 days

L11: Common Factors and Multiples 107
©Curriculum Associates, LLC Copying is not permitted.

TRY IT SOLUTIONS

14 *Solution:* 28; Students may have listed the multiples of 4 and 7 until they found the least common multiple.

15 *Solution:* 24; Students may have listed the multiples of 6 and 8 until they found the least common multiple.

ERROR ALERT: Students who wrote 48 found a multiple of 6 and 8 but not the least common multiple.

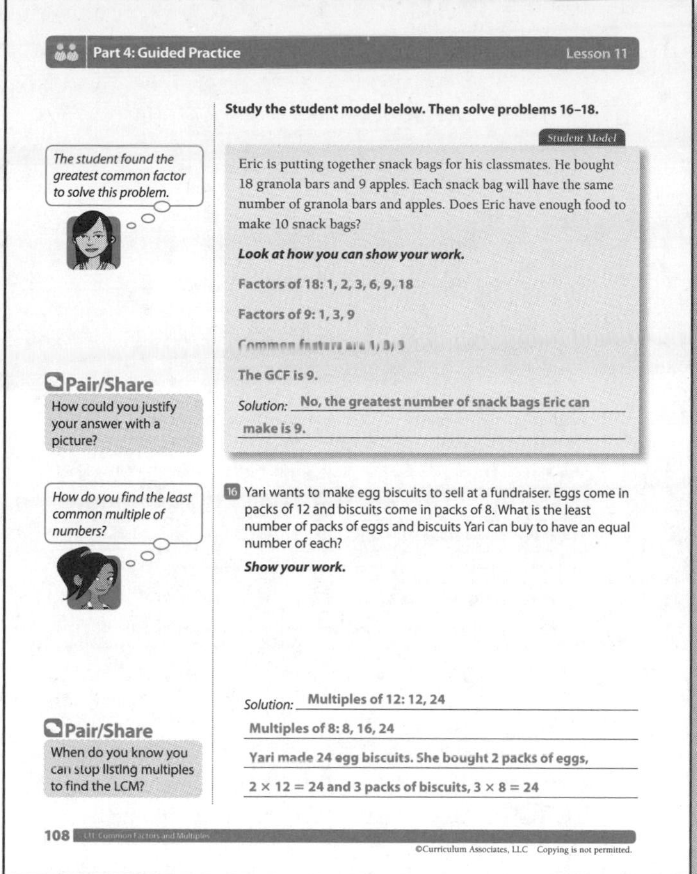

Part 4: Guided Practice Lesson 11

Study the student model below. Then solve problems 16–18.

Student Model

The student found the greatest common factor to solve this problem.

Eric is putting together snack bags for his classmates. He bought 18 granola bars and 9 apples. Each snack bag will have the same number of granola bars and apples. Does Eric have enough food to make 10 snack bags?

Look at how you can show your work.

Factors of 18: 1, 2, 3, 6, 9, 18

Factors of 9: 1, 3, 9

Common factors are 1, 3, 9

The GCF is 9.

Solution: No, the greatest number of snack bags Eric can make is 9.

Pair/Share
How could you justify your answer with a picture?

How do you find the least common multiple of numbers?

16 Yari wants to make egg biscuits to sell at a fundraiser. Eggs come in packs of 12 and biscuits come in packs of 8. What is the least number of packs of eggs and biscuits Yari can buy to have an equal number of each?

Show your work.

Solution: Multiples of 12: 12, 24
Multiples of 8: 8, 16, 24
Yari made 24 egg biscuits. She bought 2 packs of eggs, $2 \times 12 = 24$ and 3 packs of biscuits, $3 \times 8 = 24$

Pair/Share
When do you know you can stop listing multiples to find the LCM?

108 L11: Common Factors and Multiples ©Curriculum Associates, LLC Copying is not permitted.

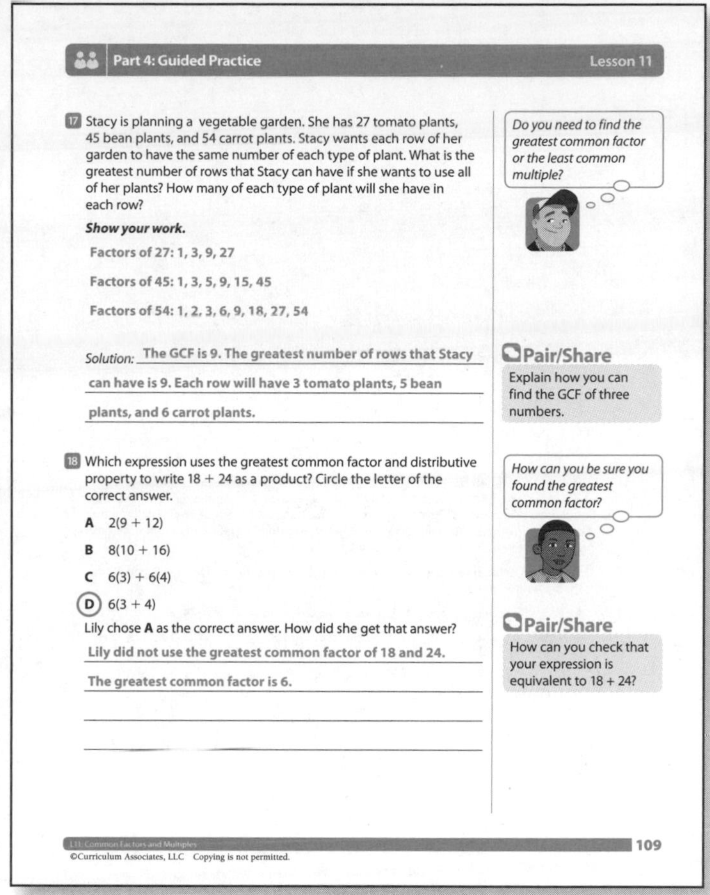

Part 4: Guided Practice Lesson 11

17 Stacy is planning a vegetable garden. She has 27 tomato plants, 45 bean plants, and 54 carrot plants. Stacy wants each row of her garden to have the same number of each type of plant. What is the greatest number of rows that Stacy can have if she wants to use all of her plants? How many of each type of plant will she have in each row?

Show your work.

Factors of 27: 1, 3, 9, 27

Factors of 45: 1, 3, 5, 9, 15, 45

Factors of 54: 1, 2, 3, 6, 9, 18, 27, 54

Solution: The GCF is 9. The greatest number of rows that Stacy can have is 9. Each row will have 3 tomato plants, 5 bean plants, and 6 carrot plants.

Do you need to find the greatest common factor or the least common multiple?

Pair/Share
Explain how you can find the GCF of three numbers.

18 Which expression uses the greatest common factor and distributive property to write 18 + 24 as a product? Circle the letter of the correct answer.

A $2(9 + 12)$

B $8(10 + 16)$

C $6(3) + 6(4)$

(D) $6(3 + 4)$

Lily chose **A** as the correct answer. How did she get that answer?

Lily did not use the greatest common factor of 18 and 24. The greatest common factor is 6.

How can you be sure you found the greatest common factor?

Pair/Share
How can you check that your expression is equivalent to 18 + 24?

L11: Common Factors and Multiples ©Curriculum Associates, LLC Copying is not permitted. 109

AT A GLANCE

Students use factors and multiples to solve problems.

STEP BY STEP

- Ask students to solve the problems individually and show how they used factors or multiples to find the solution.
- When students have completed each problem, have them Pair/Share to discuss their solutions with a partner or in a group.

SOLUTIONS

Ex Lists of factors and common factors are shown as one way to solve the problem.

16 *Solution:* 24 egg biscuits; 2 packs of eggs and 3 packs of biscuits. Students could find the LCM of 8 and 12. ***(DOK 2)***

17 *Solution:* The greatest common factor is 9, which gives the greatest number of rows that Stacy can have. ***(DOK 2)***

18 *Solution:* **D**; Lily used the common factor 2 instead of the greatest common factor, 6.

Explain to students why the other two answer choices are not correct:

B is not correct because the distributive property is applied incorrectly.

C is not correct because the expression is not completely rewritten. ***(DOK 3)***

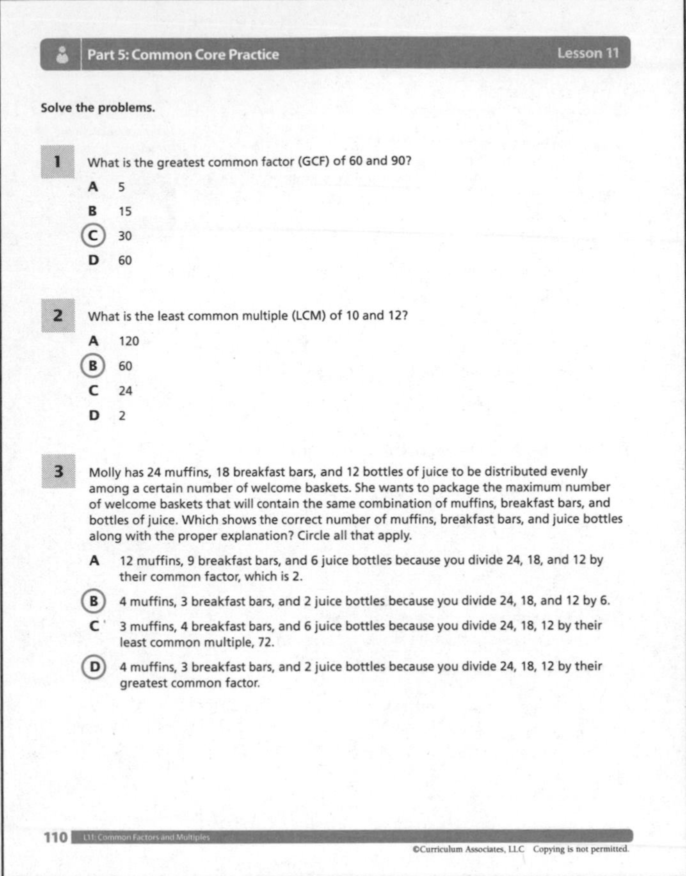

Part 5: Common Core Practice Lesson 11

Solve the problems.

1 What is the greatest common factor (GCF) of 60 and 90?

A 5

B 15

(C) 30

D 60

2 What is the least common multiple (LCM) of 10 and 12?

A 120

(B) 60

C 24

D 2

3 Molly has 24 muffins, 18 breakfast bars, and 12 bottles of juice to be distributed evenly among a certain number of welcome baskets. She wants to package the maximum number of welcome baskets that will contain the same combination of muffins, breakfast bars, and bottles of juice. Which shows the correct number of muffins, breakfast bars, and juice bottles along with the proper explanation? Circle all that apply.

A 12 muffins, 9 breakfast bars, and 6 juice bottles because you divide 24, 18, and 12 by their common factor, which is 2.

(B) 4 muffins, 3 breakfast bars, and 2 juice bottles because you divide 24, 18, and 12 by 6.

C 3 muffins, 4 breakfast bars, and 6 juice bottles because you divide 24, 18, 12 by their least common multiple, 72.

(D) 4 muffins, 3 breakfast bars, and 2 juice bottles because you divide 24, 18, 12 by their greatest common factor.

110 L11: Common Factors and Multiples

©Curriculum Associates, LLC Copying is not permitted.

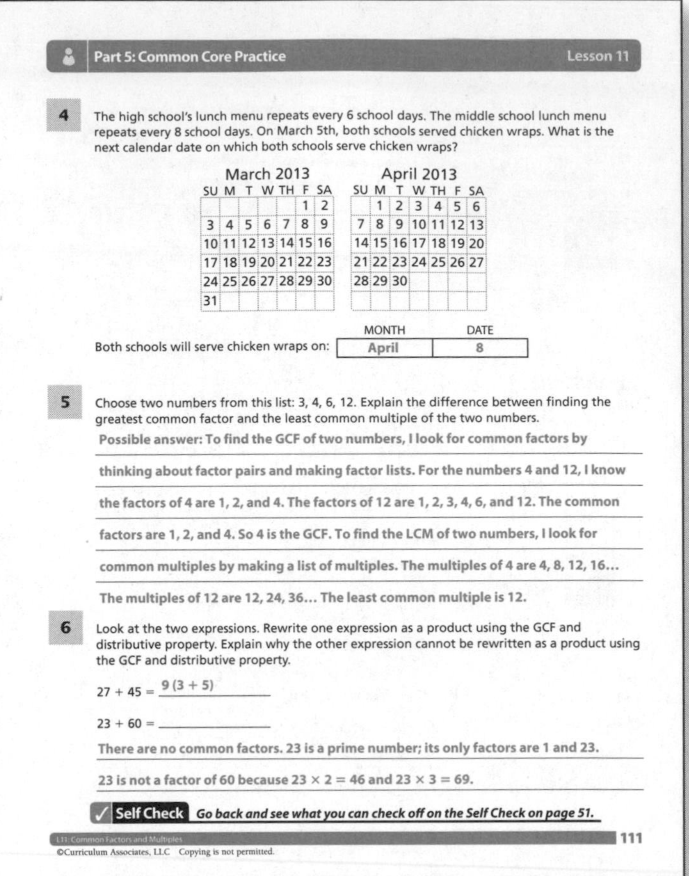

Part 5: Common Core Practice Lesson 11

4 The high school's lunch menu repeats every 6 school days. The middle school lunch menu repeats every 8 school days. On March 5th, both schools served chicken wraps. What is the next calendar date on which both schools serve chicken wraps?

March 2013

SU	M	T	W	TH	F	SA
					1	2
3	4	5	6	7	8	9
10	11	12	13	14	15	16
17	18	19	20	21	22	23
24	25	26	27	28	29	30
31						

April 2013

SU	M	T	W	TH	F	SA
	1	2	3	4	5	6
7	8	9	10	11	12	13
14	15	16	17	18	19	20
21	22	23	24	25	26	27
28	29	30				

Both schools will serve chicken wraps on: MONTH April DATE 8

5 Choose two numbers from this list: 3, 4, 6, 12. Explain the difference between finding the greatest common factor and the least common multiple of the two numbers.

Possible answer: To find the GCF of two numbers, I look for common factors by thinking about factor pairs and making factor lists. For the numbers 4 and 12, I know the factors of 4 are 1, 2, and 4. The factors of 12 are 1, 2, 3, 4, 6, and 12. The common factors are 1, 2, and 4. So 4 is the GCF. To find the LCM of two numbers, I look for common multiples by making a list of multiples. The multiples of 4 are 4, 8, 12, 16… The multiples of 12 are 12, 24, 36… The least common multiple is 12.

6 Look at the two expressions. Rewrite one expression as a product using the GCF and distributive property. Explain why the other expression cannot be rewritten as a product using the GCF and distributive property.

$27 + 45 = 9(3 + 5)$

$23 + 60 =$ ______

There are no common factors. 23 is a prime number; its only factors are 1 and 23. 23 is not a factor of 60 because $23 \times 2 = 46$ and $23 \times 3 = 69$.

Self Check Go back and see what you can check off on the Self Check on page 51.

L11: Common Factors and Multiples 111

©Curriculum Associates, LLC Copying is not permitted.

AT A GLANCE

Students use greatest common multiples and least common factors to solve problems that might appear on a mathematics test.

SOLUTIONS

1 *Solution:* **C**; List factors of 60 and 90 and find the greatest factor in common. ***(DOK 1)***

2 *Solution:* **B**; List multiples of 10 and 12 and find the least multiple in common. ***(DOK 1)***

3 *Solution:* **B** and **D**; Find the greatest number of baskets by finding the greatest common factor of all three numbers. Then divide each number of items by the greatest common factor to find how many of each to put in each basket. ***(DOK 2)***

4 *Solution:* April 8; Start on March 5. Count every 6 days and also every 8 days. Find the earliest day after March 5 that a multiple of 6 days is on the same day as a multiple of 8 days. ***(DOK 2)***

5 *Possible answer*: Find the GCF by listing the factors of each number and finding the greatest factor they share. To find the LCM, list several multiples of each number and find the least multiple they share. The student might include specific examples. ***(DOK 3)***

6 *Possible answer*: The first expression can be rewritten as $9(3 + 5)$ because the GCF is 9. The second expression cannot be rewritten because the GCF is 1, and 23 and 60 have no common factors. ***(DOK 3)***

Assessment and Remediation

- Ask students to find the greatest common factor of 20 and 28. [4]
- For students who are struggling, use the chart below to guide remediation.
- After providing remediation, check students' understanding. Ask students to find the greatest common factor of 18 and 45. [9]
- If a student is still having difficulty, use ***Ready Instruction, Level 4,*** Lesson 7.

If the error is . . .	Students may . . .	To remediate . . .
2	have found a common factor but not the greatest common factor.	Remind students that a pair of numbers may have many factors in common, but the greatest common factor is the greatest one they have in common.
140	have found the least common multiple.	Review the difference between greatest common factor and the least common multiple.
any other number.	have found the factors incorrectly.	Remind students to use an organized list to find the factors accurately and completely.

Hands-On Activity

Use area models to find factors and greatest common factor.

Materials: cubes, grid paper, colored pencils

- Give each pair of students a set of cubes.
- Ask them to show all the ways they can make a rectangle using 12 cubes. Have them record their work on grid paper using a colored pencil. Have them label each rectangle with its dimensions.
- Then have students show all the ways they can make a rectangle using 16 cubes. Have them record and label their work on grid paper using another color of pencil.
- Have students list the possible dimensions for the two rectangles with one list below the other. Have them circle the numbers that appear in both lists and identify the greatest of those numbers.

Challenge Activity

Explore the product of the greatest common factor and the least common multiple.

- Ask students to find the product of 6 and 16. [96] Have them use the prime factor methods to find the greatest common factor and the least common multiple of 6 and 16. Have them find the product of the GCF and LCM. [2 and 48; 96] Have them compare the two products.
- Give students other number pairs such as 8 and 20 or 9 and 15. Then have them find the product of the number pairs and the product of their greatest common factor and least common multiple.
- Have students generalize about the results. Then have students examine the prime factor methods of finding each and explain why the product of two numbers is always the same as the product of their greatest common factor and least common multiple.

Lesson 12 (Student Book pages 112–117)

Understand Positive and Negative Numbers

LESSON OBJECTIVES

- Relate positive and negative numbers to the real world.
- Understand integers and other rational numbers as points on a number line.
- Understand the sign of a number indicates its direction on the number line from zero.
- Recognize that the opposite of an opposite of a number is the number itself; 0 is its own opposite.

PREREQUISITE SKILLS

- Know where positive integers are on a number line.
- Understand that zero represents a position.
- Draw a number line and represent real-life contexts on a number line.

VOCABULARY

positive numbers: numbers that are greater than 0 and located to the right of 0 on a number line

negative numbers: numbers that are less than 0 and located to the left of 0 on a number line

signed numbers: positive and negative whole numbers

opposite numbers: numbers that are the same distance from zero but in opposite directions

integers: all whole numbers and their opposites

THE LEARNING PROGRESSION

In previous grades, students learned about whole numbers as well as positive fractions and decimals. This year they will learn about negative numbers. They will see that every number has an opposite and that the opposite of a positive number is a negative number. They will use vertical and horizontal number lines to show negative numbers. They will see that opposite numbers are the same distance from 0 but in different directions. Students will relate negative numbers to real-world situations and use them to solve simple problems. Students will demonstrate their understanding of positive and negative numbers by translating among words, numbers, and models.
A solid understanding is necessary for success in later grades because integers are an essential part of algebra.

Ready *Teacher Toolbox* Teacher-Toolbox.com

	Prerequisite Skills	*6.NS.C.5, 6.NS.C.6a, 6.NS.C.6c*
Ready Lessons		✓
Tools for Instruction		
Interactive Tutorials		✓

CCSS Focus

6.NS.C.5 Understand that positive and negative numbers are used together to describe quantities having opposite directions or values (e.g., temperature above/below zero, elevation above/below sea level, credits/debits, positive/negative electric charge); use positive and negative numbers to represent quantities in real-world contexts, explaining the meaning of 0 in each situation.

6.NS.C.6 Understand a rational number as a point on the number line. Extend number line diagrams and coordinate axes familiar from previous grades to represent points on the line with negative number coordinates.

a. Recognize opposite signs of numbers as indicating locations on opposite sides of 0 on the number line; recognize that the opposite of the opposite of a number is the number itself, e.g., $-(-3) = 3$, and that 0 is its own opposite.

c. Find and position integers and other rational numbers on a horizontal or vertical number line diagram; find and position pairs of integers and other rational numbers on a coordinate plane.

ADDITIONAL STANDARDS: ***6.NS.C.7*** *(see page A42 for full text)*

STANDARDS FOR MATHEMATICAL PRACTICE: ***SMP 1, 2, 4*** *(see page A9 for full text)*

AT A GLANCE

Students explore positive and negative numbers using the idea of opposite numbers.

STEP BY STEP

- Introduce the Question at the top of the page.
- Read the description of positive and negative numbers. Discuss how the number line relates to the definition.
- Have students describe how a thermometer is like a number line. Discuss what negative numbers mean in terms of temperatures.
- Ask students to explain the difference between 20 and −20 as well as 30 and −30.

SMP Tip: Students learn to model with mathematics (*SMP 4*) as they picture signed numbers on number lines and thermometers. Using a variety of concrete representations to represent abstract concepts such as negative numbers builds a deeper understanding of the concepts.

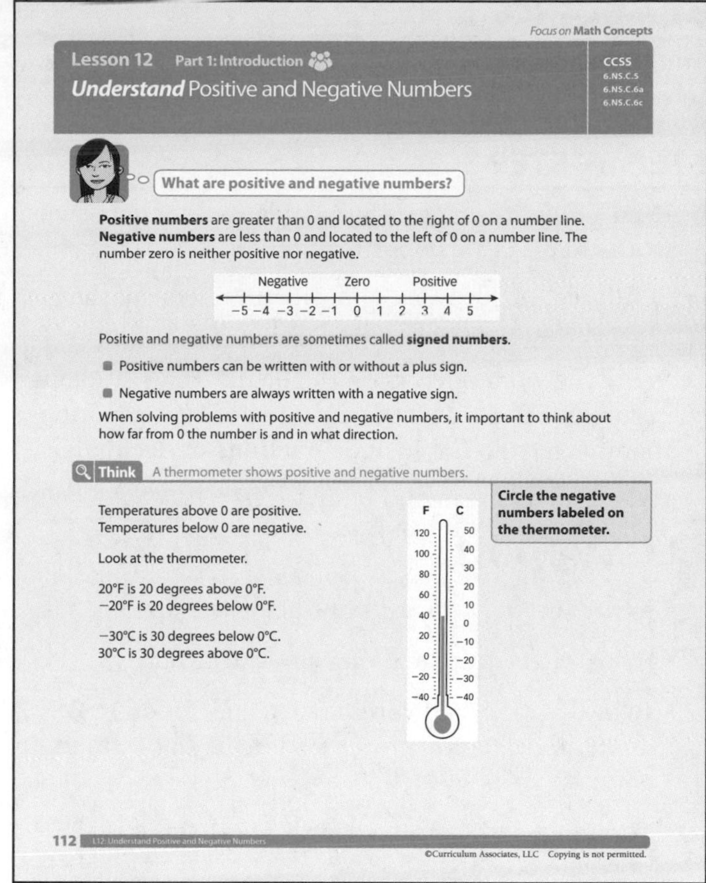

Focus on Math Concepts
Lesson 12 Part 1: Introduction
Understand Positive and Negative Numbers
CCSS
6.NS.C.5
6.NS.C.6a
6.NS.C.6c
What are positive and negative numbers?
Positive numbers are greater than 0 and located to the right of 0 on a number line. Negative numbers are less than 0 and located to the left of 0 on a number line. The number zero is neither positive nor negative.
Negative Zero Positive
−5 −4 −3 −2 −1 0 1 2 3 4 5
Positive and negative numbers are sometimes called signed numbers.
Positive numbers can be written with or without a plus sign.
Negative numbers are always written with a negative sign.
When solving problems with positive and negative numbers, it important to think about how far from 0 the number is and in what direction.
Think A thermometer shows positive and negative numbers.
Temperatures above 0 are positive.
Temperatures below 0 are negative.
Look at the thermometer.
20°F is 20 degrees above 0°F.
−20°F is 20 degrees below 0°F.
−30°C is 30 degrees below 0°C.
30°C is 30 degrees above 0°C.
Circle the negative numbers labeled on the thermometer.
F C
112
©Curriculum Associates, LLC Copying is not permitted.

Mathematical Discourse

- *What can you show on a number line?*

  The distance each whole number is from zero.

- *What are numbers less than zero?*

  Listen for students' responses about negative numbers and the concept that they are opposites of positive numbers.

  How are −3 and +3 different? −3 is a negative number and +3 is a positive number. *How are they the same?* They are both the same distance from zero.

AT A GLANCE

Students explore numbers and their opposites. They are introduced to the term *integer.*

STEP BY STEP

- Read Think as a class. Have students use their own words to describe opposite numbers.
- Reinforce the idea that opposite numbers are the same distance from 0, but in different directions.
- Write the word *integers* on the board. Have students pronounce it. Review the meaning of *integer* noting that integers do not include fractions or decimals.
- Have students read and reply to the Reflect.

ELL Support

- Write the word *opposite* on the board.
- Ask students to name the opposite of hot.
- Repeat with other words such as tall, good, up, and dark until you are sure students understand what opposite means.
- Write −4 and 4 on the board. Say that −4 is the opposite of +4.
- Write −5 and 5 on the board. Say that +5 is the opposite of −5.
- Have students name the opposites of +11 and −7.

Visual Model

Find opposite numbers on a number line.

- Draw a number line the length of the board, spacing the tick marks evenly. Number it from −5 to 5.
- Call on a student to stand in front of a number and say the number using the term *positive* or *negative.*
- Have another student stand in front of the opposite number and name the number, using the term *positive* or *negative.*
- Note that the students are the same distance from zero, but on opposite sides of zero.
- Continue the activity by having the first student sit down and the second student stand in front of a different number.

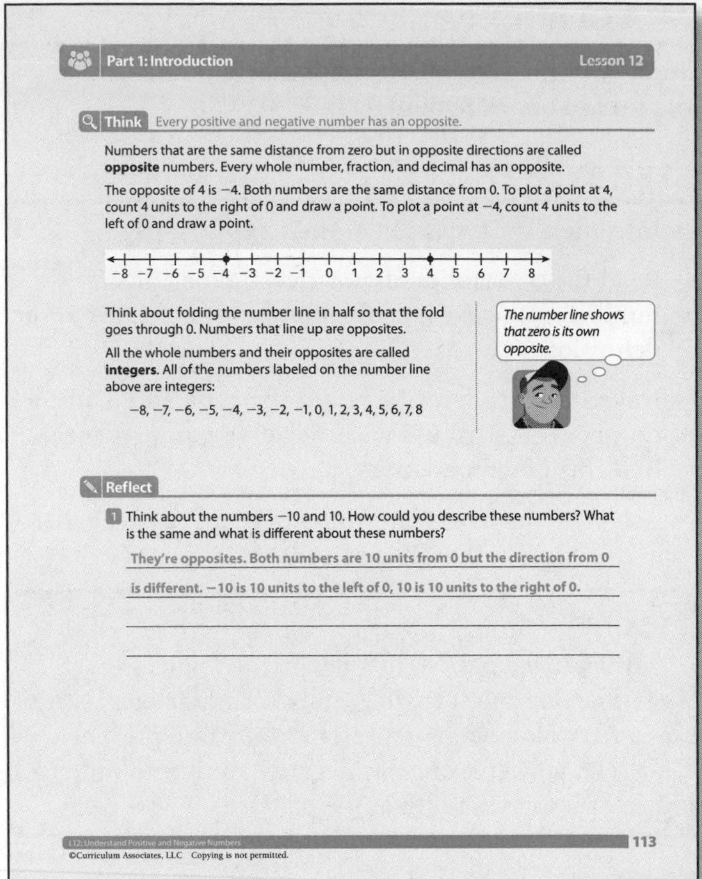

Part 1: Introduction Lesson 12

Think Every positive and negative number has an opposite.

Numbers that are the same distance from zero but in opposite directions are called **opposite** numbers. Every whole number, fraction, and decimal has an opposite.

The opposite of 4 is −4. Both numbers are the same distance from 0. To plot a point at 4, count 4 units to the right of 0 and draw a point. To plot a point at −4, count 4 units to the left of 0 and draw a point.

Think about folding the number line in half so that the fold goes through 0. Numbers that line up are opposites.

All the whole numbers and their opposites are called **integers**. All of the numbers labeled on the number line above are integers:

−8, −7, −6, −5, −4, −3, −2, −1, 0, 1, 2, 3, 4, 5, 6, 7, 8

The number line shows that zero is its own opposite.

Reflect

1 Think about the numbers −10 and 10. How could you describe these numbers? What is the same and what is different about these numbers?

They're opposites. Both numbers are 10 units from 0 but the direction from 0 is different. −10 is 10 units to the left of 0, 10 is 10 units to the right of 0.

L12: Understand Positive and Negative Numbers 113

©Curriculum Associates, LLC Copying is not permitted.

Real-World Connection

Have students describe real-world situations in which negative numbers are used.

Examples: Cold temperatures, owing or spending money, losing points, elevations below sea level.

AT A GLANCE

Students use a number line to explore numbers and their opposites.

STEP BY STEP

- Tell students that they will have time to work individually on the Explore It problems on this page and then share their responses in groups. You may choose to work through the first problem together as a class.
- As students work individually, circulate among them. This is an opportunity to assess student understanding and address student misconceptions. Use the Mathematical Discourse questions to engage student thinking.
- Check to see that students label the number line correctly before they use it to answer questions.
- If students need more support, continue to stress that opposite numbers are only opposite in the direction away from zero, but they are identical in the distance from zero.
- Check students' number lines for problem 9. Note that 4 and −4 are opposites of each other.
- Take note of students who are still having difficulty and wait to see if their understanding progresses as they work in their groups during the next part of the lesson.

STUDENT MISCONCEPTION ALERT: Some students may confuse direction with distance and think that the direction influences how far a point is from 0. Have students consider real-world examples of direction and distance. Ask questions such as, *Suppose Katie walks to the library which is 5 blocks east of her house and her sister walks to the park which is 5 blocks west of her house. Who walks the farthest? Explain.*

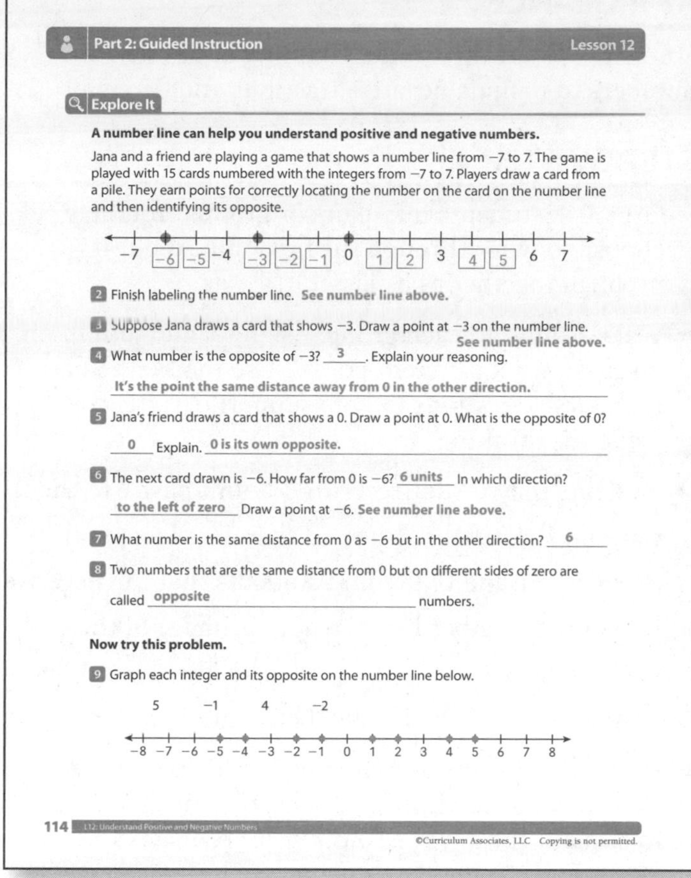

Part 2: Guided Instruction Lesson 12

Explore It

A number line can help you understand positive and negative numbers.

Jana and a friend are playing a game that shows a number line from −7 to 7. The game is played with 15 cards numbered with the integers from −7 to 7. Players draw a card from a pile. They earn points for correctly locating the number on the card on the number line and then identifying its opposite.

2 Finish labeling the number line. **See number line above.**

3 Suppose Jana draws a card that shows −3. Draw a point at −3 on the number line. **See number line above.**

4 What number is the opposite of −3? **3**. Explain your reasoning.

It's the point the same distance away from 0 in the other direction.

5 Jana's friend draws a card that shows a 0. Draw a point at 0. What is the opposite of 0?

0 Explain. **0 is its own opposite.**

6 The next card drawn is −6. How far from 0 is −6? **6 units** In which direction?

to the left of zero Draw a point at −6. **See number line above.**

7 What number is the same distance from 0 as −6 but in the other direction? **6**

8 Two numbers that are the same distance from 0 but on different sides of zero are called **opposite** numbers.

Now try this problem.

9 Graph each integer and its opposite on the number line below.

5 −1 4 −2

114 L12: Understand Positive and Negative Numbers

©Curriculum Associates, LLC Copying is not permitted.

Mathematical Discourse

- *How do you write increasing numbers on a number line?*

  A series of positive numbers growing in value (e.g., 5, 6, 7) increases. Likewise, a series of decreasing negative numbers (e.g., −4, −3, −2) also increases in value.

- *A student notices that the negative numbers are written −5, −4, −3, −2, −1 on the number line. He says the numbers are backwards and −5 should be greater than −1. Do you agree? Explain.*

  Explanations should include that numbers decrease as they go to the left. The farther away from zero, the less the value, so −5 is less than −1 because it is farther from zero. Some may say that the student is partly correct because the numbers without the negative sign increase, but the negative sign means each number that is farther left of 0 is less in value.

AT A GLANCE

Students extend their understanding of negative numbers to include negative fractions and decimals.

STEP BY STEP

- Organize students into pairs or groups. You may choose to work through the first Talk About It problem together as a class.
- Walk around to each group, listen to, and join in on discussions at different points. Use the Mathematical Discourse questions to help support or extend students' thinking.
- Students may visualize $1\frac{1}{2}$ as $\frac{1}{2}$ a unit past 1 to the right on the number line and therefore locate $-1\frac{1}{2}$ between -1 and 0. Remind students that the negative side of the number line is a mirror image of the positive side. Note that $1\frac{1}{2}$ is located between 1 and 2, so $-1\frac{1}{2}$ would be located between -1 and -2.
- Direct the group's attention to Try It Another Way. Have a volunteer from each group come to the board to explain the group's solutions to problem 13.

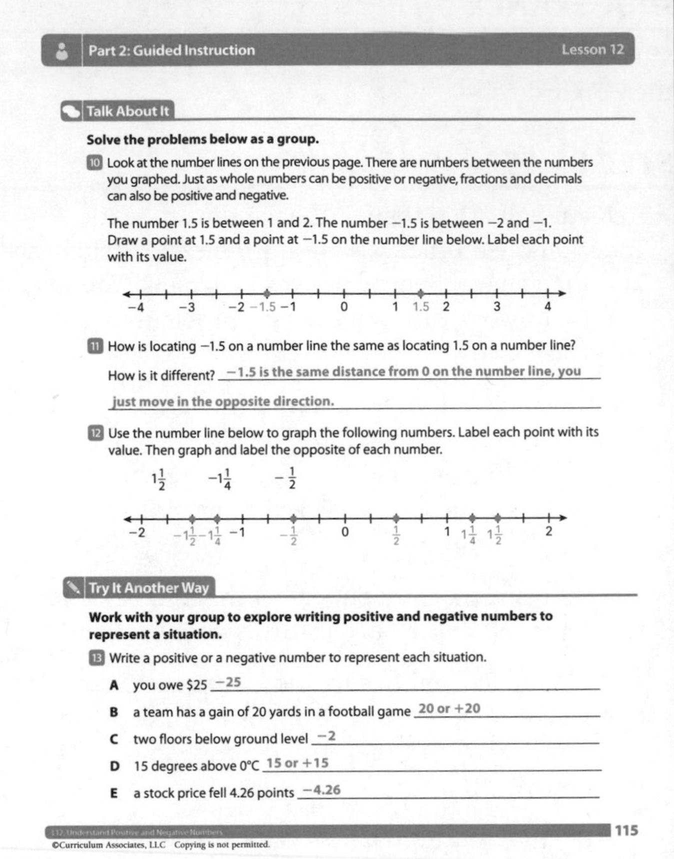

Part 2: Guided Instruction Lesson 12

Talk About It

Solve the problems below as a group.

10 Look at the number lines on the previous page. There are numbers between the numbers you graphed. Just as whole numbers can be positive or negative, fractions and decimals can also be positive and negative.

The number 1.5 is between 1 and 2. The number −1.5 is between −2 and −1. Draw a point at 1.5 and a point at −1.5 on the number line below. Label each point with its value.

11 How is locating −1.5 on a number line the same as locating 1.5 on a number line? How is it different? −1.5 is the same distance from 0 on the number line, you just move in the opposite direction.

12 Use the number line below to graph the following numbers. Label each point with its value. Then graph and label the opposite of each number.

$1\frac{1}{2}$ $-1\frac{1}{4}$ $-\frac{1}{2}$

Try It Another Way

Work with your group to explore writing positive and negative numbers to represent a situation.

13 Write a positive or a negative number to represent each situation.

A you owe $25 −25

B a team has a gain of 20 yards in a football game 20 or +20

C two floors below ground level −2

D 15 degrees above 0°C 15 or +15

E a stock price fell 4.26 points −4.26

L12: Understand Positive and Negative Numbers 115

©Curriculum Associates, LLC Copying is not permitted.

Visual Model

- Have students look at a metric ruler. Have them describe the lines between each centimeter mark. Tell them that a number line showing tenths is similar to a metric ruler.
- On the board, replicate the first 3 centimeters, but enlarge the drawing so students can see the tenths. Mark and label a number line 0, 1, 2, and 3 and also show the smaller marks that represent tenths.
- Call volunteers to the board to locate and label numbers such as 2.4, 0.7, and 0.5.
- Ask how you could show negative decimals. Extend the number line to −3, showing the tenths with smaller marks.
- Have volunteers find and label the opposite of each number marked on the positive side.

Mathematical Discourse

- *How can you use the point $1\frac{1}{2}$ to help you locate $1\frac{1}{4}$?*

  I know that 1 is the same as $1\frac{0}{4}$ and $1\frac{1}{2}$ is the same as $1\frac{2}{4}$. That tells me that $1\frac{1}{4}$ would go between 1 and $1\frac{1}{2}$.
- *How can you use the location of $-1\frac{1}{2}$ to help you locate $-1\frac{1}{4}$?*

  It is a lot like locating $+1\frac{1}{4}$ because -1 is the same as $-1\frac{0}{4}$ and $-1\frac{1}{2}$ is the same as $-1\frac{2}{4}$. I know that $-1\frac{1}{4}$ would go between -1 and $-1\frac{1}{2}$.

AT A GLANCE

Students demonstrate their understanding of positive and negative numbers as they talk through these problems.

STEP BY STEP

- Discuss each Connect It problem as a class using the discussion points outlined below.

Conclude

- When asking for the opposite of the opposite, you may want to break the question into 3 parts. Ask: *What is the opposite of 5?* [−5] *What is the opposite of −5?* [5] *What is the opposite of the opposite of 5?* [5]

Interpret

- Read the problem as a class. Ask: *What operation would you use to find the difference between the pounds collected and the goal of 1,000 pounds?* [Subtraction]
- Have students explain how they could show whether or not the difference was the amount above or below the goal.

Analyze

- Have students explain what they know from the position of a point in relation to zero.
- Discuss how to use the number line to decide which letter has the greatest value even though they don't know exactly which integer each letter represents.

SMP Tip: As students use signed numbers to solve problems involving real-world situations, they must reason abstractly and quantitatively (*SMP 2*) to describe the problem and solution using mathematical terms. When students use models to show the situations, help them use concrete representations to understand the abstract concepts involved.

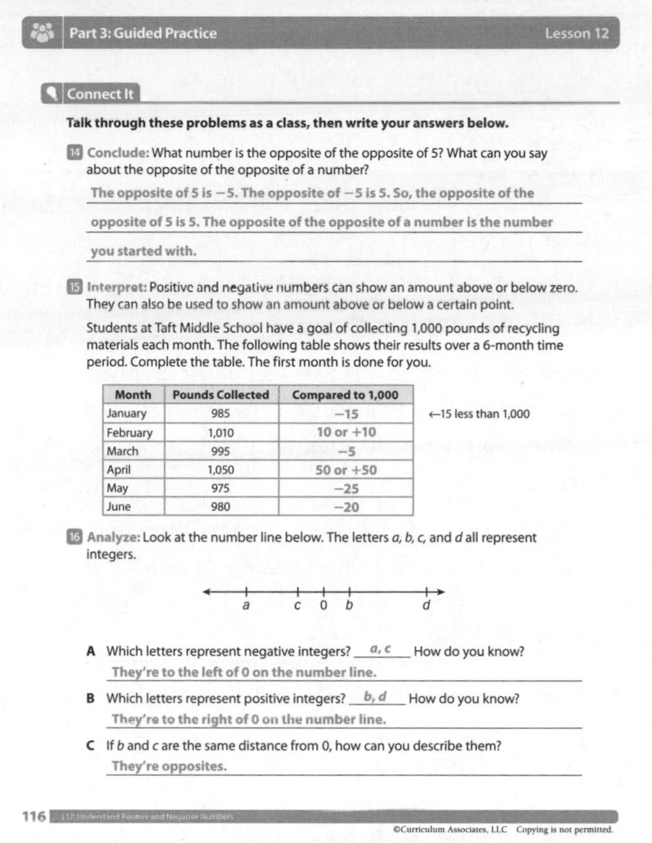

Part 3: Guided Practice Lesson 12

Connect It

Talk through these problems as a class, then write your answers below.

14 **Conclude:** What number is the opposite of the opposite of 5? What can you say about the opposite of the opposite of a number?
The opposite of 5 is −5. The opposite of −5 is 5. So, the opposite of the opposite of 5 is 5. The opposite of the opposite of a number is the number you started with.

15 **Interpret:** Positive and negative numbers can show an amount above or below zero. They can also be used to show an amount above or below a certain point.

Students at Taft Middle School have a goal of collecting 1,000 pounds of recycling materials each month. The following table shows their results over a 6-month time period. Complete the table. The first month is done for you.

Month	Pounds Collected	Compared to 1,000
January	985	−15
February	1,010	10 or +10
March	995	−5
April	1,050	50 or +50
May	975	−25
June	980	−20

←15 less than 1,000

16 **Analyze:** Look at the number line below. The letters *a*, *b*, *c*, and *d* all represent integers.

A Which letters represent negative integers? a, c How do you know?
They're to the left of 0 on the number line.

B Which letters represent positive integers? b, d How do you know?
They're to the right of 0 on the number line.

C If *b* and *c* are the same distance from 0, how can you describe them?
They're opposites.

116 L12: Understand Positive and Negative Numbers

AT A GLANCE

Students write and solve a problem about a real-world situation that involves opposite integers.

STEP BY STEP

- Direct students to complete the Put It Together task on their own.
- Encourage students to read the instructions carefully so that they complete the task as directed.
- As students work on their own, walk around to assess their progress and understanding, to answer their questions, and to give additional support, if needed.
- If time permits, have students share their problems with classmates and discuss the answer.

SCORING RUBRICS

See student facsimile page for possible student answers.

A

Points	Expectations
2	The problem is about money or temperature and involves an integer and its opposite. The answer is zero.
1	The problem involves money or temperature and integers, but not opposite integers.
0	The problem does not involve money, temperature, or integers.

B

Points	Expectations
2	The numbers in the student's problem are graphed correctly on a number line.
1	The graph of the numbers is only partially complete or correct.
0	The numbers are incorrectly graphed or not graphed at all.

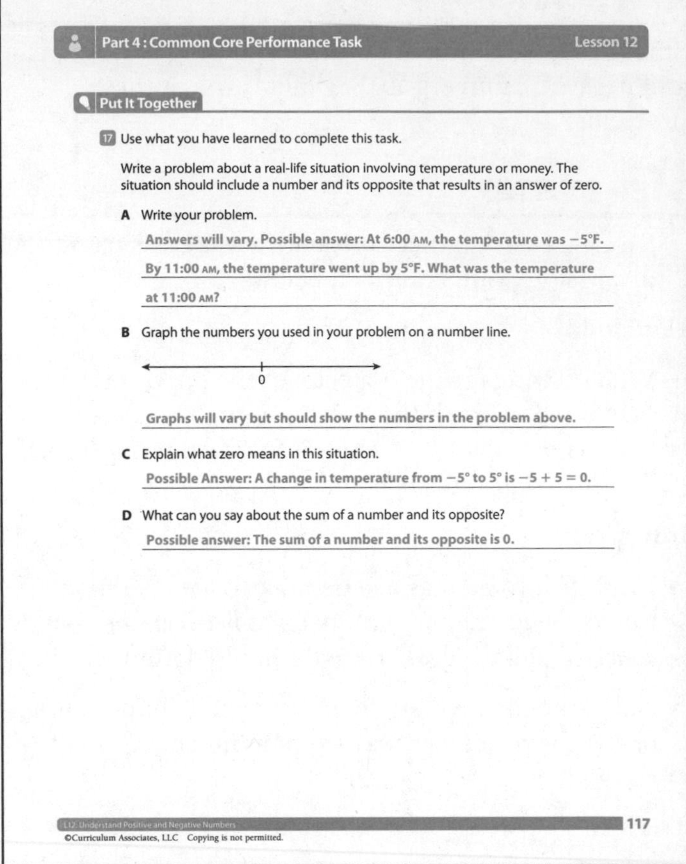

Part 4 : Common Core Performance Task Lesson 12

Put It Together

17 Use what you have learned to complete this task.

Write a problem about a real-life situation involving temperature or money. The situation should include a number and its opposite that results in an answer of zero.

A Write your problem.

Answers will vary. Possible answer: At 6:00 AM, the temperature was -5°F. By 11:00 AM, the temperature went up by 5°F. What was the temperature at 11:00 AM?

B Graph the numbers you used in your problem on a number line.

Graphs will vary but should show the numbers in the problem above.

C Explain what zero means in this situation.

Possible Answer: A change in temperature from -5° to 5° is $-5 + 5 = 0$.

D What can you say about the sum of a number and its opposite?

Possible answer: The sum of a number and its opposite is 0.

L12: Understand Positive and Negative Numbers 117

©Curriculum Associates, LLC Copying is not permitted.

C

Points	Expectations
2	Student shows that 0 is the result of adding opposite integers and relates the 0 to the context of the problem.
1	Student shows that 0 is the result of adding opposite integers but does not relate it to the context of the problem.
0	Student did not answer or the answer has nothing to do with opposite integers or the context of the problem.

D

Points	Expectations
2	Student explains that the sum is always 0.
1	Student writes 0 but does not explain why.
0	Student gives a number other than 0 or no response at all.

Intervention Activity

Explore Opposite Integers.

Materials: tape, paper, markers

Write the integers from −8 to +8 on sheets of paper. Use the papers and tape to create a number line on the floor. Have a student stand on −5. Ask how many spaces and in what direction the student would have to move to end up on 0. Have the student confirm it by moving that number of spaces. Write $-5 + 5 = 0$ on the board. Have another student stand on +7. Repeat the questions. Have the student move to 0, counting the number of spaces. Write $+7 + -7 = 0$ on the board. Repeat until students have the idea of opposite integers.

Draw students' attention to the equations on the board. Reinforce the concept of opposite integers. Have students explain the result of adding opposite integers in their own words.

On-Level Activity

Illustrate signed numbers involving fractions.

Materials: colored pencils

Have students draw a number line labeled with the integers from −3 to +3. Ask students to show $\frac{1}{4}$, $\frac{1}{2}$, and $\frac{3}{4}$ between 0 and +1. Then have them show the fourths between +1 and +2 and between +2 and +3. Check the number lines for accuracy.

Ask students to describe how to use the right side of the number line to label the left side. Emphasize that it should be a mirror image. Once students understand how the two sides are related, have them label the left side with fourths and halves between the integers.

Have students use 5 different colors to mark 5 different points. Have them find the opposite of each point and mark it using the color of the original point. Discuss why the numbers marked with the same color are considered to be opposites.

Challenge Activity

Apply signed numbers to real-world context.

Ask students to think of real-world situations in which they would use signed numbers. Then have them write down 2 specific examples, such as owing $10 (−10) or a seawall 15 feet above the water level (+15). Call on a student to share one example, including both the situation and the signed number. The student will call on a volunteer to give the opposite situation, including the signed number. If the response is incorrect, have another volunteer try another response. The student that gives the correct response will start the activity again with another example. Repeat the activity until all students have had a chance to share at least one example.

Lesson 13 (Student Book pages 118–127)

Absolute Value and Ordering Numbers

LESSON OBJECTIVES

- Write, interpret, and explain statements of order for rational numbers.
- Understand absolute value of a rational number as the distance from 0 on the number line.
- Interpret absolute value as the magnitude of the number from 0 in a real-world situation.
- Distinguish comparisons of absolute value from statements about order.

PREREQUISITE SKILLS

- Compare and order whole numbers.
- Use horizontal and vertical number lines to show rational numbers and represent quantities.
- Describe quantities having opposite values.

VOCABULARY

absolute value: a number's distance from 0 on the number line

THE LEARNING PROGRESSION

In previous grades, students learned to graph, compare, and order positive numbers. They also learned to compare and order positive numbers. This year they extend these skills to the set of rational numbers which includes negative numbers. They solve simple problems involving rational numbers and absolute value. In later grades, students will perform operations on rational numbers. They will use rational numbers throughout their study of algebra.

Ready ***Teacher Toolbox*** Teacher-Toolbox.com

	Prerequisite Skills	6.NS.C.5, 6.NS.C.7a, 6.NS.C.7b 6.NS.C.7c, 6.NS.C.7d
Ready Lessons		✓
Tools for Instruction	✓	✓
Interactive Tutorials		✓

CCSS Focus

6.NS.C.5 Understand that positive and negative numbers are used together to describe quantities having opposite directions or values (e.g., temperature above/below zero, elevation above/below sea level, credits/debits, positive/negative electric charge); use positive and negative numbers to represent quantities in real-world contexts, explaining the meaning of 0 in each situation.

6.NS.C.7 Understand ordering and absolute value of rational numbers.

a. Interpret statements of inequality as statements about the relative position of two numbers on a number line. *For example, interpret $-3 > -7$ as a statement that -3 is located to the right of -7 on a number line oriented from left to right.*

b. Write, interpret, and explain statements of order for rational numbers in real-world contexts. *For example, write $-3°C > -7°C$ to express the fact that $-3°C$ is warmer than $-7°C$.*

c. Understand the absolute value of a rational number as its distance from 0 on the number line; interpret absolute value as magnitude for a positive or negative quantity in a real-world situation. *For example, for an account balance of -30 dollars, write $|-30| = 30$ to describe the size of the debt in dollars.*

d. Distinguish comparisons of absolute value from statements about order. *For example, recognize that an account balance less than -30 dollars represents a debt greater than 30 dollars.*

ADDITIONAL STANDARDS: ***6.NS.C.6*** *(see page A42 for full text)*

STANDARDS FOR MATHEMATICAL PRACTICE: ***SMP 1–4, 6*** *(see page A9 for full text)*

AT A GLANCE

Students read a problem and answer a series of questions. Students use a vertical number line to visualize the distance of a point from 0.

STEP BY STEP

- Tell students this page models the distance a number is from zero. Mention that the distance is also called the absolute value.
- Have students read the problem at the top of the page.
- Work through Explore It as a class.
- Discuss the numbering of the number line. Point out that the positive numbers increase from 0 and the negative numbers decrease from 0. Note that they are a mirror image of each other.
- Ask student pairs or groups to explain their answers for questions about the distance from 0.

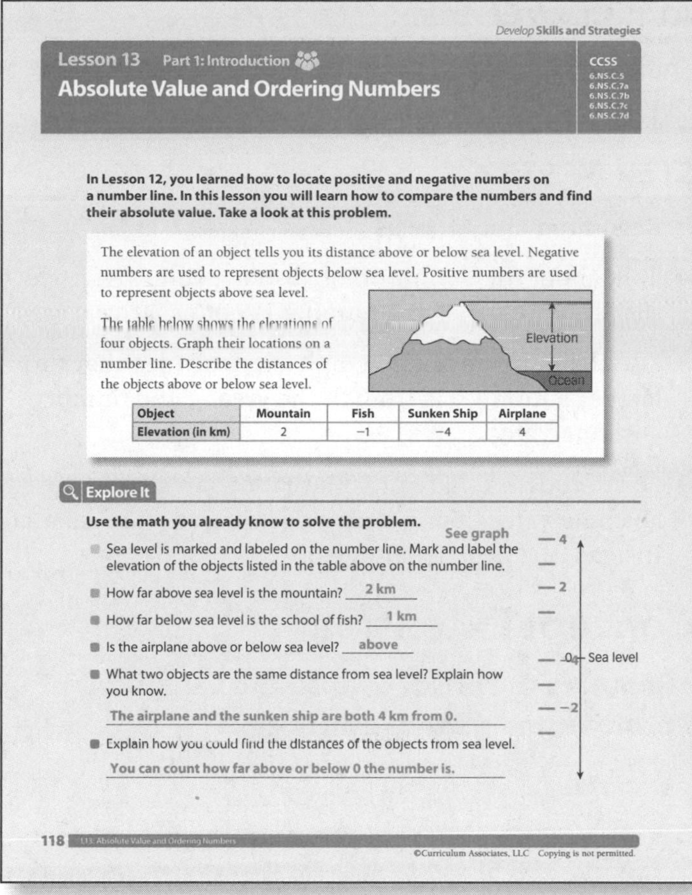

Develop **Skills and Strategies**

Lesson 13 Part 1: Introduction

Absolute Value and Ordering Numbers

CCSS 6.NS.C.5 6.NS.C.7a 6.NS.C.7b 6.NS.C.7c 6.NS.C.7d

In Lesson 12, you learned how to locate positive and negative numbers on a number line. In this lesson you will learn how to compare the numbers and find their absolute value. Take a look at this problem.

The elevation of an object tells you its distance above or below sea level. Negative numbers are used to represent objects below sea level. Positive numbers are used to represent objects above sea level.

The table below shows the elevations of four objects. Graph their locations on a number line. Describe the distances of the objects above or below sea level.

Object	Mountain	Fish	Sunken Ship	Airplane
Elevation (in km)	2	−1	−4	4

Explore It

Use the math you already know to solve the problem.

- Sea level is marked and labeled on the number line. Mark and label the elevation of the objects listed in the table above on the number line. **See graph**
- How far above sea level is the mountain? **2 km**
- How far below sea level is the school of fish? **1 km**
- Is the airplane above or below sea level? **above**
- What two objects are the same distance from sea level? Explain how you know. **The airplane and the sunken ship are both 4 km from 0.**
- Explain how you could find the distances of the objects from sea level. **You can count how far above or below 0 the number is.**

ELL Support

- Draw two rectangles on the board, one above the other. In the top rectangle, write *above* and in the bottom rectangle write *below*.
- Discuss the words *above* and *below*. Hold a pen above a pencil. Say, *The pen is above the pencil. The pencil is below the pen*. Have volunteers give other examples.
- Write *higher* in the top rectangle and *lower* in the bottom rectangle. Again, discuss and illustrate the meaning of the words.
- Repeat with other phrases such as *greater than (more than)* and *less than*.

SMP Tip: When students use number lines to illustrate the relative values of rational numbers, they are modeling with mathematics. Encourage them to create a model using the information in the problem and then use the relationships shown by the model to solve the problem (*SMP 4*).

Mathematical Discourse

- *The table shows fish and a sunken ship as things below sea level. What other examples can you add?*

  Responses might include coral reefs, submarines, tunnels and cables, or underwater volcanoes and vents. Most students will be able to offer ideas given a bit of wait time. If possible, keep a written list, and when suggestions slow down, ask students to think about the item on the list that is the farthest below sea level.

- *How can you use a number line to show distances above and below sea level?*

  Student responses should note that the distances above sea level are above or to the right of 0 and distances below sea level are below or to the left of 0.

AT A GLANCE

Students relate the distance from zero to the absolute value of a number.

STEP BY STEP

- Read Find Out More as a class.
- Talk about the definition of absolute value. Ask why the absolute value of a number is not negative.
- Use the number line to emphasize the idea that the farther a number is from 0, the greater the number's absolute value.
- Have students share other situations in which an absolute value, along with a descriptive word, is used instead of a negative number.

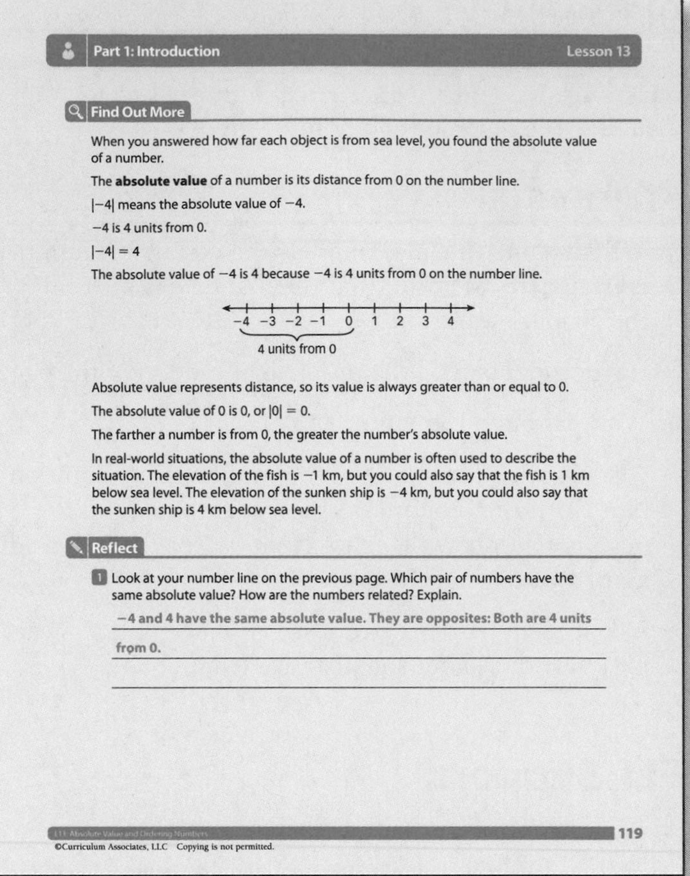

Part 1: Introduction Lesson 13

Find Out More

When you answered how far each object is from sea level, you found the absolute value of a number.

The **absolute value** of a number is its distance from 0 on the number line.

$|-4|$ means the absolute value of -4.

-4 is 4 units from 0.

$|-4| = 4$

The absolute value of -4 is 4 because -4 is 4 units from 0 on the number line.

Absolute value represents distance, so its value is always greater than or equal to 0.

The absolute value of 0 is 0, or $|0| = 0$.

The farther a number is from 0, the greater the number's absolute value.

In real-world situations, the absolute value of a number is often used to describe the situation. The elevation of the fish is -1 km, but you could also say that the fish is 1 km below sea level. The elevation of the sunken ship is -4 km, but you could also say that the sunken ship is 4 km below sea level.

Reflect

1 Look at your number line on the previous page. Which pair of numbers have the same absolute value? How are the numbers related? Explain.

-4 and 4 have the same absolute value. They are opposites: Both are 4 units from 0.

L13: Absolute Value and Ordering Numbers 119

©Curriculum Associates, LLC Copying is not permitted.

Concept Extension

Compare the effect of absolute values on positive and negative integers.

Materials: colored pencils

- On a number line, have students use green Xs to locate 3, 4, 5, and 6. Ask, *Do the numbers increase or decrease as they go from 3 to 6?* [increase]
- On the same number line, have students use blue Xs to locate $|3|$, $|4|$, $|5|$, and $|6|$. Ask, *Do the absolute values increase or decrease as they go from $|3|$ to $|6|$?* [increase]
- On another number line, have students use red Xs to locate -3, -4, -5, and -6. Ask, *Do the numbers increase or decrease as they go from -3 to -6?* [decrease]
- On the same number line, have students use purple Xs to locate $|-3|$, $|-4|$, $|-5|$, and $|-6|$. Ask, *Do the absolute values increase or decrease as they go from $|-3|$ to $|-6|$?* [increase]
- Discuss the following: When the numbers are positive, the absolute values increase as the numbers increase, but when the numbers are negative, the absolute values increase as the numbers decrease. Have students explain why.

Real-World Connection

Encourage students to think of everyday situations in which positive and negative numbers are used in the same context.

Examples: temperatures above and below zero, having money and owing money

AT A GLANCE

Students use a number line and inequality symbols to compare positive and negative numbers.

STEP BY STEP

- Read the problem at the top of the page as a class.
- As students look at Picture It, discuss that on a horizontal number line, the number on the right is greater than the number on the left.
- As students read each Model It, review the meaning of the symbols $<$ and $>$. Read each inequality aloud using the proper terminology.

SMP Tip: Students use the number line as a tool for comparing numbers and absolute value. Regularly ask students to use the number line in their work and explanations so they develop a strong mental association between these concepts and the model (*SMP 5*).

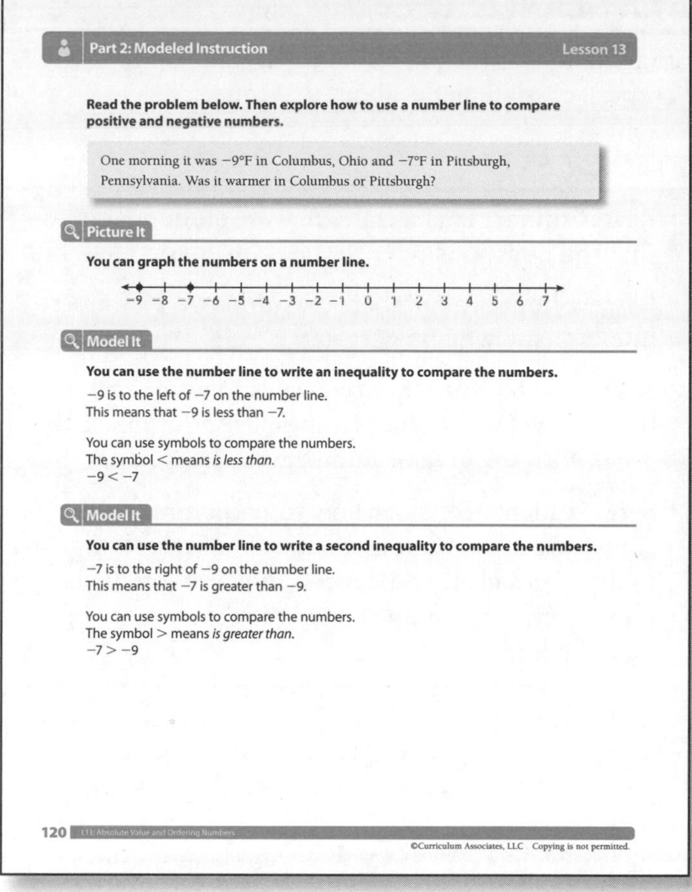

Part 2: Modeled Instruction Lesson 13

Read the problem below. Then explore how to use a number line to compare positive and negative numbers.

One morning it was -9°F in Columbus, Ohio and -7°F in Pittsburgh, Pennsylvania. Was it warmer in Columbus or Pittsburgh?

Picture It

You can graph the numbers on a number line.

Model It

You can use the number line to write an inequality to compare the numbers.

-9 is to the left of -7 on the number line.
This means that -9 is less than -7.

You can use symbols to compare the numbers.
The symbol $<$ means *is less than.*
$-9 < -7$

Model It

You can use the number line to write a second inequality to compare the numbers.

-7 is to the right of -9 on the number line.
This means that -7 is greater than -9.

You can use symbols to compare the numbers.
The symbol $>$ means *is greater than.*
$-7 > -9$

120 L13: Absolute Value and Ordering Numbers

©Curriculum Associates, LLC Copying is not permitted.

Concept Extension

Illustrate the converse nature of $a < b$ and $b > a$.

- Write 6 and -7 on the board. Ask students to tell which number is less. Circle the -7.
- Tell students that the inequality symbol points to the lesser number. Add the $>$ symbol to show the number sentence $6 > -7$. Read it aloud as a class.
- Reverse the order of the numbers and repeat the process so that the final inequality is $-7 < 6$. Read it aloud as a class.
- Have students compare and contrast $6 > -7$ and $-7 < 6$. Make sure they notice that not only is the order reversed, but the sign is also reversed.
- Go through the steps again with -4 and -2. Discuss why $-4 < -2$ and $-2 > -4$ mean the same thing even though they seem to be opposite.

Mathematical Discourse

- *You know that $9 > 7$, so why isn't $-9 > -7$?*

  Student responses should indicate that 9 is to the right of 7 on the horizontal number line, so it is greater, and -9 is to the left of -7 on the horizontal number line, so it is less.

- *How can you use the numbers' positions on a number line to compare them?*

  Student responses should note that the lesser number is to the left of the other number on a horizontal number line and below it on a vertical number line.

- *One way to remember what the inequality symbols mean is that the symbol points to the lesser number. Have you learned or created other ways to remember what the symbols mean?*

AT A GLANCE

Students revisit the problem on page 120 and make comparison statements about two integers.

STEP BY STEP

- Read Connect It as a class. Be sure students know that the questions refer to the problem on page 120.
- Review how two numbers' positions on a number line indicate which is greater.
- Point out that there are two ways to write each inequality. One begins with the lesser number, the other with the greater number.
- After students consider how to use a number line to compare any two numbers, have them work together to develop a clear and concise explanation. Once they agree, write it on the board or on a piece of poster board.

SMP Tip: Students must attend to precision when they develop a set of instructions that tells how to compare numbers. Listen for anything students omit or are unclear about. Challenge them to refine their instructions so that other students could follow them easily (*SMP 6*).

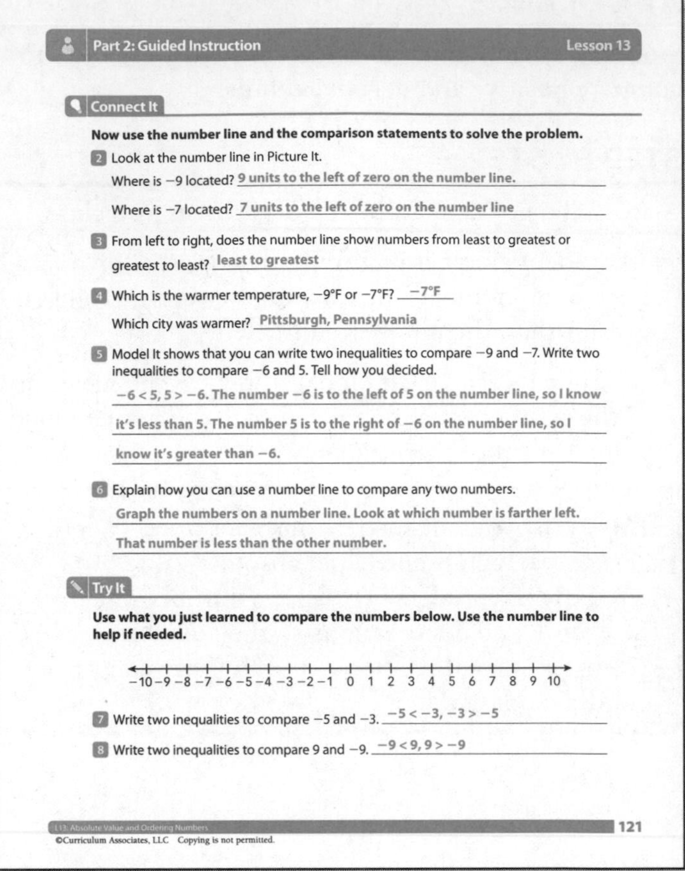

Part 2: Guided Instruction Lesson 13

Connect It

Now use the number line and the comparison statements to solve the problem.

2 Look at the number line in Picture It.

Where is −9 located? 9 units to the left of zero on the number line.

Where is −7 located? 7 units to the left of zero on the number line

3 From left to right, does the number line show numbers from least to greatest or greatest to least? least to greatest

4 Which is the warmer temperature, −9°F or −7°F? −7°F

Which city was warmer? Pittsburgh, Pennsylvania

5 Model It shows that you can write two inequalities to compare −9 and −7. Write two inequalities to compare −6 and 5. Tell how you decided.

−6 < 5, 5 > −6. The number −6 is to the left of 5 on the number line, so I know it's less than 5. The number 5 is to the right of −6 on the number line, so I know it's greater than −6.

6 Explain how you can use a number line to compare any two numbers.

Graph the numbers on a number line. Look at which number is farther left. That number is less than the other number.

Try It

Use what you just learned to compare the numbers below. Use the number line to help if needed.

7 Write two inequalities to compare −5 and −3. −5 < −3, −3 > −5

8 Write two inequalities to compare 9 and −9. −9 < 9, 9 > −9

L13: Absolute Value and Ordering Numbers 121

©Curriculum Associates, LLC Copying is not permitted.

TRY IT SOLUTIONS

7 *Solution:* $-5 < -3$ and $-3 > -5$. Students may visualize the location of the integers on a number line.

ERROR ALERT: Students who wrote $-3 < -5$ and $-5 > -3$ may have disregarded the negative signs or compared the absolute values of the integers instead of the integers themselves.

8 *Solution:* $-9 < 9$ and $9 > -9$. Students may visualize the location of the integers on a number line.

AT A GLANCE

Students read a problem and solve it by ordering positive and negative numbers.

STEP BY STEP

- Read the problem at the top of the page as a class.
- Point out that instead of having two numbers to compare, the problem has four numbers. Ask for student ideas how to put the numbers in order.
- Study the number line in Picture It. Have students explain how you would know where to plot −3.5 and 1.5 even though the number line is labeled with integers.
- As students discuss the information in the first Model It, make sure they express that when a number is to the left of another number, it is less than that number.
- As students read through the second Model It, they should understand that when a number is to the right of another number, it is greater than that number.

SMP Tip: As students discuss possible strategies they might use to solve a problem, they begin to make sense of problems and persevere in solving them. If the first strategy students suggest does not work, encourage them to refine it or develop a new strategy based on reasons it was not successful. *(SMP 1)*

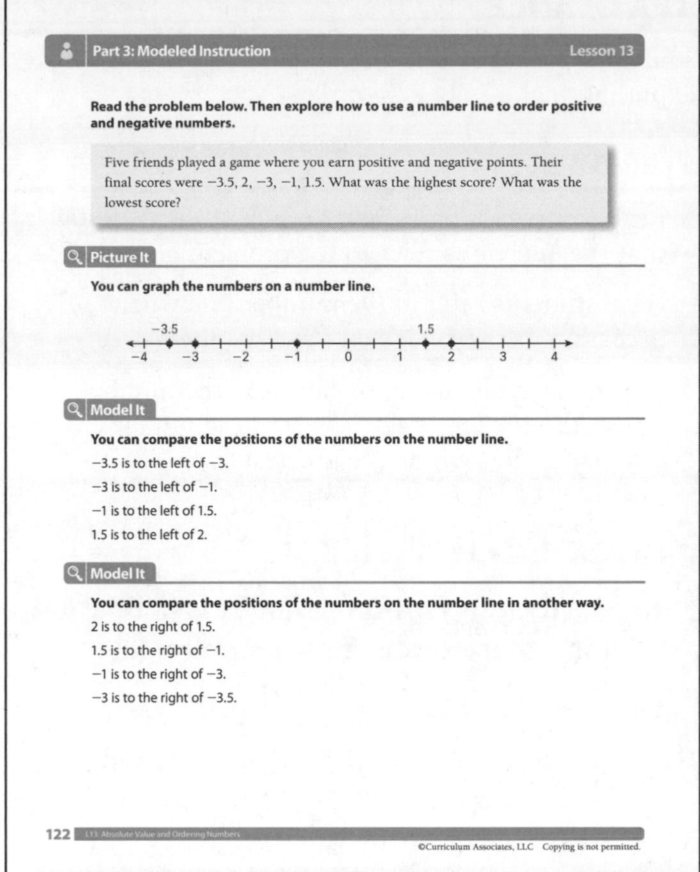
Part 3: Modeled Instruction Lesson 13

Read the problem below. Then explore how to use a number line to order positive and negative numbers.

Five friends played a game where you earn positive and negative points. Their final scores were −3.5, 2, −3, −1, 1.5. What was the highest score? What was the lowest score?

Picture It

You can graph the numbers on a number line.

Model It

You can compare the positions of the numbers on the number line.

−3.5 is to the left of −3.

−3 is to the left of −1.

−1 is to the left of 1.5.

1.5 is to the left of 2.

Model It

You can compare the positions of the numbers on the number line in another way.

2 is to the right of 1.5.

1.5 is to the right of −1.

−1 is to the right of −3.

−3 is to the right of −3.5.

122 L13: Absolute Value and Ordering Numbers

©Curriculum Associates, LLC Copying is not permitted.

Mathematical Discourse

- *Look at the number line. Why is +1.5 to the right of +1, but −3.5 is to the left of −3?*

  Students may explain that +1.5 is between +1 and +2 and −3.5 is between −3 and −4. They may also note that 1.5 is 0.5 greater than 1, so it is to the right of 1, and −3.5 is 0.5 less than −3, so it is to the left of −3.

- *How can you locate numbers that are not integers on a number line?*

  Students may say that they would estimate where to plot a number between two integers. Listen for responses that reveal students are misapplying positive number reasoning to negative numbers.

AT A GLANCE

Students revisit the problem on page 122 to learn how to put rational numbers in order.

STEP BY STEP

- Read Connect It as a class. Be sure students know that the questions refer to the problem on page 122.
- Have students refer to the number line when necessary as they work on the Try It items.
- Encourage students to explain why the number farthest to the left is the least and the number farthest to the right is the greatest.

Hands-On Activity

Practice locating rational numbers in relation to 0 and other numbers on a number line.

Materials: chalkboard, markers, paper, tape

- Draw a blank number line on the board and tape a sheet of paper with the number 0 to the center.
- Instruct students to prepare 6 sheets of paper, 3 with positive numbers and 3 with negative numbers.
- Call on one student to tape one number on the number line, locating it in relation to the 0. Have the class decide if the number is located correctly.
- Choose another student to tape another number on the board, deciding how to locate the number in relation to the 0 and the other number on the board. (If necessary, the student may move the first number to make space for the new number.) The class will decide if the numbers are in proper order.
- Continue until 6 numbers are taped to the board in the correct order from lowest to highest. As a class, read the numbers aloud. Then take down all except the 0 and begin again.

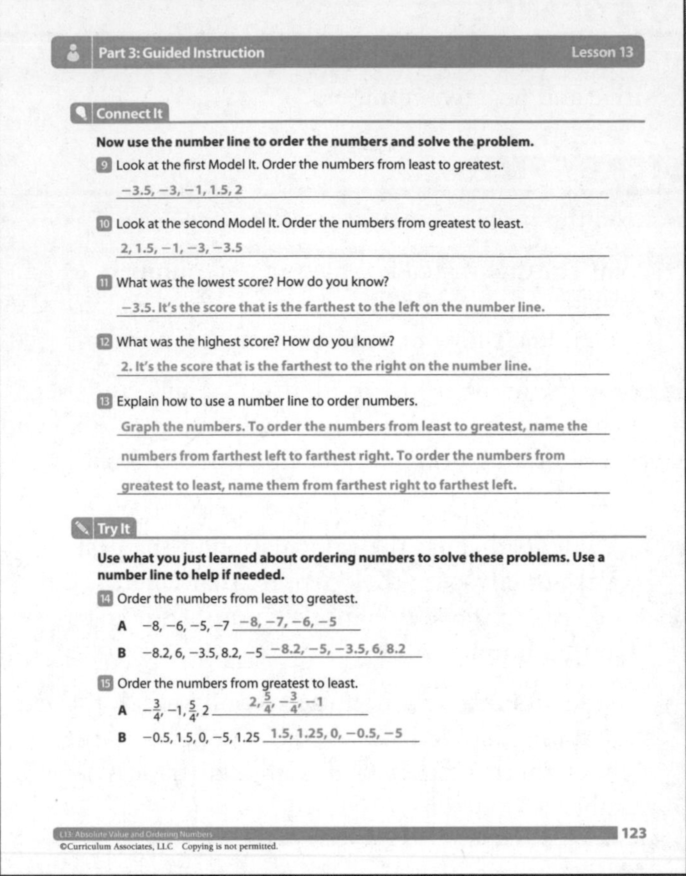

Part 3: Guided Instruction Lesson 13

Connect It

Now use the number line to order the numbers and solve the problem.

9 Look at the first Model It. Order the numbers from least to greatest.

−3.5, −3, −1, 1.5, 2

10 Look at the second Model It. Order the numbers from greatest to least.

2, 1.5, −1, −3, −3.5

11 What was the lowest score? How do you know?

−3.5. It's the score that is the farthest to the left on the number line.

12 What was the highest score? How do you know?

2. It's the score that is the farthest to the right on the number line.

13 Explain how to use a number line to order numbers.

Graph the numbers. To order the numbers from least to greatest, name the numbers from farthest left to farthest right. To order the numbers from greatest to least, name them from farthest right to farthest left.

Try It

Use what you just learned about ordering numbers to solve these problems. Use a number line to help if needed.

14 Order the numbers from least to greatest.

A −8, −6, −5, −7 −8, −7, −6, −5

B −8.2, 6, −3.5, 8.2, −5 −8.2, −5, −3.5, 6, 8.2

15 Order the numbers from greatest to least.

A $-\frac{3}{4}, -1, \frac{5}{4}, 2$ $2, \frac{5}{4}, -\frac{3}{4}, -1$

B −0.5, 1.5, 0, −5, 1.25 1.5, 1.25, 0, −0.5, −5

L13: Absolute Value and Ordering Numbers 123

©Curriculum Associates, LLC Copying is not permitted.

TRY IT SOLUTIONS

14 *Solution:* A. −8, −7, −6, −5;
B. −8.2, −5, −3.5, 6, 8.2;
Students may arrange the numbers by plotting them as points on a number line.

15 *Solution:* A. $2, \frac{5}{4}, -\frac{3}{4}, -1$;
B. 1.5, 1.25, 0, −0.5, −5;
Students may arrange the numbers by plotting them as points on a number line.

ERROR ALERT: Students who wrote 1.25, 1.5, 0, −0.5, −5 may need to review decimal place value because they assume 1.25 > 1.5 because 25 > 5.

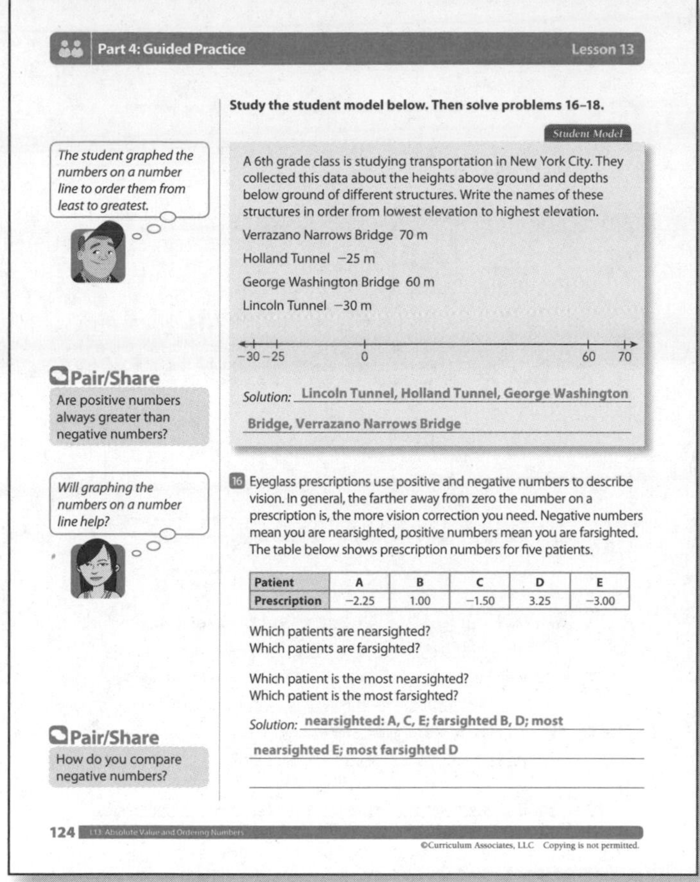

Part 4: Guided Practice Lesson 13

The student graphed the numbers on a number line to order them from least to greatest.

Study the student model below. Then solve problems 16–18.

Student Model

A 6th grade class is studying transportation in New York City. They collected this data about the heights above ground and depths below ground of different structures. Write the names of these structures in order from lowest elevation to highest elevation.

Verrazano Narrows Bridge 70 m

Holland Tunnel −25 m

George Washington Bridge 60 m

Lincoln Tunnel −30 m

Solution: **Lincoln Tunnel, Holland Tunnel, George Washington Bridge, Verrazano Narrows Bridge**

Pair/Share

Are positive numbers always greater than negative numbers?

Will graphing the numbers on a number line help?

16 Eyeglass prescriptions use positive and negative numbers to describe vision. In general, the farther away from zero the number on a prescription is, the more vision correction you need. Negative numbers mean you are nearsighted, positive numbers mean you are farsighted. The table below shows prescription numbers for five patients.

Patient	A	B	C	D	E
Prescription	−2.25	1.00	−1.50	3.25	−3.00

Which patients are nearsighted?
Which patients are farsighted?

Which patient is the most nearsighted?
Which patient is the most farsighted?

Solution: **nearsighted: A, C, E; farsighted B, D; most nearsighted E; most farsighted D**

Pair/Share

How do you compare negative numbers?

124 L13: Absolute Value and Ordering Numbers

©Curriculum Associates, LLC Copying is not permitted.

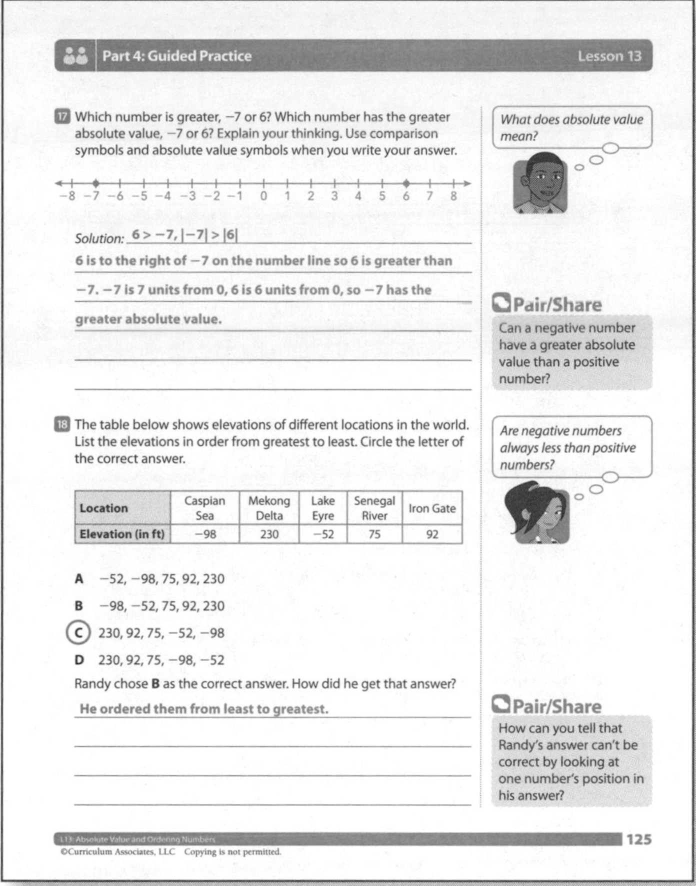

Part 4: Guided Practice Lesson 13

17 Which number is greater, −7 or 6? Which number has the greater absolute value, −7 or 6? Explain your thinking. Use comparison symbols and absolute value symbols when you write your answer.

Solution: **6 > −7, |−7| > |6|**

6 is to the right of −7 on the number line so 6 is greater than −7. −7 is 7 units from 0, 6 is 6 units from 0, so −7 has the greater absolute value.

What does absolute value mean?

Pair/Share

Can a negative number have a greater absolute value than a positive number?

18 The table below shows elevations of different locations in the world. List the elevations in order from greatest to least. Circle the letter of the correct answer.

Location	Caspian Sea	Mekong Delta	Lake Eyre	Senegal River	Iron Gate
Elevation (in ft)	−98	230	−52	75	92

A −52, −98, 75, 92, 230

B −98, −52, 75, 92, 230

C 230, 92, 75, −52, −98

D 230, 92, 75, −98, −52

Randy chose **B** as the correct answer. How did he get that answer?

He ordered them from least to greatest.

Are negative numbers always less than positive numbers?

Pair/Share

How can you tell that Randy's answer can't be correct by looking at one number's position in his answer?

L13: Absolute Value and Ordering Numbers 125

©Curriculum Associates, LLC Copying is not permitted.

AT A GLANCE

Students use number lines to solve problems involving comparing rational numbers and their absolute values.

STEP BY STEP

- Ask students to solve the problems individually on pages 124 and 125. Circulate and monitor students' work.
- When students have completed each problem, have them Pair/Share to discuss their solutions with a partner or in a group.

SOLUTIONS

Ex A number line is shown as one way to solve the problem.

16 *Solution:* nearsighted: A, C, E; farsighted: B, D; most nearsighted E; most farsighted D. Students could solve the problem using a number line or using the concept of absolute value. ***(DOK 1)***

17 *Solution:* 6 > −7, is to the right of −7; |−7| > |6|, −7 is farther from 0 than 6 is. Students could solve the problem by comparing the positions on a number line. ***(DOK 3)***

18 *Solution:* **C**; Randy listed the numbers from least to greatest.

Explain to students why the other two answer choices are not correct:

A is not correct because they are listed from least to greatest and −98 and −52 are out of order.

D is not correct because −98 is the least number. ***(DOK 3)***

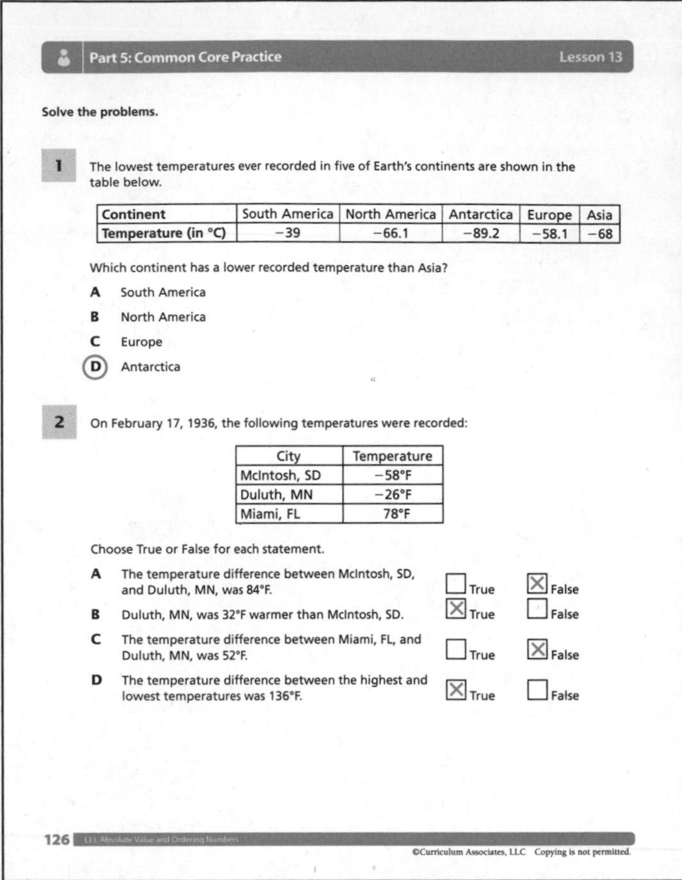

Part 5: Common Core Practice Lesson 13

Solve the problems.

1 The lowest temperatures ever recorded in five of Earth's continents are shown in the table below.

Continent	South America	North America	Antarctica	Europe	Asia
Temperature (in °C)	−39	−66.1	−89.2	−58.1	−68

Which continent has a lower recorded temperature than Asia?

A South America

B North America

C Europe

(D) Antarctica

2 On February 17, 1936, the following temperatures were recorded:

City	Temperature
McIntosh, SD	−58°F
Duluth, MN	−26°F
Miami, FL	78°F

Choose True or False for each statement.

A The temperature difference between McIntosh, SD, and Duluth, MN, was 84°F. ☐ True ☒ False

B Duluth, MN, was 32°F warmer than McIntosh, SD. ☒ True ☐ False

C The temperature difference between Miami, FL, and Duluth, MN, was 52°F. ☐ True ☒ False

D The temperature difference between the highest and lowest temperatures was 136°F. ☒ True ☐ False

126 L13: Absolute Value and Ordering Numbers ©Curriculum Associates, LLC Copying is not permitted.

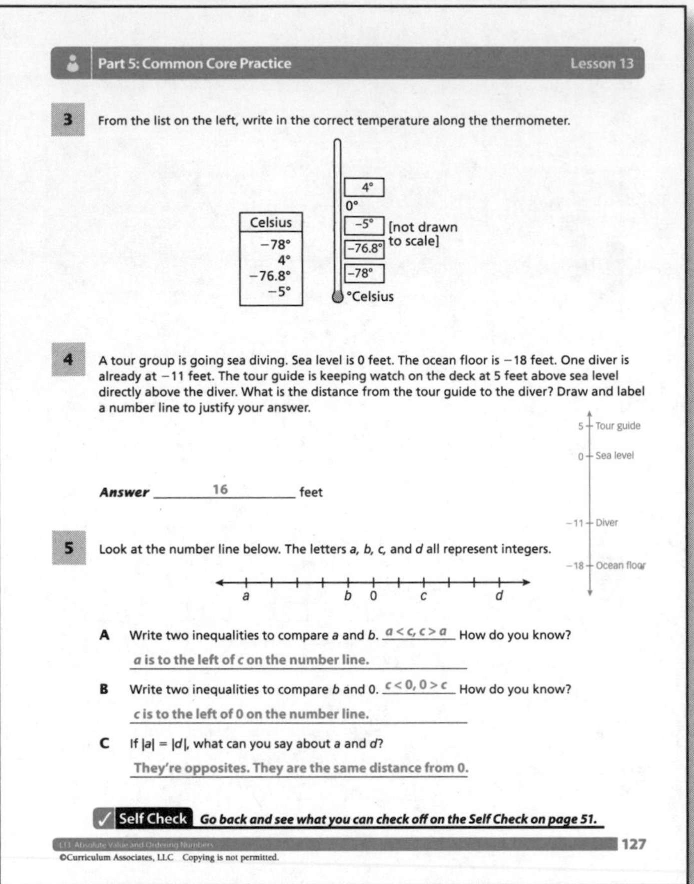

Part 5: Common Core Practice Lesson 13

3 From the list on the left, write in the correct temperature along the thermometer.

Celsius
−78°
4°
−76.8°
−5°

4 A tour group is going sea diving. Sea level is 0 feet. The ocean floor is −18 feet. One diver is already at −11 feet. The tour guide is keeping watch on the deck at 5 feet above sea level directly above the diver. What is the distance from the tour guide to the diver? Draw and label a number line to justify your answer.

Answer 16 feet

5 Look at the number line below. The letters *a*, *b*, *c*, and *d* all represent integers.

A Write two inequalities to compare *a* and *b*. $a < c, c > a$ How do you know?
a is to the left of *c* on the number line.

B Write two inequalities to compare *b* and 0. $c < 0, 0 > c$ How do you know?
c is to the left of 0 on the number line.

C If $|a| = |d|$, what can you say about *a* and *d*?
They're opposites. They are the same distance from 0.

✓ Self Check *Go back and see what you can check off on the Self Check on page 51.*

L13: Absolute Value and Ordering Numbers 127 ©Curriculum Associates, LLC Copying is not permitted.

AT A GLANCE

Students compare and order rational numbers to solve word problems that might appear on a mathematics test.

SOLUTIONS

1 *Solution:* **D**; Show that on a number line −89.2 is the farthest left. ***(DOK 1)***

2 *Solution:* A **False**; B **True**; C **False**; D **True** ***(DOK 2)***

3 *Solution:* See student book page above for solution. Write the temperatures in their correct locations on the thermometer. ***(DOK 2)***

4 *Solution:* 16; See student book page above for possible student number line. ***(DOK 3)***

5 *Solution:* A. $a < b$, $b > a$, *a* is to the left of *b*;
B. $b < 0$, $0 > b$, *b* is left of 0;
C. They are opposites and the same distance from 0.
(DOK 3)

Assessment and Remediation

- Ask students to list −2, 3, −4, and 1 in order from least to greatest. [−4, −2, 1, 3]
- For students who are struggling, use the chart below to guide remediation.
- After providing remediation, check students' understanding. Ask students to list 3, −5, −1, and 4 in order from least to greatest. [−5, −1, 3, 4]

If the error is . . .	Students may . . .	To remediate . . .
1, −2, 3, −4	have disregarded the negative signs.	Have students graph the numbers on a number line and note that the negative numbers are less than the positive numbers.
3, 1, −2, −4	have listed them from greatest to least.	Have students reread the instructions, highlighting the order.
−2, −4, 1, 3	have listed −2 as less than −4.	Have students compare the positions of −4 and −2 on a number line, noting that −4 is to the left of −2 and is therefore less than −2.

Hands-On Activity

Use number lines to compare integers.

Materials: number cube, coin, masking tape

Give each pair of students a number cube and a coin that has a small piece of masking tape on each side. The students should write a plus sign on one side of the coin and a minus sign on the other.

For each round, students will make a number line on a sheet of paper. The first student will roll the number cube and flip the coin and then mark the location of the integer formed on the number line. The second student will do the same thing. The students will then decide which integer is greater. Under the number line, they will write two inequalities, one using $<$ and the other using $>$.

If the integers are the same, they should write an equation.

Challenge Activity

Ask students to order the numbers 5, 7, 9, and 2. Then have them order $|5|$, $|7|$, $|9|$, and $|2|$. Have them compare the two lists of numbers.

Next, have them order −5, −7, −9, and −2 as well as $|-5|$, $|-7|$, $|-9|$, and $|-2|$. Again, have them compare the two lists.

Consider why the order seems the same for positive integers but backwards for negative integers.

Then have them order 5, −7, −9, and 2 and their absolute values $|5|$, $|-7|$, $|-9|$, and $|2|$. Talk about how the two lists are different. Discuss the effect of absolute value on the order of the numbers.

Lesson 14 (Student Book pages 128–139)

The Coordinate Plane

LESSON OBJECTIVES

- Identify the origin and four quadrants of the coordinate plane. Plot ordered pairs in all quadrants.
- Use the signs of coordinates to locate points in quadrants. Recognize that if the coordinates only differ by the signs, the points are reflections across one or both axes.
- Use coordinates and absolute values to find distances between points.
- Solve real-world problems by graphing points in all quadrants.

PREREQUISITE SKILLS

- Understand absolute value as a number's distance from zero.
- Describe quantities having opposite values.
- Graph on a number line and a coordinate plane.

VOCABULARY

quadrants: the four spaces of the coordinate plane that are created when the *x*-axis and *y*-axis intersect at the origin

THE LEARNING PROGRESSION

In elementary school, students worked with positive fractions, decimals, and whole numbers on the number line and in the first quadrant of the coordinate plane.

In Grade 6, students extend the number line to represent all rational numbers. They combine horizontal and vertical number lines to form the coordinate plane. Students locate and describe points within the four quadrants. Students understand how the coordinates change when a point is reflected across an axis. They find the distance between two points when the *x* or *y* coordinate are the same.

A solid understanding of points on the coordinate plane and fluency in plotting them is essential for success in algebra and geometry. Students need to graph accurately and efficiently as they study functions in algebra. The study of geometry requires students to use coordinate planes when studying distances, midpoints, transformations, and many other topics.

Ready *Teacher Toolbox* Teacher-Toolbox.com

	Prerequisite Skills	*6.NS.C.6b, 6.NS.C.6c 6.NS.C.8*
Ready Lessons	✓	✓
Tools for Instruction	✓	✓
Interactive Tutorials	✓	✓

CCSS Focus

6.NS.C.6 Understand a rational number as a point on the number line. Extend number line diagrams and coordinate axes familiar from previous grades to represent points on the line and in the plane with negative number coordinates.

b. Understand signs of numbers in ordered pairs as indicating locations in quadrants of the coordinate plane; recognize that when two ordered pairs differ only by signs, the locations of the points are related by reflections across one or both axes.

c. Find and position integers and other rational numbers on a horizontal or vertical number line; find and position pairs of integers and other rational numbers on a coordinate plane.

6.NS.C.8 Solve real-world and mathematical problems by graphing points in all four quadrants of the coordinate plane. Include use of coordinates and absolute value to find distances between points with the same first coordinate or the same second coordinate.

ADDITIONAL STANDARDS: ***6.NS.C.5, 6.NS.C.7*** *(see page A42 for full text)*

STANDARDS FOR MATHEMATICAL PRACTICE: ***SMP 1, 2, 4–7*** *(see page A9 for full text)*

AT A GLANCE

Students read a problem and answer questions that help them use coordinates to locate points on a coordinate plane.

STEP BY STEP

- Tell students that this page models how to describe locations on the coordinate plane.
- Have students read the problem at the top of the page.
- Work through Explore It as a class.
- Say that the horizontal number line is the *x*-axis. It tells how far left or right a point is from the origin. The vertical number line is the *y*-axis and tells how far above or below the origin a point is.
- Work through the questions, stressing that the first number gives the horizontal distance and the second number tells the vertical distance.
- Ask student pairs or groups to explain their answers for the coordinates of each point. Stress the need for accuracy as they name the coordinates.

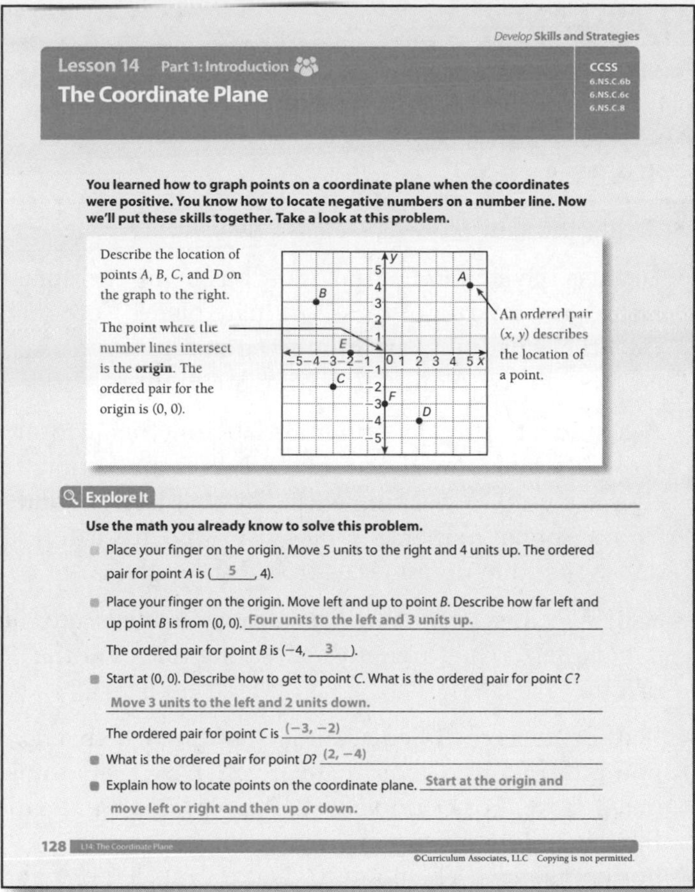

Develop Skills and Strategies

Lesson 14 Part 1: Introduction

The Coordinate Plane

CCSS 6.NS.C.6b 6.NS.C.6c 6.NS.C.8

You learned how to graph points on a coordinate plane when the coordinates were positive. You know how to locate negative numbers on a number line. Now we'll put these skills together. Take a look at this problem.

Describe the location of points *A*, *B*, *C*, and *D* on the graph to the right.

The point where the number lines intersect is the **origin**. The ordered pair for the origin is (0, 0).

An ordered pair (*x*, *y*) describes the location of a point.

Explore It

Use the math you already know to solve this problem.

- Place your finger on the origin. Move 5 units to the right and 4 units up. The ordered pair for point *A* is (_5_, 4).
- Place your finger on the origin. Move left and up to point *B*. Describe how far left and up point *B* is from (0, 0). Four units to the left and 3 units up.

  The ordered pair for point *B* is (−4, _3_).
- Start at (0, 0). Describe how to get to point *C*. What is the ordered pair for point *C*? Move 3 units to the left and 2 units down.

  The ordered pair for point *C* is (−3, −2)
- What is the ordered pair for point *D*? (2, −4)
- Explain how to locate points on the coordinate plane. Start at the origin and move left or right and then up or down.

128 L14: The Coordinate Plane

©Curriculum Associates, LLC Copying is not permitted.

ELL Support

- Review the meanings of *horizontal, vertical, up, down, above, below, left,* and *right*. Use visual examples and verbal explanations.
- Give students a series of instructions using the terms such as these:

  Draw a horizontal line. Write 6 above it and 3 below it.

  Draw a vertical line. Draw a triangle to the right of it and a circle to the left of it.
- After each set of instructions, have students compare drawings. Discuss errors to clear up misconceptions.

SMP Tip: As you stress the need for accuracy when students describe the location of points on a coordinate plane, you encourage them to attend to precision (*SMP 6*). Observe that the coordinate plane is used to communicate exact locations to others, so it is important to be precise when naming the coordinates.

Mathematical Discourse

- *How do you know whether the point is to the left or right of the origin? How do you know how far to move it?*

  Students should say that the sign of the first number of the coordinate tells the direction and the absolute value of that number tells the distance.
- *How do you know whether the point is above or below the origin? How do you know how far to move it?*

  Students should say that the sign of the second number of the coordinate tells the direction and the absolute value of that number tells the distance.

AT A GLANCE

Students learn about the quadrants of a coordinate plane and use them to describe the location of points.

STEP BY STEP

- Read Find Out More as a class.
- Discuss the location of quadrant I as being the upper right-hand quarter of the coordinate plane. Note that the other quadrants are numbered in a counterclockwise direction from quadrant I.
- Ask students why the numerals labeling the quadrant look different from the numbers 1, 2, 3, and 4 that they are used to working with. Say that I, II, III, and IV are Roman numerals. Make sure students can read and write Roman numerals from I through IV.
- Ask, *Why aren't points with a zero coordinate located in a quadrant?* [They are on the dividing line or at the origin.]
- If students have difficulty understanding which axis points with a zero coordinate are on, have them think of a 0 move. For example, (−2, 0) is located 2 units to the left and 0 units up or down, so it stays on the horizontal axis. The point (0, 3) is 0 units left or right and 3 units up, so it stays on the vertical axis.

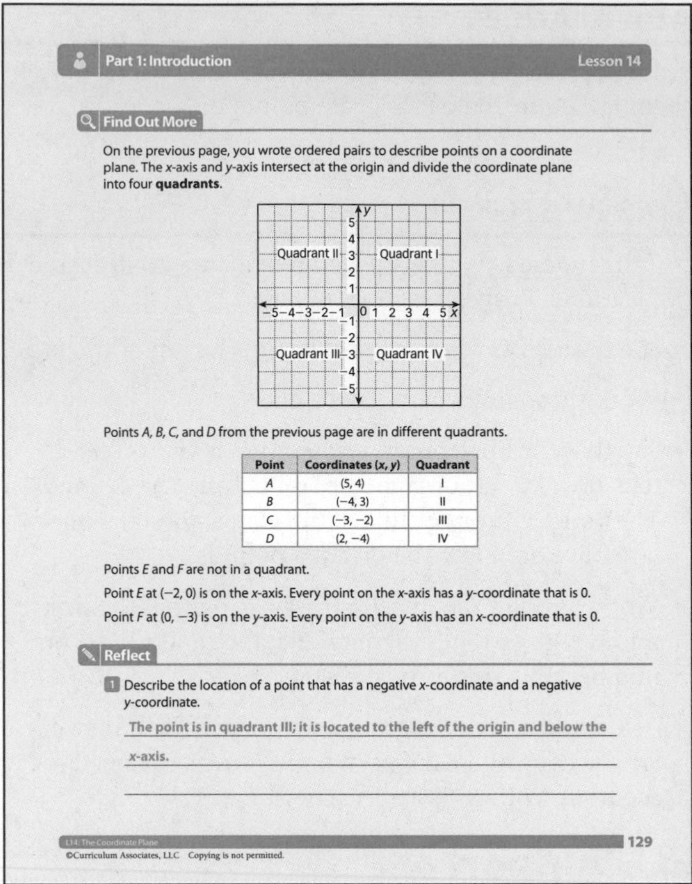

Part 1: Introduction Lesson 14

Find Out More

On the previous page, you wrote ordered pairs to describe points on a coordinate plane. The *x*-axis and *y*-axis intersect at the origin and divide the coordinate plane into four **quadrants**.

Points *A*, *B*, *C*, and *D* from the previous page are in different quadrants.

Point	Coordinates (*x*, *y*)	Quadrant
A	(5, 4)	I
B	(−4, 3)	II
C	(−3, −2)	III
D	(2, −4)	IV

Points *E* and *F* are not in a quadrant.

Point *E* at (−2, 0) is on the *x*-axis. Every point on the *x*-axis has a *y*-coordinate that is 0.

Point *F* at (0, −3) is on the *y*-axis. Every point on the *y*-axis has an *x*-coordinate that is 0.

Reflect

1 Describe the location of a point that has a negative *x*-coordinate and a negative *y*-coordinate.

The point is in quadrant III; it is located to the left of the origin and below the *x*-axis.

L14: The Coordinate Plane 129

©Curriculum Associates, LLC Copying is not permitted.

Concept Extension

Generalize about the signs of coordinates in each quadrant.

- Draw a coordinate plane on the board. Label the quadrants.
- Ask students to identify where the *x*-coordinates are negative and where they are positive. In each quadrant, write *x is negative* or *x is positive.*
- Ask students to identify where the *y*-coordinates are negative and where they are positive. In each quadrant, write *y is negative* or *y is positive.*
- Point to quadrant II. Say that in quadrant II, the *x*-coordinate is always negative and the *y*-coordinate is always positive.
- Call on students to make generalizations about the other three quadrants.

Real-World Connection

Encourage students to think of professions in which giving accurate locations is important.

Examples: air traffic controllers, military planners, forest rangers, oceanographers, geographers, architects

AT A GLANCE

Students use a coordinate plane to model a real-world situation.

STEP BY STEP

- Read the problem at the top of the page as a class.
- Read Model It and discuss how the directions in the second table are based on the coordinates in the first table. Note that all the directions start from the origin.
- Ask students why there is only one direction each for the education building and the dining hall. Discuss what that will mean in terms of the graph.
- Look at the coordinate plane in Graph It. Have students describe the positions of the buildings relative to both the origin and the other buildings.

SMP Tip: When students represent real-world situations on a coordinate plane, they are modeling with mathematics (*SMP 4*). Observe that the model allows people to see both the direction the buildings are from each other as well as how far apart they are.

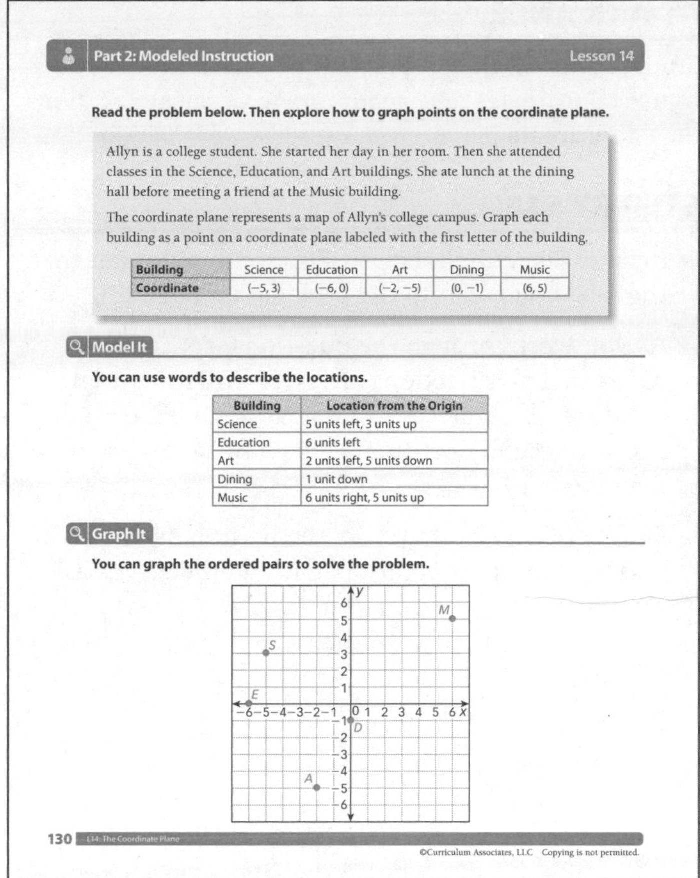

Part 2: Modeled Instruction Lesson 14

Read the problem below. Then explore how to graph points on the coordinate plane.

Allyn is a college student. She started her day in her room. Then she attended classes in the Science, Education, and Art buildings. She ate lunch at the dining hall before meeting a friend at the Music building.

The coordinate plane represents a map of Allyn's college campus. Graph each building as a point on a coordinate plane labeled with the first letter of the building.

Building	Science	Education	Art	Dining	Music
Coordinate	(−5, 3)	(−6, 0)	(−2, −5)	(0, −1)	(6, 5)

Model It

You can use words to describe the locations.

Building	Location from the Origin
Science	5 units left, 3 units up
Education	6 units left
Art	2 units left, 5 units down
Dining	1 unit down
Music	6 units right, 5 units up

Graph It

You can graph the ordered pairs to solve the problem.

130 L14: The Coordinate Plane

©Curriculum Associates, LLC Copying is not permitted.

Mathematical Discourse

- *How would you graph the points using the coordinates only? Explain.*

  Students should explain the thinking process they would use if graphing a point directly from the coordinates. Listen for responses that are similar to the table with words.

- *Would you prefer to graph from a table with words or directly from the coordinates? What are the advantages of each method?*

  Students will have different preferences. However, they should mention that the table gives clear directions and they would be less likely to make a mistake, but graphing directly from the coordinates is faster.

AT A GLANCE

Students revisit the problem on page 130 to learn how to use coordinates and quadrants to describe locations on a coordinate plane.

STEP BY STEP

- Read Connect It as a class. Be sure to point out that the questions refer to the problem on page 130.
- As you work through the questions, continue to stress that all directions are given from the origin. The first coordinate tells how far to go left or right, and the second coordinate tells how far to go up or down.
- Have students explain why the point falls on the y-axis when the x-coordinate is 0 and vice versa.

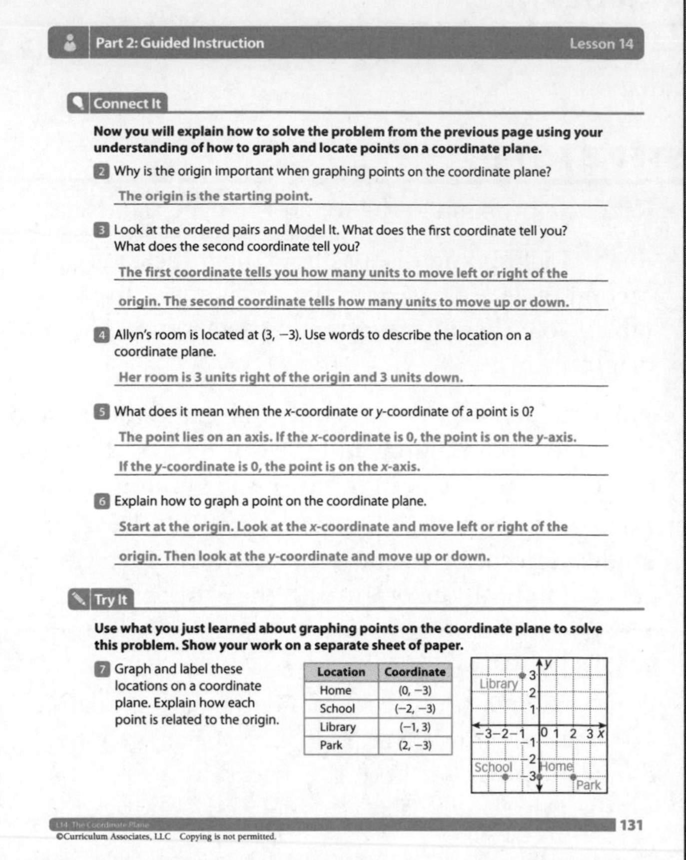
Part 2: Guided Instruction Lesson 14

Connect It

Now you will explain how to solve the problem from the previous page using your understanding of how to graph and locate points on a coordinate plane.

2 Why is the origin important when graphing points on the coordinate plane?

The origin is the starting point.

3 Look at the ordered pairs and Model It. What does the first coordinate tell you? What does the second coordinate tell you?

The first coordinate tells you how many units to move left or right of the origin. The second coordinate tells how many units to move up or down.

4 Allyn's room is located at (3, −3). Use words to describe the location on a coordinate plane.

Her room is 3 units right of the origin and 3 units down.

5 What does it mean when the x-coordinate or y-coordinate of a point is 0?

The point lies on an axis. If the x-coordinate is 0, the point is on the y-axis. If the y-coordinate is 0, the point is on the x-axis.

6 Explain how to graph a point on the coordinate plane.

Start at the origin. Look at the x-coordinate and move left or right of the origin. Then look at the y-coordinate and move up or down.

Try It

Use what you just learned about graphing points on the coordinate plane to solve this problem. Show your work on a separate sheet of paper.

7 Graph and label these locations on a coordinate plane. Explain how each point is related to the origin.

Location	Coordinate
Home	(0, −3)
School	(−2, −3)
Library	(−1, 3)
Park	(2, −3)

L14: The Coordinate Plane 131
©Curriculum Associates, LLC Copying is not permitted.

TRY IT SOLUTION

7 *Solution:* Home: 3 units down from the origin; school: 2 units left, 3 units down; Library: 1 unit left, 3 units up; Park: 2 units right, 3 units down; Students may graph the points and then explain their location using proper mathematical terminology such as coordinates or quadrants.

ERROR ALERT: Students who located home on the x-axis graphed the point (−3, 0) instead of (0, −3).

AT A GLANCE

Students explore the changes in the coordinates of a figure when it is reflected across the *x*- and *y*-axes.

STEP BY STEP

- Read the problem at the top of the page as a class.
- Have students study *ΔABC* and *ΔDEF* on the graph. Ask, *Which vertex in ΔDEF corresponds to point A?* [*D*] *To point B?* [*E*] *To point C?* [*F*] It may be helpful to circle each pair of corresponding vertices with a different color.
- Ask students to identify the corresponding vertices of *ΔABC* and *ΔGHI*.
- Have students study the table in Picture It. Ask them how the coordinates of the corresponding vertices are the same and how they are different.

SMP Tip: When students compare the corresponding coordinates of reflected figures, they are looking for and making use of structure (*SMP 7*). As they develop the ability to recognize and use patterns, they are better able to internalize the concepts being presented.

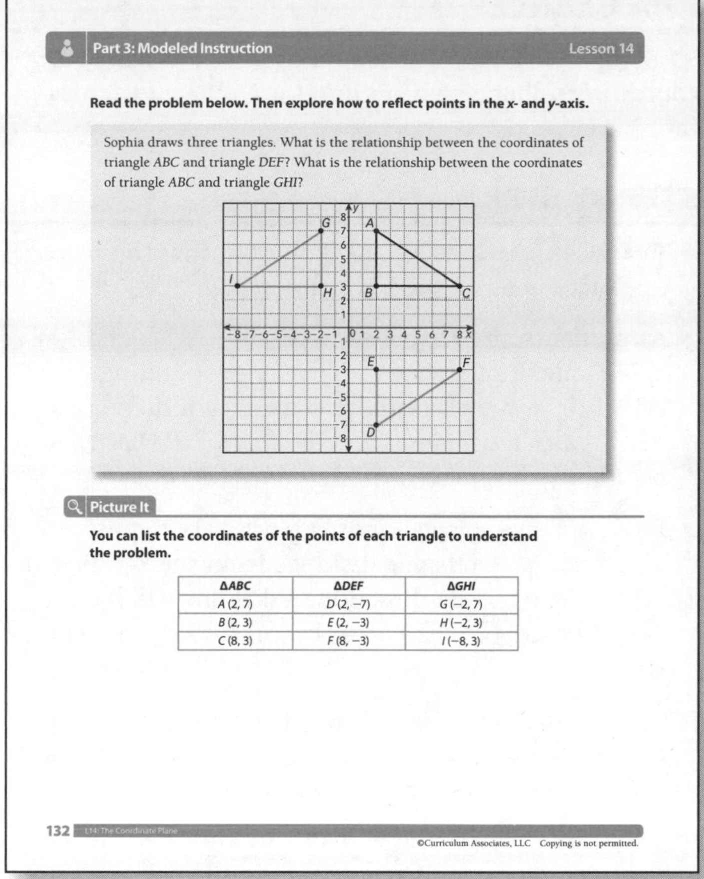

Read the problem below. Then explore how to reflect points in the *x*- and *y*-axis.

Sophia draws three triangles. What is the relationship between the coordinates of triangle *ABC* and triangle *DEF*? What is the relationship between the coordinates of triangle *ABC* and triangle *GHI*?

Picture It

You can list the coordinates of the points of each triangle to understand the problem.

ΔABC	ΔDEF	ΔGHI
A (2, 7)	D (2, −7)	G (−2, 7)
B (2, 3)	E (2, −3)	H (−2, 3)
C (8, 3)	F (8, −3)	I (−8, 3)

Mathematical Discourse

- *Are the triangles shown on the coordinate plane the same shape and size? Explain.*

  Some students may count and compare the number of units on each side of each triangle. Others may cite the definition of reflection, which says that the reflected image is congruent to the original shape. If students respond only that the triangles look—or do not look—the same, follow up by asking them how they could prove their point of view.

- *How do ΔDEF and ΔGHI look different than ΔABC?*

  Students will use their own words to describe the different orientations of the triangles. They may use expressions such as "upside-down" and "sideways" to describe the reflections.

AT A GLANCE

Students revisit the problem on page 132 to learn how coordinates change when figures are reflected across the *x*- and *y*-axes.

STEP BY STEP

- Read Connect It as a class. Point out that the questions refer to the problem on page 132.
- As students answer questions about ΔABC and ΔDEF, make sure they see that corresponding coordinates are the same distance from the *y*-axis. Ask, *Which coordinate stays the same if the horizontal or sideways distance stays the same?* [*x*]
- Point out that corresponding points are opposite integers; they are same distance from the *x*-axis, but are in the opposite direction. Ask, *How will the y-coordinates be different?* [They will have opposite signs.]
- Look at the table. Have students check their hypothesis that the *x*-coordinates are the same and the *y*-coordinates are opposite integers.
- Use similar reasoning with ΔABC and ΔGHI to show that when a figure is reflected over the *y*-axis, corresponding *x*-coordinates are opposite integers and corresponding *y*-coordinates are the same.

Visual Model

- Draw a triangle with vertices (−2, 3), (1, −1), and (−4, 2) on a coordinate plane on the board. Ask students to name the coordinates of each vertex. Label the vertices, using red for the *x*-coordinates and blue for the *y*-coordinates.
- Discuss how to reflect the triangle over the *y*-axis. Draw the reflected triangle. As students name the coordinates of the vertices, label them using the same colors as before. Compare the red *x*- and blue *y*-coordinates of corresponding vertices. Have students make a general rule about a reflection over the *y*-axis.
- Reflect the original triangle over the *x*-axis. Again, have students compare the coordinates and draw conclusions about a reflection over the *x*-axis.

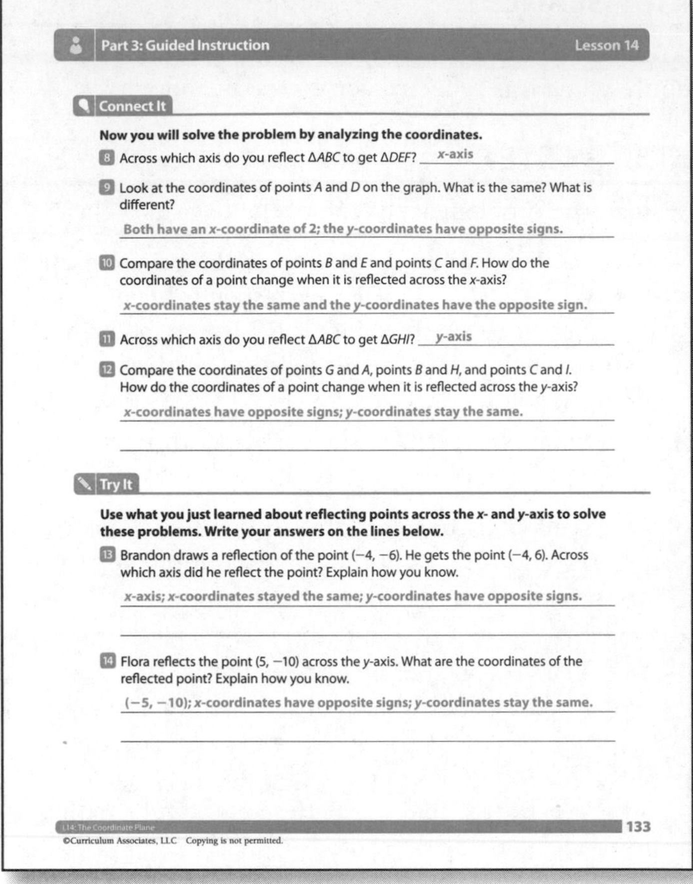

Part 3: Guided Instruction Lesson 14

Connect It

Now you will solve the problem by analyzing the coordinates.

8 Across which axis do you reflect ΔABC to get ΔDEF? *x*-axis

9 Look at the coordinates of points *A* and *D* on the graph. What is the same? What is different?

Both have an *x*-coordinate of 2; the *y*-coordinates have opposite signs.

10 Compare the coordinates of points *B* and *E* and points *C* and *F*. How do the coordinates of a point change when it is reflected across the *x*-axis?

x-coordinates stay the same and the *y*-coordinates have the opposite sign.

11 Across which axis do you reflect ΔABC to get ΔGHI? *y*-axis

12 Compare the coordinates of points *G* and *A*, points *B* and *H*, and points *C* and *I*. How do the coordinates of a point change when it is reflected across the *y*-axis?

x-coordinates have opposite signs; *y*-coordinates stay the same.

Try It

Use what you just learned about reflecting points across the *x*- and *y*-axis to solve these problems. Write your answers on the lines below.

13 Brandon draws a reflection of the point (−4, −6). He gets the point (−4, 6). Across which axis did he reflect the point? Explain how you know.

x-axis; *x*-coordinates stayed the same; *y*-coordinates have opposite signs.

14 Flora reflects the point (5, −10) across the *y*-axis. What are the coordinates of the reflected point? Explain how you know.

(−5, −10); *x*-coordinates have opposite signs; *y*-coordinates stay the same.

L14: The Coordinate Plane 133

©Curriculum Associates, LLC Copying is not permitted.

TRY IT SOLUTIONS

13 *Solution:* The *x*-axis, because the *x*-coordinates stayed the same. Students may use the rules about reflections or plot and analyze the points.

14 *Solution:* (−5, −10), because when a point is reflected across the *y*-axis, the *y*-coordinate stays the same but the *x*-coordinate becomes the opposite. Students may use the rules about reflections or plot and analyze the points.

ERROR ALERT: Students who wrote (5, 10) reflected the point across the *x*-axis instead of the *y*-axis.

AT A GLANCE

Students explore how to solve a problem by finding the distance between points with the same *x*- or *y*-coordinate.

STEP BY STEP

- Read the problem at the top of the page as a class. Have students restate what points *J* and *Z* represent as well as what the problem is asking for.
- Read the first Model It. Remind students that when they count from 4 to −6, they do not count the 4.
- Read the second Model It. Review the meaning of absolute value, stressing that it tells the distance but not the direction. Ask students why they would add the two absolute values to get the total distance.

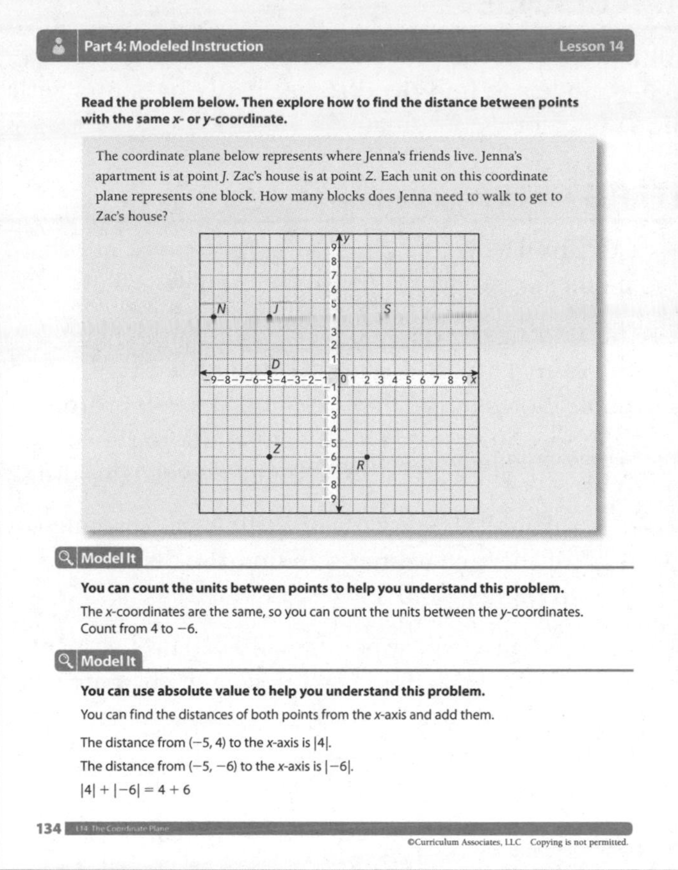

Part 4: Modeled Instruction Lesson 14

Read the problem below. Then explore how to find the distance between points with the same *x*- or *y*-coordinate.

The coordinate plane below represents where Jenna's friends live. Jenna's apartment is at point *J*. Zac's house is at point *Z*. Each unit on this coordinate plane represents one block. How many blocks does Jenna need to walk to get to Zac's house?

Model It

You can count the units between points to help you understand this problem.

The *x*-coordinates are the same, so you can count the units between the *y*-coordinates. Count from 4 to −6.

Model It

You can use absolute value to help you understand this problem.

You can find the distances of both points from the *x*-axis and add them.

The distance from (−5, 4) to the *x*-axis is |4|.

The distance from (−5, −6) to the *x*-axis is |−6|.

|4| + |−6| = 4 + 6

134 L14: The Coordinate Plane

©Curriculum Associates, LLC Copying is not permitted.

Hands-On Activity

Find distance between points.

Materials: grid paper (at least 1-inch grid), pennies

- Give each student a sheet of grid paper and 2 pennies. Instruct students to draw, label, and number the axes on the grid paper. Write (−3, 4) and (5, 4) on the board. Have students mark and label the points and place one penny on each.
- Have students move the penny on (−3, 4) to the *y*-axis and tell how far they moved it. Write 3 under the coordinates (−3, 4) on the board. Have students move the other penny to the *y*-axis and tell how far they moved it. Record 5 under (5, 4).
- Write 3 + 5 = 8. Ask students how the 3 and 5 are related to the coordinates and why the equation represents the distance between the two points.
- Repeat with other pairs of points such as (6, −2) and (−4, −2).

Mathematical Discourse

- *Explain how you can use addition to find the distance between the two points.*

  Students' responses should include how to find the distance of each point from the *x*- or *y*-axis and then the reason for adding the distances.

- *Which is easier for you, counting or adding the absolute values? Explain why.*

  Students' responses will vary.

- *In what situations would adding the absolute values be the most accurate and efficient?*

  Students might mention situations when the distances involve big numbers, fractions, or decimals.

AT A GLANCE

Students revisit the problem on page 134 to learn how to use models to find the distance between points with the same *x*- or *y*-coordinates.

STEP BY STEP

- Read Connect It as a class. Be sure to point out that the questions refer to the problem on page 134.
- After finding the distances between points *J* and *Z* and points *J* and *S*, discuss why you used the *y*-coordinates in the first case and the *x*-coordinates in the second case. Have students refer to the coordinate plane to build a concrete understanding.
- Work through the process of adding the absolute values of the *x*-coordinates to find the distance between points *J* and *S*.
- Have students look at points *J* and *N*. Have students discuss how they could use the idea of absolute value to find the distance between two points in the same quadrant.

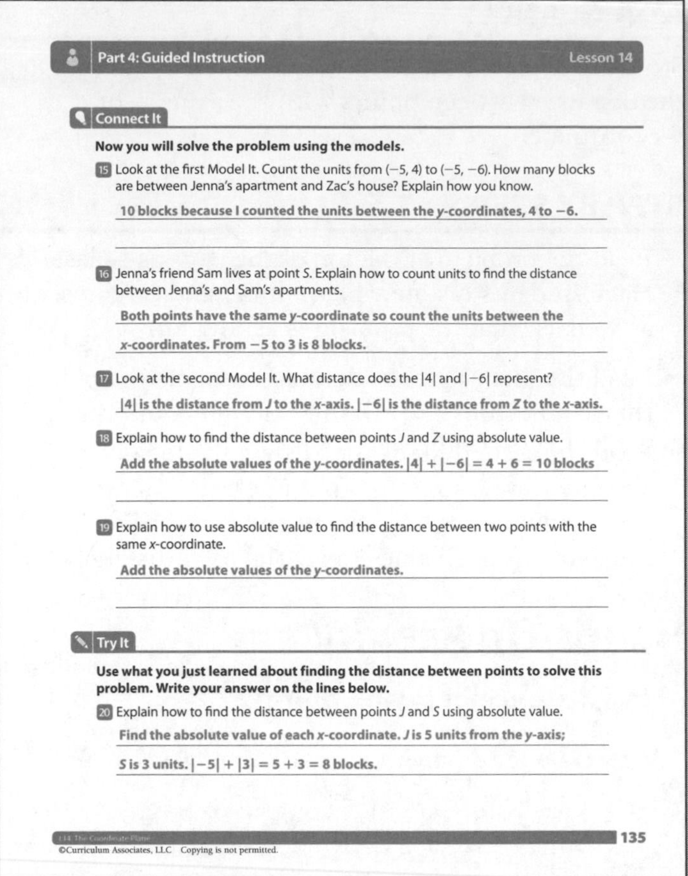

Part 4: Guided Instruction Lesson 14

Connect It

Now you will solve the problem using the models.

15 Look at the first Model It. Count the units from (−5, 4) to (−5, −6). How many blocks are between Jenna's apartment and Zac's house? Explain how you know.

10 blocks because I counted the units between the *y*-coordinates, 4 to −6.

16 Jenna's friend Sam lives at point *S*. Explain how to count units to find the distance between Jenna's and Sam's apartments.

Both points have the same *y*-coordinate so count the units between the *x*-coordinates. From −5 to 3 is 8 blocks.

17 Look at the second Model It. What distance does the |4| and |−6| represent?

|4| is the distance from *J* to the *x*-axis. |−6| is the distance from *Z* to the *x*-axis.

18 Explain how to find the distance between points *J* and *Z* using absolute value.

Add the absolute values of the *y*-coordinates. |4| + |−6| = 4 + 6 = 10 blocks

19 Explain how to use absolute value to find the distance between two points with the same *x*-coordinate.

Add the absolute values of the *y*-coordinates.

Try It

Use what you just learned about finding the distance between points to solve this problem. Write your answer on the lines below.

20 Explain how to find the distance between points *J* and *S* using absolute value.

Find the absolute value of each *x*-coordinate. *J* is 5 units from the *y*-axis; *S* is 3 units. |−5| + |3| = 5 + 3 = 8 blocks.

L14: The Coordinate Plane 135

©Curriculum Associates, LLC Copying is not permitted.

TRY IT SOLUTION

20 *Solution:* 8 blocks. Students may give an explanation such as this: Find the absolute value of each *x*-coordinate. *J* is |−5|, or 5 units from the *y*-axis. *S* is |3|, or 3 units. |−5| + |3| = 5 + 3 = 8.

ERROR ALERT: Students who wrote 2 blocks may have incorrectly thought that −5 is the absolute value of −5.

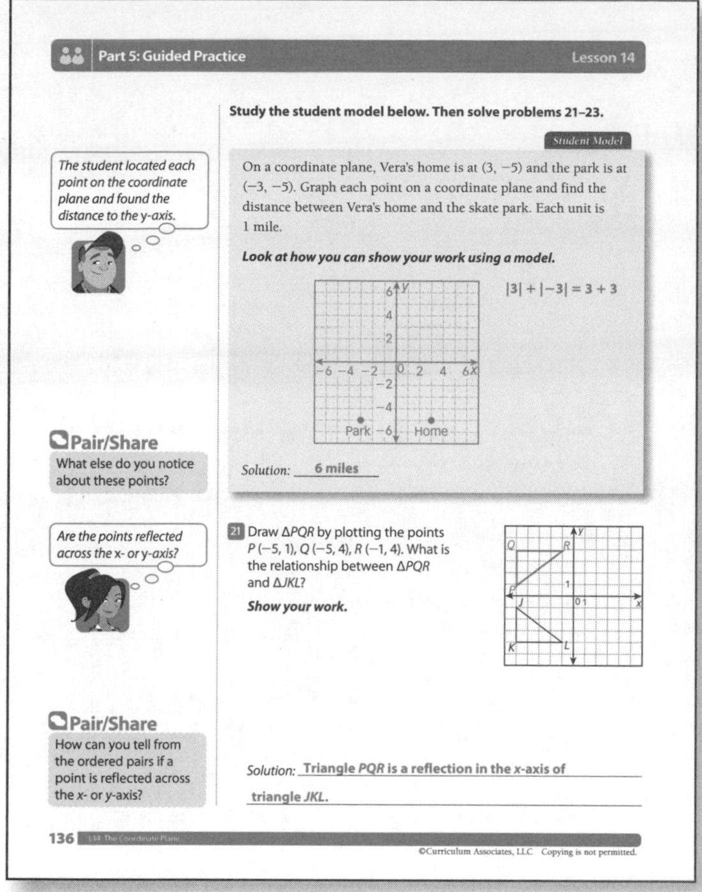

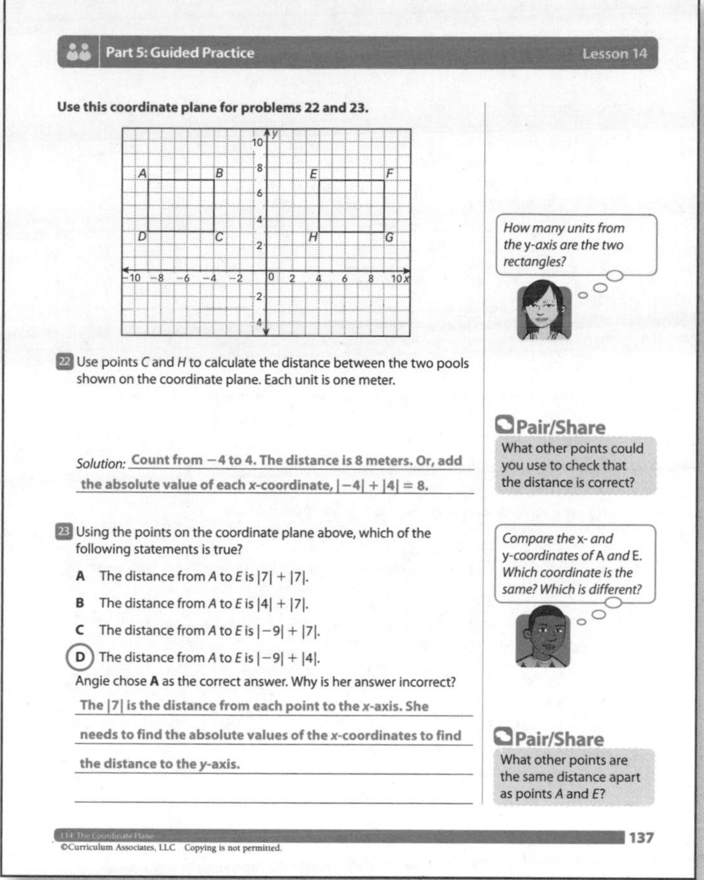

AT A GLANCE

Students will use coordinate planes to plot points, analyze reflected figures, and find distances between points.

STEP BY STEP

- Ask students to solve the problems individually and show their work on a coordinate plane.
- When students have completed each problem, have them Pair/Share to discuss their solutions with a partner or in a group.

SOLUTIONS

Ex A coordinate plane is shown as a model of the problem. The distance is found by adding absolute values.

21 *Solution:* The points in ΔPQR are reflections of those in ΔJKL across the x-axis, or the y-coordinates of P, Q, and R are opposites of the y-coordinates of J, K, and L. Students could analyze the differences between ΔJKL and ΔPQR. ***(DOK 2)***

22 *Solution:* 8. Students could add the absolute values of the x-coordinates, or they could count. ***(DOK 1)***

23 *Solution:* **D**. Angie added the absolute values of the y-coordinates instead of the x-coordinates.

Explain to students why the other two answer choices are not correct:

B is not correct because the x-coordinate of A is -9, not 7.

C is not correct because the x-coordinate of E is 4, not 7. ***(DOK 3)***

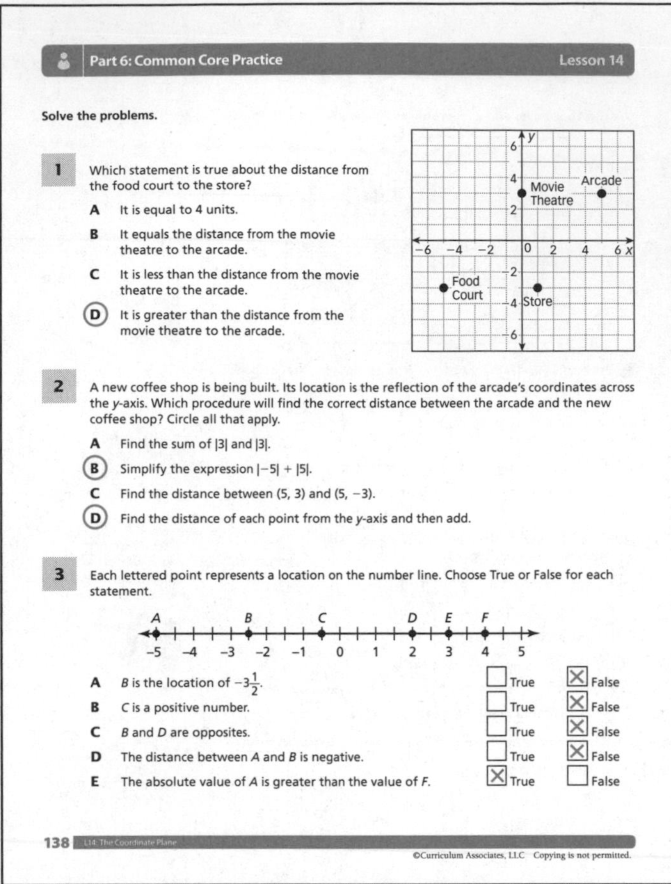

Part 6: Common Core Practice Lesson 14

Solve the problems.

1 Which statement is true about the distance from the food court to the store?

A It is equal to 4 units.

B It equals the distance from the movie theatre to the arcade.

C It is less than the distance from the movie theatre to the arcade.

(D) It is greater than the distance from the movie theatre to the arcade.

2 A new coffee shop is being built. Its location is the reflection of the arcade's coordinates across the *y*-axis. Which procedure will find the correct distance between the arcade and the new coffee shop? Circle all that apply.

A Find the sum of |3| and |3|.

(B) Simplify the expression |−5| + |5|.

C Find the distance between (5, 3) and (5, −3).

(D) Find the distance of each point from the *y*-axis and then add.

3 Each lettered point represents a location on the number line. Choose True or False for each statement.

		True	False
A	*B* is the location of $-3\frac{1}{2}$.	☐ True	☒ False
B	*C* is a positive number.	☐ True	☒ False
C	*B* and *D* are opposites.	☐ True	☒ False
D	The distance between *A* and *B* is negative.	☐ True	☒ False
E	The absolute value of *A* is greater than the value of *F*.	☒ True	☐ False

138 L14: The Coordinate Plane ©Curriculum Associates, LLC Copying is not permitted.

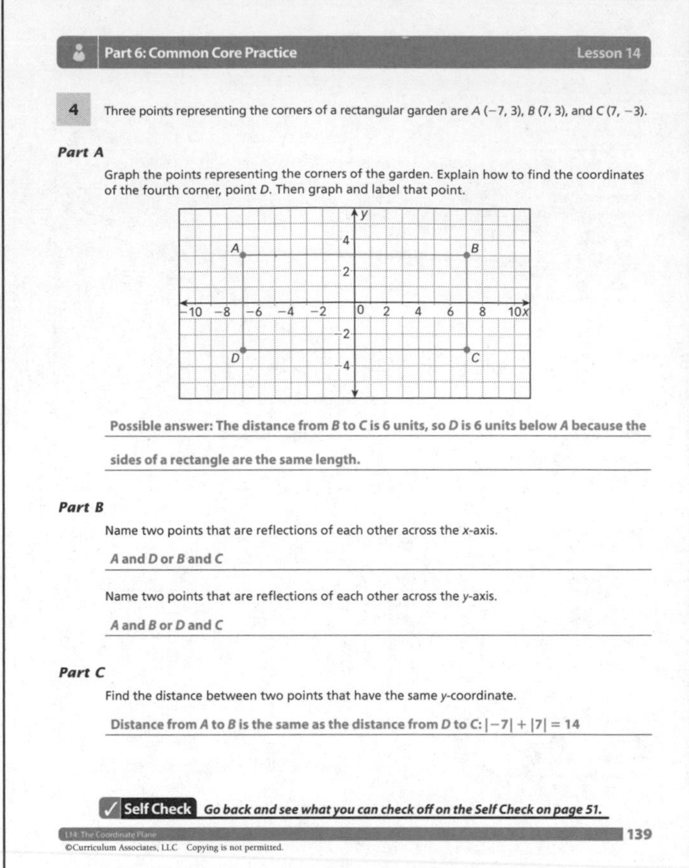

Part 6: Common Core Practice Lesson 14

4 Three points representing the corners of a rectangular garden are *A* (−7, 3), *B* (7, 3), and *C* (7, −3).

Part A

Graph the points representing the corners of the garden. Explain how to find the coordinates of the fourth corner, point *D*. Then graph and label that point.

Possible answer: The distance from *B* to *C* is 6 units, so *D* is 6 units below *A* because the sides of a rectangle are the same length.

Part B

Name two points that are reflections of each other across the *x*-axis.

A and D or B and C

Name two points that are reflections of each other across the *y*-axis.

A and B or D and C

Part C

Find the distance between two points that have the same *y*-coordinate.

Distance from *A* to *B* is the same as the distance from *D* to *C*: |−7| + |7| = 14

✓ Self Check *Go back and see what you can check off on the Self Check on page 51.*

L14: The Coordinate Plane 139 ©Curriculum Associates, LLC Copying is not permitted.

AT A GLANCE

Students use points on a coordinate plane to solve word problems that might appear on a mathematics test.

SOLUTIONS

1 *Solution:* **D**; Find the distance between each pair of locations by counting or by adding the absolute values. ***(DOK 2)***

2 *Solution:* **B**; Add the absolute value of the *x*-coordinate for the location of the coffee shop, −5, to the absolute value of the *x*-coordinate for the location of the arcade, 5.

D; The coffee shop is located 5 units to the left of the *y*-axis, and the arcade is located 5 units to the right of the *y*-axis, so add 5 + 5. ***(DOK 2)***

3 *Solution:* A **False**; B **False**; C **False**; D **False**; E **True** ***(DOK 2)***

4 *Part A Solution:* Point *D* is at (−7, −3) because the distance from *C* to *D* should be the same as the distance from *A* to *B*, and the distance from *A* to *D* should be the same as the distance from *B* to *C*.

Part B Solution: *A* and *D* or *B* and *C*; *A* and *B* or *D* and *C*.

Part C Solution: It is 14 units from *A* to *B* or from *D* to *C*.

The distance between *A* and *B* or between *D* and *C* is |−7| + |7| = 14. ***(DOK 3)***

Assessment and Remediation

- Ask students to find the distance between (4, −8) and (4, 1) without counting. [9 units]
- For students who are struggling, use the chart below to guide remediation.
- After providing remediation, check students' understanding. Ask students to find the distance between (−4, −2) and (7, −2) without counting. [11 units]
- If a student is still having difficulty, use ***Ready Instruction, Level 6***, Lesson 12 and Lesson 13.

If the error is . . .	Students may . . .	To remediate . . .
−7	have added without finding the absolute value.	Remind students that distances must be positive.
7	have subtracted the absolute values.	Point out that (4, −8) is 8 units from the *x*-axis and the other point is on the other side of it. The distance must be greater than 8.
8	have added the *x*-coordinates.	Point out that the distance is caused by a change in the *y*-coordinates, not the *x*-coordinates.

Hands-On Activity

Explore the effect of reflections on coordinates.

Materials: grid paper (at least 1-inch grid), paper clips, colored pencils

Have students draw, label, and number the axes on a sheet of grid paper. Have them mark a point with a paper clip. Ask, *If you reflect the clip across the y-axis, how would its position compare to the original position?* [The vertical position would remain the same. The horizontal position would be the same distance from the *y*-axis but in the other direction.] Have students place another clip to show the reflection. Then have them record the coordinates of each clip in red. Compare the coordinates and relate them to their answer to the previous question. Repeat twice, using different colors for the coordinates. Have students generalize a rule for reflecting points across the *y*-axis. Continue the activity with reflections across the *x*-axis, following the same steps as before.

Challenge Activity

Find distance between points in the same quadrant.

Have students plot (1, −2) and (1, 7) on a coordinate plane. Have them review the use of absolute value to find the distance between those points. [9] Count to confirm the distance. Then have them plot (3, 2) and (3, 7) and use absolute values to find the distance. Count to confirm it. Discuss why adding the absolute values of the *y*-coordinates does not work to find the distance between points in the same quadrant. Help students develop the idea that they would subtract absolute values to find the distance for points in the same quadrant.

Have students plot (−2, 6) and (−2, −4). Discuss how to find the distance between them without counting. Repeat with (−4, −6) and (−4, −1). Have students summarize how to find the distances between points in different quadrants and in the same quadrants.

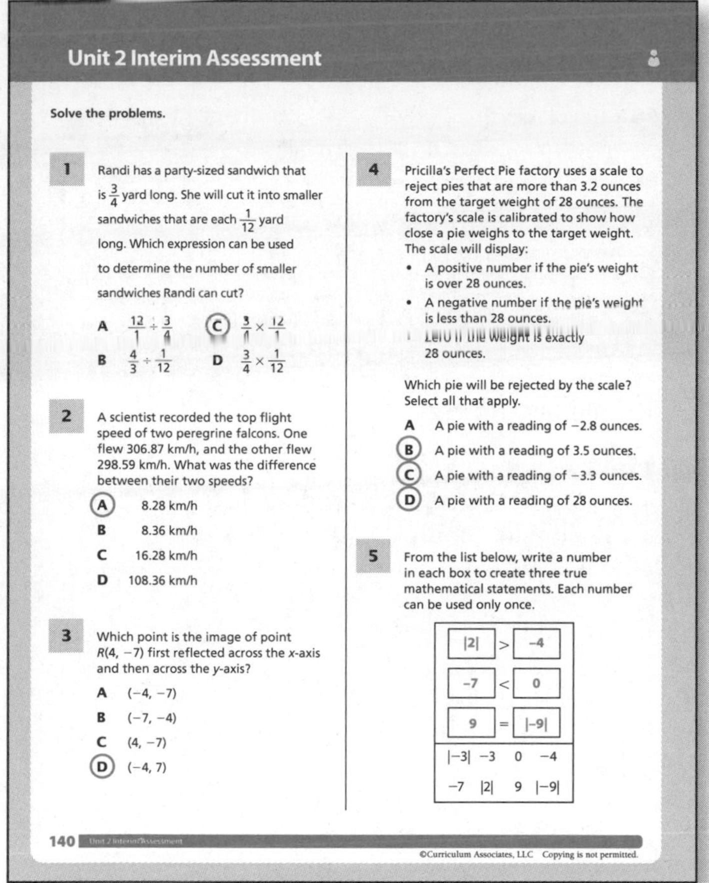

Unit 2 Interim Assessment

Solve the problems.

1 Randi has a party-sized sandwich that is $\frac{3}{4}$ yard long. She will cut it into smaller sandwiches that are each $\frac{1}{12}$ yard long. Which expression can be used to determine the number of smaller sandwiches Randi can cut?

A $\frac{12}{1} \div \frac{3}{4}$

(C) $\frac{3}{4} \times \frac{12}{1}$

B $\frac{4}{3} \div \frac{1}{12}$

D $\frac{3}{4} \times \frac{1}{12}$

2 A scientist recorded the top flight speed of two peregrine falcons. One flew 306.87 km/h, and the other flew 298.59 km/h. What was the difference between their two speeds?

(A) 8.28 km/h

B 8.36 km/h

C 16.28 km/h

D 108.36 km/h

3 Which point is the image of point $R(4, -7)$ first reflected across the x-axis and then across the y-axis?

A (−4, −7)

B (−7, −4)

C (4, −7)

(D) (−4, 7)

4 Pricilla's Perfect Pie factory uses a scale to reject pies that are more than 3.2 ounces from the target weight of 28 ounces. The factory's scale is calibrated to show how close a pie weighs to the target weight. The scale will display:

- A positive number if the pie's weight is over 28 ounces.
- A negative number if the pie's weight is less than 28 ounces.
- Zero if the weight is exactly 28 ounces.

Which pie will be rejected by the scale? Select all that apply.

A A pie with a reading of −2.8 ounces.

(B) A pie with a reading of 3.5 ounces.

(C) A pie with a reading of −3.3 ounces.

(D) A pie with a reading of 28 ounces.

5 From the list below, write a number in each box to create three true mathematical statements. Each number can be used only once.

|2| > −4

−7 < 0

9 = |−9|

|−3|	−3	0	−4
−7	|2|	9	|−9|

140 Unit 2 Interim Assessment

©Curriculum Associates, LLC Copying is not permitted.

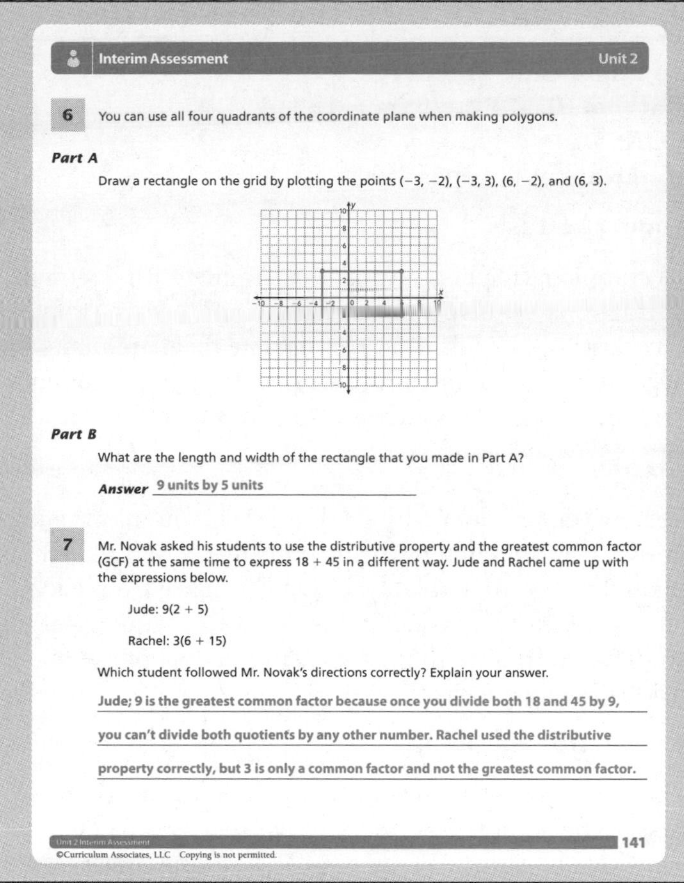

Interim Assessment Unit 2

6 You can use all four quadrants of the coordinate plane when making polygons.

Part A

Draw a rectangle on the grid by plotting the points (−3, −2), (−3, 3), (6, −2), and (6, 3).

Part B

What are the length and width of the rectangle that you made in Part A?

Answer 9 units by 5 units

7 Mr. Novak asked his students to use the distributive property and the greatest common factor (GCF) at the same time to express 18 + 45 in a different way. Jude and Rachel came up with the expressions below.

Jude: 9(2 + 5)

Rachel: 3(6 + 15)

Which student followed Mr. Novak's directions correctly? Explain your answer.

Jude; 9 is the greatest common factor because once you divide both 18 and 45 by 9, you can't divide both quotients by any other number. Rachel used the distributive property correctly, but 3 is only a common factor and not the greatest common factor.

Unit 2 Interim Assessment 141

©Curriculum Associates, LLC Copying is not permitted.

SCORING GUIDE AND ANSWER ANALYSIS

1 *Solution:* **C**; To find the number of smaller sandwiches, divide the total length by the length of each smaller sandwich. To divide by a fraction, multiply by the reciprocal. ***(DOK 2)***

2 *Solution:* **A**; Subtract to find the difference between the two speeds. ***(DOK 1)***

3 *Solution:* **D**; When a point is reflected across the x-axis, the sign of the y-coordinate changes. When a point is reflected across the y-axis, the sign of the x-coordinate changes. Here, the signs of both coordinates change. ***(DOK 2)***

4 *Solution:* **B**; 3.5 is greater than 3.2.

C; |−3.3| is greater than 3.2.

D; 28 is greater than 3.2. ***(DOK 2)***

5 *Solution:* Answers will vary. See student book page above for possible student responses. ***(DOK 2)***

6 *Part A Solution:*
See student work above.

Part B Solution:
9 units × 5 units; Find the lengths of each side by finding the distance between the x-coordinates and the distance between the y-coordinates. ***(DOK 2)***

7 *Solution:* Jude; See student book page above for possible student explanation. ***(DOK 3)***

PERFORMANCE TASK TEACHER NOTES

Common Core Standards: 6.NS.A.1, 6.NS.B.3
Mathematical Practices: SMP 1, 2, 3, 4, 5, 6
DOK: 3
Materials: grid paper, rulers

About the Task

To complete this task, students compute with decimals or fractions to solve a measurement and design problem. The task involves finding appropriate measurements to fit design criteria and allow for equal spacing. Students also draw a diagram with all measurements labeled.

Getting Started

Review the problem with the students. You may wish to draw a rough sketch of the wood centered left to right on the hallway wall, explaining that the space from each end of the wood to each end of the wall is equal. Remind students to be sure that all measurements are expressed using the same unit.

Completing the Task

There are multiple parts to this task, and they do not have to be completed in a specific order. Students may draw one or multiple diagrams. Before drawing a detailed diagram, students may sketch the situation and make notes to begin to address the problem. ***(SMP 4)***

Some students may begin by calculating the amount of space not covered by the wood to determine how much space will be on either side of the coat rack. You may wish to engage students in a discussion about how they calculated this. Ask if they could find how much space is left on either side of the coat rack by subtracting half the length of the wood from half the length of the hallway. ***(SMP 3)***

Next, students need to calculate the length of wood available for the hooks, since the hooks cannot be placed at the edge of the board. They also need to devise a plan for determining how many hooks will fit in that space. Encourage them to estimate first. If students want to account for width of the hooks in their plans, demonstrate how the equal spacing can represent the distance from the center of each hook. Some students may find a double number line useful for tracking the distance between the hooks and the actual position of the hooks on the board. ***(SMP 4)***

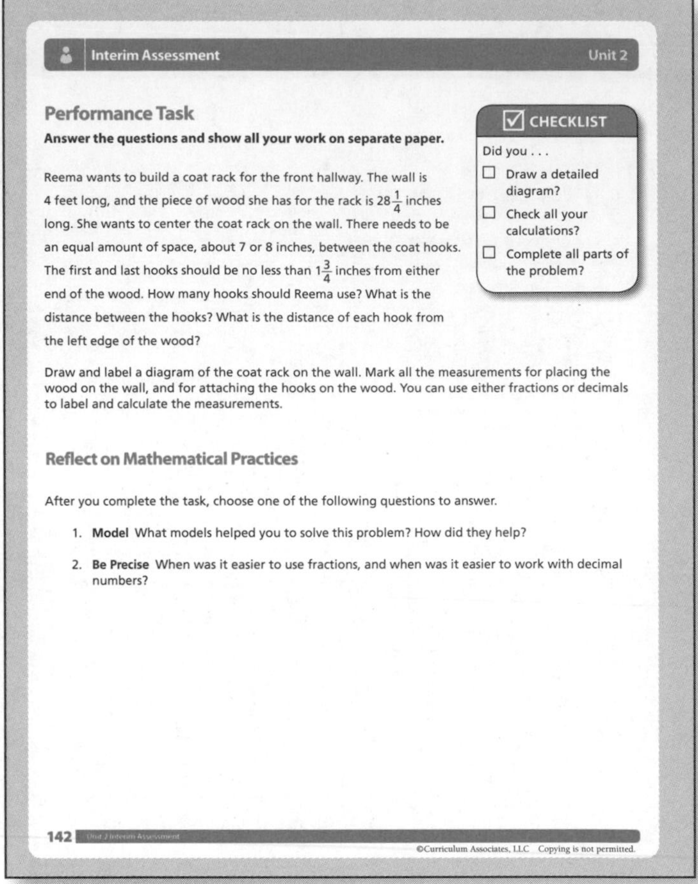
Interim Assessment Unit 2

Performance Task

Answer the questions and show all your work on separate paper.

Reema wants to build a coat rack for the front hallway. The wall is 4 feet long, and the piece of wood she has for the rack is $28\frac{1}{4}$ inches long. She wants to center the coat rack on the wall. There needs to be an equal amount of space, about 7 or 8 inches, between the coat hooks. The first and last hooks should be no less than $1\frac{3}{4}$ inches from either end of the wood. How many hooks should Reema use? What is the distance between the hooks? What is the distance of each hook from the left edge of the wood?

CHECKLIST
Did you . . .
- ☐ Draw a detailed diagram?
- ☐ Check all your calculations?
- ☐ Complete all parts of the problem?

Draw and label a diagram of the coat rack on the wall. Mark all the measurements for placing the wood on the wall, and for attaching the hooks on the wood. You can use either fractions or decimals to label and calculate the measurements.

Reflect on Mathematical Practices

After you complete the task, choose one of the following questions to answer.

1. **Model** What models helped you to solve this problem? How did they help?
2. **Be Precise** When was it easier to use fractions, and when was it easier to work with decimal numbers?

142 Unit 2 Interim Assessment

©Curriculum Associates, LLC Copying is not permitted.

The students need to draw and label a diagram of the coat rack on the wall. While the drawing does not need to be to scale, it should be a fairly reasonable representation. Supplying the students with graph paper and rulers may help them with their models. ***(SMP 5)***

Remind students to check their calculations and diagrams to make sure they have fulfilled all the requirements. ***(SMP 1, 6)***

Extension

If some students have more time to spend on this problem, you can have them solve this extension:

Reema wants to make a tile mosaic to hang on the wall next to the coat rack. If the mosaic is a square with $7\frac{1}{2}$-inch sides, how many $\frac{3}{4}$-inch square tiles does she need?

PERFORMANCE TASK SAMPLE RESPONSES AND RUBRIC

4-Point Solution

The wall is 4 feet long, which is $4 \times 12 = 48$ inches. Subtract the length of the wood from the length of the wall: $48 - 28.25 = 19.75$ inches. Divide the remaining length into two equal parts: $19.75 \div 2 = 9.875$.

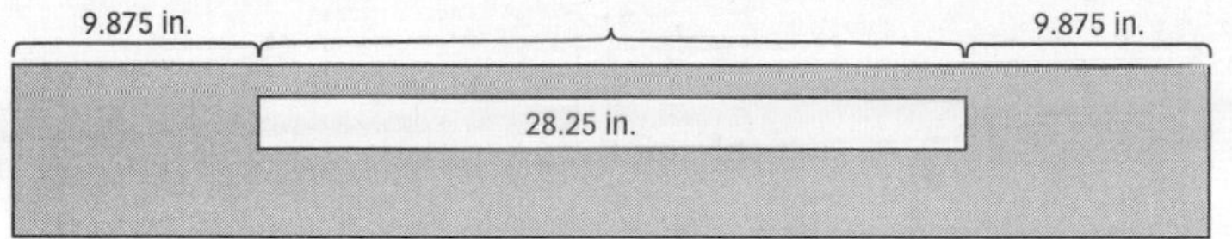

The end hooks are 1.75 inches from each end of the wood: $1.75 \times 2 = 3.5$ inches. Subtract from the length of the wood ($28.25 - 3.5 = 24.75$ inches) to find the total length between the end hooks.

If there are 4 hooks, there are 3 equal spaces between them. Model on a number line.

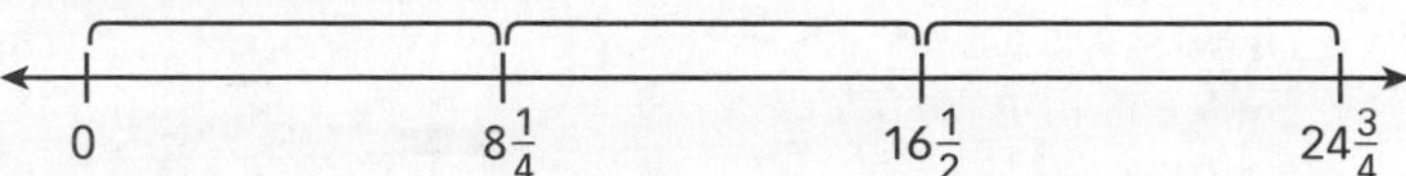

Find the distance from the left edge of the wood to each hook. Since the first hook has to be 1.75 inches in from the edge, it will be placed at 1.75. The second hook will be at $1.75 + 8.25$ (the equal space), or 10 inches. Continue to add 8.25 inches to find the position of each hook.

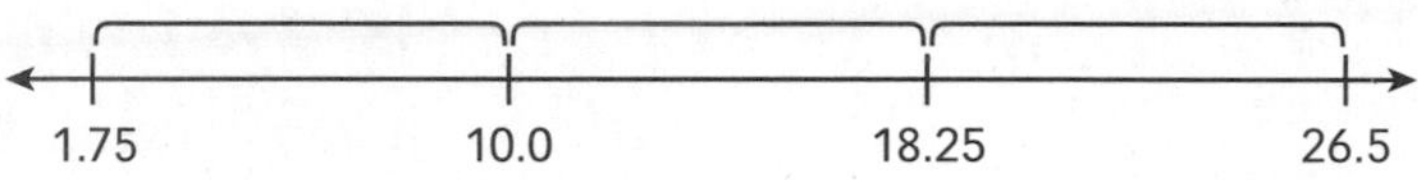

REFLECT ON MATHEMATICAL PRACTICES

1. Look for the use of models that show equal parts and that represent lengths along a line. ***(SMP 4)***
2. Students may have different preferences for using fractions or decimals. Look for an understanding that both forms can be used interchangeably. ***(SMP 6)***

SCORING RUBRIC

4 points The student's response is accurate and complete. All calculations are correct and contain appropriate labels. The student computes correctly and easily with decimals or fractions. The diagram is detailed and accurate.

3 points The student has attempted all parts of the task and may have minor errors in calculations. The diagram is sufficient but may have minor errors.

2 points The student's response contains several computational errors. The student may not have completed all parts of the task.

1 point The response contains an incorrect solution. The student's diagram is incomplete, incorrect, or missing.

SOLUTION TO THE EXTENSION

The area of the mosaic is 7.5×7.5, or 56.25 square inches. The area of one tile is 0.75×0.75, or 0.5625 square inches. Since $56.25 \div 0.5625 = 100$, she needs 100 tiles for the mosaic.

Unit 3: Expressions and Equations

Which lessons are students building upon?

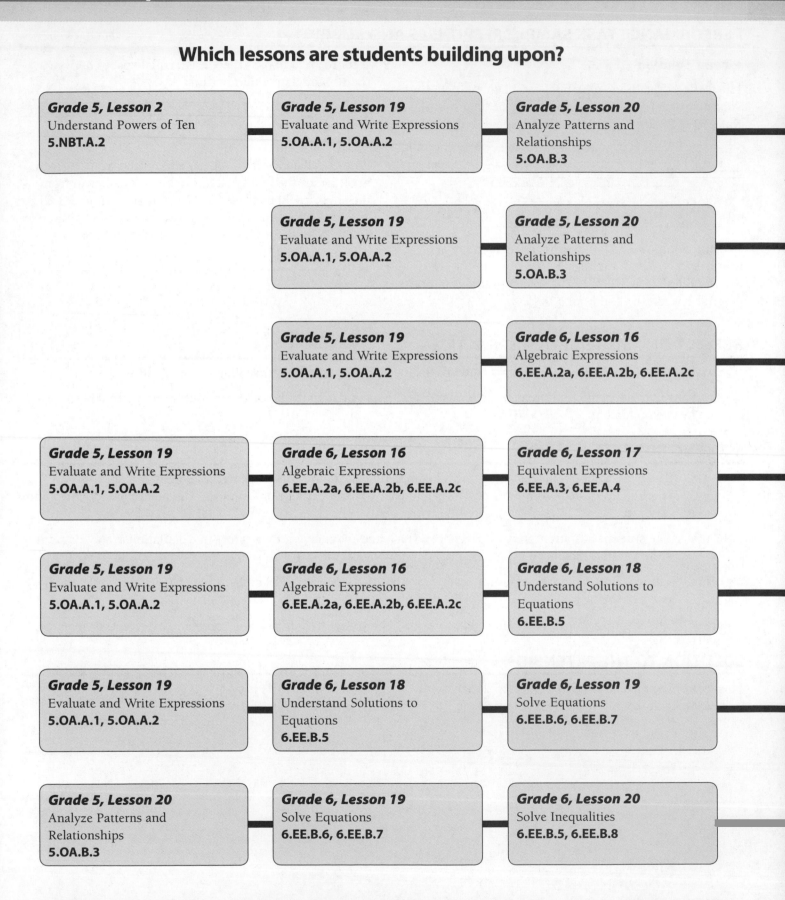

Grade 5, Lesson 2 Understand Powers of Ten **5.NBT.A.2**	***Grade 5, Lesson 19*** Evaluate and Write Expressions **5.OA.A.1, 5.OA.A.2**	***Grade 5, Lesson 20*** Analyze Patterns and Relationships **5.OA.B.3**
	Grade 5, Lesson 19 Evaluate and Write Expressions **5.OA.A.1, 5.OA.A.2**	***Grade 5, Lesson 20*** Analyze Patterns and Relationships **5.OA.B.3**
	Grade 5, Lesson 19 Evaluate and Write Expressions **5.OA.A.1, 5.OA.A.2**	***Grade 6, Lesson 16*** Algebraic Expressions **6.EE.A.2a, 6.EE.A.2b, 6.EE.A.2c**
Grade 5, Lesson 19 Evaluate and Write Expressions **5.OA.A.1, 5.OA.A.2**	***Grade 6, Lesson 16*** Algebraic Expressions **6.EE.A.2a, 6.EE.A.2b, 6.EE.A.2c**	***Grade 6, Lesson 17*** Equivalent Expressions **6.EE.A.3, 6.EE.A.4**
Grade 5, Lesson 19 Evaluate and Write Expressions **5.OA.A.1, 5.OA.A.2**	***Grade 6, Lesson 16*** Algebraic Expressions **6.EE.A.2a, 6.EE.A.2b, 6.EE.A.2c**	***Grade 6, Lesson 18*** Understand Solutions to Equations **6.EE.B.5**
Grade 5, Lesson 19 Evaluate and Write Expressions **5.OA.A.1, 5.OA.A.2**	***Grade 6, Lesson 18*** Understand Solutions to Equations **6.EE.B.5**	***Grade 6, Lesson 19*** Solve Equations **6.EE.B.6, 6.EE.B.7**
Grade 5, Lesson 20 Analyze Patterns and Relationships **5.OA.B.3**	***Grade 6, Lesson 19*** Solve Equations **6.EE.B.6, 6.EE.B.7**	***Grade 6, Lesson 20*** Solve Inequalities **6.EE.B.5, 6.EE.B.8**

Unit 3

Which lessons are students preparing for?

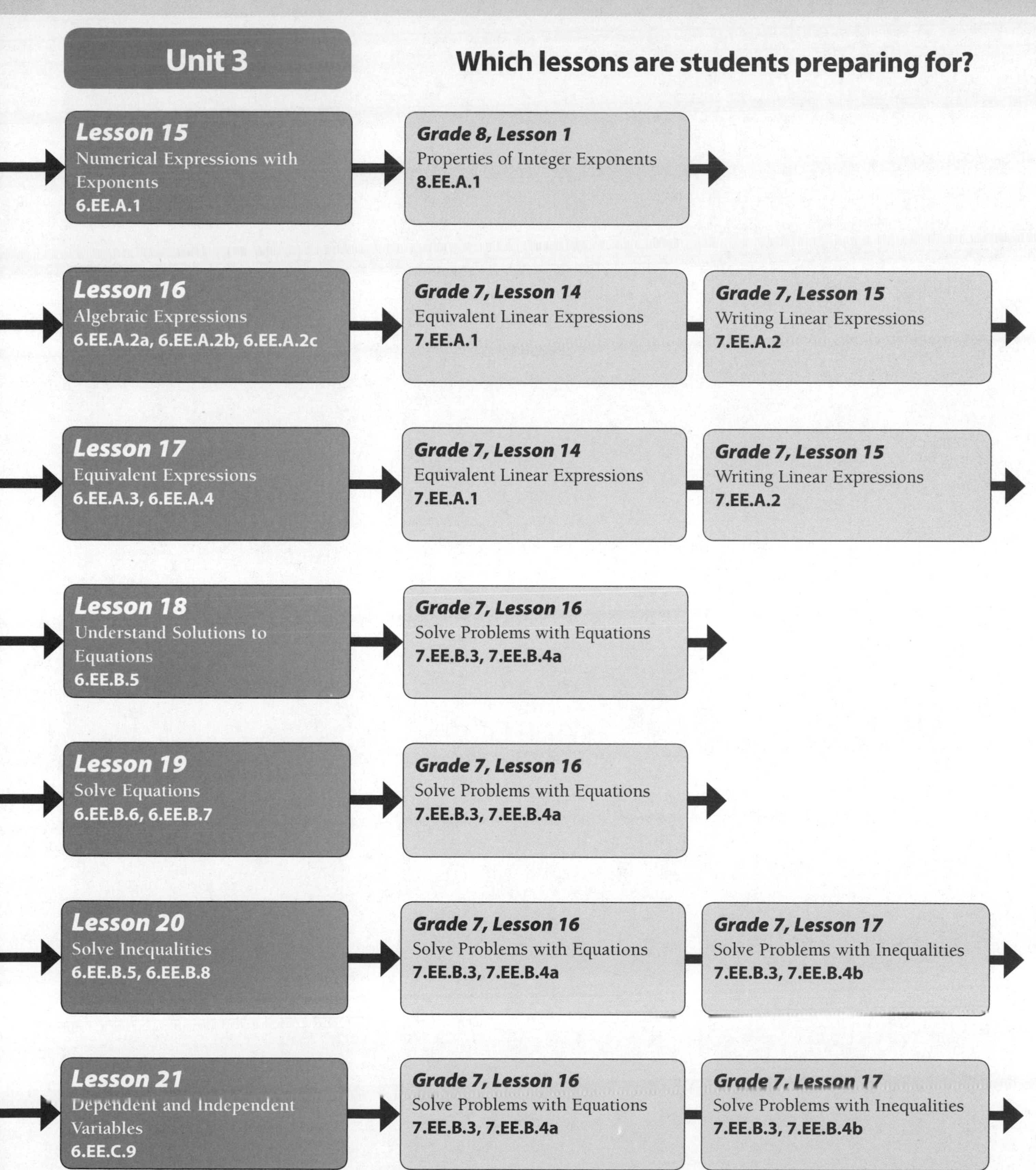

Unit 3 Lesson	Preparing for	Then
Lesson 15 Numerical Expressions with Exponents **6.EE.A.1**	***Grade 8, Lesson 1*** Properties of Integer Exponents **8.EE.A.1**	
Lesson 16 Algebraic Expressions **6.EE.A.2a, 6.EE.A.2b, 6.EE.A.2c**	***Grade 7, Lesson 14*** Equivalent Linear Expressions **7.EE.A.1**	***Grade 7, Lesson 15*** Writing Linear Expressions **7.EE.A.2**
Lesson 17 Equivalent Expressions **6.EE.A.3, 6.EE.A.4**	***Grade 7, Lesson 14*** Equivalent Linear Expressions **7.EE.A.1**	***Grade 7, Lesson 15*** Writing Linear Expressions **7.EE.A.2**
Lesson 18 Understand Solutions to Equations **6.EE.B.5**	***Grade 7, Lesson 16*** Solve Problems with Equations **7.EE.B.3, 7.EE.B.4a**	
Lesson 19 Solve Equations **6.EE.B.6, 6.EE.B.7**	***Grade 7, Lesson 16*** Solve Problems with Equations **7.EE.B.3, 7.EE.B.4a**	
Lesson 20 Solve Inequalities **6.EE.B.5, 6.EE.B.8**	***Grade 7, Lesson 16*** Solve Problems with Equations **7.EE.B.3, 7.EE.B.4a**	***Grade 7, Lesson 17*** Solve Problems with Inequalities **7.EE.B.3, 7.EE.B.4b**
Lesson 21 Dependent and Independent Variables **6.EE.C.9**	***Grade 7, Lesson 16*** Solve Problems with Equations **7.EE.B.3, 7.EE.B.4a**	***Grade 7, Lesson 17*** Solve Problems with Inequalities **7.EE.B.3, 7.EE.B.4b**

Lesson 15 (Student Book pages 144–153)

Numerical Expressions with Exponents

LESSON OBJECTIVES

- Write numerical expressions involving whole-number exponents.
- Evaluate numerical expressions involving whole-number exponents.

PREREQUISITE SKILLS

- Use the order of operations to evaluate expressions.
- Fluently multiply with decimals using a standard algorithm.
- Fluently multiply with fractions using a standard algorithm.
- Evaluate powers of 10.
- Use whole-number exponents to denote powers of 10.

VOCABULARY

base: the number that is multiplied by itself when it is raised to a certain power

exponent: a number that shows how many times a base is multiplied by itself

exponential expression: expressions written with exponents

THE LEARNING PROGRESSION

In keeping with the Common Core goal of developing deeper student understanding of expressions and equations, this lesson extends students' understanding of writing and evaluating numeric expressions to include powers with whole-number exponents. Students will write numeric expressions. They will also evaluate powers with whole-number exponents to solve real-world problems.

Ready *Teacher Toolbox* Teacher-Toolbox.com

	Prerequisite Skills	6.EE.A.1
Ready Lessons	✓	✓
Tools for Instruction	✓	✓
Interactive Tutorials		✓

CCSS Focus

6.EE.A.1 Write and evaluate numerical expressions involving whole-number exponents.

STANDARDS FOR MATHEMATICAL PRACTICE: ***SMP 1–8*** *(see page A9 for full text)*

AT A GLANCE

Students read a word problem and answer questions that connect repeated multiplication and powers.

STEP BY STEP

- Tell students this page models how to use powers to write numerical expressions.
- Have students read the problem at the top of the page.
- Work through Explore It as a class.
- Emphasize the value of 10^3 as $10 \cdot 10 \cdot 10 = 1{,}000$ and not $10 \cdot 3$ or 30.
- Point out to students that 10, the base, is being multiplied by itself 3 times.
- Ask, *What is the base number for* 6^3? [6] *Following the pattern used to find the value of* 10^3, *what expression do you predict to be equivalent to* 6^3? [$6 \cdot 6 \cdot 6$]
- Ask student pairs or groups to explain how to calculate the number of table tennis balls in the box.

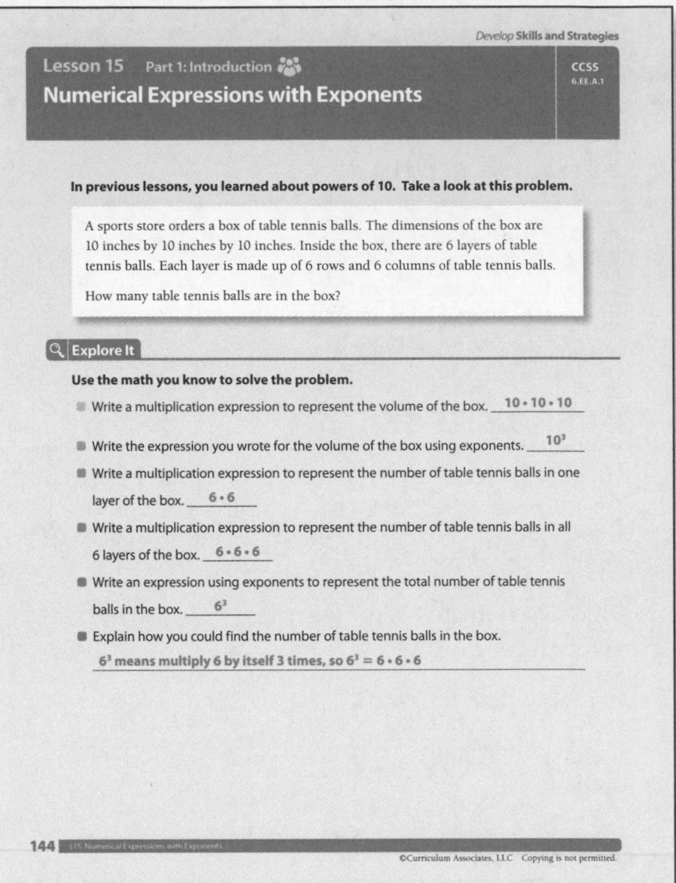

Develop Skills and Strategies

Lesson 15 Part 1: Introduction

Numerical Expressions with Exponents

CCSS 6.EE.A.1

In previous lessons, you learned about powers of 10. Take a look at this problem.

A sports store orders a box of table tennis balls. The dimensions of the box are 10 inches by 10 inches by 10 inches. Inside the box, there are 6 layers of table tennis balls. Each layer is made up of 6 rows and 6 columns of table tennis balls.

How many table tennis balls are in the box?

Explore It

Use the math you know to solve the problem.

- Write a multiplication expression to represent the volume of the box. $10 \cdot 10 \cdot 10$
- Write the expression you wrote for the volume of the box using exponents. 10^3
- Write a multiplication expression to represent the number of table tennis balls in one layer of the box. $6 \cdot 6$
- Write a multiplication expression to represent the number of table tennis balls in all 6 layers of the box. $6 \cdot 6 \cdot 6$
- Write an expression using exponents to represent the total number of table tennis balls in the box. 6^3
- Explain how you could find the number of table tennis balls in the box. 6^3 means multiply 6 by itself 3 times, so $6^3 = 6 \cdot 6 \cdot 6$

144 L15: Numerical Expressions with Exponents ©Curriculum Associates, LLC Copying is not permitted.

ELL Support

Display 10^3 and 6^3 for students numerically and in words. Point to and label the parts of the power as the vocabulary is used.

SMP Tip: Recognizing the structure of 10^3 as $10 \cdot 10 \cdot 10$ prepares students to make use of the same structure in determining the value of 6^3 (*SMP 7*).

Visual Model

Model powers with unit cubes.

Materials: unit cubes

- Model $2 \cdot 2$, $3 \cdot 3$, and $4 \cdot 4$ with unit cubes. (2 rows of 2, etc).
- Ask, *Which powers are being represented?* [2^2, 3^2, 4^2]
- Represent $2 \cdot 2 \cdot 2 \cdot 2$ (two sets of 2^2). Stack the sets. Model 3^3 and 4^3.
- Discuss what observations students have made.

Mathematical Discourse

- *Why is it important to know the value of the base and the exponent?*

  The base tells you which number is being multiplied by itself. The exponent tells you how many times to multiply the base by itself.

- *Explain why* 3^2 *and* 2^3 *are not equivalent.*

  3^2 is $3 \cdot 3 = 9$, and 2^3 is $2 \cdot 2 \cdot 2 = 8$. Even though the same two numbers are used, they are not representing the same expression.

AT A GLANCE

Students write numerical expressions using powers with whole numbers. Students will explore a visual model to understand exponents.

STEP BY STEP

- Read Find Out More as a class.
- Clarify the vocabulary. The *power* is the entire expression, which includes the base and the exponent. The *base* is the number which is being multiplied by itself. The *exponent* represents the number of times the base is multiplied by itself.

ELL Support

Base has multiple meanings. Show the base of a figure. Discuss how it is the support of the figure. A good example is to show a cylinder and describe how the circle is repeated to create the cylinder.

Concept Extension

Model exponents.

Materials: counters

- Tell students you will create a model to show 2^4.
- Use chips to show 2^2 or $2 \cdot 2$. Ask, *What happens to the number of counters when I show the next power of 2 or* 2^3? [The number of counters is multiplied by 2.] Show this new number of counters. [8 counters]
- Repeat this question and process for 2^4. Show this new number of counters. [16 counters]
- Ask students to predict the number of counters for 2^1. Have a volunteer show the model to the class and explain their reasoning. [The number of counters is 2. Following the model backwards, the number of counters is divided by two, so 4 divided by 2 is 2 counters, for 2^1.]
- Ask students to predict the number of counters for 2^0. Have a volunteer show this model and explain. [The number of counters is one. Following the model backwards, the number of counters is divided by two, so 2 divided by 2 would be 1 counter for 2^0.]

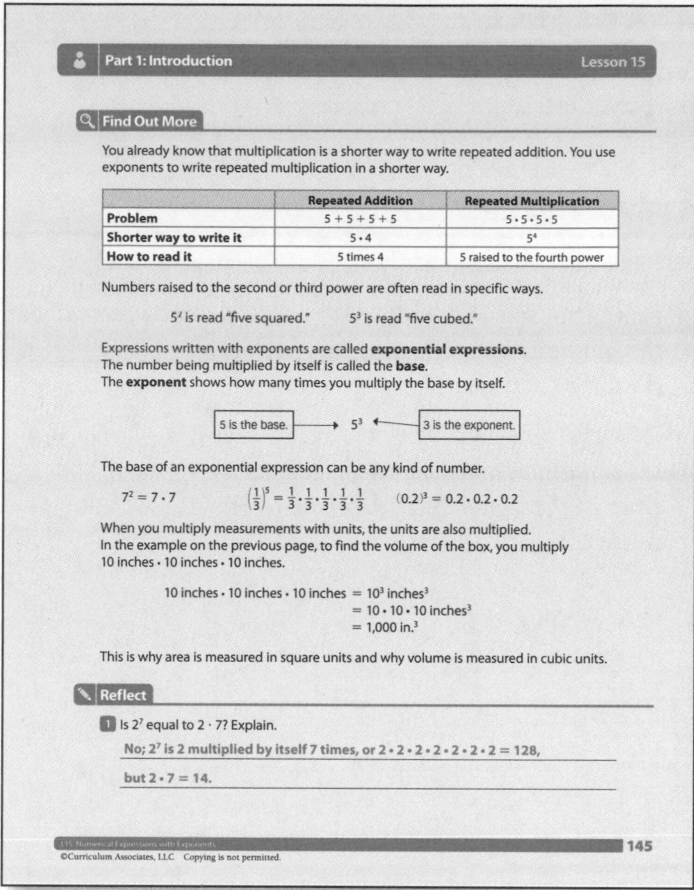

Part 1: Introduction Lesson 15

Find Out More

You already know that multiplication is a shorter way to write repeated addition. You use exponents to write repeated multiplication in a shorter way.

	Repeated Addition	Repeated Multiplication
Problem	$5 + 5 + 5 + 5$	$5 \cdot 5 \cdot 5 \cdot 5$
Shorter way to write it	$5 \cdot 4$	5^4
How to read it	5 times 4	5 raised to the fourth power

Numbers raised to the second or third power are often read in specific ways.

5^2 is read "five squared." 5^3 is read "five cubed."

Expressions written with exponents are called **exponential expressions**.
The number being multiplied by itself is called the **base**.
The **exponent** shows how many times you multiply the base by itself.

5 is the base. → 5^3 ← 3 is the exponent.

The base of an exponential expression can be any kind of number.

$7^2 = 7 \cdot 7$ $\left(\frac{1}{3}\right)^5 = \frac{1}{3} \cdot \frac{1}{3} \cdot \frac{1}{3} \cdot \frac{1}{3} \cdot \frac{1}{3}$ $(0.2)^3 = 0.2 \cdot 0.2 \cdot 0.2$

When you multiply measurements with units, the units are also multiplied.
In the example on the previous page, to find the volume of the box, you multiply 10 inches • 10 inches • 10 inches.

$$\begin{aligned} 10 \text{ inches} \cdot 10 \text{ inches} \cdot 10 \text{ inches} &= 10^3 \text{ inches}^3 \\ &= 10 \cdot 10 \cdot 10 \text{ inches}^3 \\ &= 1{,}000 \text{ in.}^3 \end{aligned}$$

This is why area is measured in square units and why volume is measured in cubic units.

Reflect

1 Is 2^7 equal to $2 \cdot 7$? Explain.

No; 2^7 is 2 multiplied by itself 7 times, or $2 \cdot 2 \cdot 2 \cdot 2 \cdot 2 \cdot 2 \cdot 2 = 128$, but $2 \cdot 7 = 14$.

L15: Numerical Expressions with Exponents 145
©Curriculum Associates, LLC Copying is not permitted.

Real-World Connection

Encourage students to think about everyday situations where people may need to write and evaluate expressions with powers. Have volunteers share their ideas.

Examples: sewing (material for a square quilt), volume of a cubic container, epidemiologist (to study the growth and spread of disease)

AT A GLANCE

Students write and use powers to solve a real-world problem. Students will explore visual models to understand exponents.

STEP BY STEP

- Read the problem at the top of the page as a class.
- Read the first Model It. Ask, *What do you notice about the amount of money Julie has each day?* [The amount doubles each day.]
- Direct students to the second Model It. Ask, *Do you see a pattern in the number of 2s as we go down the rows of the table? If so, describe it.* [Each row adds one more 2.]

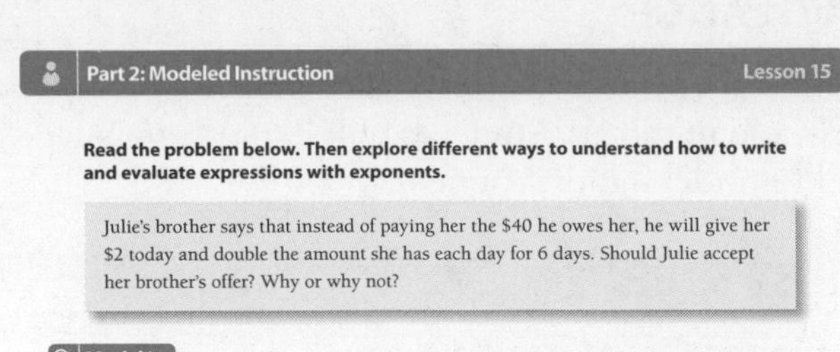

Part 2: Modeled Instruction Lesson 15

Read the problem below. Then explore different ways to understand how to write and evaluate expressions with exponents.

Julie's brother says that instead of paying her the $40 he owes her, he will give her $2 today and double the amount she has each day for 6 days. Should Julie accept her brother's offer? Why or why not?

Model It

Use multiplication to represent the problem.

Find the amount of money Julie has each day and then double it to find the amount she has the next day.

Day 1	Day 2	Day 3	Day 4	Day 5	Day 6
2	$2 \cdot 2 = 4$	$4 \cdot 2 = 8$	$8 \cdot 2 = 16$	$16 \cdot 2 = 32$	$32 \cdot 2 = 64$

Model It

Represent the problem with repeated multiplication.

Each day, Julie gets two times the amount of money she got the previous day.

Day	Amount of Money Julie Has from Her Brother
1	2
2	$2 \cdot 2$
3	$2 \cdot 2 \cdot 2$
4	$2 \cdot 2 \cdot 2 \cdot 2$
5	$2 \cdot 2 \cdot 2 \cdot 2 \cdot 2$
6	$2 \cdot 2 \cdot 2 \cdot 2 \cdot 2 \cdot 2$

146 L15: Numerical Expressions with Exponents

©Curriculum Associates, LLC Copying is not permitted.

AT A GLANCE

Students revisit the problem on page 146 to write and evaluate numerical expressions using whole numbers in a real-world application.

STEP BY STEP

- Read Connect It as a class. Point out that the questions refer to the problem from page 146.
- Review the meaning of *base* (the number being multiplied by itself), *exponent* (the number of times the base is being multiplied by itself), and *power* (the expression which includes the base and the exponent).
- Have students work the Try It problems by themselves or in small groups.

SMP Tip: Mathematical vocabulary allows students to share ideas clearly and precisely (*SMP 6*) in discussions and explanations of their reasoning. Use the words *base*, *exponent*, and *power* regularly and share your expectation that students use them in class.

Concept Extension

Use a table to evaluate exponents.

- Create a 3-column table. Write 5^2 in the left column. Ask a volunteer to write an equivalent expression in the middle column and another volunteer to record the whole-number value of the expression in the right column.
- Repeat this process for 5^3, 5^4, and 5^5.
- Ask students to describe patterns they may see in the table. [As the exponent increases, the number of 5s in the expression increases; values for each expression are multiplied by 5 as the exponent increases; values are divided by 5 as the exponent decreases.]
- Repeat with other powers. Discuss if the patterns appear to hold true.
- Ask students to compare their tables. Ask, *What mathematical conjectures can you make?* [The powers with a large base increase in value at a faster rate than those with a smaller base.]

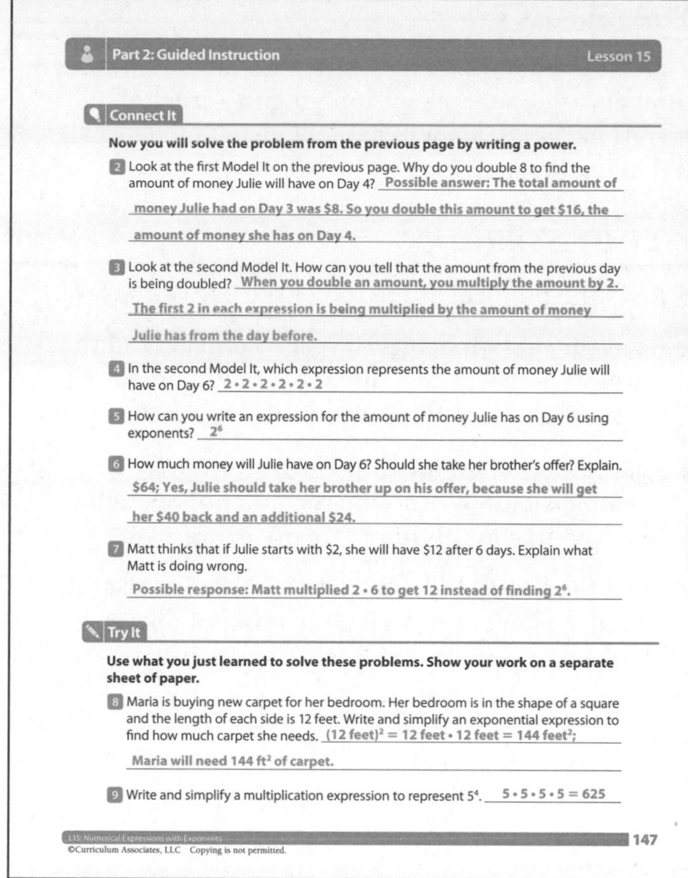
Part 2: Guided Instruction Lesson 15

Connect It

Now you will solve the problem from the previous page by writing a power.

2 Look at the first Model It on the previous page. Why do you double 8 to find the amount of money Julie will have on Day 4? **Possible answer: The total amount of money Julie had on Day 3 was $8. So you double this amount to get $16, the amount of money she has on Day 4.**

3 Look at the second Model It. How can you tell that the amount from the previous day is being doubled? **When you double an amount, you multiply the amount by 2. The first 2 in each expression is being multiplied by the amount of money Julie has from the day before.**

4 In the second Model It, which expression represents the amount of money Julie will have on Day 6? **$2 \cdot 2 \cdot 2 \cdot 2 \cdot 2 \cdot 2$**

5 How can you write an expression for the amount of money Julie has on Day 6 using exponents? **2^6**

6 How much money will Julie have on Day 6? Should she take her brother's offer? Explain. **$64; Yes, Julie should take her brother up on his offer, because she will get her $40 back and an additional $24.**

7 Matt thinks that if Julie starts with $2, she will have $12 after 6 days. Explain what Matt is doing wrong. **Possible response: Matt multiplied $2 \cdot 6$ to get 12 instead of finding 2^6.**

Try It

Use what you just learned to solve these problems. Show your work on a separate sheet of paper.

8 Maria is buying new carpet for her bedroom. Her bedroom is in the shape of a square and the length of each side is 12 feet. Write and simplify an exponential expression to find how much carpet she needs. **$(12 \text{ feet})^2 = 12 \text{ feet} \cdot 12 \text{ feet} = 144 \text{ feet}^2$; Maria will need 144 ft^2 of carpet.**

9 Write and simplify a multiplication expression to represent 5^4. **$5 \cdot 5 \cdot 5 \cdot 5 = 625$**

L15: Numerical Expressions with Exponents 147
©Curriculum Associates, LLC Copying is not permitted.

TRY IT SOLUTIONS

8 *Solution:* $12^2 = 12 \times 12 = 144$ square feet

9 *Solution:* $5 \times 5 \times 5 \times 5 = 625$

ERROR ALERT: Students who write $5 \times 4 = 20$ misunderstand the meaning of base and exponent.

AT A GLANCE

Students evaluate expressions which include whole numbers as exponents by applying the order of operations. Students will explore visual models to understand exponents.

STEP BY STEP

- Read the problem at the top of the page as a class.
- Read the first Model It. Have a volunteer read the example aloud or describe the order of operations involved in simplifying Michael's expression.
- Read the second Model It. Have a volunteer read the example aloud or describe the order of operations involved in simplifying Morgan's expression.
- Read the third Model It. Have a volunteer read the example aloud or describe the order of operations involved in simplifying Keegan's expression.

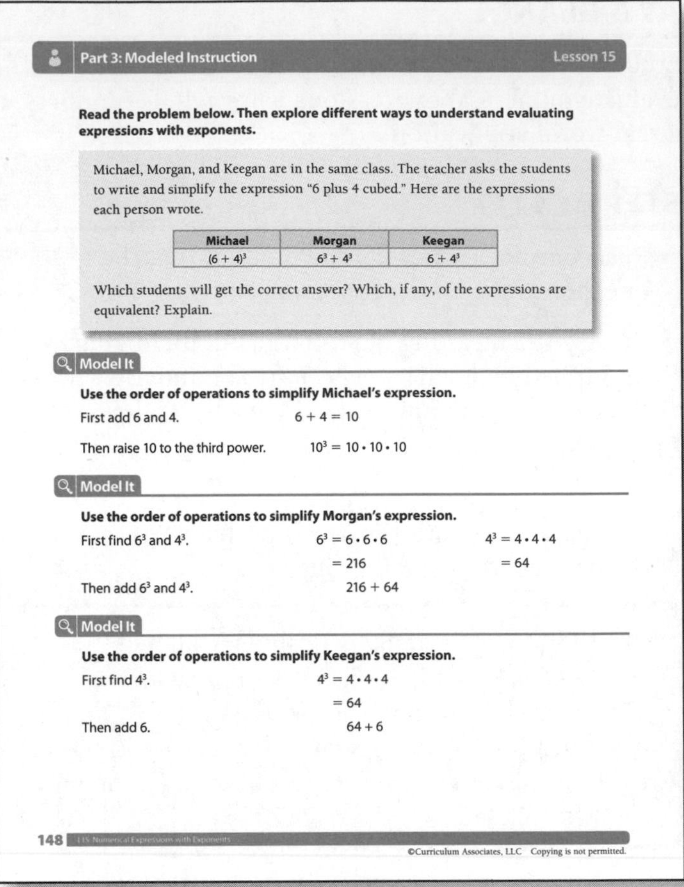

Part 3: Modeled Instruction Lesson 15

Read the problem below. Then explore different ways to understand evaluating expressions with exponents.

Michael, Morgan, and Keegan are in the same class. The teacher asks the students to write and simplify the expression "6 plus 4 cubed." Here are the expressions each person wrote.

Michael	Morgan	Keegan
$(6 + 4)^3$	$6^3 + 4^3$	$6 + 4^3$

Which students will get the correct answer? Which, if any, of the expressions are equivalent? Explain.

Model It

Use the order of operations to simplify Michael's expression.

First add 6 and 4. $6 + 4 = 10$

Then raise 10 to the third power. $10^3 = 10 \cdot 10 \cdot 10$

Model It

Use the order of operations to simplify Morgan's expression.

First find 6^3 and 4^3. $6^3 = 6 \cdot 6 \cdot 6$ $= 216$ $4^3 = 4 \cdot 4 \cdot 4$ $= 64$

Then add 6^3 and 4^3. $216 + 64$

Model It

Use the order of operations to simplify Keegan's expression.

First find 4^3. $4^3 = 4 \cdot 4 \cdot 4$ $= 64$

Then add 6. $64 + 6$

148 L15: Numerical Expressions with Exponents

©Curriculum Associates, LLC Copying is not permitted.

Hands-On Activity

Use cubes to understand exponents and model volume.

Materials: unit cubes

- Distribute unit cubes to groups of 2–4 students.
- Have students create models for 1^3, 2^3, 3^3, and 4^3. Then ask volunteers to share their models.
- Lead a discussion with students about how their models connect the concept of exponents with that of volume.
- Guiding questions for students may be: *What is the smallest cube?* [The smallest square is one cube itself.] *What is the largest cube?* [This will depend on the number of cubes available.] *How can the volume of each cube be determined?* [By counting the individual cubic units or writing a power.] *How can the volume of each cube be written as a power?* [Possible powers include 1^3, 2^3, 3^3, 4^3, etc.]

Mathematical Discourse

- *Use the numbers 2, 3, and 6 to write mathematical expressions that include the exponents as whole numbers. You may use any mathematical operations with which you are familiar.*

  Display student expressions for all to see.
- *Can you predict which expressions will have a greater value without performing the mathematical operations? Explain how you know.*

  Predictions will vary. Expressions with large exponents will likely have greater values than those with small exponents or no exponents.
- *What expression can you create to get the smallest value using these 3 numbers? What expression can you create to get the largest value using these 3 numbers?*

  Expressions will vary. Encourage students to offer new expressions during the discussion as their understanding of exponents change.

AT A GLANCE

Students revisit the problem on page 148.

STEP BY STEP

- Read Connect It as a class. Be sure to point out that the questions refer to the problem from page 148.
- Emphasize the importance of the order of operations. Review the correct order of operations with students: parentheses, exponents, multiplication and division (left to right rule), and finally addition and subtraction (left to right rule).
- For problem 14, discuss as a class Corwin's error and evaluate correctly. Have students show each step and explain why each step was completed in that order.

$4^2 \cdot 5 + 6$

$16 \cdot 5 + 6$ — *(exponents come first)*

$80 + 6$ — *(multiplication comes next)*

86 — *(addition is the only operation left)*

ELL Support

Provide students with a graphic organizer to remember the order of operations.

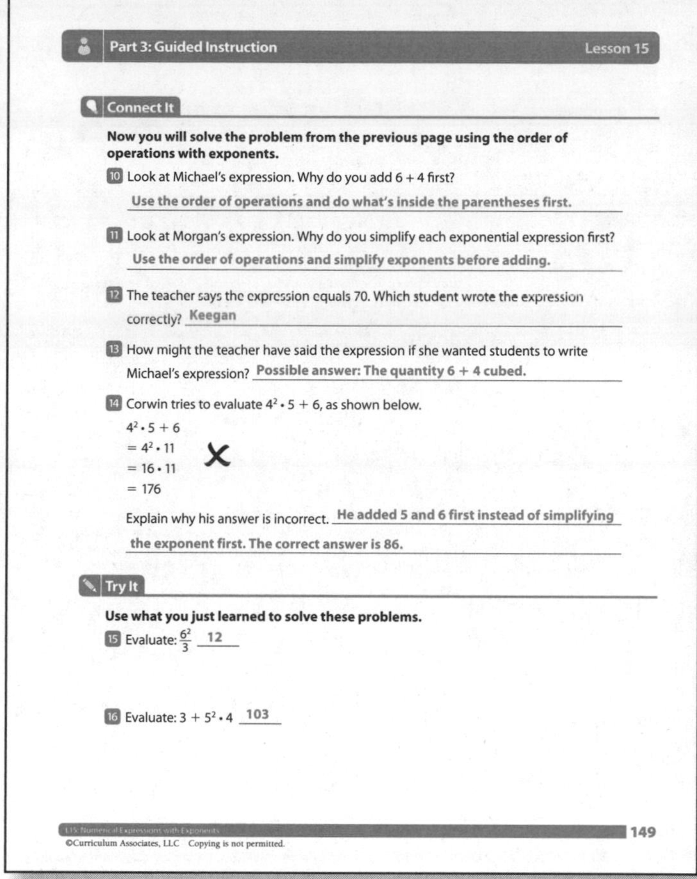

Part 3: Guided Instruction Lesson 15

Connect It

Now you will solve the problem from the previous page using the order of operations with exponents.

10 Look at Michael's expression. Why do you add 6 + 4 first? **Use the order of operations and do what's inside the parentheses first.**

11 Look at Morgan's expression. Why do you simplify each exponential expression first? **Use the order of operations and simplify exponents before adding.**

12 The teacher says the expression equals 70. Which student wrote the expression correctly? **Keegan**

13 How might the teacher have said the expression if she wanted students to write Michael's expression? **Possible answer: The quantity 6 + 4 cubed.**

14 Corwin tries to evaluate $4^2 \cdot 5 + 6$, as shown below.

$4^2 \cdot 5 + 6$

$= 4^2 \cdot 11$ ✗

$= 16 \cdot 11$

$= 176$

Explain why his answer is incorrect. **He added 5 and 6 first instead of simplifying the exponent first. The correct answer is 86.**

Try It

Use what you just learned to solve these problems.

15 Evaluate: $\frac{6^2}{3}$ **12**

16 Evaluate: $3 + 5^2 \cdot 4$ **103**

L15: Numerical Expressions with Exponents 149

©Curriculum Associates, LLC Copying is not permitted.

TRY IT SOLUTIONS

15 *Solution:* 12; $6 \cdot 6 = 36$. 36 divided by 3 is 12. Students may write $\frac{36}{3}$. Remind them to simplify.

16 *Solution:* 103; Apply the order of operations. $5^2 = 25$. $25 \cdot 4$ is 100. $3 + 100 = 103$.

ERROR ALERT: Students who wrote 112 added before multiplying, thus violating the order of operations.

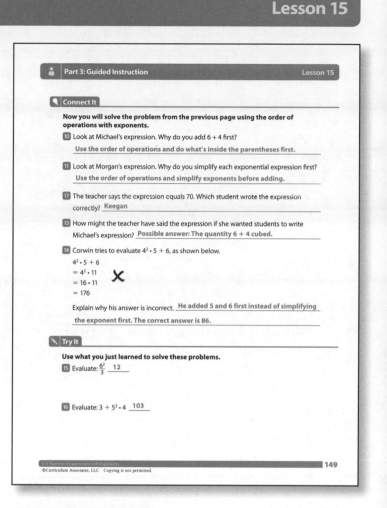

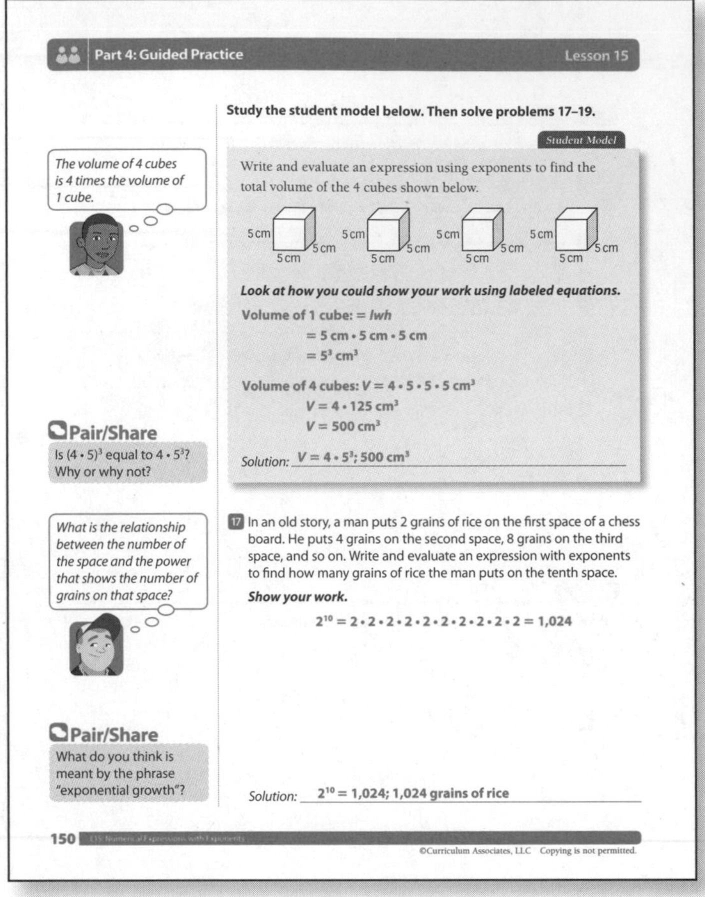

Part 4: Guided Practice — Lesson 15

Study the student model below. Then solve problems 17–19.

Student Model

Write and evaluate an expression using exponents to find the total volume of the 4 cubes shown below.

The volume of 4 cubes is 4 times the volume of 1 cube.

Look at how you could show your work using labeled equations.

Volume of 1 cube: $= lwh$

$= 5 \text{ cm} \cdot 5 \text{ cm} \cdot 5 \text{ cm}$

$= 5^3 \text{ cm}^3$

Volume of 4 cubes: $V = 4 \cdot 5 \cdot 5 \cdot 5 \text{ cm}^3$

$V = 4 \cdot 125 \text{ cm}^3$

$V = 500 \text{ cm}^3$

Solution: $V = 4 \cdot 5^3$; 500 cm³

Pair/Share

Is $(4 \cdot 5)^3$ equal to $4 \cdot 5^3$? Why or why not?

17 In an old story, a man puts 2 grains of rice on the first space of a chess board. He puts 4 grains on the second space, 8 grains on the third space, and so on. Write and evaluate an expression with exponents to find how many grains of rice the man puts on the tenth space.

What is the relationship between the number of the space and the power that shows the number of grains on that space?

Show your work.

$2^{10} = 2 \cdot 2 \cdot 2 \cdot 2 \cdot 2 \cdot 2 \cdot 2 \cdot 2 \cdot 2 \cdot 2 = 1{,}024$

Solution: $2^{10} = 1{,}024$; 1,024 grains of rice

Pair/Share

What do you think is meant by the phrase "exponential growth"?

150 L15: Numerical Expressions with Exponents

©Curriculum Associates, LLC Copying is not permitted.

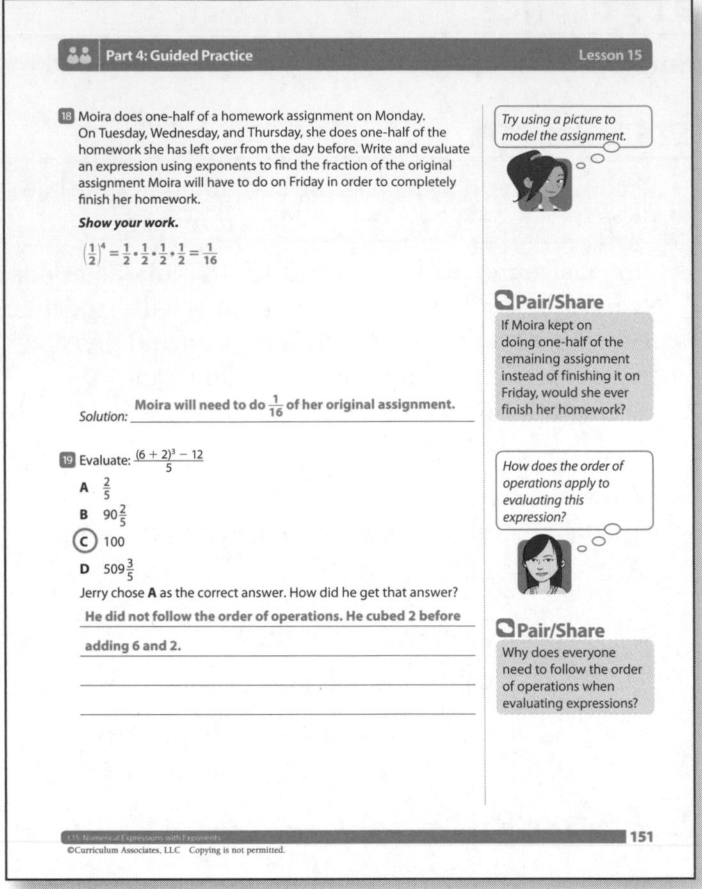

Part 4: Guided Practice — Lesson 15

18 Moira does one-half of a homework assignment on Monday. On Tuesday, Wednesday, and Thursday, she does one-half of the homework she has left over from the day before. Write and evaluate an expression using exponents to find the fraction of the original assignment Moira will have to do on Friday in order to completely finish her homework.

Try using a picture to model the assignment.

Show your work.

$\left(\frac{1}{2}\right)^4 = \frac{1}{2} \cdot \frac{1}{2} \cdot \frac{1}{2} \cdot \frac{1}{2} = \frac{1}{16}$

Solution: Moira will need to do $\frac{1}{16}$ of her original assignment.

Pair/Share

If Moira kept on doing one-half of the remaining assignment instead of finishing it on Friday, would she ever finish her homework?

19 Evaluate: $\frac{(6 + 2)^3 - 12}{5}$

How does the order of operations apply to evaluating this expression?

A $\frac{2}{5}$

B $90\frac{2}{5}$

(C) 100

D $509\frac{3}{5}$

Jerry chose **A** as the correct answer. How did he get that answer?

He did not follow the order of operations. He cubed 2 before adding 6 and 2.

Pair/Share

Why does everyone need to follow the order of operations when evaluating expressions?

L15: Numerical Expressions with Exponents 151

©Curriculum Associates, LLC Copying is not permitted.

AT A GLANCE

Students write and evaluate numerical expressions involving whole-number exponents.

STEP BY STEP

- Ask students to solve the problems individually and interpret their answers in the context of the problems.
- When students have completed each problem, have them Pair/Share to discuss their solutions with a partner or in a group.

SOLUTIONS

Ex The example shows how to write and evaluate a numerical expression involving whole-number exponents.

17 *Solution:* 1,024 grains of rice; Students could solve the problem by evaluating the following: $2^{10} = 2 \cdot 2 \cdot 2 \cdot 2 \cdot 2 \cdot 2 \cdot 2 \cdot 2 \cdot 2 \cdot 2$. ***(DOK 2)***

18 *Solution:* Moira will need to do $\frac{1}{16}$ of her original homework; Students could solve the problem by evaluating $\left(\frac{1}{2}\right)^4 = \frac{1}{2} \cdot \frac{1}{2} \cdot \frac{1}{2} \cdot \frac{1}{2}$. ***(DOK 2)***

19 *Solution:* **C**; Jerry did not follow the order of operations, instead cubing 2 before adding 6 and 2.

Explain to students why the other two answer choices are not correct:

B is not correct because $\frac{500}{5}$ does not simplify to $90\frac{2}{5}$.

D is not correct because the entire numerator should be divided by 5. ***(DOK 3)***

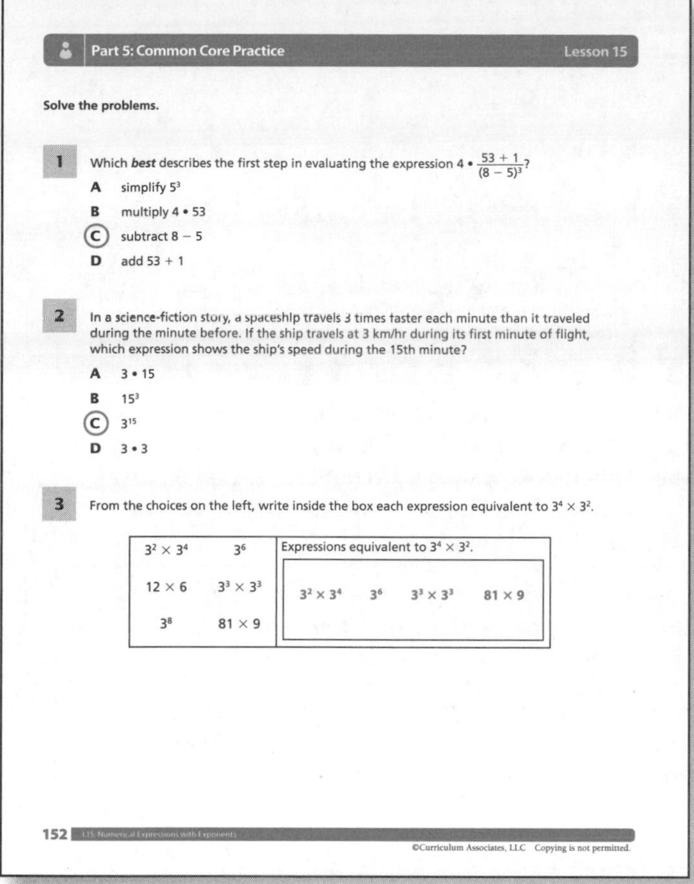

Part 5: Common Core Practice Lesson 15

Solve the problems.

1 Which *best* describes the first step in evaluating the expression $4 \cdot \frac{53 + 1}{(8 - 5)^3}$?

A simplify 5^3

B multiply $4 \cdot 53$

Ⓒ subtract $8 - 5$

D add $53 + 1$

2 In a science-fiction story, a spaceship travels 3 times faster each minute than it traveled during the minute before. If the ship travels at 3 km/hr during its first minute of flight, which expression shows the ship's speed during the 15th minute?

A $3 \cdot 15$

B 15^3

Ⓒ 3^{15}

D $3 \cdot 3$

3 From the choices on the left, write inside the box each expression equivalent to $3^4 \times 3^2$.

		Expressions equivalent to $3^4 \times 3^2$.
$3^2 \times 3^4$	3^6	
12×6	$3^3 \times 3^3$	$3^2 \times 3^4$ 3^6 $3^3 \times 3^3$ 81×9
3^8	81×9	

152 L15: Numerical Expressions with Exponents ©Curriculum Associates, LLC Copying is not permitted.

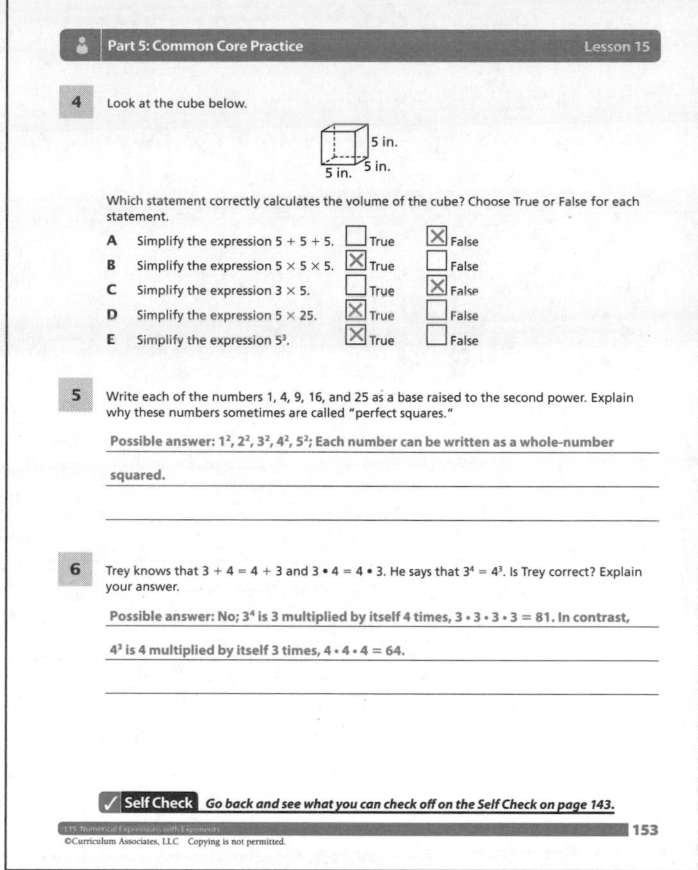

Part 5: Common Core Practice Lesson 15

4 Look at the cube below.

5 in. 5 in. 5 in.

Which statement correctly calculates the volume of the cube? Choose True or False for each statement.

A Simplify the expression $5 + 5 + 5$. ☐ True ☒ False

B Simplify the expression $5 \times 5 \times 5$. ☒ True ☐ False

C Simplify the expression 3×5. ☐ True ☒ False

D Simplify the expression 5×25. ☒ True ☐ False

E Simplify the expression 5^3. ☒ True ☐ False

5 Write each of the numbers 1, 4, 9, 16, and 25 as a base raised to the second power. Explain why these numbers sometimes are called "perfect squares."

Possible answer: $1^2, 2^2, 3^2, 4^2, 5^2$; Each number can be written as a whole-number squared.

6 Trey knows that $3 + 4 = 4 + 3$ and $3 \cdot 4 = 4 \cdot 3$. He says that $3^4 = 4^3$. Is Trey correct? Explain your answer.

Possible answer: No; 3^4 is 3 multiplied by itself 4 times, $3 \cdot 3 \cdot 3 \cdot 3 = 81$. In contrast, 4^3 is 4 multiplied by itself 3 times, $4 \cdot 4 \cdot 4 = 64$.

✓ Self Check *Go back and see what you can check off on the Self Check on page 143.*

L15: Numerical Expressions with Exponents 153 ©Curriculum Associates, LLC Copying is not permitted.

AT A GLANCE

Students write and evaluate numeric expressions which include powers with whole-number exponents to solve problems that might appear on a mathematics test.

SOLUTIONS

1 *Solution:* **C**: Apply the order of operations to evaluate the parentheses first, $(8 - 5)$. ***(DOK 2)***

2 *Solution:* **C**: The spaceship is going "3 times" faster each time (the base). This happens for 15 minutes (the exponent); 3^{15} ***(DOK 2)***

3 *Solution:* $3^2 \times 3^4$, 3^6, $3^3 \times 3^3$, 81×9; Evaluate each expression to find equivalent expressions. ***(DOK 1)***

4 *Solution:* A **False**; B **True**; C **False**; D **True**; E **True** ***(DOK 2)***

5 *Solution:* $1^2, 2^2, 3^2, 4^2, 5^2$; Each number can be written as a whole number squared. ***(DOK 3)***

6 *Solution:* No; 3^4 is 3 multiplied by itself 4 times, $3 \cdot 3 \cdot 3 \cdot 3 = 81$. In contrast, 4^3 is 4 multiplied by itself 3 times, $4 \cdot 4 \cdot 4 = 64$. ***(DOK 3)***

Assessment and Remediation

- Ask students to evaluate $5 + 7^2 \cdot (8 - 6)$. [$5 + 49 \cdot 2 = 5 + 98 = 103$]
- For students who are struggling, use the chart below to guide remediation.
- After providing remediation, check students' understanding. Ask students to evaluate $28 - (5 - 2)^3$. [$28 - (3)^3 = 28 - 27 = 1$]
- If a student is still having difficulty, review this lesson, and consult ***Ready Instruction, Level 5,*** Lesson 19.

If the error is . . .	Students may . . .	To remediate . . .
108	not have followed the order of operations.	Review the order of operations; parentheses, exponents, multiplication and division (follow the left to right rule), and finally addition and subtraction (follow the left to right rule). Explain that $8 - 6$ should be evaluated first. The difference, 2, should then be multiplied by 49 (from 7^2). Finally, add 5.
33	have evaluated the power incorrectly.	Reteach the meaning of powers; 7^2 is equivalent to $7 \cdot 7$, not $7 + 7$ or $7 \cdot 2$. Model exponential growth to see how the multiplication is growing by using counters or an area model.
38	not have followed the order of operations AND additionally evaluated the power incorrectly.	Provide a graphic organizer as a reference for the order of operations. Ask students to create a model to represent the power being evaluated.
Any other answer	have made a simple calculator error.	Consider the use of a multiplication table or basic calculator.

Hands-On Activity

- Revisit page 150, problem 17 with students.
- Ask, *How would the problem change if the man put 3 grains of rice on the first space, 9 grains on the second space, 27 grains on the third space, and so on? How many grains of rice would be on space 11?*
- Ask students to use a table, numeric expressions involving exponents, and/or a model to support their solution. [The model should support 3^{11} as their resulting solution.]
- Note: Students will question the effectiveness of the model as it grows rapidly. Ask students to provide a model to show initial growth.

Challenge Activity

- Revisit page 150, problem 17 with students.
- Tell students, *A friend of the man wants to follow a similar pattern by putting 4 grains of rice on the first space, 16 grains of rice on the second space, 64 grains of rice on the third space, and so on.*
- Now say, *Compare and contrast the two friends by creating a table, using numerical expressions involving exponents, and modeling the growth. Explain to the friends the observations you have made.* [Student observations should indicate the friend used powers of 4, while the man used powers of 2. Observations should also indicate that the friend's pattern grows at a much faster rate.]
- Note: The model will grow rapidly. Ask students to provide a model to show initial growth.

Lesson 16 (Student Book pages 154–165)

Algebraic Expressions

LESSON OBJECTIVES

- Write, read, and evaluate variable expressions.
- Apply the order of operations on expressions with variables, including those with exponents.
- Translate an expression from its word form to an algebraic expression and vice versa.
- Identify parts of expressions using appropriate mathematical vocabulary.

PREREQUISITE SKILLS

- Write, interpret, and evaluate numerical expressions, including those involving exponents.
- Interpret a fraction as division.
- Know that expressions do not include equals, greater than, or less than signs.
- Know that variables represent unknown quantities.
- Apply order of operations.

THE LEARNING PROGRESSION

In Grade 6, students will apply and extend previous understanding of arithmetic to algebraic expressions.

This lesson focuses on writing, reading, and evaluating expressions in which letters stand for numbers. Students will write expressions to record operations with letters standing for numbers. Students will identify parts of expressions using mathematical terms to include the viewing of one or more parts of an expression as a single entity. Students will also evaluate expressions at specific values of their variables, including expressions which arise from formulas used in the real world.

Ready ***Teacher Toolbox*** *Teacher-Toolbox.com*

	Prerequisite Skills	6.EE.A.2a, 6.EE.A.2b 6.EE.A.2c
Ready Lessons		✓
Tools for Instruction		
Interactive Tutorials		✓

VOCABULARY

variable: a letter that stands for an unknown number

term: a known number, a variable, or the product of a known number and variable(s)

variable term: a term that includes variables

constant: a term that is a known number without variables

coefficient: the known number that is a factor of a variable term

CCSS Focus

6.EE.A.2 Write, read, and evaluate expressions in which letters stand for numbers.

a. Write expressions that record operations with numbers and with letters standing for numbers. *For example, express the calculation "Subtract y from 5" as* $5 - y$.

b. Identify parts of an expression using mathematical terms (sum, term, product, factor, quotient, coefficient); view one or more parts of an expression as a single entity. *For example, describe the expression* $2(8 + 7)$ *as a product of two factors; view* $(8 + 7)$ *as both a single entity and a sum of two terms.*

c. Evaluate expressions at specific values of their variables. Include expressions that arise from formulas used in real-world problems. Perform arithmetic operations, including those involving whole-number exponents, in the conventional order when there are no parentheses to specify a particular order (Order of Operations). *For example, use the formulas* $V = s^3$ *and* $A = 6s^2$ *to find the volume and surface area of a cube with sides of length* $s = \frac{1}{2}$.

ADDITIONAL STANDARDS: ***6.EE.B.6*** *(see page A42 for full text)*

STANDARDS FOR MATHEMATICAL PRACTICE: ***SMP 1–4, 6*** *(see page A9 for full text)*

AT A GLANCE

Students view an expression and are guided to describe it using mathematical terms such as product and sum.

STEP BY STEP

- Tell students that this page guides them in understanding and describing an expression that includes variables and mathematical operations.
- Have students read the problem at the top of the page. Explain that we can tell a lot about an expression without evaluating it, or performing the calculation, or knowing the values of all the terms.
- Work through Explore It as a class.
- Emphasize the variable, x, in the expression. Ask students if they know what this represents. [It could be any number; an unknown number.]
- Point out the term $2x$ and the lack of an operational sign. Tell students that representing multiplication this way avoids any confusion of the variable x with a multiplication symbol. The expression $2x$ means "two times x."
- Ask student pairs or groups to explain what the whole expression $2x + 5$ represents.

SMP Tip: When students describe an expression without evaluating it, they come to understand that an expression is a single object that can also be seen as a combination of objects (*SMP 7*).

Concept Extension

Create verbal translations of expressions.

Materials: index cards with $9 - 3$, $3 + 8$, 5×6, $x - 3$, $x + 3$, $\frac{x}{3}$, $\frac{10}{2}$, and $6x$

- Assign pairs or groups expressions to read aloud.
- Create as many different verbal translations of the expression as possible.
- Write story problems to represent each expression.
- Share verbal translations with the class.

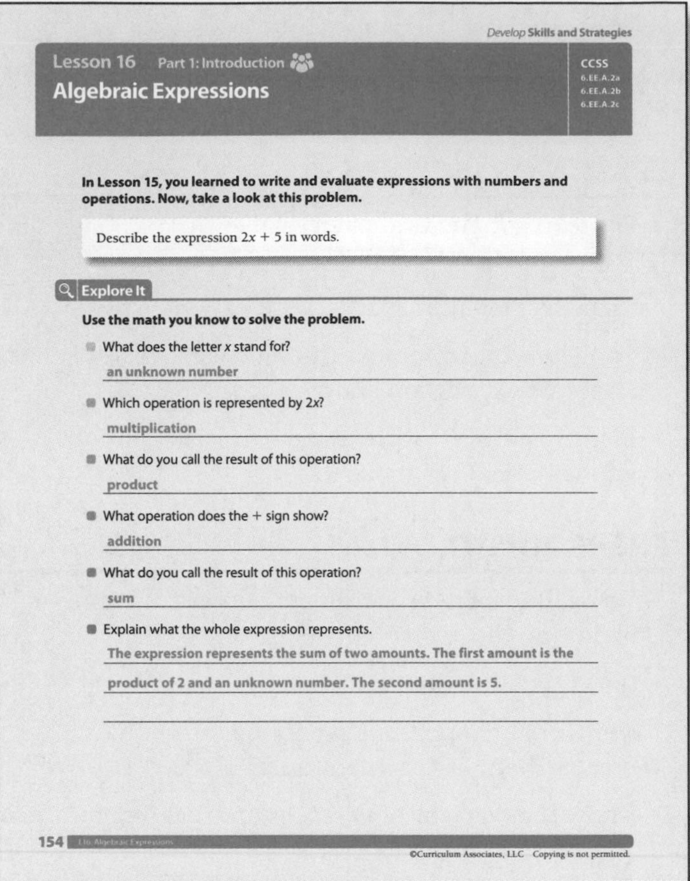

Develop Skills and Strategies

Lesson 16 Part 1: Introduction

Algebraic Expressions

CCSS 6.EE.A.2a 6.EE.A.2b 6.EE.A.2c

In Lesson 15, you learned to write and evaluate expressions with numbers and operations. Now, take a look at this problem.

Describe the expression $2x + 5$ in words.

Explore It

Use the math you know to solve the problem.

- What does the letter x stand for? an unknown number
- Which operation is represented by $2x$? multiplication
- What do you call the result of this operation? product
- What operation does the + sign show? addition
- What do you call the result of this operation? sum
- Explain what the whole expression represents. The expression represents the sum of two amounts. The first amount is the product of 2 and an unknown number. The second amount is 5.

154 L16: Algebraic Expressions ©Curriculum Associates, LLC Copying is not permitted.

Mathematical Discourse

- *Kristen says that if x is positive, then 2x + 5 is greater than 5. Do you agree?*

  Listen for reasoning that the expression has to be greater than 5 because some positive number is added to 5.

- *Is 2x + 5 is a sum or a product? Why?*

  Students may recognize that it is a sum. They may say that $2x$ is the product of 2 and x. Others may be unsure or insist that you can't know without knowing the value of x.

- *What else can you say about this expression?*

  Allow plenty of wait time. Have students respond rather than commenting yourself. Responses may include that it has two parts, that its value is positive, or that it can be rewritten as $x + x + 5$.

AT A GLANCE

Students will identify parts of an expression using mathematical terms and view one or more parts of an expression as a single entity.

STEP BY STEP

- Read Find Out More as a class.
- Write the expression $2x + 5$ on the board. Circle and label the variable term, the coefficient, and the constant.
- Point out to students another way to show multiplication is using "·" such as $2 \cdot x$.
- Read Reflect as a class. Clarify the operations being used. [multiplication and evaluating a power]
- Ask student pairs or groups to share their explanations as to why Claire was correct or incorrect.

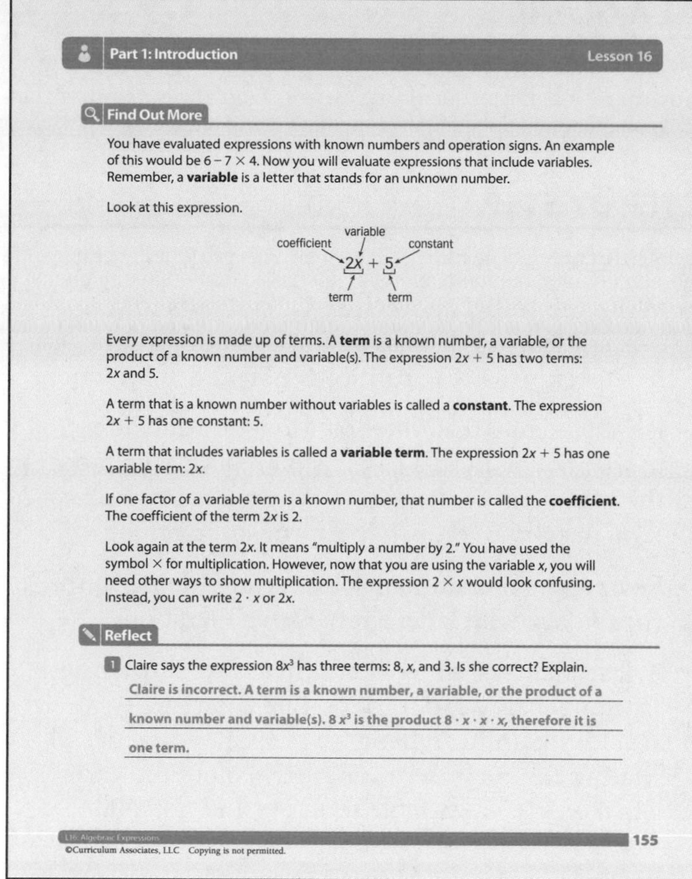

Part 1: Introduction Lesson 16

Find Out More

You have evaluated expressions with known numbers and operation signs. An example of this would be $6 - 7 \times 4$. Now you will evaluate expressions that include variables. Remember, a **variable** is a letter that stands for an unknown number.

Look at this expression.

Every expression is made up of terms. A **term** is a known number, a variable, or the product of a known number and variable(s). The expression $2x + 5$ has two terms: $2x$ and 5.

A term that is a known number without variables is called a **constant**. The expression $2x + 5$ has one constant: 5.

A term that includes variables is called a **variable term**. The expression $2x + 5$ has one variable term: $2x$.

If one factor of a variable term is a known number, that number is called the **coefficient**. The coefficient of the term $2x$ is 2.

Look again at the term $2x$. It means "multiply a number by 2." You have used the symbol $\times$ for multiplication. However, now that you are using the variable x, you will need other ways to show multiplication. The expression $2 \times x$ would look confusing. Instead, you can write $2 \cdot x$ or $2x$.

Reflect

1 Claire says the expression $8x^3$ has three terms: 8, x, and 3. Is she correct? Explain.

Claire is incorrect. A term is a known number, a variable, or the product of a known number and variable(s). $8x^3$ is the product $8 \cdot x \cdot x \cdot x$, therefore it is one term.

L16: Algebraic Expressions 155
©Curriculum Associates, LLC Copying is not permitted.

Visual Model

Study expressions with algebra tiles.

Materials: algebra tiles

- Present students with algebra tiles. Introduce the small square as one unit, the rectangular tile as x, and the large square as x^2. The red side represents a negative, and the green side represents a positive.
- Use tiles to model the following expressions: $2x + 5$, $3x$, 4, $x^2 + 1$, $2x^2 - 3x$, $^-2x^2 - 3$, and $^-5$.
- Write expressions for the following:

  2 red rectangles and 3 small green squares ($^-2x + 3$)

  4 green rectangles ($4x$)

  3 large red squares ($^-3x^2$)
- Explain to students that each grouping of tiles represents a term in the expression.
- Identify addition as the operation which describes the combining of the groups.

Real-World Connection

Encourage students to create real-world applications of the expression $2x + 5$. Have students share expressions that could be used in the real world.

Examples: Bob earns 2 dollars for each pile of leaves he bags, x, and 5 dollars for helping.

AT A GLANCE

Students will explore ways to write expressions using numbers, variables, and operational symbols from verbal descriptions.

STEP BY STEP

- Read the problem at the top of the page as a class.
- Write the verbal expression for students to see. Ask students to determine the operations to be used in this expression. [multiplication and subtraction]
- Have students read the first Model It. Call attention to the model. Lead a discussion relating the model to the verbal expression. Ask, *Why are there two boxes?* [You need two terms to perform subtraction.]
- Review the remaining problems and highlight the vocabulary which determines the operation.
- Ask students to show alternative ways of writing "a number times four." [Possible answers: $4x$, $x \cdot 4$, $x(4)$.] Explain to students the common practice of writing the coefficient (number) before the variable when writing a variable term ($4x$ and not $x4$).

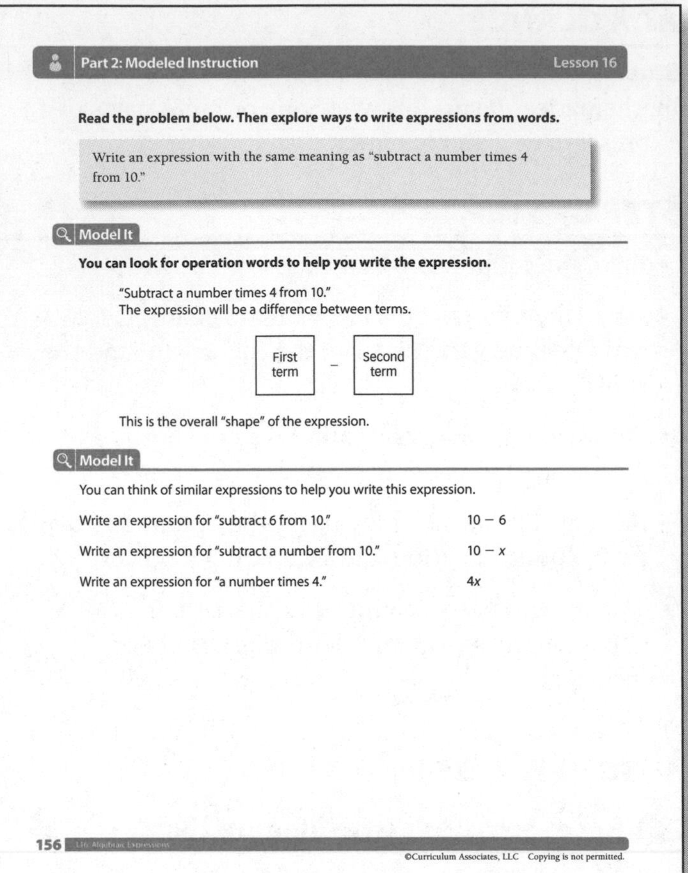

Part 2: Modeled Instruction Lesson 16

Read the problem below. Then explore ways to write expressions from words.

Write an expression with the same meaning as "subtract a number times 4 from 10."

Model It

You can look for operation words to help you write the expression.

"Subtract a number times 4 from 10."
The expression will be a difference between terms.

First term – Second term

This is the overall "shape" of the expression.

Model It

You can think of similar expressions to help you write this expression.

Write an expression for "subtract 6 from 10." $10 - 6$

Write an expression for "subtract a number from 10." $10 - x$

Write an expression for "a number times 4." $4x$

156 L16: Algebraic Expressions

©Curriculum Associates, LLC Copying is not permitted.

Concept Extension

Identify parts of a term and like terms.

Materials: cards (x, x^2, x^3, m, m^2, m^3, $2m$, $2x$, $3x$, $3m$, $4x^2$, $4x^3$, $4m^2$, $4m^3$); Cards may be duplicated.

- Give each student one card.
- Ask students who have a term without a coefficient to add one.
- List all terms for students to see.
- Ask students to find others who have a term that is "like" the one they are holding. Clarify for students that *like terms* are terms that have the same variable or variable with the same exponent.
- Once students are in groups of like terms, have students write an expression that would combine their terms and include a simplified expression of the like terms.
- Ask groups to combine their simplified expressions to write a class expression.

AT A GLANCE

Students revisit the problem on page 156 and identify parts of an expression. They then write an expression from words.

STEP BY STEP

- Read Connect It as a class. Be sure to point out that the questions refer to the problem on page 156.
- Read the Try It problems as a class.

ELL Support

Ask students to use a different color to highlight the different operations. Use the same color for similar operations.

SMP Tip: Ask students to state the meaning of the symbols they choose. This provides an opportunity for students to communicate their reasoning precisely and appropriately (*SMP 6*) with clear definitions.

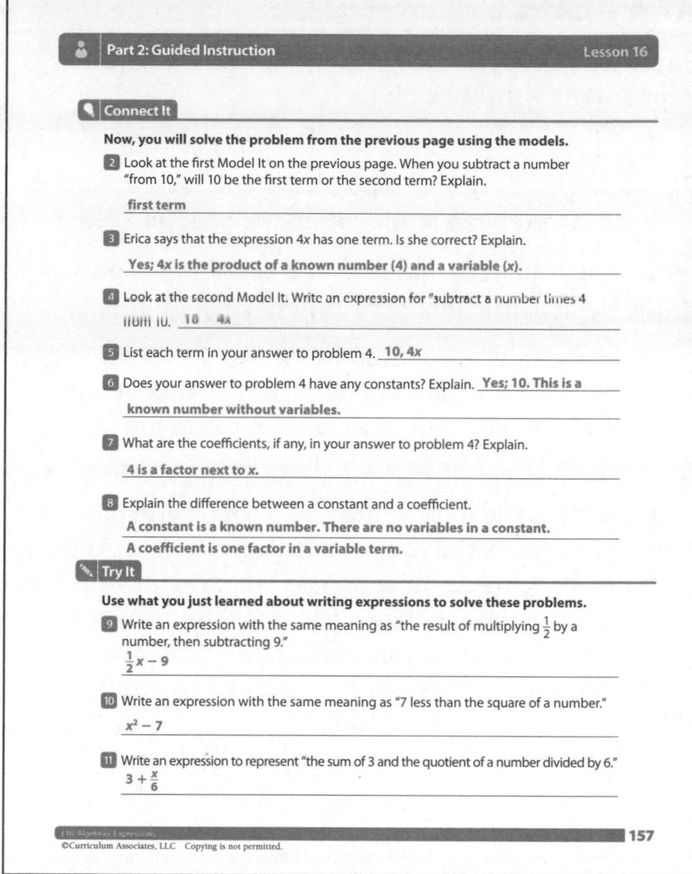

Part 2: Guided Instruction Lesson 16

Connect It

Now, you will solve the problem from the previous page using the models.

2 Look at the first Model It on the previous page. When you subtract a number "from 10," will 10 be the first term or the second term? Explain.

first term

3 Erica says that the expression $4x$ has one term. Is she correct? Explain.

Yes; $4x$ is the product of a known number (4) and a variable (x).

4 Look at the second Model It. Write an expression for "subtract a number times 4 from 10." **10 4x**

5 List each term in your answer to problem 4. **10, $4x$**

6 Does your answer to problem 4 have any constants? Explain. **Yes; 10. This is a known number without variables.**

7 What are the coefficients, if any, in your answer to problem 4? Explain.

4 is a factor next to x.

8 Explain the difference between a constant and a coefficient.

A constant is a known number. There are no variables in a constant.
A coefficient is one factor in a variable term.

Try It

Use what you just learned about writing expressions to solve these problems.

9 Write an expression with the same meaning as "the result of multiplying $\frac{1}{2}$ by a number, then subtracting 9."

$\frac{1}{2}x - 9$

10 Write an expression with the same meaning as "7 less than the square of a number."

$x^2 - 7$

11 Write an expression to represent "the sum of 3 and the quotient of a number divided by 6."

$3 + \frac{x}{6}$

L16: Algebraic Expressions 157
©Curriculum Associates, LLC Copying is not permitted.

TRY IT SOLUTIONS

9 *Solution*: $\frac{1}{2}x - 9$; Students may use the decimal representation of one half as 0.5.

10 *Solution*: $x^2 - 7$; Students may write $x \cdot x - 7$.

ERROR ALERT: Students who wrote "$2x - 7$" did not use their knowledge of exponents to represent a number being multiplied by itself.

11 *Solution*: $3 + \frac{x}{6}$; Students may write "$3 + x \div 6$" instead of writing the fraction bar or a model to determine the terms.

AT A GLANCE

Students will explore ways to write and evaluate expressions with variables.

STEP BY STEP

- Read the problem at the top of the page as a class.
- Read Picture It. What does the variable p represent in the model? [the pieces of gum in each mint pack]
- Guide students to connect the facts to the model (1 pack of orange gum, 3 packs of mint gum, orange gum has 8 pieces, unknown number of mint pieces in each pack).
- Ask a volunteer to read the second sentence in Model It ("The total number...."). Draw attention to the operating word "sum," which generally means two items are being combined. Ask, *What two items will be added?* [number of orange packs and number of mint packs] *What will the sum of these two terms determine?* [the total number of pieces purchased by Jennifer]

SMP Tip: Writing expressions to represent real-world situations and interpreting expressions in terms of the situation are examples of modeling with mathematics (*SMP 4*).

Concept Extension

Evaluate expressions by substitution.

Materials: index cards with the digits 0–9; symbols $+, -, \cdot, \div$; exponents 2, 3, a variable card (such as x)

- Explain to students that they will be asked to evaluate expressions by substitution.
- Provide students with these expressions:

  $(2 + 4) \cdot x^2$, $\frac{x^3}{(14 - 5)}$, $(-9 + 3) + x^2$,

  $2x + 3$, $\frac{4x}{2}$, $5(x + 3)^2$
- Have students work in groups. Direct students to show an expression with the cards.
- Ask students to replace the variable with any digit or with a digit directed by the teacher.
- Students should show the steps for evaluating the expression by using the order of operations.

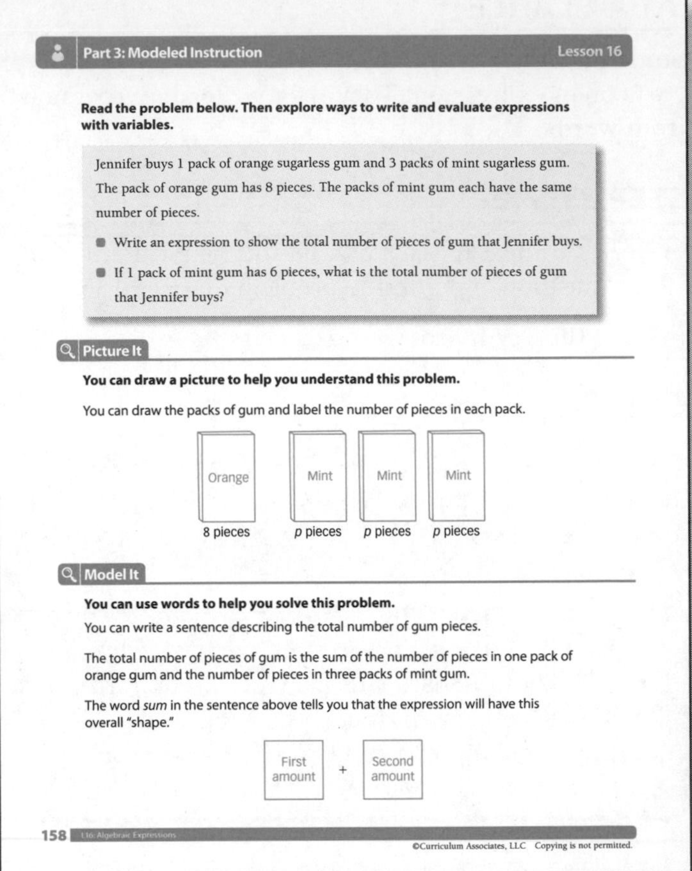

Part 3: Modeled Instruction Lesson 16

Read the problem below. Then explore ways to write and evaluate expressions with variables.

Jennifer buys 1 pack of orange sugarless gum and 3 packs of mint sugarless gum. The pack of orange gum has 8 pieces. The packs of mint gum each have the same number of pieces.

- Write an expression to show the total number of pieces of gum that Jennifer buys.
- If 1 pack of mint gum has 6 pieces, what is the total number of pieces of gum that Jennifer buys?

Picture It

You can draw a picture to help you understand this problem.

You can draw the packs of gum and label the number of pieces in each pack.

Model It

You can use words to help you solve this problem.

You can write a sentence describing the total number of gum pieces.

The total number of pieces of gum is the sum of the number of pieces in one pack of orange gum and the number of pieces in three packs of mint gum.

The word *sum* in the sentence above tells you that the expression will have this overall "shape."

158 L16: Algebraic Expressions

©Curriculum Associates, LLC Copying is not permitted.

Mathematical Discourse

- *Is there another box model that would work here? Explain.*

  Yes; this is an addition problem, and the order in which addition occurs does not matter. The second and first terms could change position.
- *How would you change the problem to increase the number of pieces of gum Jennifer buys? Can you write an expression for this? Is there another way to rewrite the problem?*

  Possible answers: change the number of orange pieces in a pack to a number greater than 8, increase the number of mint packs she purchases.

AT A GLANCE

Students revisit the problem on page 158 and solve problems by writing and evaluating expressions.

STEP BY STEP

- Read Connect It as a class. Be sure to point out that the questions refer to the problem on page 158.
- Refer students to the number of terms in the expression (2) and how they are separated (by an addition sign).
- Remind students to highlight operating words and to create a box model.

Visual Model

Model expressions with algebra tiles.

Materials: algebra tiles

- As a class, review the value of each of the algebra tiles. [The small square is one unit, the rectangular tile is x, and the large square is x^2. The red side represents a negative value, and the green side represents a positive value.]
- Ask students to use algebra tiles to model the gum problem. [8 small squares and 3 rectangles]
- Ask students, *How many terms are represented?* [2; two different groupings of shapes] *What operation would describe the combining of the groups of tiles?* [addition]
- Model for students some changes to the number of orange and mint packs Jennifer bought. Ask, *How does this change the expression?* [The constant or coefficient may change, but the number of terms remains the same.]
- Ask volunteers to change the problem and model the changed expression. [Models will vary.]

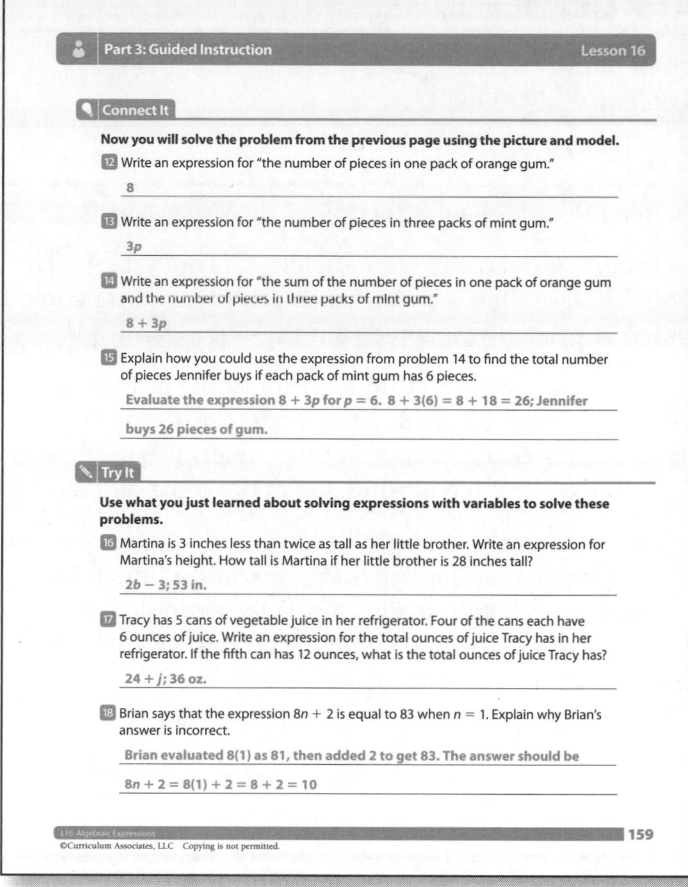
Part 3: Guided Instruction Lesson 16

Connect It

Now you will solve the problem from the previous page using the picture and model.

12 Write an expression for "the number of pieces in one pack of orange gum."

8

13 Write an expression for "the number of pieces in three packs of mint gum."

$3p$

14 Write an expression for "the sum of the number of pieces in one pack of orange gum and the number of pieces in three packs of mint gum."

$8 + 3p$

15 Explain how you could use the expression from problem 14 to find the total number of pieces Jennifer buys if each pack of mint gum has 6 pieces.

Evaluate the expression $8 + 3p$ for $p = 6$. $8 + 3(6) = 8 + 18 = 26$; Jennifer buys 26 pieces of gum.

Try It

Use what you just learned about solving expressions with variables to solve these problems.

16 Martina is 3 inches less than twice as tall as her little brother. Write an expression for Martina's height. How tall is Martina if her little brother is 28 inches tall?

$2b - 3$; 53 in.

17 Tracy has 5 cans of vegetable juice in her refrigerator. Four of the cans each have 6 ounces of juice. Write an expression for the total ounces of juice Tracy has in her refrigerator. If the fifth can has 12 ounces, what is the total ounces of juice Tracy has?

$24 + j$; 36 oz.

18 Brian says that the expression $8n + 2$ is equal to 83 when $n = 1$. Explain why Brian's answer is incorrect.

Brian evaluated 8(1) as 81, then added 2 to get 83. The answer should be $8n + 2 = 8(1) + 2 = 8 + 2 = 10$

L16: Algebraic Expressions 159
©Curriculum Associates, LLC Copying is not permitted.

TRY IT SOLUTIONS

16 *Solution:* $2b - 3$; 53 in.; Students write and evaluate an expression for twice the brother's height minus 3 inches.

ERROR ALERT: Students who wrote $3 - 2b$ did not take into account the order of "3 less than twice as tall" meaning "3 removed from twice as tall."

17 *Solution:* $24 + j$; 36 oz; Students write and evaluate an expression for the cans and ounces of juice.

18 *Solution:* Brian evaluated 8(1) as 81, then added 2 to get 83. The answer is $8n + 2 = 8(1) + 2 = 8 + 2 = 10$.

AT A GLANCE

Students will continue exploring ways to write and evaluate expressions.

STEP BY STEP

- Read the problem at the top of the page as a class.
- Prompt students to state the facts. [This year's prize is \$20 less than 3 times last year's prize; two people win a prize; two people split the prize evenly.]
- Refer students to Picture It. Connect the facts described by the class to the model. Lead a discussion on the differences between this model and the previous gum model. What do students notice to be different?
- Guide students to Model It. Ask students to identify the phrase that describes the operation [less than] and the operation it signifies [subtraction]. Refer students to the model with two terms for subtraction. Point out the importance of the order of the terms.
- Refer students to Evan's prize money: "Evan gets half of the prize." Ask, *What operation does this ask us to use?* [Divide by 2 or multiply by $\frac{1}{2}$ or multiply by 0.5.]

SMP Tip: Identifying facts lets students make sense of problems *(SMP 1)* by using simpler forms of the original problem to gain insight into its solution.

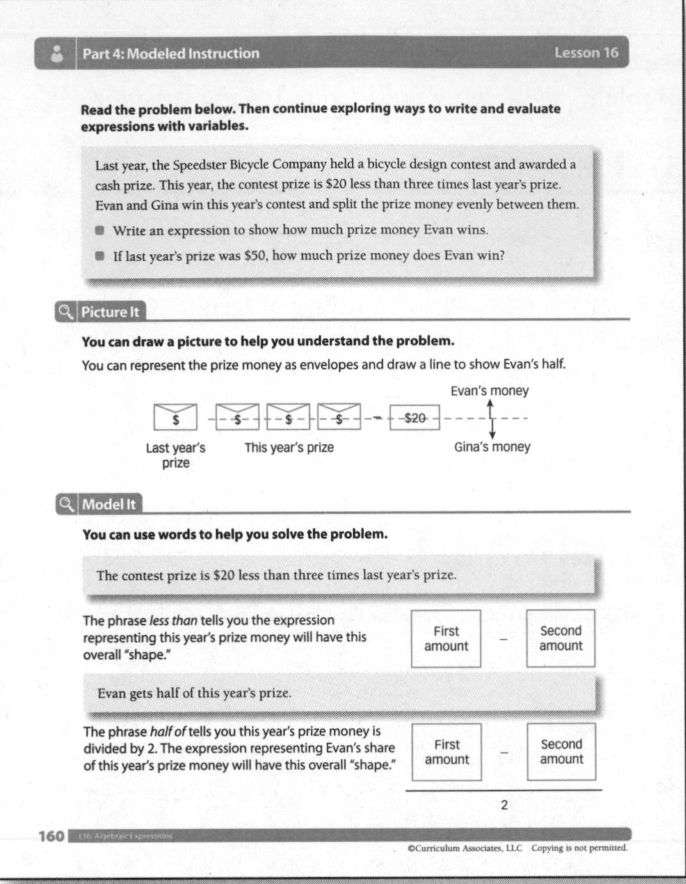

Part 4: Modeled Instruction Lesson 16

Read the problem below. Then continue exploring ways to write and evaluate expressions with variables.

Last year, the Speedster Bicycle Company held a bicycle design contest and awarded a cash prize. This year, the contest prize is \$20 less than three times last year's prize. Evan and Gina win this year's contest and split the prize money evenly between them.

- Write an expression to show how much prize money Evan wins.
- If last year's prize was \$50, how much prize money does Evan win?

Picture It

You can draw a picture to help you understand the problem.

You can represent the prize money as envelopes and draw a line to show Evan's half.

Model It

You can use words to help you solve the problem.

The contest prize is \$20 less than three times last year's prize.

The phrase *less than* tells you the expression representing this year's prize money will have this overall "shape."

First amount − Second amount

Evan gets half of this year's prize.

The phrase *half of* tells you this year's prize money is divided by 2. The expression representing Evan's share of this year's prize money will have this overall "shape."

$\frac{\text{First amount} - \text{Second amount}}{2}$

160 L16: Algebraic Expressions ©Curriculum Associates, LLC Copying is not permitted.

Mathematical Discourse

- *A student wrote "$\frac{1}{2}$(first amount − second amount)" to represent Evan's share of this year's prize money. Do you agree or disagree? Can you explain why this makes sense? Can you write another expression to represent Evan's share of this year's prize money?*

  Possible answers: Agree, multiplying by $\frac{1}{2}$ or 0.5 or dividing by 2 are equivalent. Students may also take $\frac{1}{2}$ of the second amount and subtract it from $\frac{1}{2}$ of the first amount.

Concept Extension

Use a table to evaluate expressions.

- Provide students with the following situation: *You work at a store that rents video games for \$4.*
- Ask a volunteer to share the expression that represents the amount the store earns when it rents g games. [4g]
- Complete the table by substituting the given number of games into the expression to determine the amount earned.

Number of Games	Expressions	Amount Earned
g	$4 \cdot g$	4g
15		
40		
45		

AT A GLANCE

Students revisit the problem on page 160 to write and evaluate expressions. Then students solve problems by writing and evaluating expressions.

STEP BY STEP

- Read Connect It as a class. Be sure to point out that the questions refer to the problem on page 160.
- Clarify different ways to represent "3 times last year's prize." [$3x$, $3 \cdot x$, $3(x)$, and noting that $3xx$ is incorrect]
- Regarding problem 22, ask the class to share alternate ways which Chandler could write the expression $\frac{1}{2}(3x - 20)$.
  [Examples: $\frac{(3x - 20)}{2}$, $0.5(3x - 20)$]
- Remind students to follow the order of operations when evaluating expressions.

ELL Support

Emphasize that the word "than" in "is less than" means the operation is written in a different order. Refer students to alternative phrases to aid in clarification. For example: "20 less than a number" can be phrased as "20 removed from a number" or "20 subtracted from a number."

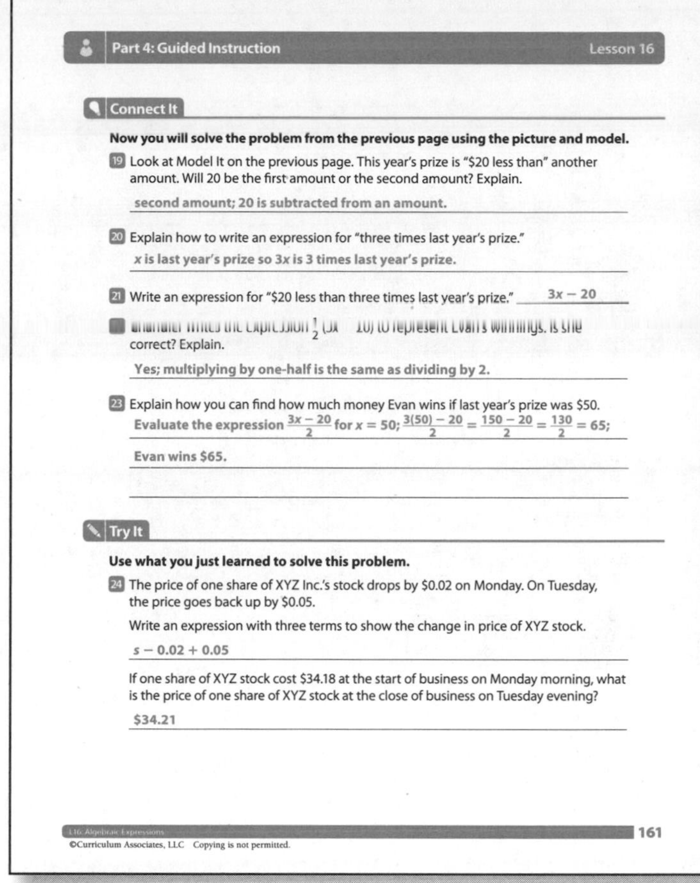

Part 4: Guided Instruction — Lesson 16

Connect It

Now you will solve the problem from the previous page using the picture and model.

19 Look at Model It on the previous page. This year's prize is "$20 less than" another amount. Will 20 be the first amount or the second amount? Explain.
second amount; 20 is subtracted from an amount.

20 Explain how to write an expression for "three times last year's prize."
x is last year's prize so $3x$ is 3 times last year's prize.

21 Write an expression for "$20 less than three times last year's prize." $3x - 20$

22 Chandler writes the expression $\frac{1}{2}(3x - 20)$ to represent Evan's winnings. Is she correct? Explain.
Yes; multiplying by one-half is the same as dividing by 2.

23 Explain how you can find how much money Evan wins if last year's prize was $50.
Evaluate the expression $\frac{3x - 20}{2}$ for $x = 50$; $\frac{3(50) - 20}{2} = \frac{150 - 20}{2} = \frac{130}{2} = 65$;
Evan wins $65.

Try It

Use what you just learned to solve this problem.

24 The price of one share of XYZ Inc.'s stock drops by $0.02 on Monday. On Tuesday, the price goes back up by $0.05.

Write an expression with three terms to show the change in price of XYZ stock.
$s - 0.02 + 0.05$

If one share of XYZ stock cost $34.18 at the start of business on Monday morning, what is the price of one share of XYZ stock at the close of business on Tuesday evening?
$34.21

L16: Algebraic Expressions 161
©Curriculum Associates, LLC Copying is not permitted.

TRY IT SOLUTION

24 *Solutions:* $s - 0.02 + 0.05$; $34.21; Students find an expression with three terms to show the change in the price of XYZ stock, then evaluate it.

ERROR ALERT: Students who wrote $s - 0.2 + 0.5$ did not transfer the numeric values accurately.

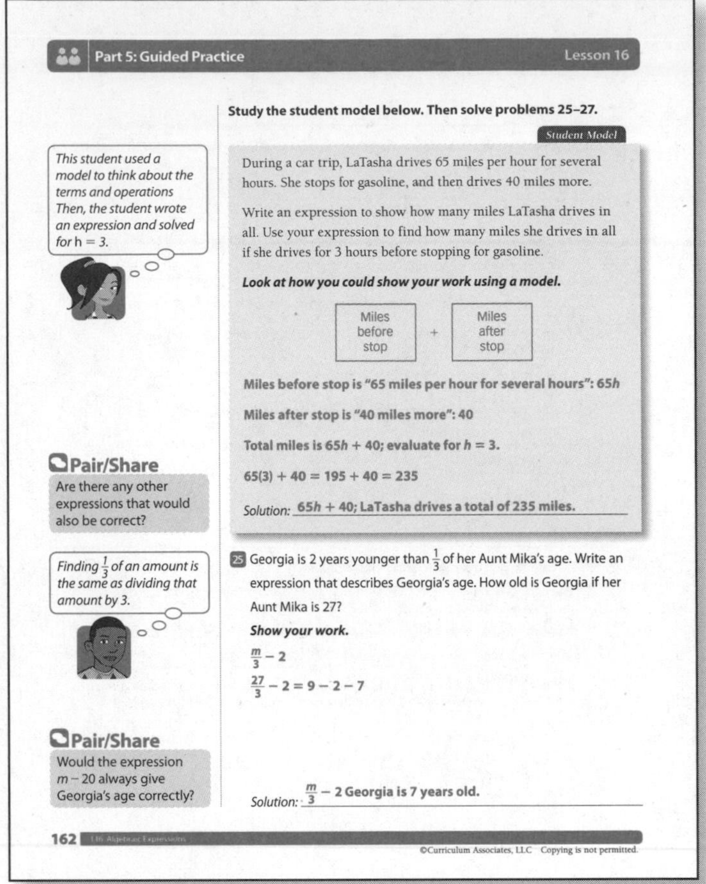

Part 5: Guided Practice — Lesson 16

Study the student model below. Then solve problems 25–27.

Student Model

This student used a model to think about the terms and operations. Then, the student wrote an expression and solved for h = 3.

During a car trip, LaTasha drives 65 miles per hour for several hours. She stops for gasoline, and then drives 40 miles more.

Write an expression to show how many miles LaTasha drives in all. Use your expression to find how many miles she drives in all if she drives for 3 hours before stopping for gasoline.

Look at how you could show your work using a model.

Miles before stop	+	Miles after stop

Miles before stop is "65 miles per hour for several hours": $65h$

Miles after stop is "40 miles more": 40

Total miles is $65h + 40$; evaluate for $h = 3$.

$65(3) + 40 = 195 + 40 = 235$

Solution: **$65h + 40$; LaTasha drives a total of 235 miles.**

Pair/Share
Are there any other expressions that would also be correct?

Finding $\frac{1}{3}$ of an amount is the same as dividing that amount by 3.

25 Georgia is 2 years younger than $\frac{1}{3}$ of her Aunt Mika's age. Write an expression that describes Georgia's age. How old is Georgia if her Aunt Mika is 27?

Show your work.

$\frac{m}{3} - 2$

$\frac{27}{3} - 2 = 9 - 2 - 7$

Solution: $\frac{m}{3} - 2$ Georgia is 7 years old.

Pair/Share
Would the expression $m - 20$ always give Georgia's age correctly?

162 L16: Algebraic Expressions
©Curriculum Associates, LLC Copying is not permitted.

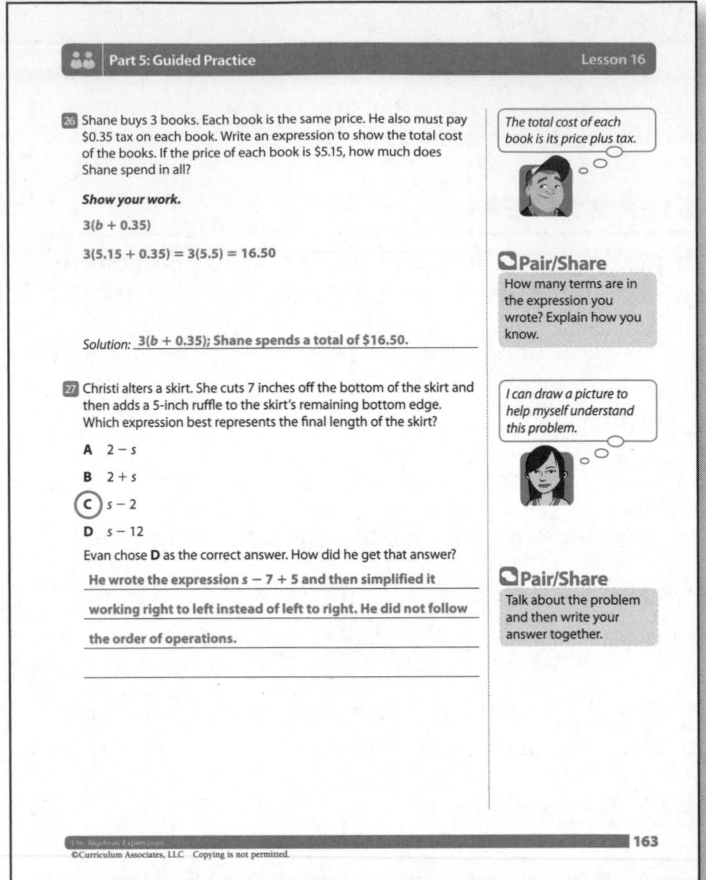

Part 5: Guided Practice — Lesson 16

26 Shane buys 3 books. Each book is the same price. He also must pay \$0.35 tax on each book. Write an expression to show the total cost of the books. If the price of each book is \$5.15, how much does Shane spend in all?

Show your work.

$3(b + 0.35)$

$3(5.15 + 0.35) = 3(5.5) = 16.50$

Solution: **$3(b + 0.35)$; Shane spends a total of \$16.50.**

The total cost of each book is its price plus tax.

Pair/Share
How many terms are in the expression you wrote? Explain how you know.

27 Christi alters a skirt. She cuts 7 inches off the bottom of the skirt and then adds a 5-inch ruffle to the skirt's remaining bottom edge. Which expression best represents the final length of the skirt?

A $2 - s$

B $2 + s$

(C) $s - 2$

D $s - 12$

Evan chose **D** as the correct answer. How did he get that answer?

He wrote the expression $s - 7 + 5$ and then simplified it working right to left instead of left to right. He did not follow the order of operations.

I can draw a picture to help myself understand this problem.

Pair/Share
Talk about the problem and then write your answer together.

L16: Algebraic Expressions
©Curriculum Associates, LLC Copying is not permitted. 163

AT A GLANCE

Students will solve problems by writing and evaluating expressions.

STEP BY STEP

- Ask students to solve the problems individually by writing and evaluating expressions.
- When students have completed each problem, have them Pair/Share to discuss their solutions with a partner or in a group.

SOLUTIONS

Ex *Solution*: $65x + 40$; 235 miles; when $x = 3$, $65(3) + 40 = 235$.

25 *Solution*: $\frac{m}{3} - 2$, Georgia is 7 years old; Students could solve the problem by $\frac{m}{3} - 2 = \frac{27}{3} - 2 = 9 - 2 = 7$. ***(DOK 2)***

26 *Solution*: $3(b + 0.35)$; Shane spends a total of \$16.50; Students could solve the problem by $3(b + 0.35) = 3(5.15 + 0.35) = 3(5.5) = 16.50$. ***(DOK 2)***

27 *Solution*: **C**; Evan wrote the expression $s - 7 + 5$, then simplified it working right to left instead of left to right. He did not follow the order of operations.

Explain to students why the other two answer choices are not correct.

A is not correct because 2 is being removed from the skirt $(s - 2)$.

B is not correct because 2 is the amount being removed from the skirt, not added. ***(DOK 3)***

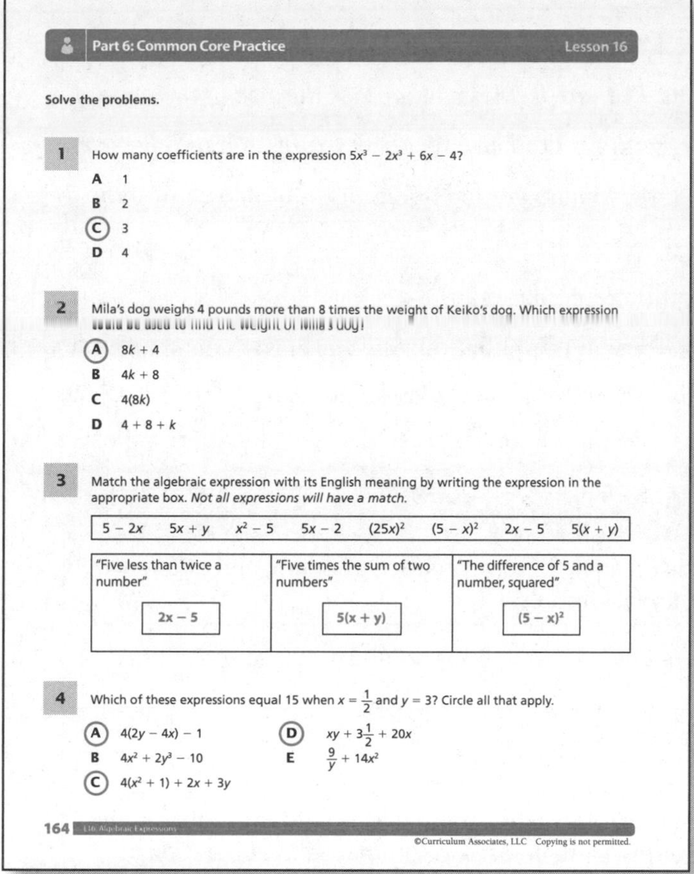

Solve the problems.

1 How many coefficients are in the expression $5x^3 - 2x^3 + 6x - 4$?

A 1
B 2
(C) 3
D 4

2 Mila's dog weighs 4 pounds more than 8 times the weight of Keiko's dog. Which expression could be used to find the weight of Mila's dog?

(A) $8k + 4$
B $4k + 8$
C $4(8k)$
D $4 + 8 + k$

3 Match the algebraic expression with its English meaning by writing the expression in the appropriate box. *Not all expressions will have a match.*

$5 - 2x$	$5x + y$	$x^2 - 5$	$5x - 2$	$(25x)^2$	$(5 - x)^2$	$2x - 5$	$5(x + y)$

"Five less than twice a number"	"Five times the sum of two numbers"	"The difference of 5 and a number, squared"
$2x - 5$	$5(x + y)$	$(5 - x)^2$

4 Which of these expressions equal 15 when $x = \frac{1}{2}$ and $y = 3$? Circle all that apply.

(A) $4(2y - 4x) - 1$
B $4x^2 + 2y^3 - 10$
(C) $4(x^2 + 1) + 2x + 3y$
(D) $xy + 3\frac{1}{2} + 20x$
E $\frac{9}{y} + 14x^2$

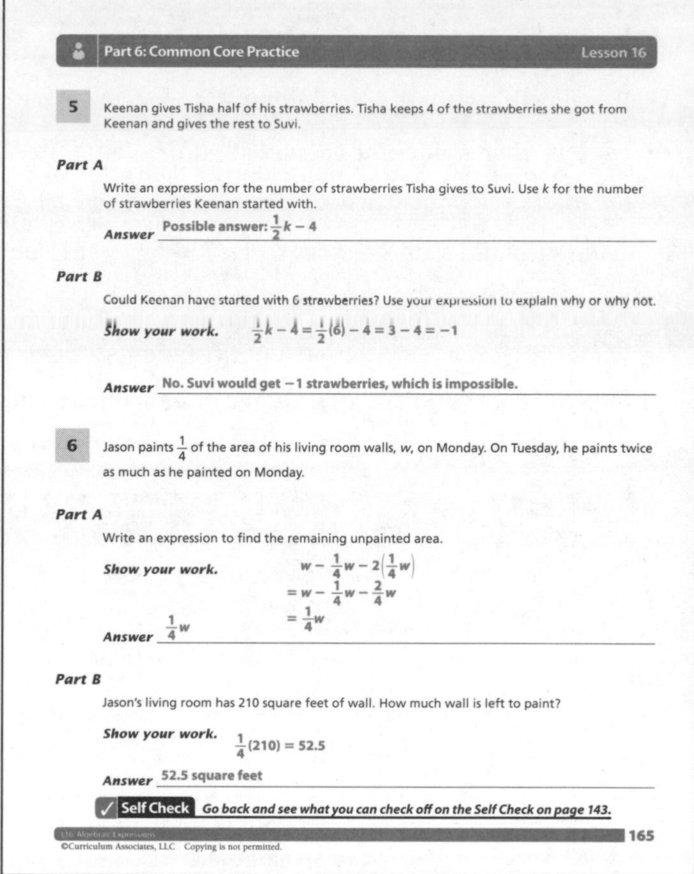

5 Keenan gives Tisha half of his strawberries. Tisha keeps 4 of the strawberries she got from Keenan and gives the rest to Suvi.

Part A

Write an expression for the number of strawberries Tisha gives to Suvi. Use k for the number of strawberries Keenan started with.

Answer Possible answer: $\frac{1}{2}k - 4$

Part B

Could Keenan have started with 6 strawberries? Use your expression to explain why or why not.

Show your work. $\frac{1}{2}k - 4 = \frac{1}{2}(6) - 4 = 3 - 4 = -1$

Answer No. Suvi would get −1 strawberries, which is impossible.

6 Jason paints $\frac{1}{4}$ of the area of his living room walls, w, on Monday. On Tuesday, he paints twice as much as he painted on Monday.

Part A

Write an expression to find the remaining unpainted area.

Show your work.

$$w - \frac{1}{4}w - 2\left(\frac{1}{4}w\right)$$
$$= w - \frac{1}{4}w - \frac{2}{4}w$$
$$= \frac{1}{4}w$$

Answer $\frac{1}{4}w$

Part B

Jason's living room has 210 square feet of wall. How much wall is left to paint?

Show your work. $\frac{1}{4}(210) = 52.5$

Answer 52.5 square feet

✓ **Self Check** *Go back and see what you can check off on the Self Check on page 143.*

AT A GLANCE

Students write, read, and evaluate expressions which contain variables that might appear on a mathematics test.

SOLUTIONS

1 *Solution:* **C**; $5x^3$, $^-2x^3$ and $6x$ are variable terms, each with a coefficient. $^-4$ is the constant term. ***(DOK 1)***

2 *Solution:* **A**; Mila's dog weighs $8 \cdot k$ or $8k$ and an additional 4 more pounds. So, Mila's dog weighs $8k + 4$ pounds. ***(DOK 2)***

3 *Solution:* See student book page above for solution. Find the mathematical expression the matches the verbal description. ***(DOK 1)***

4 *Solution:* **A**; Substitute $\frac{1}{2}$ for x and 3 for y into the expression. Then evaluate.

C; Substitute $\frac{1}{2}$ for x and 3 for y into the expression. Then evaluate.

D; Substitute $\frac{1}{2}$ for x and 3 for y into the expression. Then evaluate. ***(DOK 1)***

5 *Part A Solution:* $\frac{1}{2}k - 4$

Part B Solution: No; $\frac{1}{2}(6) - 4 = {}^-1$. Tisha cannot give Suvi a negative amount of strawberries. See student book page above for possible student work. ***(DOK 3)***

6 *Part A Solution:* $w - \frac{1}{4}w - 2(\frac{1}{4}w) = \frac{1}{4}w$; See student book page above for possible student work.

Part B Solution: 52.5 square feet; See student book page above for possible student work. ***(DOK 3)***

Assessment and Remediation

- Present this situation to students: *Tom's cucumber garden is 4 square feet less than twice the size of the tomato garden. Tom divides the cucumber garden into thirds to share with his brothers. Write an expression to represent the total area of the cucumber garden given to each brother. If the tomato garden is 123.5 square feet, how many square feet did each brother receive?* [$\frac{2g - 4}{3}$; 81 square feet]
- For students who are struggling, use the chart below to guide remediation.
- After providing remediation, check students' understanding. Present this situation: *Sue's farm is 4 square miles more than three times the size of Joe's. Sue shares half her farm with her sister. Write an expression to represent the size of Sue's farm. If Joe's farm is 2 square miles, how many square miles does Sue share with her sister?* [$\frac{3j + 4}{2}$; 5 square miles]

If the error is . . .	Students may . . .	To remediate . . .
incorrect operations	have vocabulary confused.	Connect the meaning of sum, product, quotient, and difference with operational symbols.
$\frac{4 - 2g}{3}$	have confused the two terms.	Focus on the importance of order when writing expressions.
$245\frac{2}{3}$	have forgotten the order of operations.	Review the order of operations.
any other answers	have trouble translating to an algebraic expression from a verbal expression.	Remediations will vary. Depending on the student, highlight the operating terms; write phrases to summarize the operations; create a box model from the phrases; use algebra tiles to model the box model; write an expression from the models; or apply the order of operations to evaluate the expression.

Hands-On Activity

Use a box model to solve problems.

Present students with the following: *A store has CDs on sale for $12 each and DVDs on sale for $15 each.*

1. Create a box model to translate the expression.
2. Write an expression that gives the total cost for CDs and DVDs.
3. Provide a table to evaluate the expression for different values of CDs and DVDs.

Challenge Activity

Use a table to evaluate different values.

Present students with the following: *A store has CDs on sale for $8 each and DVDs on sale for $15 each.*

1. Create a box model to translate the expression.
2. Write an expression that gives the total cost for CDs and DVDs.
3. Provide a table to evaluate the expression for different values of CDs and DVDs.
4. If Shannon has $150 dollars to spend, what are the possible combinations of CDs and DVDs she can purchase? Explain your possibilities.

Lesson 17 (Student Book pages 166–177)

Equivalent Expressions

LESSON OBJECTIVES

- Understand that the properties used with numbers also apply to expressions with variables.
- Recognize and generate equivalent expressions.
- Substitute values into expressions to prove equivalency.

PREREQUISITE SKILLS

- Recognize that variables stand for numbers.
- Understand properties of operations and apply each of them in numeric representations.
- Substitute values into expressions.

VOCABULARY

commutative property of addition: reordering the terms does not change the value of the expression. E.g., $a + b = b + a$

associative property of addition: regrouping the terms does not change the value of the expression. E.g., $(a + b) + c = a + (b + c)$

distributive property: distributing the common factor does not change the value of the expression

like terms: two or more terms in a variable expression that have the same variable factors

THE LEARNING PROGRESSION

In Grade 5, students wrote, interpreted, and evaluated numerical expressions. Students in Grade 6 will apply the properties of operations to generate equivalent expressions. In Grade 7, students will continue using the properties of operations to generate equivalent expressions.

This lesson focuses on understanding that the properties used with numbers also apply to expressions with variables. Students will show properties of operations. They will recognize equivalent expressions via modeling with manipulatives, diagrams, or story contexts. Students will also apply the properties of operations with expressions involving variables to generate equivalent expressions and substitute values into expressions to prove equivalency.

Ready *Teacher Toolbox* Teacher-Toolbox.com

	Prerequisite Skills	6.EE.A.3 6.EE.A.4
Ready Lessons		✓
Tools for Instruction		✓✓
Interactive Tutorials		✓

CCSS Focus

6.EE.A.3 Apply the properties of operations to generate equivalent expressions. *For example, apply the distributive property to the expression $3(2 + x)$ to produce the equivalent expression $6 + 3x$; apply the distributive property to the expression $24x + 18y$ to produce the equivalent expression $6(4x + 3y)$; apply properties of operations to $y + y + y$ to produce the equivalent expression $3y$.*

6.EE.A.4 Identify when two expressions are equivalent (i.e., when the two expressions name the same number regardless of which value is substituted into them). *For example, the expressions $y + y + y$ and $3y$ are equivalent because they name the same number regardless of which number y stands for.*

ADDITIONAL STANDARDS: 6.EE.B.6 *(see page A42 for full text)*

STANDARDS FOR MATHEMATICAL PRACTICE: *SMP 2, 3* *(see page A9 for full text)*

AT A GLANCE

Students view an expression and are guided to write equivalent expressions using mathematical properties.

STEP BY STEP

- Tell students that this page guides them in writing an equivalent expression using mathematical properties.
- Have students read the problem at the top of the page. Explain that by using properties of numbers we can write equivalent expressions.
- Work through Explore It as a class.
- Ask, *Which property allows values in an addition problem to be added in any order?* [commutative property]
- Ask, *Which property allows values in an addition problem to be regrouped?* [associative property]
- Ask students how they might prove that the expressions have the same value. [possible answer: using manipulatives to show the combinations]
- Ask student pairs or groups to explain their answers for writing equivalent expressions.

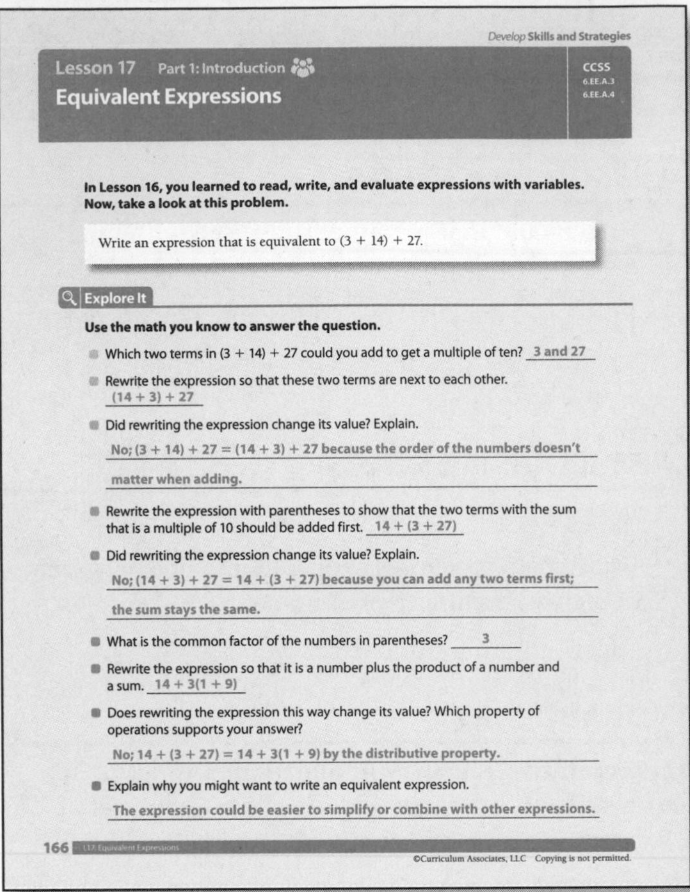

Develop **Skills and Strategies**

Lesson 17 Part 1: Introduction

Equivalent Expressions

CCSS 6.EE.A.3 6.EE.A.4

In Lesson 16, you learned to read, write, and evaluate expressions with variables. Now, take a look at this problem.

Write an expression that is equivalent to $(3 + 14) + 27$.

Explore It

Use the math you know to answer the question.

- Which two terms in $(3 + 14) + 27$ could you add to get a multiple of ten? **3 and 27**
- Rewrite the expression so that these two terms are next to each other. **$(14 + 3) + 27$**
- Did rewriting the expression change its value? Explain. **No; $(3 + 14) + 27 = (14 + 3) + 27$ because the order of the numbers doesn't matter when adding.**
- Rewrite the expression with parentheses to show that the two terms with the sum that is a multiple of 10 should be added first. **$14 + (3 + 27)$**
- Did rewriting the expression change its value? Explain. **No; $(14 + 3) + 27 = 14 + (3 + 27)$ because you can add any two terms first; the sum stays the same.**
- What is the common factor of the numbers in parentheses? **3**
- Rewrite the expression so that it is a number plus the product of a number and a sum. **$14 + 3(1 + 9)$**
- Does rewriting the expression this way change its value? Which property of operations supports your answer? **No; $14 + (3 + 27) = 14 + 3(1 + 9)$ by the distributive property.**
- Explain why you might want to write an equivalent expression. **The expression could be easier to simplify or combine with other expressions.**

166 L17: Equivalent Expressions

©Curriculum Associates, LLC Copying is not permitted.

ELL Support

Connect the words *commutative* to *commuting* (changing positions), *associative* to *associating with* people, and *distributive* to *distribute* (sending to others). Relate these base words and real-world examples to the mathematical definitions.

Mathematical Discourse

- *Of the expressions you wrote on this page, which expression is easier for you to evaluate? Explain.*

  Listen for student use of number sense and the composition of numbers.

- *Explain why the commutative and associative properties do not apply to subtraction and division. How can you support your reasoning?*

  Look for students to justify their reasoning with models or by disproving a property with an example.

AT A GLANCE

Students will explore the usage of the commutative, associative, and distributive properties in writing equivalent expressions. They will understand that the properties used with numbers also apply to expressions with variables.

STEP BY STEP

- Read Find Out More as a class.
- Ask students to explain how the equivalent expressions illustrate the property. Review that a *term* is a part of an expression separated by addition or subtraction.
- Point out the similarities and differences between the comparable expressions. Guide students to realize that the operations on expressions with numbers can also be performed on expressions with variables.
- Ask groups or pairs of students to share answers and to explain their reasoning for Reflect by using their mathematical definitions.

SMP Tip: Reading arguments of others and deciding if they make sense allows students to construct their own viable arguments (*SMP 3*) by using mathematical definitions. Occasionally ask students to determine the validity of the reasoning of their peers: Ask students, *Does the reasoning make sense? Does that always work?*

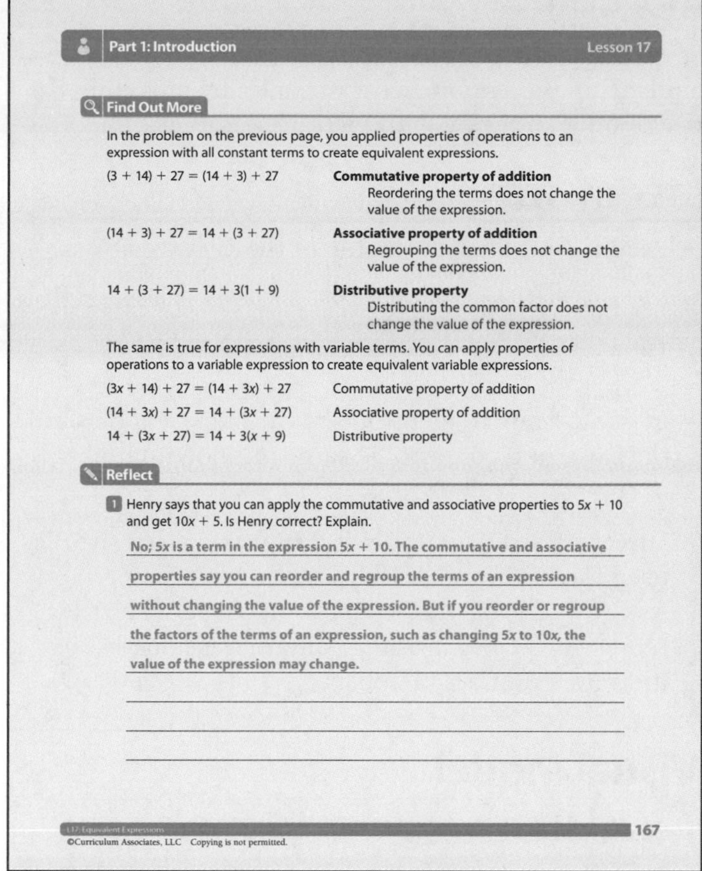

Part 1: Introduction Lesson 17

Find Out More

In the problem on the previous page, you applied properties of operations to an expression with all constant terms to create equivalent expressions.

$(3 + 14) + 27 = (14 + 3) + 27$	**Commutative property of addition** Reordering the terms does not change the value of the expression.
$(14 + 3) + 27 = 14 + (3 + 27)$	**Associative property of addition** Regrouping the terms does not change the value of the expression.
$14 + (3 + 27) = 14 + 3(1 + 9)$	**Distributive property** Distributing the common factor does not change the value of the expression.

The same is true for expressions with variable terms. You can apply properties of operations to a variable expression to create equivalent variable expressions.

$(3x + 14) + 27 = (14 + 3x) + 27$	Commutative property of addition
$(14 + 3x) + 27 = 14 + (3x + 27)$	Associative property of addition
$14 + (3x + 27) = 14 + 3(x + 9)$	Distributive property

Reflect

1 Henry says that you can apply the commutative and associative properties to $5x + 10$ and get $10x + 5$. Is Henry correct? Explain.

No; $5x$ is a term in the expression $5x + 10$. The commutative and associative properties say you can reorder and regroup the terms of an expression without changing the value of the expression. But if you reorder or regroup the factors of the terms of an expression, such as changing $5x$ to $10x$, the value of the expression may change.

L17: Equivalent Expressions 167
©Curriculum Associates, LLC Copying is not permitted.

Real-World Connection

Ask students to provide real-world situations which can be represented with numerical or algebraic expressions that can be rewritten using one of the mathematical properties.

Example: 5 families ordered the same meal of 6 chicken sandwiches, 3 desserts, and 2 drinks. What expressions would let you find the total number of food items the family bought?
$5(6) + 5(3) + 5(2) = 5(6 + 3 + 2)$

AT A GLANCE

Students will use properties of operations to write equivalent expressions with variables by modeling the distributive property with pictures and tiles.

STEP BY STEP

- Read the problem at the top of the page as a class.
- Review Picture It as a class. Ask, *Why is an* x *used on each bag?* [The number of apples in each bag is unknown.]
- Lead students to identify that the bags of apples are the same and contain the same unknown number of apples.
- Direct students to Model It. Emphasize that the tiles used for Jamie and Ashley are the same shape. Ask, *Why are the tiles all the same shape?* [The tiles represent the bags, which contain the same unknown number of apples.]

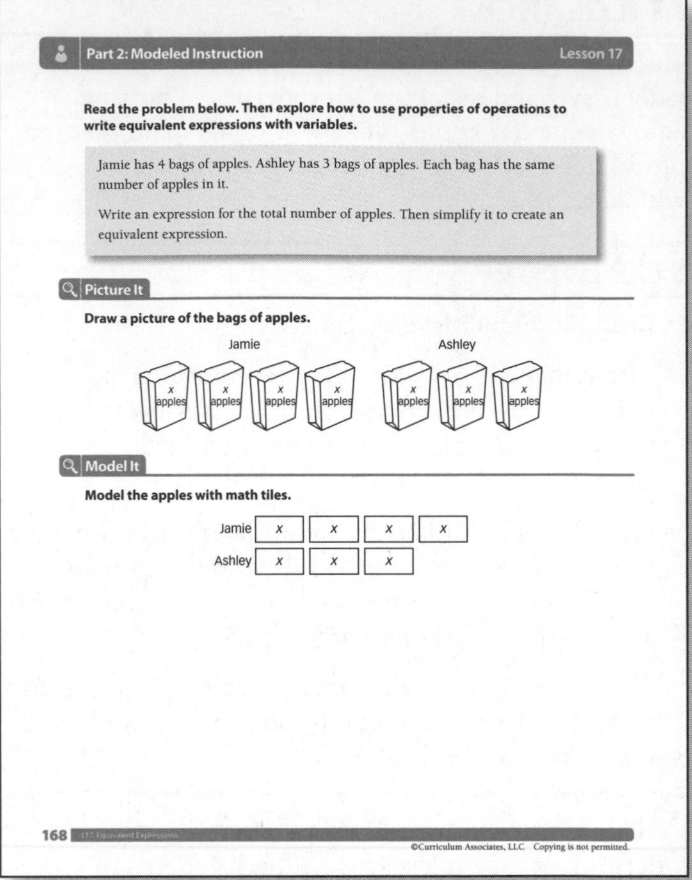

Part 2: Modeled Instruction Lesson 17

Read the problem below. Then explore how to use properties of operations to write equivalent expressions with variables.

Jamie has 4 bags of apples. Ashley has 3 bags of apples. Each bag has the same number of apples in it.

Write an expression for the total number of apples. Then simplify it to create an equivalent expression.

Picture It

Draw a picture of the bags of apples.

Model It

Model the apples with math tiles.

168 L17: Equivalent Expressions

©Curriculum Associates, LLC Copying is not permitted.

Visual Model

Model the distribution of factors.

Materials: mathematical situations; colored candies or counters, including:

three groups of 2 yellow and 1 red

two groups of 1 brown and 5 blue

three groups of 3 orange and 2 green

two groups of 5 red and 3 blue

twelve groups of 4 green and 8 yellow

- Ask students to work in pairs to use colored candies to model the mathematical situations.
- Ask pairs of students to write two equivalent expressions. The second expression should demonstrate the application of the distributive property on the first expression.
- Have volunteers share their models and expressions with the class.

Mathematical Discourse

- *What can you say about the diagrams shown in Picture It and Model It?*

  Listen for student discussion supporting ideas such as: the bags contain an equal number of apples; the diagrams in Picture It and Model It are equivalent; and the value of x must be a positive number.

- *How would the diagrams be different if Jamie's bags held a different number of apples than Ashley's bags? How would the expression be different?*

  Listen for responses that show that students understand how to use variables to represent a real-world problem situation.

AT A GLANCE

Students revisit the problem on page 168 to write equivalent expressions by identifying like terms and applying the distributive property to expressions with variables.

STEP BY STEP

- Read Connect It as a class. Be sure to point out that the questions refer to the problem on page 168.
- Identify the terms in the expression. [$4x$ and $3x$]
- Point out to students the new vocabulary *like term* as connected to $4x$ and $3x$ and that both terms have a common factor of x which makes them "like."
- Ask, *What does the common factor of* x *represent in the real world?* [the number of apples in each bag]
- Read Try It as a class. Prompt students to use pictures or tiles to model the expressions, if necessary.

ELL Support

Review the meanings of *term*, *like terms*, *common factor*, *factor*, and *distribute*.

SMP Tip: Students reason quantitatively when they use properties of operations to recognize or write equivalent expressions (*SMP 2*). Regularly ask students to look for ways they can compose or decompose numbers or use properties of operations to simplify calculations.

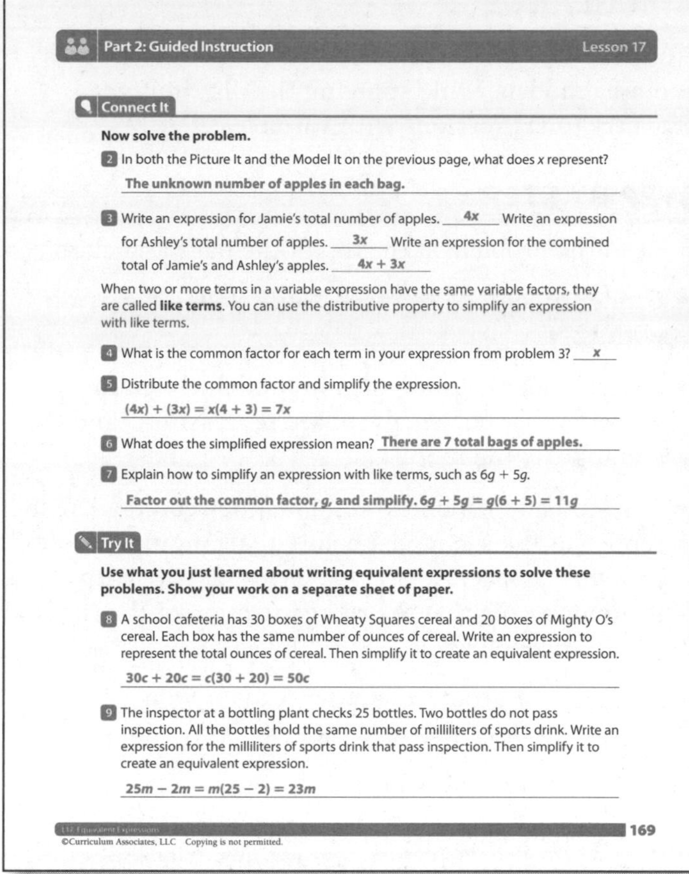
Part 2: Guided Instruction Lesson 17

Connect It

Now solve the problem.

2 In both the Picture It and the Model It on the previous page, what does x represent?
The unknown number of apples in each bag.

3 Write an expression for Jamie's total number of apples. **$4x$** Write an expression for Ashley's total number of apples. **$3x$** Write an expression for the combined total of Jamie's and Ashley's apples. **$4x + 3x$**

When two or more terms in a variable expression have the same variable factors, they are called **like terms**. You can use the distributive property to simplify an expression with like terms.

4 What is the common factor for each term in your expression from problem 3? **x**

5 Distribute the common factor and simplify the expression.
$(4x) + (3x) = x(4 + 3) = 7x$

6 What does the simplified expression mean? **There are 7 total bags of apples.**

7 Explain how to simplify an expression with like terms, such as $6g + 5g$.
Factor out the common factor, g, and simplify. $6g + 5g = g(6 + 5) = 11g$

Try It

Use what you just learned about writing equivalent expressions to solve these problems. Show your work on a separate sheet of paper.

8 A school cafeteria has 30 boxes of Wheaty Squares cereal and 20 boxes of Mighty O's cereal. Each box has the same number of ounces of cereal. Write an expression to represent the total ounces of cereal. Then simplify it to create an equivalent expression.
$30c + 20c = c(30 + 20) = 50c$

9 The inspector at a bottling plant checks 25 bottles. Two bottles do not pass inspection. All the bottles hold the same number of milliliters of sports drink. Write an expression for the milliliters of sports drink that pass inspection. Then simplify it to create an equivalent expression.
$25m - 2m = m(25 - 2) = 23m$

L17: Equivalent Expressions 169
©Curriculum Associates, LLC Copying is not permitted.

TRY IT SOLUTIONS

8 *Solution:* $30c + 20c = c(30 + 20) = 50c$; Students may combine like terms without directly using the distributive property. They might also create a model to support their work.

ERROR ALERT: Students who wrote $10c(3 + 2)$ need to be reminded that the second factor should represent the number of boxes while the common factor is the value both terms have in common, c.

9 *Solution:* $25m - 2m = m(25 - 2) = 23m$; Students may combine like terms without directly using the distributive property. They might also create a model to support their work.

AT A GLANCE

Students will write equivalent expressions from tiles and area models while applying the distributive property to expressions with variables.

STEP BY STEP

- Read the problem at the top of the page as a class.
- Guide students to connect "more than 2 feet wide" with "$2 + x$."
- Direct students to the tiles in Model It. Remind students that one small square represents 1 and the rectangular tile represents x.
- Ask students which expressions they could write to represent the tile model before rearranging the tiles. [possible answer: $2 + x + 2 + x + 2 + x$] Help students to see that the reorganization of the tiles did not change the value.
- Ask pairs or groups of students to explain connections see between the two expressions.
- Review Picture It as a class.
- Guide students to determine the area of each smaller rectangle within the picture. [$3 \cdot 2 = 6$ and $3 \cdot x = 3x$]
- Ask students to compare the expressions developed in Model It and Picture It. What do they notice? [There are several ways to write the same expression.]

Visual Model

Calculate area using the distributive property.

Materials: graph paper, scissors

- Draw a rectangle on graph paper with a length of 12 units and a width of 9 units. What expression represents the area of the rectangle?
- Draw a second rectangle with a length of 12 units and a width of 15 units. What expression represents the area of this rectangle?
- Cut out the rectangles and place them next to each other to create a rectangle which is still 12 units long. What expression represents the area of this rectangle?
- What equivalent expressions can you create from this area model?

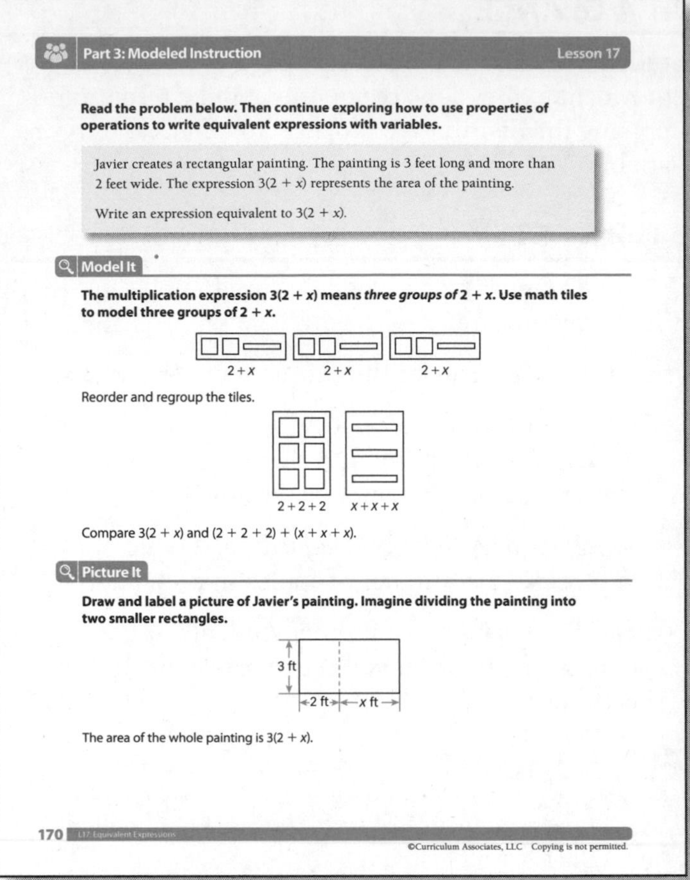
Part 3: Modeled Instruction Lesson 17

Read the problem below. Then continue exploring how to use properties of operations to write equivalent expressions with variables.

Javier creates a rectangular painting. The painting is 3 feet long and more than 2 feet wide. The expression $3(2 + x)$ represents the area of the painting.

Write an expression equivalent to $3(2 + x)$.

Model It

The multiplication expression $3(2 + x)$ means *three groups of* $2 + x$. Use math tiles to model three groups of $2 + x$.

Reorder and regroup the tiles.

Compare $3(2 + x)$ and $(2 + 2 + 2) + (x + x + x)$.

Picture It

Draw and label a picture of Javier's painting. Imagine dividing the painting into two smaller rectangles.

The area of the whole painting is $3(2 + x)$.

170 L17: Equivalent Expressions

©Curriculum Associates, LLC Copying is not permitted.

Mathematical Discourse

- *Describe in your own words how the picture in Picture It shows $3(2 + x)$.*

  Listen for responses that students see $(2 + x)$ as a single entity that represents the length of the painting, and that it can be multiplied by 3, the height of the painting.

- *How do the different ways to show the problem lead to different equivalent expressions?*

  Listen for responses that indicate that the model helps you see equivalent expressions for $3(2 + x)$ that use either addition (because you can add the tiles) or multiplication (because you can think of 3 times 2 and 3 times x).

AT A GLANCE

Students revisit the problem on page 170 using the distributive property to compare and write equivalent expressions involving variables.

STEP BY STEP

- Read Connect It as a class. Be sure to point out that the questions refer to the problem on page 170.
- Refer students to the various expressions and models used in Model It and Picture It.
- Emphasize that applying the properties of operations to expressions does not change the value of the expression. This can be proven in many ways as shown in Model It and Picture It.

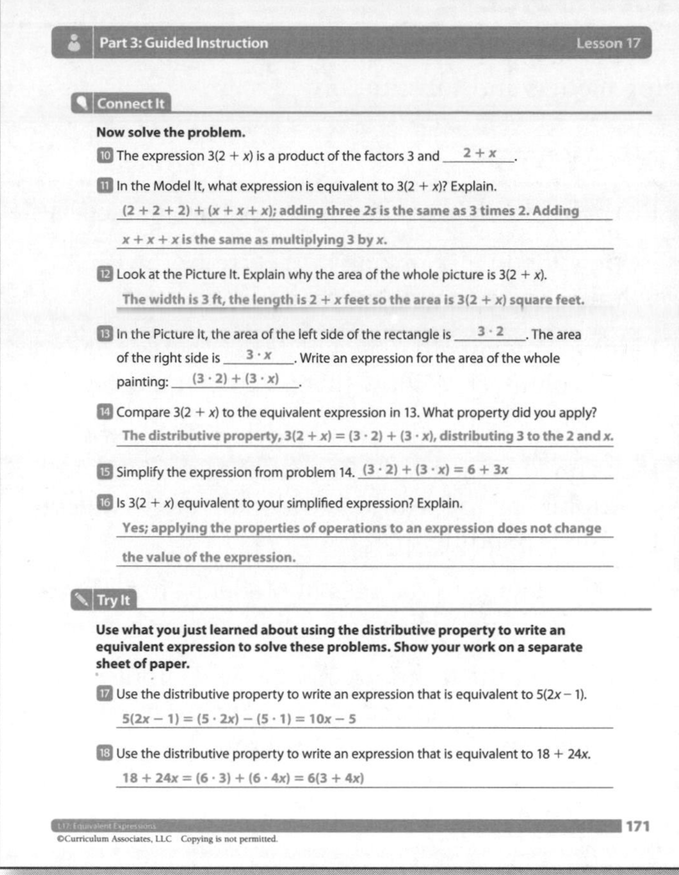

Part 3: Guided Instruction Lesson 17

Connect It

Now solve the problem.

10 The expression $3(2 + x)$ is a product of the factors 3 and $2 + x$.

11 In the Model It, what expression is equivalent to $3(2 + x)$? Explain.
$(2 + 2 + 2) + (x + x + x)$; adding three 2s is the same as 3 times 2. Adding $x + x + x$ is the same as multiplying 3 by x.

12 Look at the Picture It. Explain why the area of the whole picture is $3(2 + x)$.
The width is 3 ft, the length is $2 + x$ feet so the area is $3(2 + x)$ square feet.

13 In the Picture It, the area of the left side of the rectangle is $3 \cdot 2$. The area of the right side is $3 \cdot x$. Write an expression for the area of the whole painting: $(3 \cdot 2) + (3 \cdot x)$.

14 Compare $3(2 + x)$ to the equivalent expression in 13. What property did you apply?
The distributive property, $3(2 + x) = (3 \cdot 2) + (3 \cdot x)$, distributing 3 to the 2 and x.

15 Simplify the expression from problem 14. $(3 \cdot 2) + (3 \cdot x) = 6 + 3x$

16 Is $3(2 + x)$ equivalent to your simplified expression? Explain.
Yes; applying the properties of operations to an expression does not change the value of the expression.

Try It

Use what you just learned about using the distributive property to write an equivalent expression to solve these problems. Show your work on a separate sheet of paper.

17 Use the distributive property to write an expression that is equivalent to $5(2x - 1)$.
$5(2x - 1) = (5 \cdot 2x) - (5 \cdot 1) = 10x - 5$

18 Use the distributive property to write an expression that is equivalent to $18 + 24x$.
$18 + 24x = (6 \cdot 3) + (6 \cdot 4x) = 6(3 + 4x)$

L17: Equivalent Expressions 171
©Curriculum Associates, LLC Copying is not permitted.

Hands-On Activity

Use the distributive property to write expressions.

Materials: colored counters

- Sort the counters by color. Count the number of counters of each color.
- Ask, *If you were given two identical bags of counters, how could you use the distributive property to write an expression to represent the total number of counters? For example, 2(10r + 15g + 12y).*
- Ask students to share other expressions to represent the total number of counters in the two bags. For example, $20r + 30g + 24y$.
- Use the distributive property to write expressions showing how many counters of each color would be in 5 bags, 10 bags, and so on.

TRY IT SOLUTIONS

17 *Solution:* $10x - 5$; Students may evaluate the expression by $5(2x) - 5(1)$ or use a model.

18 *Solution:* $6(3 + 4x)$; Students may also write $6(4x + 3)$ or use a model.

ERROR ALERT: Students who wrote $3(6 + 8x)$ did not choose the greatest factor of the two terms.

AT A GLANCE

Students will prove the equivalency of expressions using models and substitution.

STEP BY STEP

- Read the problem at the top of the page as a class.
- Review the line segments in Picture It. Have a volunteer confirm the accuracy of the lengths.
- Remind students that $5h$ and $2h^2$ are being combined. Ask a volunteer to show this combined model.
- Direct students to the area models with a particular focus on h^2. Discuss the area of h^2 as the length multiplied by the width. Show students the algebra tile corresponding to h^2.
- Direct students to the tiles in Model It. Emphasize the use of various shapes to represent each term.
- Clarify that the terms are not being combined but instead being compared; $5h$ and $2h^2$ are in one grouping, and $7h$ is in another grouping.

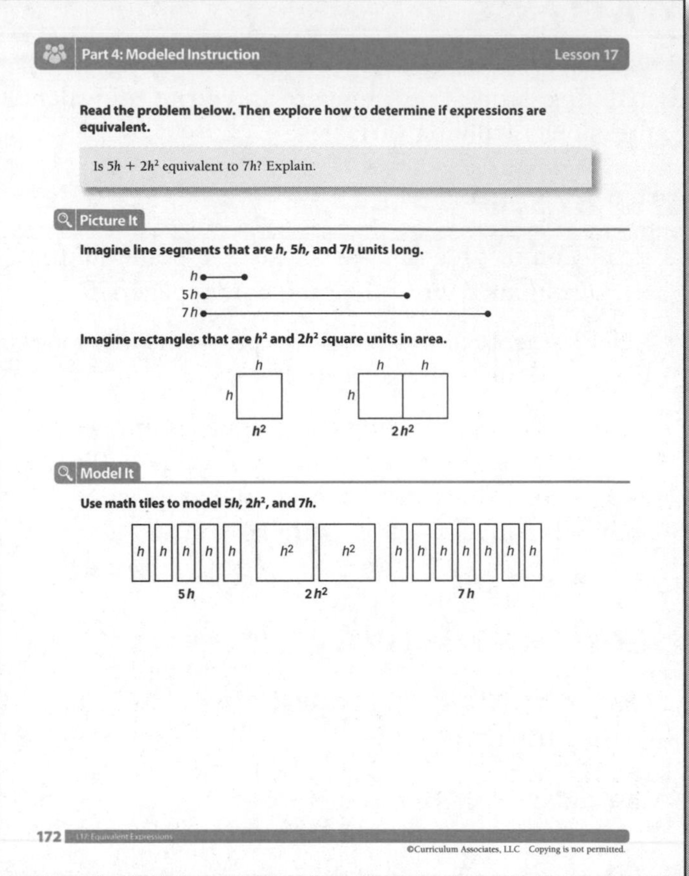

Visual Model

Use the distributive property to prove the equivalency of expressions.

Materials: tiles, graph paper, expressions

- Put students into pairs or groups.
- Display the following expressions:
  $4x + 4$, $3(2x + 5)$, $2(8 + x)$, $3(2x + 0)$,
  $0.5(x + 1)$, $2x(8x + x)$, $4(x + 1)$, $6x + 15$,
  $16 + 2x$, $6x$, $0.5x + 0.5$, $16x^2 + x^2$,
  $17x^2$, $7x^2 - 3x^2$, $4x^2$, $x^2(7 - 3)$
- Assign each pair or group of students one of the expressions you displayed.
- Ask each pair or group of students to create a model which represents the expression they have been assigned.
- Ask each pair or group of students to find another expression which is equivalent to their own.
- Students should share equivalent expressions and models with the class.

Mathematical Discourse

- *When using the tiles to model* $5h + 2h^2$, *one student models* h^2 *with two* h *tiles. What is wrong with this representation?*

  When using two h tiles, the measure of the square is 2 units by h units, which is not the same as h^2.

- *Why can't you use the line segments to represent* h^2*? Can you show any multiplication with line segments?*

  Students' responses should include that h^2 means h times h. To represent multiplication with the line segments, you have to know how many segments of length h to show. You can use a line to represent a number times a variable, but not a variable times a variable.

AT A GLANCE

Students revisit the problem on page 172 to determine if expressions are equivalent using mathematical properties, modeling, and substitution.

STEP BY STEP

- Read page 173 as a class. Be sure to point out that Connect It refers to the problem on page 172.
- Guide students to use Picture It to prove the expressions are not equivalent.
- Guide students to use Model It to prove the expressions are not equivalent.
- Review the definition of *like terms*. Students should share their reasoning as to why the expressions are not equivalent, using the phrase "like terms" in their reasoning.
- Problem 22 introduces substitution as a way of testing for equivalency. Point out that equivalent expressions will have equal values. Review the concept of a variable having any value. Students will replace (substitute) the variable with any non-zero value to test for equivalency. Ask, *Why do you think the value of the variable should not be 0?* [Unlike a non-zero value, 0 would make the statement true.]

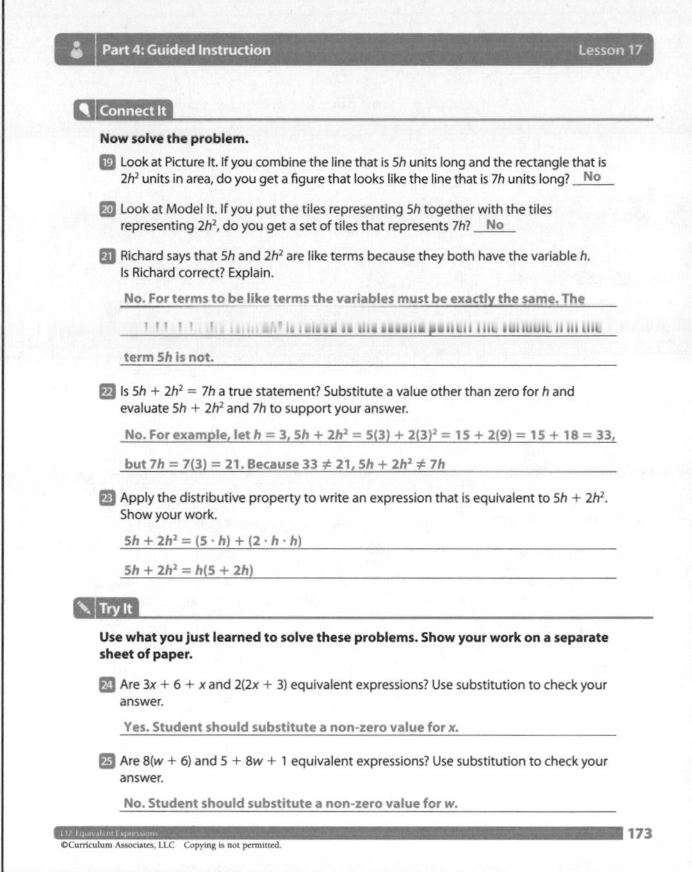

Part 4: Guided Instruction Lesson 17

Connect It

Now solve the problem.

19 Look at Picture It. If you combine the line that is $5h$ units long and the rectangle that is $2h^2$ units in area, do you get a figure that looks like the line that is $7h$ units long? **No**

20 Look at Model It. If you put the tiles representing $5h$ together with the tiles representing $2h^2$, do you get a set of tiles that represents $7h$? **No**

21 Richard says that $5h$ and $2h^2$ are like terms because they both have the variable h. Is Richard correct? Explain.

No. For terms to be like terms the variables must be exactly the same. The [illegible] is raised to the second power. The variable h in the term 5h is not.

22 Is $5h + 2h^2 = 7h$ a true statement? Substitute a value other than zero for h and evaluate $5h + 2h^2$ and $7h$ to support your answer.

No. For example, let $h = 3$, $5h + 2h^2 = 5(3) + 2(3)^2 = 15 + 2(9) = 15 + 18 = 33$, but $7h = 7(3) = 21$. Because $33 \neq 21$, $5h + 2h^2 \neq 7h$

23 Apply the distributive property to write an expression that is equivalent to $5h + 2h^2$. Show your work.

$5h + 2h^2 = (5 \cdot h) + (2 \cdot h \cdot h)$

$5h + 2h^2 = h(5 + 2h)$

Try It

Use what you just learned to solve these problems. Show your work on a separate sheet of paper.

24 Are $3x + 6 + x$ and $2(2x + 3)$ equivalent expressions? Use substitution to check your answer.

Yes. Student should substitute a non-zero value for x.

25 Are $8(w + 6)$ and $5 + 8w + 1$ equivalent expressions? Use substitution to check your answer.

No. Student should substitute a non-zero value for w.

L17: Equivalent Expressions 173

©Curriculum Associates, LLC Copying is not permitted.

TRY IT SOLUTIONS

24 *Solution:* Yes; Students should substitute a non-zero value for *x*.

ERROR ALERT: Students who wrote the correct answer may have substituted zero for the variable, coming to the correct answer using the wrong reasoning.

25 *Solution:* No; Students should substitute a non-zero value for *w*.

ELL Support

Work with students to connect the word *substitute* to "replace." Offer real-world examples, such as a substitute teacher who replaces a teacher.

Hands-On Activity

Apply substitution and the distributive property to determine temperatures.

Materials: formula card: $°C = \frac{5}{9}(°F - 32)$

- Use your knowledge of the distributive property and substitution, along with the formula card, to convert the following temperatures to degrees Celsius:

  9°F, 32°F, 23°F, ⁻4°F, ⁻45°F

- Show at least two different ways to evaluate each expression.
- As a class, discuss the method(s) which are most efficient in evaluating each expression.

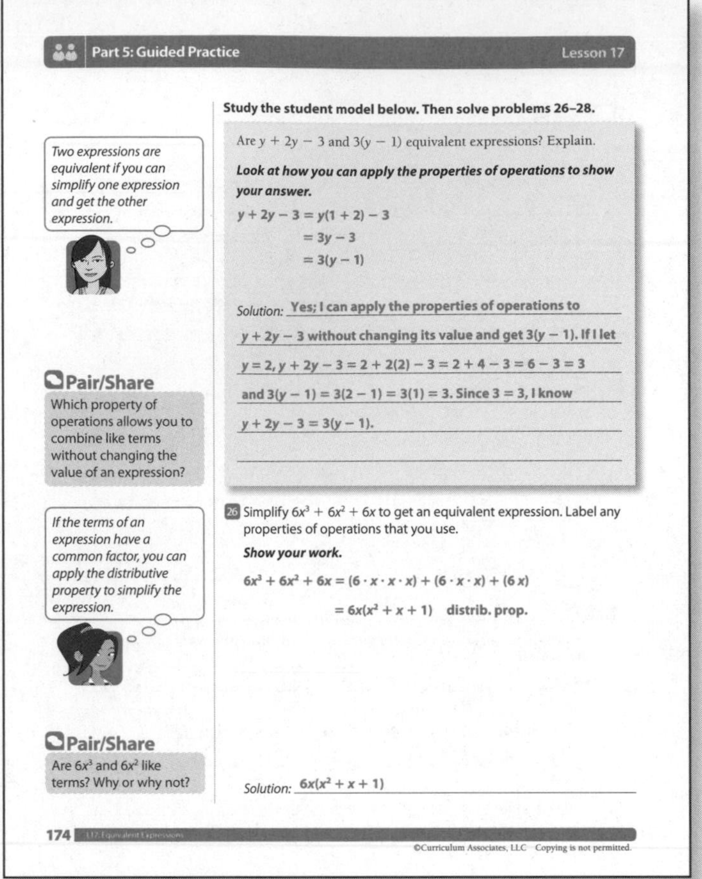
Part 5: Guided Practice Lesson 17

Study the student model below. Then solve problems 26–28.

Two expressions are equivalent if you can simplify one expression and get the other expression.

Are $y + 2y - 3$ and $3(y - 1)$ equivalent expressions? Explain.

Look at how you can apply the properties of operations to show your answer.

$$y + 2y - 3 = y(1 + 2) - 3$$
$$= 3y - 3$$
$$= 3(y - 1)$$

Solution: **Yes; I can apply the properties of operations to $y + 2y - 3$ without changing its value and get $3(y - 1)$. If I let $y = 2$, $y + 2y - 3 = 2 + 2(2) - 3 = 2 + 4 - 3 = 6 - 3 = 3$ and $3(y - 1) = 3(2 - 1) = 3(1) = 3$. Since $3 = 3$, I know $y + 2y - 3 = 3(y - 1)$.**

Pair/Share
Which property of operations allows you to combine like terms without changing the value of an expression?

26 Simplify $6x^3 + 6x^2 + 6x$ to get an equivalent expression. Label any properties of operations that you use.

Show your work.

$$6x^3 + 6x^2 + 6x = (6 \cdot x \cdot x \cdot x) + (6 \cdot x \cdot x) + (6\ x)$$
$$= 6x(x^2 + x + 1) \quad \text{distrib. prop.}$$

If the terms of an expression have a common factor, you can apply the distributive property to simplify the expression.

Pair/Share
Are $6x^3$ and $6x^2$ like terms? Why or why not?

Solution: $6x(x^2 + x + 1)$

174 L17: Equivalent Expressions
©Curriculum Associates, LLC Copying is not permitted.

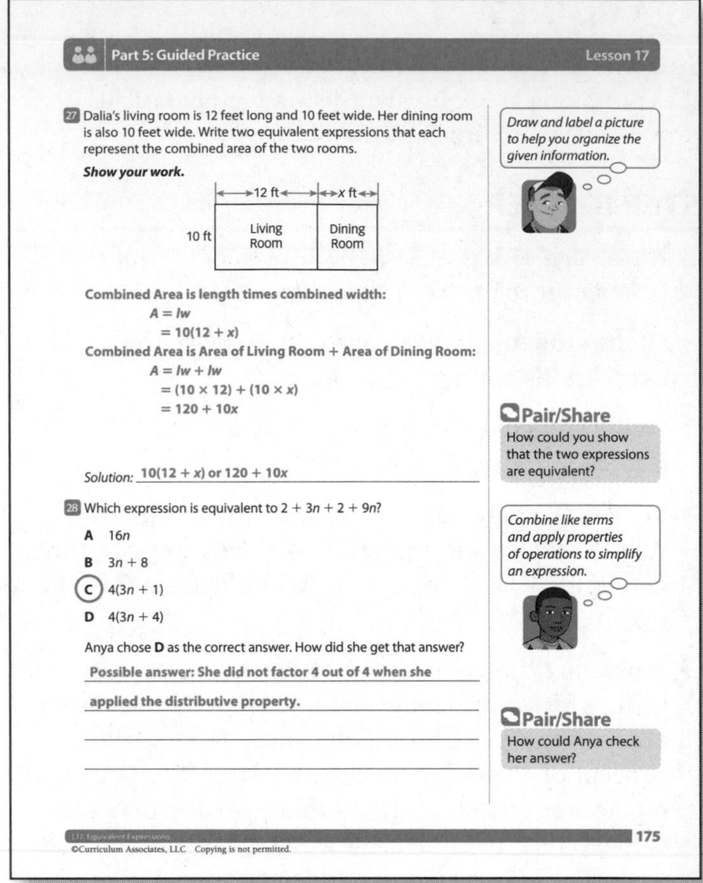
Part 5: Guided Practice Lesson 17

27 Dalia's living room is 12 feet long and 10 feet wide. Her dining room is also 10 feet wide. Write two equivalent expressions that each represent the combined area of the two rooms.

Show your work.

Combined Area is length times combined width:
$$A = lw$$
$$= 10(12 + x)$$
Combined Area is Area of Living Room + Area of Dining Room:
$$A = lw + lw$$
$$= (10 \times 12) + (10 \times x)$$
$$= 120 + 10x$$

Draw and label a picture to help you organize the given information.

Solution: **$10(12 + x)$ or $120 + 10x$**

Pair/Share
How could you show that the two expressions are equivalent?

28 Which expression is equivalent to $2 + 3n + 2 + 9n$?

A $16n$
B $3n + 8$
C $4(3n + 1)$ (circled)
D $4(3n + 4)$

Anya chose **D** as the correct answer. How did she get that answer?

Possible answer: She did not factor 4 out of 4 when she applied the distributive property.

Combine like terms and apply properties of operations to simplify an expression.

Pair/Share
How could Anya check her answer?

L17: Equivalent Expressions
©Curriculum Associates, LLC Copying is not permitted. 175

AT A GLANCE

Students will apply properties of operations to show equivalency in expressions.

STEP BY STEP

- Ask students to solve the problems individually to apply the properties of operations to show equivalency in expressions.
- When students have completed each problem, have them Pair/Share to discuss their solutions with a partner or in a group.

SOLUTIONS

Ex A problem that applies the properties of operations is shown.

26 *Solution:* $6x(x^2 + x + 1)$; distributive property; Students could solve the problem by rewriting $6x^3 + 6x^2 + 6x$ as $(6 \cdot x \cdot x \cdot x) + (6 \cdot x \cdot x) + (6 \cdot x) = 6x(x^2 + x + 1)$. ***(DOK 1)***

27 *Solution:* The combined area of the two rooms is $10(12 + x)$ or $120 + 10x$; Students could solve the problem by showing that combined area is length times combined width. Combined Area is Area of Living Room + Area of Dining Room: $A = (10 \cdot 12) + (10 \cdot x) = 120 + 10x$. ***(DOK 1)***

28 *Solution:* **C**; Anya did not factor 4 out of 4 when she applied the distributive property.

Explain to students why the other two answer choices are not correct:

A is not correct because 2, $3n$, 2, and $9n$ were combined, but they are not all like terms.

B is not correct because the factor 4 was not multiplied by $3n$ and then was just added to 4. ***(DOK 3)***

Part 6: Common Core Practice Lesson 17

Solve the problems.

1 The expression $0.25(2d + 1)$ represents the fines per day, d, for overdue books. Which expression is equivalent to $0.25(2d + 1)$?

A $0.252d + 1$

(B) $0.50d + 0.25$

C $2d + 0.25$

D $0.50d + 1$

2 A game company makes a board game that comes with 2 dice and a card game that comes with 3 dice. Which expression shows the total number of dice in b boxes of the board game and b boxes of the card game?

(A) $5b$

B $5(2b)$

C $5 + b$

D $2b + 3$

3 Look at the equations below. Choose True or False for each equation.

	Equation	True	False
A	$f + f + f = 3f$	☒ True	☐ False
B	$4 \times n \times n \times n \times n = 4n^4$	☒ True	☐ False
C	$10h - 10 = 10 - 10h$	☐ True	☒ False
D	$x^2 + 3v = (x + x) + v \times v \times v$	☐ True	☒ False
E	$6 \times (2 + 7) = (6 \times 2) + 7$	☐ True	☒ False

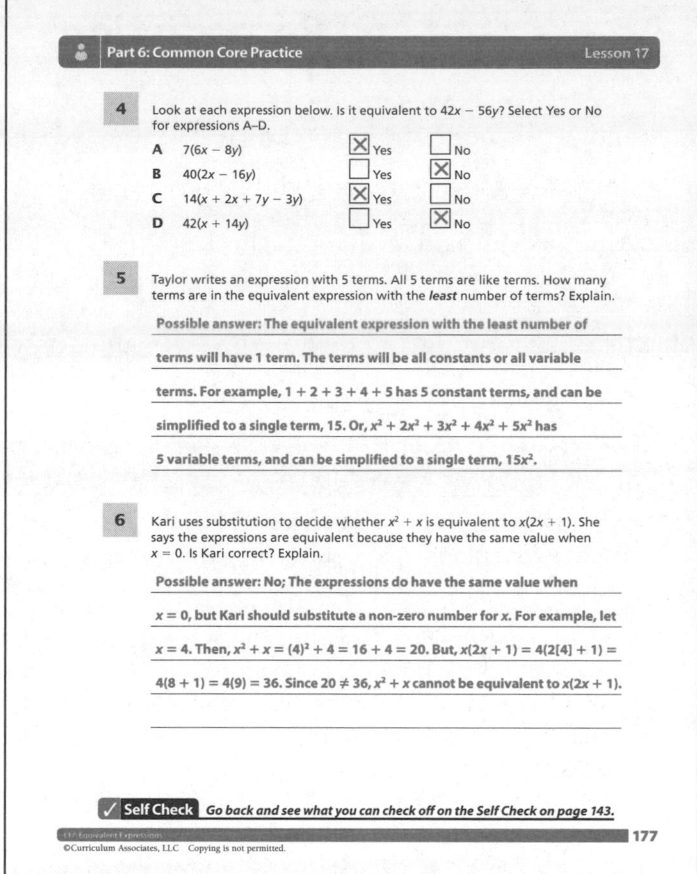

Part 6: Common Core Practice Lesson 17

4 Look at each expression below. Is it equivalent to $42x - 56y$? Select Yes or No for expressions A–D.

A	$7(6x - 8y)$	☒ Yes	☐ No
B	$40(2x - 16y)$	☐ Yes	☒ No
C	$14(x + 2x + 7y - 3y)$	☒ Yes	☐ No
D	$42(x + 14y)$	☐ Yes	☒ No

5 Taylor writes an expression with 5 terms. All 5 terms are like terms. How many terms are in the equivalent expression with the *least* number of terms? Explain.

Possible answer: The equivalent expression with the least number of terms will have 1 term. The terms will be all constants or all variable terms. For example, $1 + 2 + 3 + 4 + 5$ has 5 constant terms, and can be simplified to a single term, 15. Or, $x^2 + 2x^2 + 3x^2 + 4x^2 + 5x^2$ has 5 variable terms, and can be simplified to a single term, $15x^2$.

6 Kari uses substitution to decide whether $x^2 + x$ is equivalent to $x(2x + 1)$. She says the expressions are equivalent because they have the same value when $x = 0$. Is Kari correct? Explain.

Possible answer: No; The expressions do have the same value when $x = 0$, but Kari should substitute a non-zero number for x. For example, let $x = 4$. Then, $x^2 + x = (4)^2 + 4 = 16 + 4 = 20$. But, $x(2x + 1) = 4(2[4] + 1) = 4(8 + 1) = 4(9) = 36$. Since $20 \neq 36$, $x^2 + x$ cannot be equivalent to $x(2x + 1)$.

✓ Self Check *Go back and see what you can check off on the Self Check on page 143.*

AT A GLANCE

Students solve problems concerning equivalent expressions that might appear on a mathematics test.

SOLUTIONS

1 *Solution:* **B**; $0.25(2d) + 0.25(1) = 0.5d + 0.25$. ***(DOK 2)***

2 *Solution:* **A**; Multiply the number of dice per board game, 2, and the number of dice per card game, 3, by b boxes and add them. ***(DOK 2)***

3 *Solution:* A **True**; B **True**; C **False**; D **False**; E **False** ***(DOK 2)***

4 *Solution:* A **Yes**; B **No**; C **Yes**; D **No**; ***(DOK 2)***

5 *Solution:* 1 term; See student book page above for possible student explanation. ***(DOK 3)***

6 *Solution:* No; See student book page above for possible explanation. ***(DOK 3)***

Assessment and Remediation

- Ask students to determine if the given expressions are equivalent and to provide their reasoning: $2(2x^2 - 2)$ and $2x^2 - 2x - 4 + 2x^2 + 2x$. [Yes; $2x^2 - 2x - 4 + 2x^2 + 2x = 4x^2 - 4 = 2(2x^2 - 2)$]
- For students who are struggling, use the chart below to guide remediation.
- After providing remediation, check students' understanding. Ask students to determine if the given expressions are equivalent and to provide their reasoning: $4(5x - 6)$ and $\frac{1}{2}(30x - 12) + 5x$. [No. Substituting $x = 1$, $4(5x - 6) = {}^{-}4$ and $\frac{1}{2}(30x - 12) + 5x = 14$. Since ${}^{-}4 \neq 14$, the expressions are not equivalent.]

If the error is . . .	Students may . . .	To remediate . . .
yes, because both expressions equal ${}^{-}4$.	have tested for equivalency with zero.	Model terms such as $2x$ and x^2 which are not equivalent. Substitute zero for x showing that zero is not a valid value for substitution.
no, because the first expression does not have any x terms while the second expression does.	not recognize the result of opposites values when combining like terms.	Model expressions with algebra tiles with a focus on subtracting and negative values. Show students that ${}^{-}2x$ and $2x$ are opposites resulting in zero x terms. Practice similar expressions which require subtraction of terms.

Hands-On Activity

Create a mini-poster.

Materials: algebra tiles, graph paper, colored paper, chart paper for posters, colored pencils, recycled and/or crafting objects

- Display for students the following expression:
  $16 + 12y + 18y + 20 + 4y^2$
- Ask students to create a mini-poster which models and represents equivalent expressions for the given expression in as many ways as they can.
- Suggest that students choose a different object for each of the terms in the expression.
- Help students to think of real-world situations (for example, shopping for groceries or gifts) to represent the expressions, which might help them picture a model.
- Encourage students to be creative with their models.

Challenge Activity

Write a problem to match the expression.

- Display for students the following expression:
  $3(y + \frac{1}{2}y^2)$
- Ask students to create a word problem which models and represents the given expression.
- Help students to think of real-world situations (for example, ways to repackage sets of items) which might help them think of suitable problems.
- Encourage students to be creative with their word problems.

Lesson 18 (Student Book pages 178–183)

Understand Solutions to Equations

LESSON OBJECTIVES

- Understand the differences between equations and inequalities.
- Know that inequalities represent a range of possible values rather than a single solution.
- Use substitution to determine whether a given number in a specified set makes an equation or inequality true.

PREREQUISITE SKILLS

- Know variables can be replaced with numbers.
- Understand that for an equation to be true, expressions on either side of the equal sign must be equivalent.
- Model equations and inequalities that do not involve operations ($3 < 5$, $x > 7$, $y = 6$, etc.).

VOCABULARY

equation: a statement that shows two equivalent expressions

THE LEARNING PROGRESSION

In previous grades, students wrote and solved equations that represent problem situations. They used variables to represent unknowns and worked with expressions without evaluating them. In Grade 6, students begin to work systematically with algebraic expressions.

In this lesson, students will understand solving an equation or inequality as a process of answering a question. They will focus on modeling, writing, understanding, and determining solutions to equations using substitution. Students will model solutions for equations and inequalities with manipulatives, graphs, diagrams, or story contexts. Students will simplify numerical expressions by substituting values for given variables and use substitution to determine whether a given number in a specified set makes an equation or inequality true.

Ready *Teacher Toolbox* Teacher-Toolbox.com

	Prerequisite Skills	6.EE.B.5
Ready Lessons		✓
Tools for Instruction		✓ ✓
Interactive Tutorials		✓

CCSS Focus

6.EE.B.5 Understand solving an equation or inequality as a process of answering a question: which values from a specified set, if any, make the equation or inequality true? Use substitution to determine whether a given number in a specified set makes an equation or inequality true.

ADDITIONAL STANDARDS: 6.EE.B.6 *(see page A42 for full text)*

STANDARDS FOR MATHEMATICAL PRACTICE: SMP 1–5, 7 *(see page A9 for full text)*

AT A GLANCE

Students explore the meaning of solving equations using a pan balance to develop the concept of equality.

STEP BY STEP

- Introduce the Question at the top of the page.
- Help students relate the equality of the two expressions to the pan balance.
- Ask students how they might represent the equality of the pan balance.
- Lead students to represent the picture with an equation of $5 + 5 = 10$ or $2(5) = 10$.
- Read Think with students. Reinforce the idea of equal expressions using the pan balance.
- Guide students to recognize that 2 oz plus the unknown number of ounces on the left side of the pan balance has a sum equal to the 6 oz on the right side of the pan balance.

SMP Tip: Ask students to show how to use a model as a tool to demonstrate equivalency (*SMP 5*).

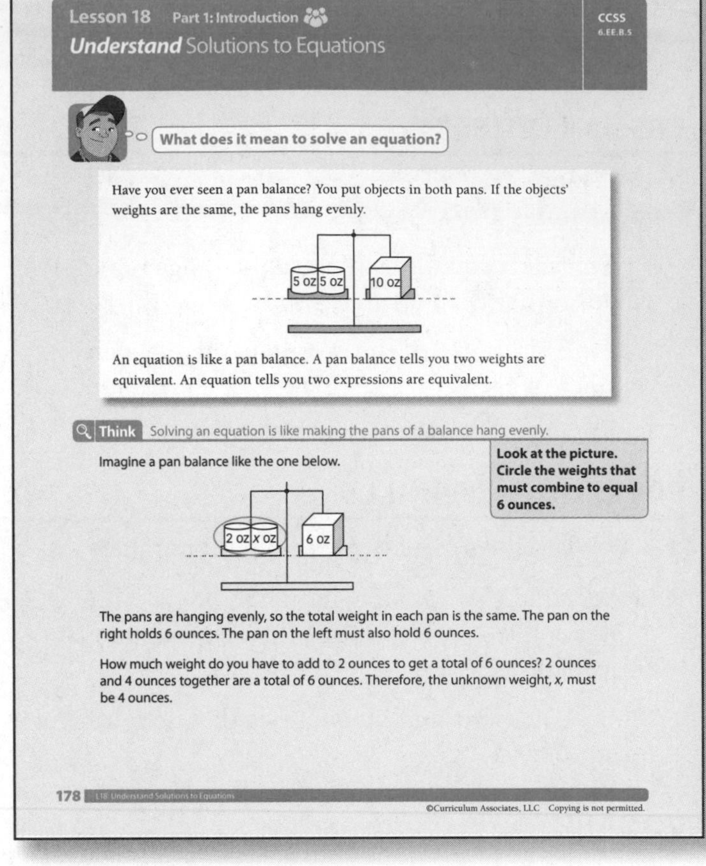

Focus on Math Concepts

Lesson 18 Part 1: Introduction CCSS 6.EE.B.5

Understand Solutions to Equations

What does it mean to solve an equation?

Have you ever seen a pan balance? You put objects in both pans. If the objects' weights are the same, the pans hang evenly.

An equation is like a pan balance. A pan balance tells you two weights are equivalent. An equation tells you two expressions are equivalent.

Think Solving an equation is like making the pans of a balance hang evenly.

Imagine a pan balance like the one below.

Look at the picture. Circle the weights that must combine to equal 6 ounces.

The pans are hanging evenly, so the total weight in each pan is the same. The pan on the right holds 6 ounces. The pan on the left must also hold 6 ounces.

How much weight do you have to add to 2 ounces to get a total of 6 ounces? 2 ounces and 4 ounces together are a total of 6 ounces. Therefore, the unknown weight, x, must be 4 ounces.

178 L18: Understand Solutions to Equations

©Curriculum Associates, LLC Copying is not permitted.

Hands-On Activity

Use a pan balance to model equivalent expressions.

Materials: a pan balance, small paper bag, blocks

- Put a bag with an unknown number of blocks and up to 10 visible blocks on one pan of a pan balance.
- Have students balance the scale by adding as many blocks as needed on the other pan.
- Ask, *What story can be used to describe the situation? Write the story as equivalent expressions.*
- Have students remove a block at a time from each pan to determine how many blocks are in the bag. Ask, *What number makes the equation true? How do you know?* Repeat the process using another bag.

Mathematical Discourse

- *Where have you seen or used a balance like this one? Have you seen or used something that is like a balance?*

  Students may or may not have had experience with pan balances. Some may have seen them in stores or recall having had balance toys as young children. They may also connect balances to seesaws or other playground equipment.

- *Is it possible for the unknown value to be equivalent to any number of ounces? How do you know? Explain.*

  Guide students to articulate that any other values would make the pans unequal in weight. One side will dip, while the opposite side will rise.

AT A GLANCE

Students explore equivalent expressions as a way of solving equations.

STEP BY STEP

- Read Think with students.
- Discuss how the equation $2 + x = 6$ is mathematical notation for what is seen on the pan balance.
- Ask a student to explain how the unknown amount can be determined for the left pan. Help students recognize that the same process can be used to determine the value of x in the equation.
- Have students read and reply to the Reflect questions.

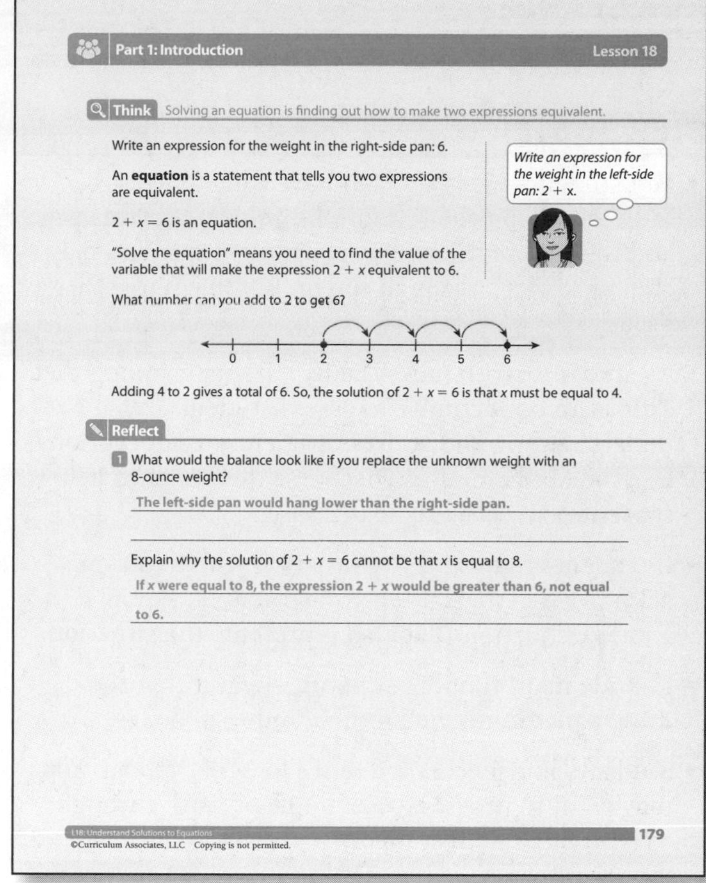

Part 1: Introduction Lesson 18

Think Solving an equation is finding out how to make two expressions equivalent.

Write an expression for the weight in the right-side pan: 6.

An **equation** is a statement that tells you two expressions are equivalent.

$2 + x = 6$ is an equation.

"Solve the equation" means you need to find the value of the variable that will make the expression $2 + x$ equivalent to 6.

Write an expression for the weight in the left-side pan: $2 + x$.

What number can you add to 2 to get 6?

Adding 4 to 2 gives a total of 6. So, the solution of $2 + x = 6$ is that x must be equal to 4.

Reflect

1 What would the balance look like if you replace the unknown weight with an 8-ounce weight?

The left-side pan would hang lower than the right-side pan.

Explain why the solution of $2 + x = 6$ cannot be that x is equal to 8.

If x were equal to 8, the expression $2 + x$ would be greater than 6, not equal to 6.

L18: Understand Solutions to Equations 179

©Curriculum Associates, LLC Copying is not permitted.

Concept Extension

Explore using mental math or writing expressions to determine unknown values.

Materials: paper

- Use mental math or write expressions to work through Steps 1–5:
  1. Think of a number.
  2. Multiply by 3.
  3. Subtract the original number.
  4. Divide by 2.
  5. Subtract the original number.
- Ask, *If the value before Step 4 is 24, what is the original number? Write an expression to explain your answer.* [The original number is 12. A possible expression representing Steps 1–3 is 3 • 12 − 12.]

Mathematical Discourse

- *What happens to the pan balance if the amount on the right side were decreased? How would you fix the left side to balance this change?*

  The pans would not be balanced. An equal amount would also have to be removed from the left side to keep the balance.

- *In the example of the pan balance, how many values can x represent? Explain. Can you create an equation where x represents many values? Explain.*

  Students should explain that only one value can be used to balance the scale. A possible scale where x could have many values is $x = x$.

AT A GLANCE

Students use bar models to write and solve equations.

STEP BY STEP

- Tell students that they will have time to work individually on the Explore It problems on this page and then share their responses in groups. You may choose to work through the first problem together as a class.
- As students work individually, circulate among them. This is an opportunity to assess student understanding and address student misconceptions. Use the Mathematical Discourse questions to help students articulate their thinking.
- If students represent the situation with addition, acknowledge that they are correct and ask for another equation that also represents the situation.
- If students need more support, suggest that they draw a picture to model the number of boxes.
- Students may need a reference for a bar model. You may want to provide an example or work through this problem with students.
- Direct students to the word "solution." Explain that the solution is the value of the variable.
- Take note of students who are still having difficulty and wait to see if their understanding progresses as they work in their groups during the next part of the lesson.

STUDENT MISCONCEPTION ALERT: Students may attempt to write equations using only addition. Encourage students to use previous knowledge of writing expressions to utilize different mathematical operations.

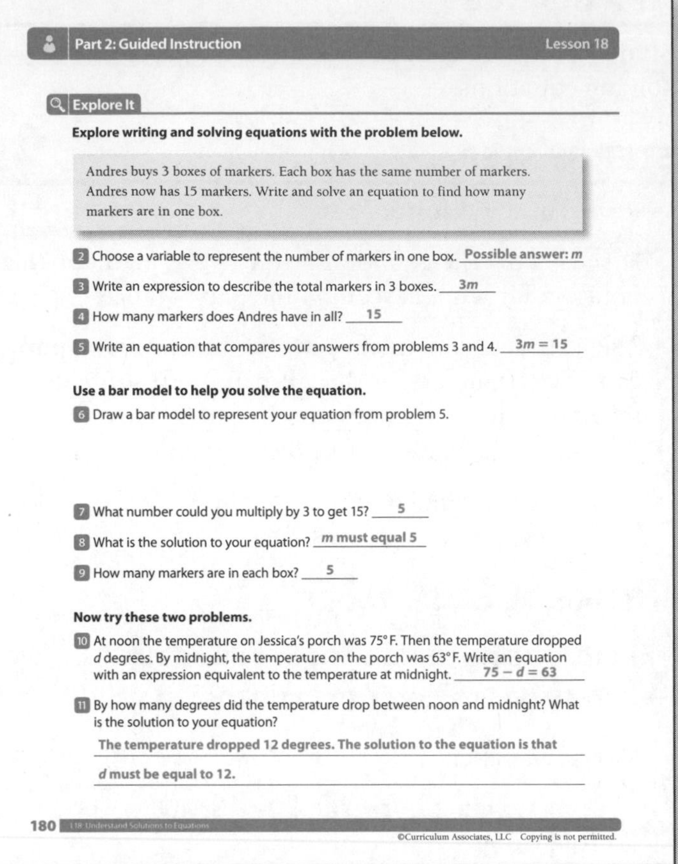

Part 2: Guided Instruction Lesson 18

Explore It

Explore writing and solving equations with the problem below.

Andres buys 3 boxes of markers. Each box has the same number of markers. Andres now has 15 markers. Write and solve an equation to find how many markers are in one box.

2 Choose a variable to represent the number of markers in one box. **Possible answer: m**

3 Write an expression to describe the total markers in 3 boxes. **$3m$**

4 How many markers does Andres have in all? **15**

5 Write an equation that compares your answers from problems 3 and 4. **$3m = 15$**

Use a bar model to help you solve the equation.

6 Draw a bar model to represent your equation from problem 5.

7 What number could you multiply by 3 to get 15? **5**

8 What is the solution to your equation? **m must equal 5**

9 How many markers are in each box? **5**

Now try these two problems.

10 At noon the temperature on Jessica's porch was 75°F. Then the temperature dropped d degrees. By midnight, the temperature on the porch was 63°F. Write an equation with an expression equivalent to the temperature at midnight. **$75 - d = 63$**

11 By how many degrees did the temperature drop between noon and midnight? What is the solution to your equation?

The temperature dropped 12 degrees. The solution to the equation is that d must be equal to 12.

180 L18: Understand Solutions to Equations ©Curriculum Associates, LLC Copying is not permitted.

Mathematical Discourse

- *What does the pan balance look like for the marker problem? How does the model compare to the bar model?*

  The pan balance will have 3 unknowns on the left and the value of 15 on the right. Both models show the total number of markers is equal to 15.

- *Explain how you determine the number of markers in each box. How is the operation similar to multiplication?*

  Guide students to connect division as the inverse operation of multiplication.

- *In the temperature problem, the story represents a difference. How could a difference be represented on a scale model? Bar model? Which is your preferred method to model this situation?*

  Students may struggle with this question. Students might try to use negative values. Help students recognize that equations are an efficient way to represent a difference.

AT A GLANCE

Students write and solve equations to solve problems.

STEP BY STEP

- Organize students into pairs or small groups. You may choose to work through the first Talk About It problem together as a class.
- Walk around to each group, listen to, and join in on discussions at different points. Use the Mathematical Discourse questions to help support or extend students' thinking.
- When using the number line to determine the distance from 12.5 to 8, remind students to use increments of 0.5.
- Direct the groups' attention to Try It Another Way. Have a volunteer from each group come to the board to share the group's solutions to problems 19–22.

SMP Tip: Students use equations to model the problem situation (*SMP 4*). As students write and solve equations, regularly ask them why they chose the terms, variables, and operations in the equation and how each relates to the problem context.

Part 2: Guided Instruction Lesson 18

Talk About It

Solve the problem below as a group.

Marta earns $12.50 from babysitting, and then spends some of her earnings on a new book. She has $8.00 of her earnings left. Write and solve an equation to find the cost of the book.

12 What is the unknown amount? cost of the book Choose a variable to represent it. *b*

13 Could the value of the variable be greater than $12.50? Explain.
No. Marta earned $12.50 and has money left over after buying the book, so she must have spent less than $12.50.

14 Write an equation with an expression equivalent to $8.00. $12.5 - b = 8$

15 Draw a number line from 7.5 to 13.5.

7.5 8.0 8.5 9.0 9.5 10.0 10.5 11.0 11.5 12.0 12.5 13.0 13.5

16 What number can you subtract from 12.5 to get 8? 4.5

17 What is the solution of your equation? 4.5

18 What is the cost of the book? $4.50

Try It Another Way

Explore using math tiles to solve an equation.

19 Write your equation from problem 14. $12.5 - b = 8$

20 Use math tiles to represent the equation.

21 What amount can you subtract from $12.50 to get $8.00? $4.50

22 What is the cost of the book? $4.50

L18: Understand Solutions to Equations 181
©Curriculum Associates, LLC Copying is not permitted.

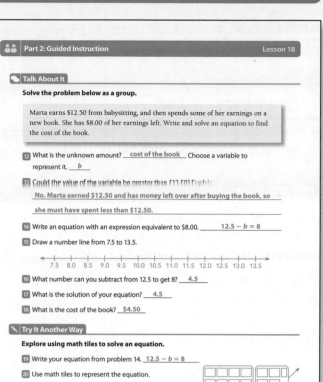

Concept Extension

Explore writing inequalities.

- Read the following problem to students: *Marta earns $12.50 from babysitting and spends some of her earnings on a book. She has less than $8.00 left.*
- Use a number line to determine the amount of money Marta spent. Ask, *What are possible solutions?*
- Ask students to discuss how this problem is different from the original. Ask, *Is this an equation?*
- Ask students to use inequality symbols (<, >) to write a mathematical sentence.
- Ask, *How would the story change if the Marta had more than $8.00 left?*

Mathematical Discourse

- *Is there another equation you can write to determine the cost of the book? How would this equation change the solution? What can you say about these two equations?*

  Encourage students to express the cost of the book as $12.50 - 8.00 = b$. Students should recognize this as an equivalent equation with the same solution.

- *How can you convince another student that your solution is correct?*

  Students could use substitution or another model to create an equivalent value.

AT A GLANCE

Students demonstrate their understanding of solutions of equations as representing equivalent expressions.

STEP BY STEP

- Discuss each Connect It problem as a class using the discussion points outlined below.

Analyze:

- Ask students to explain what would happen if the value of r is equal to or greater than 1. How does this support their explanation?
- Ask, *Would a model be useful to support your reasoning? Explain.*

Illustrate:

- How is a model for subtraction different from a model that uses addition?
- Ask students to create additional models to extend the thinking of their peers. Ask, *How many ways can students explain their reasoning?*

Create:

- Students should share their real-world problems and solutions with the class.

SMP Tip: Listening to arguments of others and deciding if they make sense allows students to construct their own viable arguments (*SMP 3*) by using mathematical definitions. Help students follow the reasoning of others by asking them to restate the idea or to use the method with a different problem. Provide sentence frames or models of language to use when critiquing arguments.

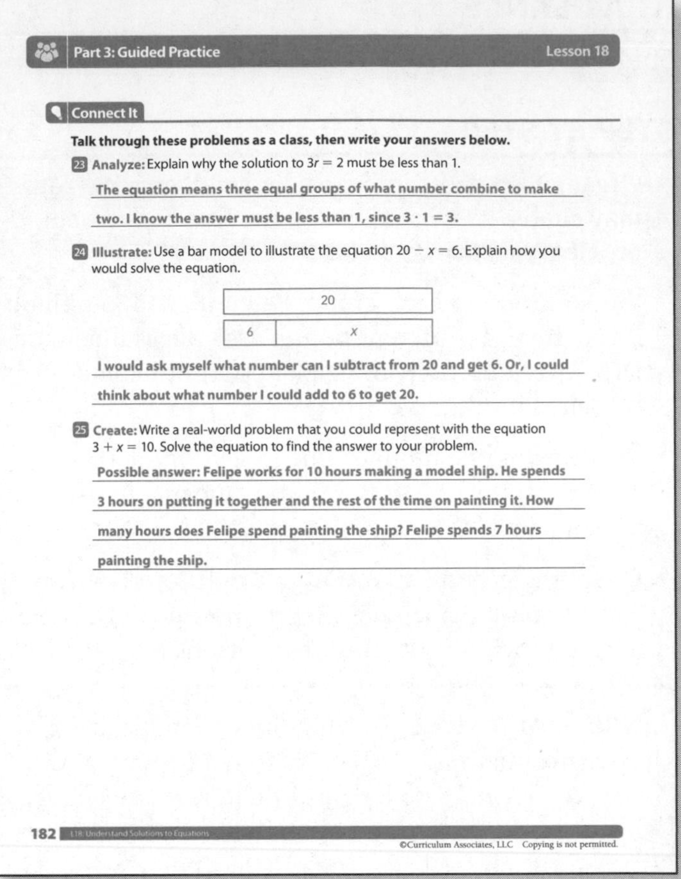
Part 3: Guided Practice Lesson 18

Connect It

Talk through these problems as a class, then write your answers below.

23 **Analyze:** Explain why the solution to $3r = 2$ must be less than 1.

The equation means three equal groups of what number combine to make two. I know the answer must be less than 1, since $3 \cdot 1 = 3$.

24 **Illustrate:** Use a bar model to illustrate the equation $20 - x = 6$. Explain how you would solve the equation.

I would ask myself what number can I subtract from 20 and get 6. Or, I could think about what number I could add to 6 to get 20.

25 **Create:** Write a real-world problem that you could represent with the equation $3 + x = 10$. Solve the equation to find the answer to your problem.

Possible answer: Felipe works for 10 hours making a model ship. He spends 3 hours on putting it together and the rest of the time on painting it. How many hours does Felipe spend painting the ship? Felipe spends 7 hours painting the ship.

182 L18: Understand Solutions to Equations

©Curriculum Associates, LLC Copying is not permitted.

AT A GLANCE

Students use the pan balance model to write and solve equations.

STEP BY STEP

- Direct students to complete the Put It Together task independently.
- As students work on their own, walk around to assess their progress and understanding, to answer their questions, and to give additional support, if needed.
- Discuss the progression of the pan balance and the changes this had on the equation.

SCORING RUBRICS

See student facsimile page for possible student answers.

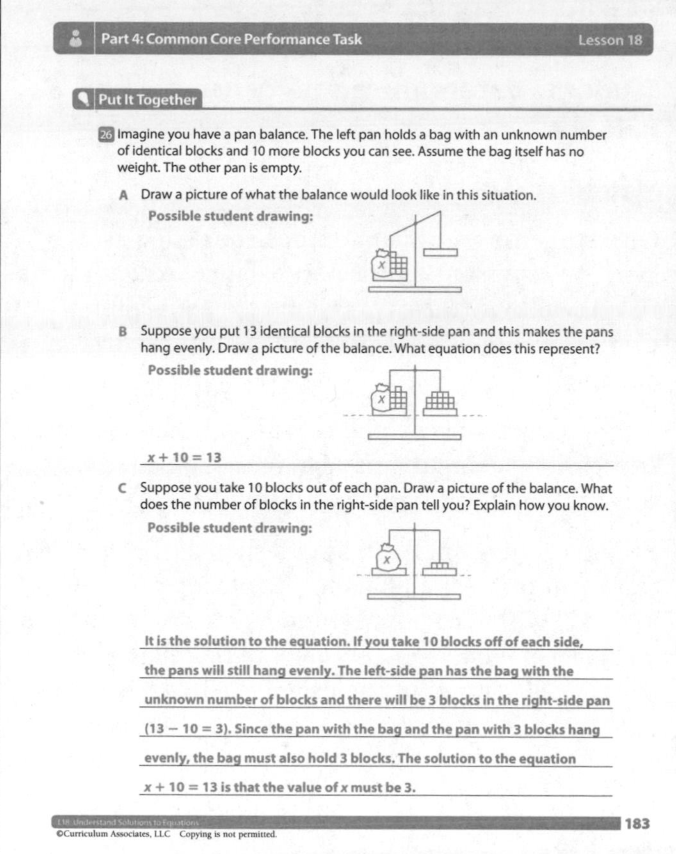

Part 4: Common Core Performance Task   Lesson 18

Put It Together

26 Imagine you have a pan balance. The left pan holds a bag with an unknown number of identical blocks and 10 more blocks you can see. Assume the bag itself has no weight. The other pan is empty.

A Draw a picture of what the balance would look like in this situation.

Possible student drawing:

B Suppose you put 13 identical blocks in the right-side pan and this makes the pans hang evenly. Draw a picture of the balance. What equation does this represent?

Possible student drawing:

$x + 10 = 13$

C Suppose you take 10 blocks out of each pan. Draw a picture of the balance. What does the number of blocks in the right-side pan tell you? Explain how you know.

Possible student drawing:

It is the solution to the equation. If you take 10 blocks off of each side, the pans will still hang evenly. The left-side pan has the bag with the unknown number of blocks and there will be 3 blocks in the right-side pan ($13 - 10 = 3$). Since the pan with the bag and the pan with 3 blocks hang evenly, the bag must also hold 3 blocks. The solution to the equation $x + 10 = 13$ is that the value of x must be 3.

L18: Understand Solutions to Equations   183
©Curriculum Associates, LLC Copying is not permitted.

A

Points	Expectations
2	The response demonstrates the student's mathematical understanding of using a pan balance to show equality.
1	The pan balance drawn may contain minor errors. Evidence in the response demonstrates that with feedback, the student can revise the work to accomplish the task.
0	There is no pan balance drawn or the pan balance shows little or no evidence of understanding.

B

Points	Expectations
2	The response demonstrates the student's mathematical understanding of using a pan balance to write an equation.
1	The response demonstrates some evidence of using a pan balance to write an equation, but the student's response may contain some misunderstandings. Evidence in the response demonstrates that with feedback, the student can revise the work to accomplish the task.
0	There is no response or the response shows little or no understanding of the task.

C

Points	Expectations
2	The response demonstrates the student's mathematical understanding of using a pan balance to write and solve an equation.
1	The response demonstrates some evidence of writing and solving an equation, but the student's response may contain some misunderstandings. Evidence in the response demonstrates that with feedback, the student can revise the work to accomplish the task.
0	There is no response or the response shows little or no understanding of the task.

Intervention Activity

Students determine equality using a pan balance.

Materials: pan balance, blocks

Give students equivalent expressions such as $2 + 5$ and 7 to represent on the pan balance. Ask students how they know the expressions are equivalent. Continue with similar problems to represent equality.

Ask students to write and represent other equivalent expressions using the pan balance. Continue with this practice to recognize equality.

Provide equivalent expressions such as $3 + x = 21$ to represent on the pan balance. Replace one of the addends with a bag. Ask students questions such as *3 plus what number is 21? How can the value be determined?* Point out the use of the inverse operation.

On-Level Activity

Model solutions for equations and inequalities.

Materials: pan balance, blocks, bags, algebra tiles

Sally is shopping at the grocery store.

She puts 6 items in the shopping cart, and then decides to double the amount. Harry removes 4 of the items. At the checkout line, Sally is able to go through the Express Lane for 12 items or fewer. How many items did Sally have at the checkout line?

Use a pan balance, bar model, tiles, or number lines to support your reasoning.

Challenge Activity

Use modeling to determine equality.

Materials: marbles, bags

Algebra Twist #1: Take an empty bag with any number of marbles inside. Add 6 marbles. Multiply the total number of marbles by 2. Subtract 4 marbles. Divide the number of marbles in half. Subtract the original number of marbles. How many marbles are in the bag?

Algebra Twist #2: Take an empty bag with any number of marbles inside. Multiply the total number of marbles by 2. Add 6 marbles. Subtract 4 marbles. Divide the number of marbles in half. Subtract the original number of marbles. How many marbles are in the bag?

Model the solutions to the two Algebra Twists.

Can you create a third Algebra Twist that has the same solution as Algebra Twist #1 or Algebra Twist #2?

Lesson 19 (Student Book pages 184–195)

Solve Equations

LESSON OBJECTIVES

- Recognize that real-world mathematical problems can be expressed using a variable to represent an unknown.
- Recognize that both sides of an equation are equal, and whatever operation is performed on one side of the equation must be done on the other side to maintain the equality.
- Write and solve equations that represent real-world mathematical problems that use variables and involve non-negative rational numbers.

PREREQUISITE SKILLS

- Understand that a variable represents a number or a specified set of numbers.
- Understand that variables can be operated upon in the same way as numbers.
- Write an expression from a real-world mathematical problem.
- Use substitution to determine if both sides of the equation are equal.

VOCABULARY

There is no new vocabulary.

THE LEARNING PROGRESSION

In earlier grades, students often solved word problems involving one operation. For example, if the total cost of 8 candles was $56, they would divide 56 by 8 to find that each candle cost $7.

In this lesson, students learn how to solve similar problems using algebraic equations of the forms $x + p = q$ and $px = q$. They first use pan scales to understand how both sides of an equation are equal. Students learn how to use inverse operations to isolate a variable, and how to perform operations on both sides of an equation in order to keep it balanced and equal. Students learn to use a variable to represent an unknown quantity and then model simple word problems with algebraic equations they can then solve.

Ready *Teacher Toolbox* Teacher-Toolbox.com

	Prerequisite Skills	*6.EE.B.6 6.EE.B.7*
Ready Lessons		✓
Tools for Instruction	✓	✓
Interactive Tutorials	✓	✓

CCSS Focus

6.EE.B.6 Use variables to represent numbers and write expressions when solving a real-world or mathematical problem; understand that a variable can represent an unknown number, or, depending on the purpose at hand, any number in a specified set.

6.EE.B.7 Solve real-world and mathematical problems by writing and solving equations of the form $x + p = q$ and $px = q$ for cases in which p, q and x are all nonnegative rational numbers.

ADDITIONAL STANDARDS: **6.EE.B.5** *(see page A42 for full text)*

STANDARDS FOR MATHEMATICAL PRACTICE: **SMP 1–4, 7** *(see page A9 for full text)*

AT A GLANCE

Students work through a problem in which a pan balance holds a number of blocks and a bag with an unknown number of blocks in each of two pans. Students use the balance to find the unknown number.

STEP BY STEP

- Tell students that this page models how both sides of an equation must be equal and balanced.
- Have students read the problem at the top of the page.
- Work through Explore It as a class.
- For the third bullet, make sure students understand how the expression represents the picture. Ask them to explain in words why $x + 2$ represents the number of blocks in the left pan. [Because the bag holds x blocks, and we can see 2 more beside it.]
- Ask student pairs or groups to explain their answers for the remaining questions.

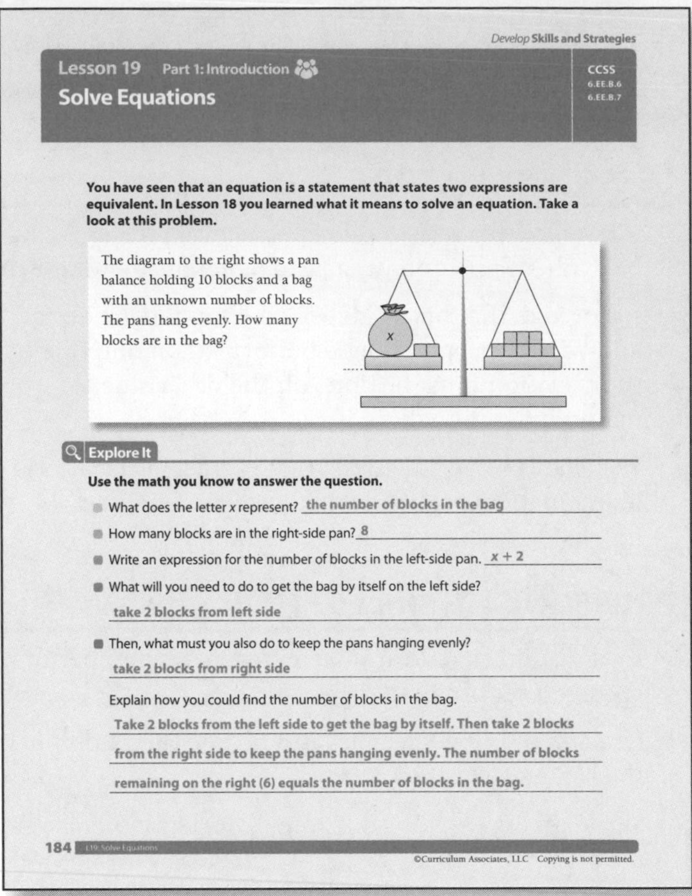

Develop Skills and Strategies

Lesson 19 Part 1: Introduction

Solve Equations

CCSS 6.EE.B.6 6.EE.B.7

You have seen that an equation is a statement that states two expressions are equivalent. In Lesson 18 you learned what it means to solve an equation. Take a look at this problem.

The diagram to the right shows a pan balance holding 10 blocks and a bag with an unknown number of blocks. The pans hang evenly. How many blocks are in the bag?

Explore It

Use the math you know to answer the question.

- What does the letter x represent? the number of blocks in the bag
- How many blocks are in the right-side pan? 8
- Write an expression for the number of blocks in the left-side pan. $x + 2$
- What will you need to do to get the bag by itself on the left side? take 2 blocks from left side
- Then, what must you also do to keep the pans hanging evenly? take 2 blocks from right side

Explain how you could find the number of blocks in the bag. Take 2 blocks from the left side to get the bag by itself. Then take 2 blocks from the right side to keep the pans hanging evenly. The number of blocks remaining on the right (6) equals the number of blocks in the bag.

184 L19: Solve Equations

©Curriculum Associates, LLC Copying is not permitted.

ELL Support

Discuss the *pan balance* with students, labeling the pans. Use the drawing and other sketches to show what the pan balance looks like balanced and not balanced.

Hands-On Activity

Use a pan balance.

Materials: at least 20 blocks, two lightweight opaque bags, a pan balance

- Put 5 blocks in the bag, and then put that bag and 2 blocks in one pan. Put blocks and the other empty bag (to balance the full bag) in the other pan until they balance (7 blocks).
- Ask students how to find the number of blocks in the bag. Guide them to follow a procedure. *How do we get the bag by itself?* [Remove 2 blocks from that pan.] *How do we get the pans to hang evenly?* [Remove 2 blocks from the other pan.] *How many blocks are in the bag? How do we know?* [5; because the pans are balanced]

Mathematical Discourse

- *You know that an equation shows two expressions are equivalent. How do you think this relates to the pan balance in this problem?*

  Listen for answers that talk about how both sides must be equal in both situations. The pan balance will not be balanced unless both sides weigh equal amounts.

- *In this problem, you take two blocks off each side of the pan balance to get the bag alone. How do you think that might apply to an equation?*

  Listen for ideas that include getting the variable, or "x," alone to find its value. Some students may see that whatever you do to get x alone on one side has to be done to the other side to keep the equation balanced.

AT A GLANCE

Students explore how solving the pan balance is related to solving equations. They learn about using inverse operations to isolate a variable.

STEP BY STEP

- Read Find Out More as a class.
- Review how the balance and blocks represent the equation $x + 2 = 8$.
- Explain that you keep the equation balanced by treating both sides the same. When you do something to one side, you must also do it to the other side.

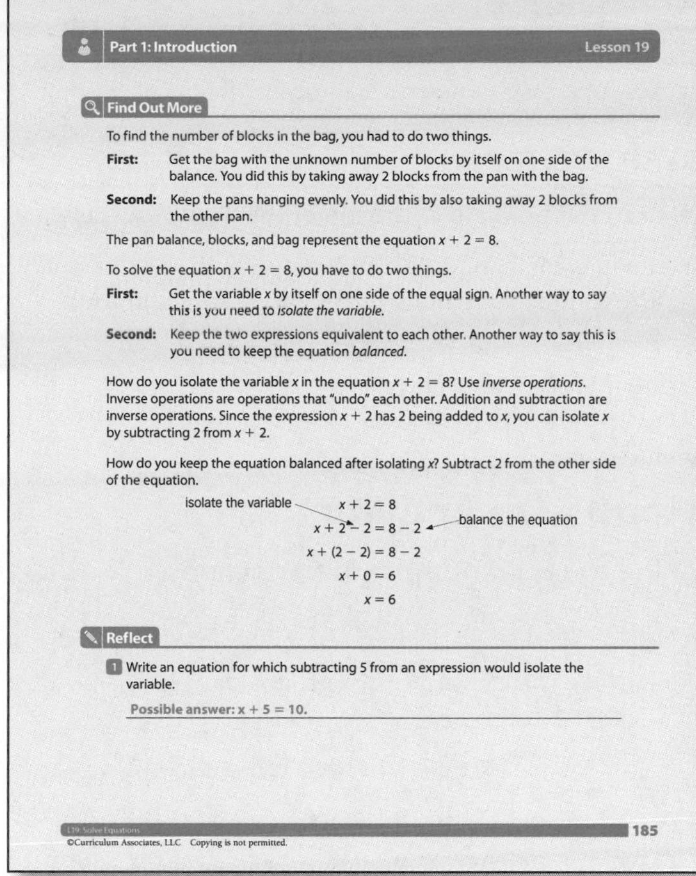

Part 1: Introduction Lesson 19

Find Out More

To find the number of blocks in the bag, you had to do two things.

First: Get the bag with the unknown number of blocks by itself on one side of the balance. You did this by taking away 2 blocks from the pan with the bag.

Second: Keep the pans hanging evenly. You did this by also taking away 2 blocks from the other pan.

The pan balance, blocks, and bag represent the equation $x + 2 = 8$.

To solve the equation $x + 2 = 8$, you have to do two things.

First: Get the variable x by itself on one side of the equal sign. Another way to say this is you need to *isolate the variable.*

Second: Keep the two expressions equivalent to each other. Another way to say this is you need to keep the equation *balanced.*

How do you isolate the variable x in the equation $x + 2 = 8$? Use *inverse operations.* Inverse operations are operations that "undo" each other. Addition and subtraction are inverse operations. Since the expression $x + 2$ has 2 being added to x, you can isolate x by subtracting 2 from $x + 2$.

How do you keep the equation balanced after isolating x? Subtract 2 from the other side of the equation.

isolate the variable

$$x + 2 = 8$$
$$x + 2 - 2 = 8 - 2$$
$$x + (2 - 2) = 8 - 2$$
$$x + 0 = 6$$
$$x = 6$$

balance the equation

Reflect

1 Write an equation for which subtracting 5 from an expression would isolate the variable.

Possible answer: $x + 5 = 10$.

L19: Solve Equations 185

©Curriculum Associates, LLC Copying is not permitted.

ELL Support

The term *isolate* may be unfamiliar to many students. Specifically tell students that to isolate something means to get it by itself, and give some examples of uses in other contexts.

Real-World Connection

Ask students to think of situations where they know a total, and part of a total, but not the other part. For example, someone might read 107 pages of a book that is 248 pages long. They could set up the equation $x + 107 = 248$ to find how many more pages they have to read. If you knew how much you paid for 3 items at a garage sale, but lost the price sticker for one of them, you could write an equation to find it using the prices on the other items. Students may say they don't need equations to solve these problems; explain that in other real situations, equations help keep track of complicated details.

AT A GLANCE

Students write an equation of the form $x - p = q$ to represent a block and pan balance problem.

STEP BY STEP

- Read the problem at the top of the page as a class.
- Discuss Picture It. Ask, *What does* x *itself represent?* [the number of blocks in the bag before you took 3 out]
- Read Solve It as a class.

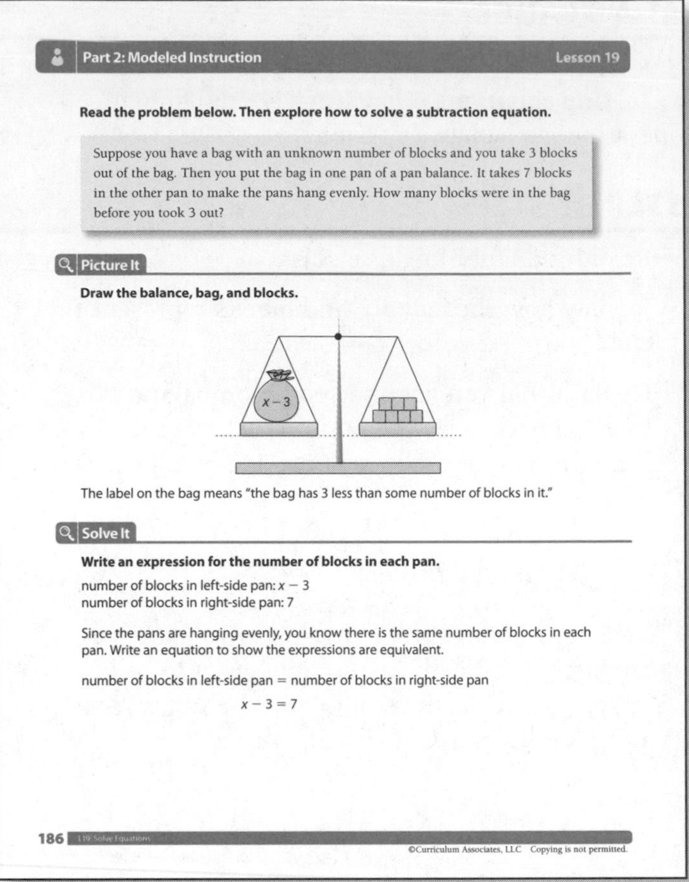

Part 2: Modeled Instruction Lesson 19

Read the problem below. Then explore how to solve a subtraction equation.

Suppose you have a bag with an unknown number of blocks and you take 3 blocks out of the bag. Then you put the bag in one pan of a pan balance. It takes 7 blocks in the other pan to make the pans hang evenly. How many blocks were in the bag before you took 3 out?

Picture It

Draw the balance, bag, and blocks.

The label on the bag means "the bag has 3 less than some number of blocks in it."

Solve It

Write an expression for the number of blocks in each pan.

number of blocks in left-side pan: $x - 3$
number of blocks in right-side pan: 7

Since the pans are hanging evenly, you know there is the same number of blocks in each pan. Write an equation to show the expressions are equivalent.

number of blocks in left-side pan = number of blocks in right-side pan

$x - 3 = 7$

186 L19: Solve Equations

©Curriculum Associates, LLC Copying is not permitted.

Hands-On Activity

Find the total number of paper clips.

Materials: a clear jar, a large number of paper clips

- Divide the class into two groups and designate a leader in each group.
- Fill the jar with paper clips. Tell students you have x paper clips in the jar. Take a portion of the paper clips $\left(\text{between } \frac{1}{3} \text{ and } \frac{1}{2}\right)$ and give them to the leader in group 1.
- Ask the students to use words to describe an expression to represent how many clips are left in the jar. [x minus the amount taken out]
- Tell students to use words to write an equation that relates the two amounts. [x − amount taken out = amount left in jar]
- Give the rest of the paper clips to the leader in group 2. Have the leaders distribute the clips among the group to count and then find the total. Ask students how to use this information in their equation. [Replace "amount taken out" with the count for group 1, and "amount left in jar" with the count for group 2.] Tell students to solve for the total amount.

Real-World Connection

Ask students to think of situations where someone might know how much was taken and how much was left, but not the original amount. For example, a mom sends 2 cheese sticks with her kids to lunch. She has 6 left in the package. How many were in the package to begin with? A company receives a shipment and unloads 16 boxes. If there are 28 boxes left on the truck, how can they find the total number that were in the shipment?

AT A GLANCE

Students revisit the problem on page 186 and investigate how to solve an equation of the form $x - p = q$. They use inverse operations to isolate the variable.

STEP BY STEP

- Point out that Connect It refers to the question on page 186.
- Remind students that isolating the variable means to get x by itself on one side of the equal sign.
- Have students work through the problems in Try It. Ask, *How did you isolate the variable to solve the equations?*

SMP Tip: Students use the context of the pan balance to set up an equation. They then reason abstractly to solve the equation using inverse operations (*SMP 2*). Review inverse properties so students will better understand how to use them to solve equations.

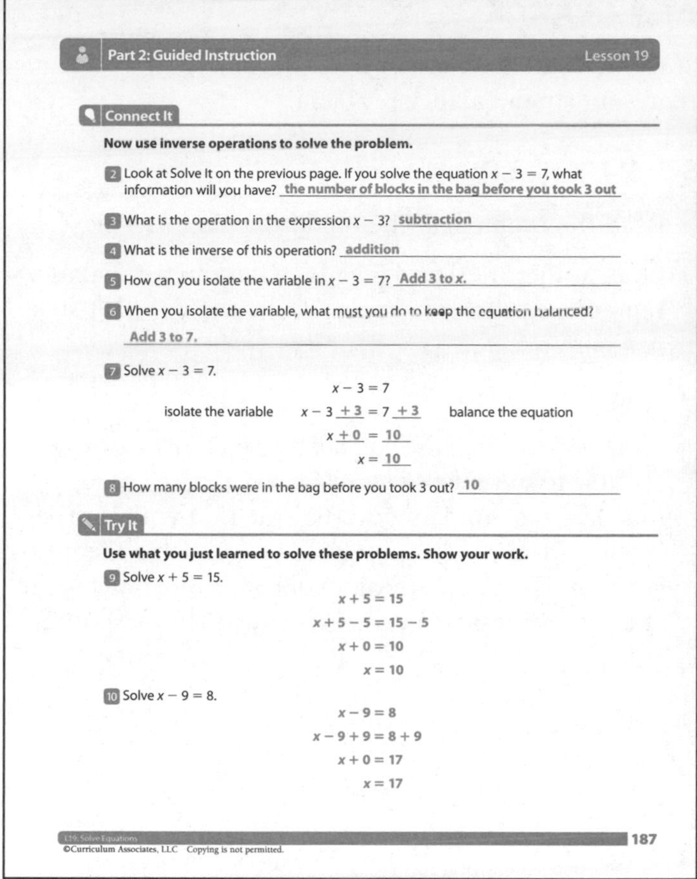

Part 2: Guided Instruction — Lesson 19

Connect It

Now use inverse operations to solve the problem.

2 Look at Solve It on the previous page. If you solve the equation $x - 3 = 7$, what information will you have? the number of blocks in the bag before you took 3 out

3 What is the operation in the expression $x - 3$? subtraction

4 What is the inverse of this operation? addition

5 How can you isolate the variable in $x - 3 = 7$? Add 3 to x.

6 When you isolate the variable, what must you do to keep the equation balanced? Add 3 to 7.

7 Solve $x - 3 = 7$.

$x - 3 = 7$

isolate the variable $\quad x - 3 + 3 = 7 + 3 \quad$ balance the equation

$x + 0 = 10$

$x = 10$

8 How many blocks were in the bag before you took 3 out? 10

Try It

Use what you just learned to solve these problems. Show your work.

9 Solve $x + 5 = 15$.

$x + 5 = 15$

$x + 5 - 5 = 15 - 5$

$x + 0 = 10$

$x = 10$

10 Solve $x - 9 = 8$.

$x - 9 = 8$

$x - 9 + 9 = 8 + 9$

$x + 0 = 17$

$x = 17$

L19: Solve Equations 187

©Curriculum Associates, LLC Copying is not permitted.

TRY IT SOLUTIONS

9 *Solution:* $x = 10$; Students may solve by subtracting 5 from both sides of the equation.

ERROR ALERT: Students who wrote $x = 20$ subtracted 5 from one side, but then added it to the other. They used the inverse of the operation they used to isolate the variable.

10 *Solution:* $x = 17$; Students may solve by adding 9 to each side of the equation.

AT A GLANCE

Students find an equation in the form $px = q$ to represent a pan balance problem.

STEP BY STEP

- Read the problem at the top of the page as a class.
- Look at Picture It and discuss what the pan balance represents. Ask, *How many blocks are in the left-side pan in terms of* x? [$x + x$, or $2x$]
- Read Solve It as a class.
- Ask, *Do you think the pan balance picture helps you to see how to solve the equation? How?* [Some students may feel they understand the equation without the model. Others may appreciate how it helps them to see that doing something to one side unbalances the equation unless you do the same thing to the other side.]

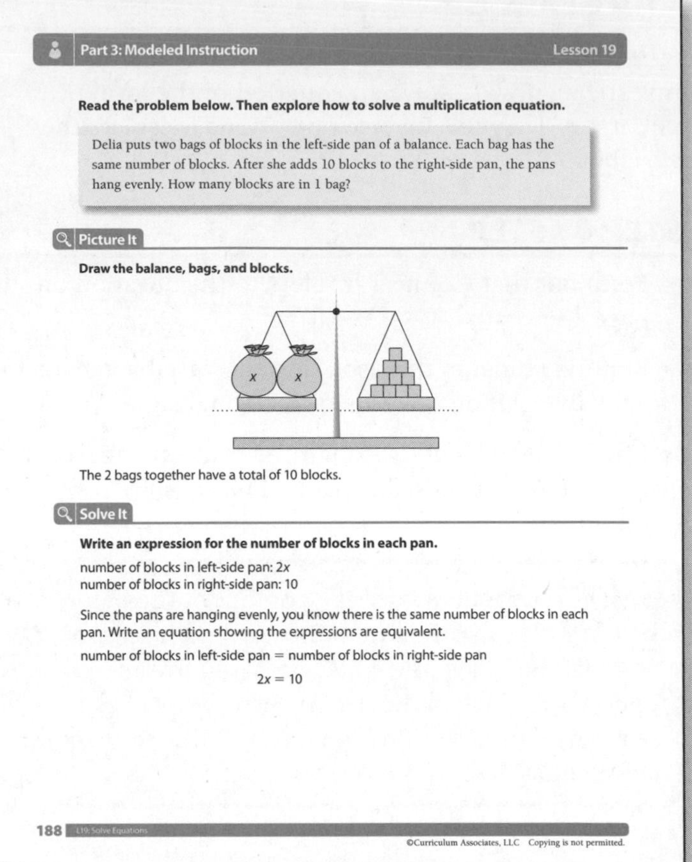

Part 3: Modeled Instruction Lesson 19

Read the problem below. Then explore how to solve a multiplication equation.

Delia puts two bags of blocks in the left-side pan of a balance. Each bag has the same number of blocks. After she adds 10 blocks to the right-side pan, the pans hang evenly. How many blocks are in 1 bag?

Picture It

Draw the balance, bags, and blocks.

The 2 bags together have a total of 10 blocks.

Solve It

Write an expression for the number of blocks in each pan.

number of blocks in left-side pan: $2x$
number of blocks in right-side pan: 10

Since the pans are hanging evenly, you know there is the same number of blocks in each pan. Write an equation showing the expressions are equivalent.

number of blocks in left-side pan = number of blocks in right-side pan

$2x = 10$

188 L19: Solve Equations

©Curriculum Associates, LLC Copying is not permitted.

Mathematical Discourse

- *How could you isolate one bag of* x *blocks on the left side? What would you then do to balance the pans?*

  Students would probably take one of the x bags off the scale, but then the question is how many blocks to take off the other side when we do not know what x is. Listen for the idea that you took half of the blocks off one side, so take half of the blocks off the other side.

- *What are some other ways you could solve this problem?*

  Allow wait time for students to offer solution strategies. Some students may use a "guess and check" strategy.

AT A GLANCE

Students revisit the problem on page 188 and investigate how to solve an equation of the form $px = q$. They use the inverse of multiplication to isolate the variable.

STEP BY STEP

- Point out the Connect It refers to the problem on page 188.
- If it seems appropriate, you may want to remind students that dividing by 2 is the same as multiplying by $\frac{1}{2}$.
- Emphasize that it is always a good idea to check your answer.
- Have students solve the problems in Try It.

Concept Extension

Solve inequalities.

Materials: pan balance, 2 opaque bags, 13 blocks

Before class, put 5 blocks in each bag. Tell students each bag holds the same number of blocks, which you will call x.

Place the 2 bags on one pan and 3 blocks on the other pan. Ask, *Do the two pans balance?* [No.] *How could you represent this problem algebraically?* If students are stuck, suggest that one pan weighs more than the other, and see if they can think of using an inequality. Try to lead them to see that $2x > 3$.

Now, working algebraically, ask, *What operation is used?* [multiplication] *What would be the inverse operation?* [division] *If you divided both sides by 2, you would get* $x > \frac{3}{2}$. *What does this mean as it applies to the pan balance? Would* $\frac{3}{2}$ *blocks make sense?* [The answer in this problem would have to be a whole number, since we're working with whole blocks.] *Can we find the exact answer?* [We can only find an answer that would make one pan heavier than the other one. Since they are not equal, we cannot find the quantity in the bag exactly.]

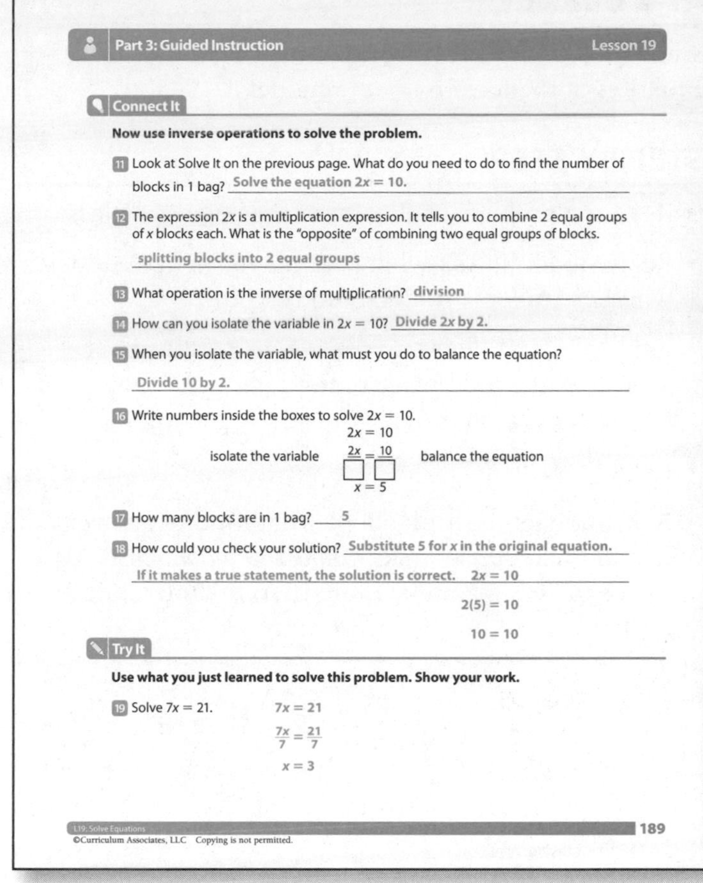

Part 3: Guided Instruction Lesson 19

Connect It

Now use inverse operations to solve the problem.

11 Look at Solve It on the previous page. What do you need to do to find the number of blocks in 1 bag? Solve the equation $2x = 10$.

12 The expression $2x$ is a multiplication expression. It tells you to combine 2 equal groups of x blocks each. What is the "opposite" of combining two equal groups of blocks?
splitting blocks into 2 equal groups

13 What operation is the inverse of multiplication? division

14 How can you isolate the variable in $2x = 10$? Divide $2x$ by 2.

15 When you isolate the variable, what must you do to balance the equation?
Divide 10 by 2.

16 Write numbers inside the boxes to solve $2x = 10$.

$2x = 10$

isolate the variable $\frac{2x}{\square} = \frac{10}{\square}$ balance the equation

$x = 5$

17 How many blocks are in 1 bag? 5

18 How could you check your solution? Substitute 5 for x in the original equation. If it makes a true statement, the solution is correct. $2x = 10$; $2(5) = 10$; $10 = 10$

Try It

Use what you just learned to solve this problem. Show your work.

19 Solve $7x = 21$. $7x = 21$; $\frac{7x}{7} = \frac{21}{7}$; $x = 3$

L19: Solve Equations 189
©Curriculum Associates, LLC Copying is not permitted.

TRY IT SOLUTION

15 *Solution:* $x = 3$; Students should use inverse operations to divide both sides of the equation by 7.

ERROR ALERT: Students who wrote $x = 147$ multiplied the right side of the equation by 7 instead of dividing by 7.

AT A GLANCE

Students explore a real world situation and write an equation of the form $px = q$ to model it.

STEP BY STEP

- Read the problem at the top of the page as a class.
- Read Model It. Ask what t stands for to determine whether students understand the problem.
- Ask, *How do we know* 6t *is equal to 84?* [Both represent the total price of the tickets, so they must be the same amount.]
- Read Solve It.
- Ask students to think about what kind of answer would make sense. Ask, *would $30 make sense?* [No. Three tickets would be more than the total, and they have 6.]

SMP Tip: Using a bar model and a word sentence helps students find their own way to make sense of the problem (*SMP 1*). Help students to find alternate ways of looking at problems to better understand how equations represent them.

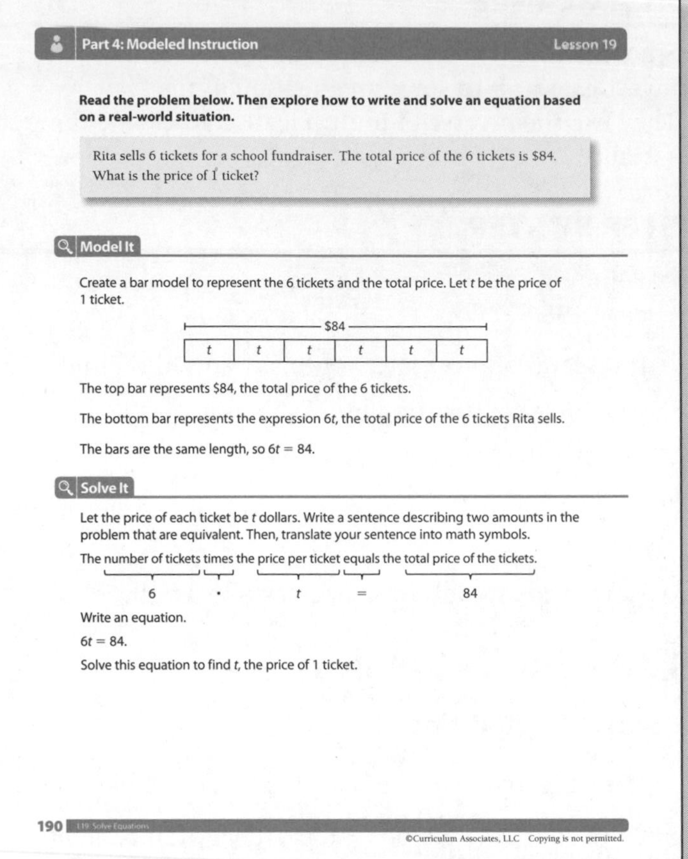

Part 4: Modeled Instruction Lesson 19

Read the problem below. Then explore how to write and solve an equation based on a real-world situation.

Rita sells 6 tickets for a school fundraiser. The total price of the 6 tickets is $84. What is the price of 1 ticket?

Model It

Create a bar model to represent the 6 tickets and the total price. Let t be the price of 1 ticket.

The top bar represents $84, the total price of the 6 tickets.

The bottom bar represents the expression $6t$, the total price of the 6 tickets Rita sells.

The bars are the same length, so $6t = 84$.

Solve It

Let the price of each ticket be t dollars. Write a sentence describing two amounts in the problem that are equivalent. Then, translate your sentence into math symbols.

The number of tickets times the price per ticket equals the total price of the tickets.

$6 \cdot t = 84$

Write an equation.

$6t = 84$.

Solve this equation to find t, the price of 1 ticket.

190 L19: Solve Equations

©Curriculum Associates, LLC Copying is not permitted.

Mathematical Discourse

- *Would you rather use the bar model or the word sentence method to help you set up an equation from a word problem? Why?*

  Some students will like the picture method. Others will prefer using word sentences. Guide students to clearly explain why they prefer their method.

- *When you had this type of problem before, you solved it by simply dividing 84 by 6. How is the equation related to this problem? Do you think it works as well? How might setting up an equation be helpful?*

  Some students will not like using equations as the process is more abstract. Students may share that both methods will get the same answer as both are correct. Some students may see an equation could be helpful when details get more complicated.

AT A GLANCE

Students revisit the problem on page 190 and work through how to solve it.

STEP BY STEP

- Note that the problem in Connect It refers to the problem on page 190.
- Ask students if they remember the two things you must do to solve an equation. [Isolate the variable, and keep the equation balanced.]
- Have students complete the problems in Try It.

SMP Tip: Allow students to review each other's explanations in the last Connect It question. Then have each student explain the other student's thinking (*SMP 3*). Tell students to give definite reasons to support their argument.

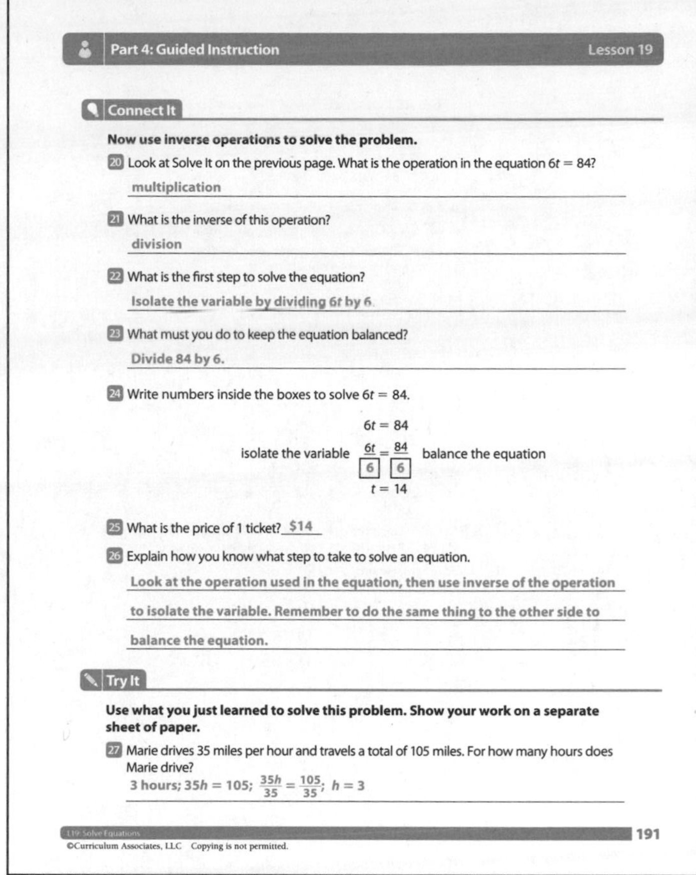

Part 4: Guided Instruction Lesson 19

Connect It

Now use inverse operations to solve the problem.

20 Look at Solve It on the previous page. What is the operation in the equation $6t = 84$?
multiplication

21 What is the inverse of this operation?
division

22 What is the first step to solve the equation?
Isolate the variable by dividing $6t$ by 6.

23 What must you do to keep the equation balanced?
Divide 84 by 6.

24 Write numbers inside the boxes to solve $6t = 84$.

$$6t = 84$$

isolate the variable $\frac{6t}{6} = \frac{84}{6}$ balance the equation

$$t = 14$$

25 What is the price of 1 ticket? $14

26 Explain how you know what step to take to solve an equation.
Look at the operation used in the equation, then use inverse of the operation to isolate the variable. Remember to do the same thing to the other side to balance the equation.

Try It

Use what you just learned to solve this problem. Show your work on a separate sheet of paper.

27 Marie drives 35 miles per hour and travels a total of 105 miles. For how many hours does Marie drive?
3 hours; $35h = 105$; $\frac{35h}{35} = \frac{105}{35}$; $h = 3$

L19: Solve Equations 191
©Curriculum Associates, LLC Copying is not permitted.

TRY IT SOLUTION

27 *Solution:* $h = 3$ hours; Students may divide both sides of the equation by 35.

ERROR ALERT: Students who wrote $h = 70$ subtracted 35 from both sides rather than dividing both sides of the equation by 35 in an attempt to isolate the variable.

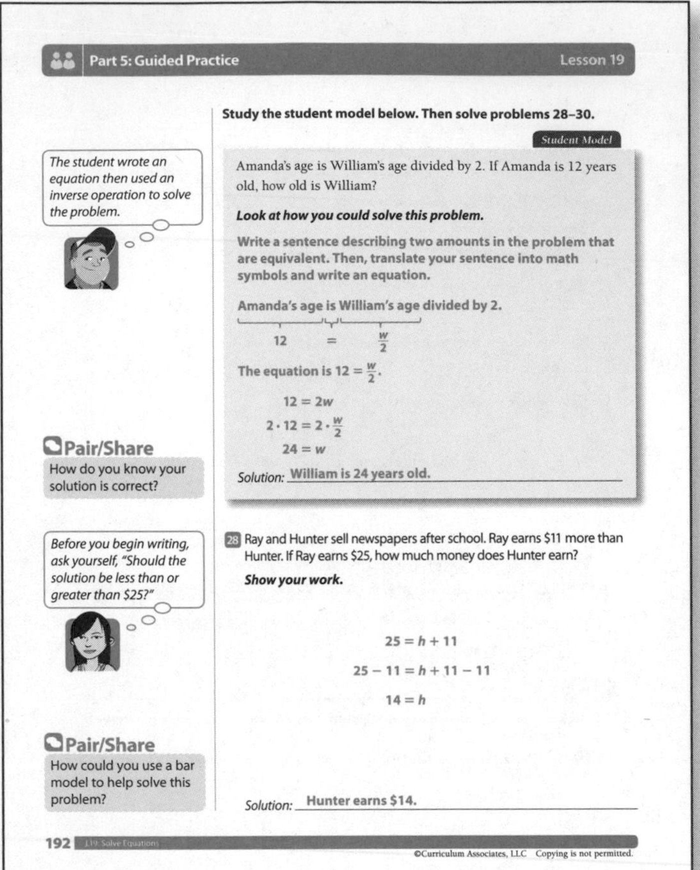

Study the student model below. Then solve problems 28–30.

Student Model

Amanda's age is William's age divided by 2. If Amanda is 12 years old, how old is William?

Look at how you could solve this problem.

Write a sentence describing two amounts in the problem that are equivalent. Then, translate your sentence into math symbols and write an equation.

Amanda's age is William's age divided by 2.

$12 = \frac{w}{2}$

The equation is $12 = \frac{w}{2}$.

$12 = 2w$

$2 \cdot 12 = 2 \cdot \frac{w}{2}$

$24 = w$

Solution: William is 24 years old.

Pair/Share
How do you know your solution is correct?

28 Ray and Hunter sell newspapers after school. Ray earns $11 more than Hunter. If Ray earns $25, how much money does Hunter earn?

Show your work.

$25 = h + 11$

$25 - 11 = h + 11 - 11$

$14 = h$

Solution: Hunter earns $14.

Pair/Share
How could you use a bar model to help solve this problem?

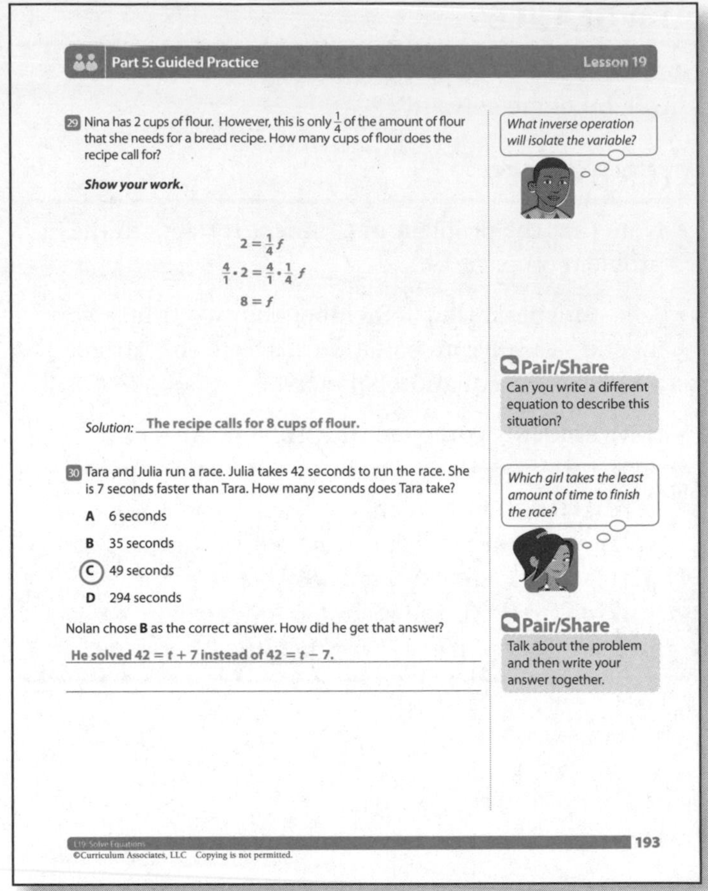

29 Nina has 2 cups of flour. However, this is only $\frac{1}{4}$ of the amount of flour that she needs for a bread recipe. How many cups of flour does the recipe call for?

Show your work.

$2 = \frac{1}{4}f$

$\frac{4}{1} \cdot 2 = \frac{4}{1} \cdot \frac{1}{4}f$

$8 = f$

Solution: The recipe calls for 8 cups of flour.

Pair/Share
Can you write a different equation to describe this situation?

30 Tara and Julia run a race. Julia takes 42 seconds to run the race. She is 7 seconds faster than Tara. How many seconds does Tara take?

A 6 seconds

B 35 seconds

(C) 49 seconds

D 294 seconds

Nolan chose **B** as the correct answer. How did he get that answer?

He solved $42 = t + 7$ instead of $42 = t - 7$.

Pair/Share
Talk about the problem and then write your answer together.

AT A GLANCE

Students use models to set up and solve simple algebraic equations.

STEP BY STEP

- Ask students to solve the problems individually. Remind students to show their equations and the steps they used to find the solution.
- When students have completed each problem, have them Pair/Share to discuss their solutions with a partner or in a group.

SOLUTIONS

Ex An equation relating their ages is $12 = \frac{w}{2}$, since William is 2 times as old as Amanda. Multiply both sides of the equation by 2; $w = 24$.

28 *Solution:* $14; Students could solve the problem by solving the equation $h + 11 = 25$. ***(DOK 1)***

29 *Solution:* 8 cups; Students could solve the problem by solving the equation $2 = \frac{1}{4}f$. ***(DOK 1)***

30 *Solution:* **C**; Nolan solved $42 = t + 7$, but it should be $42 = t - y$.

Explain to students why the other two answer choices are not correct:

A is not correct because Tara took longer than Julia so the answer must be more than 42 seconds.

D is not correct because 7 should be added, and not multiplied, by each side. ***(DOK 3)***

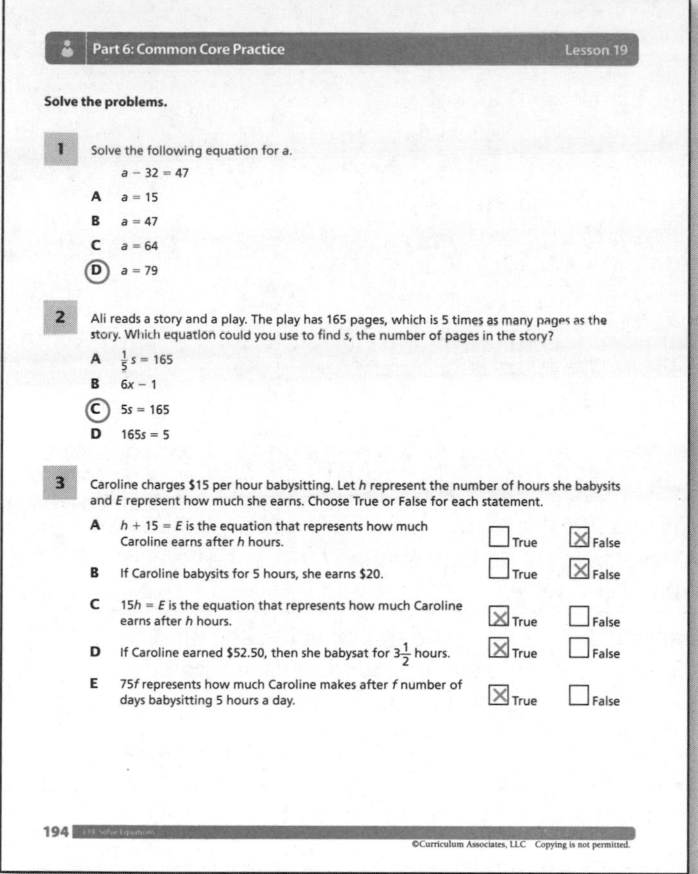

Part 6: Common Core Practice Lesson 19

Solve the problems.

1 Solve the following equation for a.

$a - 32 = 47$

A $a = 15$

B $a = 47$

C $a = 64$

(D) $a = 79$

2 Ali reads a story and a play. The play has 165 pages, which is 5 times as many pages as the story. Which equation could you use to find s, the number of pages in the story?

A $\frac{1}{5}s = 165$

B $6x - 1$

(C) $5s = 165$

D $165s = 5$

3 Caroline charges $15 per hour babysitting. Let h represent the number of hours she babysits and E represent how much she earns. Choose True or False for each statement.

A	$h + 15 = E$ is the equation that represents how much Caroline earns after h hours.	☐ True	☒ False
B	If Caroline babysits for 5 hours, she earns $20.	☐ True	☒ False
C	$15h = E$ is the equation that represents how much Caroline earns after h hours.	☒ True	☐ False
D	If Caroline earned $52.50, then she babysat for $3\frac{1}{2}$ hours.	☒ True	☐ False
E	$75f$ represents how much Caroline makes after f number of days babysitting 5 hours a day.	☒ True	☐ False

194 L19: Solve Equations ©Curriculum Associates, LLC Copying is not permitted.

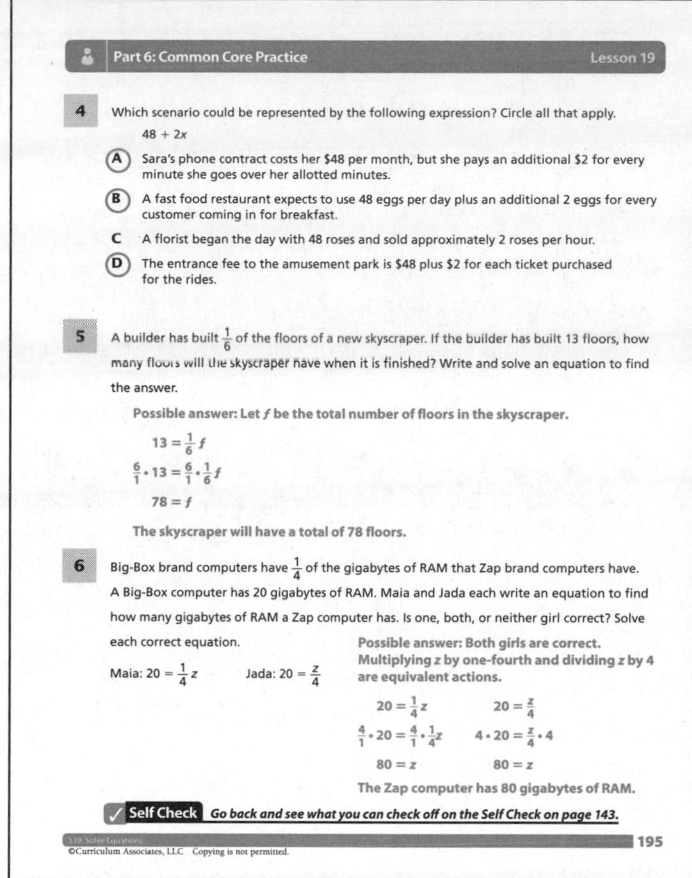

Part 6: Common Core Practice Lesson 19

4 Which scenario could be represented by the following expression? Circle all that apply.

$48 + 2x$

(A) Sara's phone contract costs her $48 per month, but she pays an additional $2 for every minute she goes over her allotted minutes.

(B) A fast food restaurant expects to use 48 eggs per day plus an additional 2 eggs for every customer coming in for breakfast.

C A florist began the day with 48 roses and sold approximately 2 roses per hour.

(D) The entrance fee to the amusement park is $48 plus $2 for each ticket purchased for the rides.

5 A builder has built $\frac{1}{6}$ of the floors of a new skyscraper. If the builder has built 13 floors, how many floors will the skyscraper have when it is finished? Write and solve an equation to find the answer.

Possible answer: Let f be the total number of floors in the skyscraper.

$13 = \frac{1}{6}f$

$\frac{6}{1} \cdot 13 = \frac{6}{1} \cdot \frac{1}{6}f$

$78 = f$

The skyscraper will have a total of 78 floors.

6 Big-Box brand computers have $\frac{1}{4}$ of the gigabytes of RAM that Zap brand computers have. A Big-Box computer has 20 gigabytes of RAM. Maia and Jada each write an equation to find how many gigabytes of RAM a Zap computer has. Is one, both, or neither girl correct? Solve each correct equation.

Maia: $20 = \frac{1}{4}z$ Jada: $20 = \frac{z}{4}$

Possible answer: Both girls are correct. Multiplying z by one-fourth and dividing z by 4 are equivalent actions.

$20 = \frac{1}{4}z$ $20 = \frac{z}{4}$

$\frac{4}{1} \cdot 20 = \frac{4}{1} \cdot \frac{1}{4}z$ $4 \cdot 20 = \frac{z}{4} \cdot 4$

$80 = z$ $80 = z$

The Zap computer has 80 gigabytes of RAM.

Self Check *Go back and see what you can check off on the Self Check on page 143.*

L19: Solve Equations ©Curriculum Associates, LLC Copying is not permitted. 195

AT A GLANCE

Students set up and solve equations to solve word problems that might appear on a mathematics test.

SOLUTIONS

1 *Solution:* **D**; Add 32 to both sides of the equation. ***(DOK 1)***

2 *Solution:* **C**; The play (165 pages) has 5 times as many pages as the short story. $165 = 5 \cdot s$ ***(DOK 2)***

3 *Solution:* A **False**; B **False**; C **True**; D **True**; E **True** ***(DOK 2)***

4 *Solution:* **A**; 48 represents her cost per month. $2x$ represents paying $2 for every minute, x, over her allotted minutes.

B; 48 represents the number of eggs used per day. $2x$ represents giving 2 extra eggs to each customer, x, coming in for breakfast.

D; 48 represents the entrance fee. $2x$ represents paying $2 for each of x ride tickets. ***(DOK 2)***

5 *Solution:* $f = 78$; See student book page above for possible student work. ***(DOK 3)***

6 *Solution:* Both girls are correct. $\frac{1}{4}z$ is equivalent to $\frac{z}{4}$. See student book above for possible student work. ***(DOK 3)***

Assessment and Remediation

- Ask students to find an equation to model the following problem and then solve it.

  John is 4 years older than his brother, Ben. If John is 12, find Ben's age. [$j = 4 + b$; $12 = b + 4$; Ben is 8.]
- For students who are struggling, use the chart below to guide remediation.
- After providing remediation, check students' understanding. Ask students to find an equation to model the following problem, and then solve it.

  Jill has twice as much money as Adi. If Jill has \$42, how much does Adi have? [$j = 2a$; $42 = 2a$; $a = \$21$]
- If a student is still having difficulty, use ***Ready Instruction, Level 5,*** Lesson 19, and ***Level 6,*** Lesson 18.

If the error is . . .	Students may . . .	To remediate . . .
16	have set up the equation $12 + 4 = b$.	Remind students that the term *is* can usually be translated to the symbol =. Have them set up the equation $j = b + 4$. Then replace j with 12 and solve.
3	have solved the equation $12 = b + 4$ by dividing both sides by 4.	Ask students to first identify the operation in the equation, which is addition. Then tell them to find the inverse operation. The inverse of addition is subtraction, so subtract 4 from both sides.
3	have set up the equation $12 = 4b$.	Ask students what operation is needed. If John is 4 years older, his age is 4 years more than Ben's. Would addition or multiplication be used? [addition]

Hands-On Activity

Model the equation.

Material: about 20 blocks (or other uniform objects), masking tape

Have students model the first question above. Have them divide their desk in two halves using a vertical strip of tape. Using tape, label one side "John's age" and the other side "Ben's age." Have students put 12 blocks on John's side. Ask, *How much older is John than Ben?* [4 years] Have students remove 4 blocks and move the remaining blocks (8) over to Ben's side. Now put 12 more blocks back on John's side. Put a strip of tape along the entire length of the bottom of the desk. Put an "=" at the point where it intersects the vertical strip of tape. Ask students what they would have to do to make both sides equal. [either subtract 4 from John or add 4 to Ben] Have them write an equation along the bottom strip of tape using the approach they chose.
[either $j - 4 = b$ or $j = b + 4$]

Challenge Activity

Write an equation to model a problem.

Ask students to find an equation to model the following problem, and then solve the equation.

If Sid receives 3 more trading cards, then he will have twice as many as Anna. If Anna has 17 trading cards, how many does Sid have? [$s + 3 = 2a$; $s + 3 = 34$; $s = 31$]

Lesson 20 (Student Book pages 196–205)

Solving Inequalities

LESSON OBJECTIVES

- Write an inequality that represents real-world mathematical problems containing a constraint or a condition ($<$, $>$).
- Recognize that a variable can stand for an infinite number of solutions when used in inequalities.
- Use substitution to determine whether a given number in a specified set makes an equation or inequality true.
- Represent inequalities on a number line.

PREREQUISITE SKILLS

- Understand the meanings of equality and inequality.
- Recognize that a variable can stand for a number.
- Substitute values for given variables.
- Write an inequality of the form $x > c$ or $c > x$ where x and c are rational numbers.

VOCABULARY

inequality: two unequal values that are compared using less than ($<$) and greater than ($>$) signs

THE LEARNING PROGRESSION

In earlier grades, students gained an understanding of simple inequalities such as $3 < 5$. They also understand the concept of algebraic equations having a solution.

In this lesson, students begin the organized study of algebraic inequalities. They learn that variables can represent infinitely many solutions when used in inequalities, and they learn how to graph those solutions. They use key word phrases such as "at most" and "no less than" to help them write symbolic inequality representations of real-world situations. They increase their mathematical proficiency through using different methods to check their answers.

Ready ***Teacher Toolbox*** Teacher-Toolbox.com

	Prerequisite Skills	*6.EE.B.5 6.EE.B.8*
Ready Lessons		✓
Tools for Instruction		✓ ✓
Interactive Tutorials		✓

CCSS Focus

6.EE.B.5 Understand solving an equation or inequality as a process of answering a question: which values from a specified set, if any, make the equation or inequality true? Use substitution to determine whether a given number in a specified set makes an equation or inequality true.

6.EE.B.8 Write an inequality of the form $x > c$ or $x < c$ to represent a constraint or condition in a real-world or mathematical problem. Recognize that inequalities of the form $x > c$ or $x < c$ have infinitely many solutions; represent solutions of such inequalities on number line diagrams.

ADDITIONAL STANDARDS: ***6.NS.B.7a, 6.EE.B.6*** *(see page A42 for full text)*

STANDARDS FOR MATHEMATICAL PRACTICE: ***SMP 1–4, 6, 7*** *(see page A9 for full text)*

AT A GLANCE

Students study a real-world situation involving a simple inequality. They use algebraic symbols to represent it.

STEP BY STEP

- Tell students that this page models mathematical representations of real-world inequalities.
- Have students read the problem at the top of the page.
- Work through Explore It as a class.
- Ask student pairs or groups to explain their answers for the last four questions.

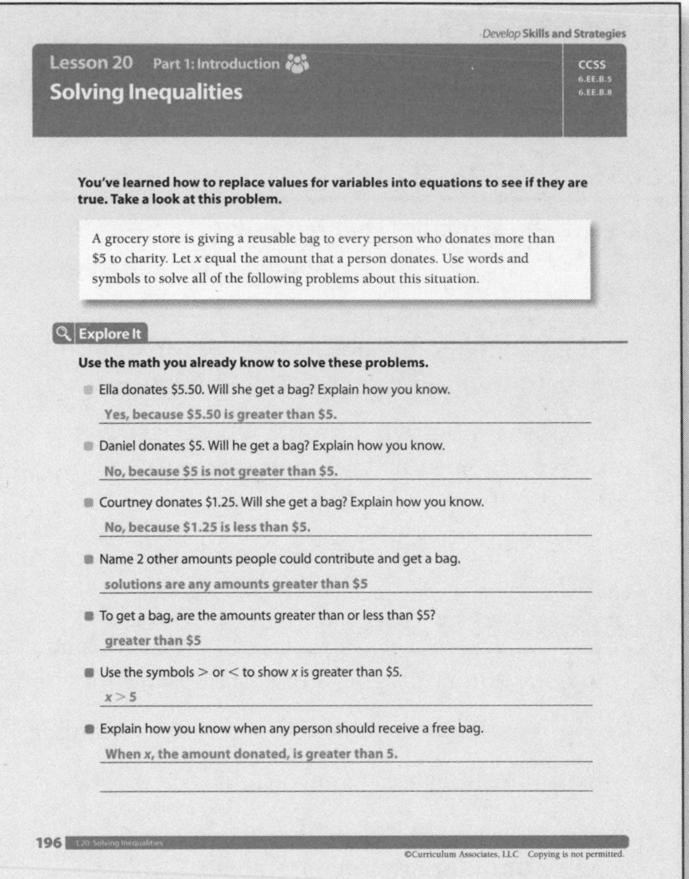

Develop **Skills and Strategies**

Lesson 20 Part 1: Introduction

Solving Inequalities

CCSS 6.EE.B.5 6.EE.B.8

You've learned how to replace values for variables into equations to see if they are true. Take a look at this problem.

A grocery store is giving a reusable bag to every person who donates more than $5 to charity. Let x equal the amount that a person donates. Use words and symbols to solve all of the following problems about this situation.

Explore It

Use the math you already know to solve these problems.

- Ella donates $5.50. Will she get a bag? Explain how you know.
  Yes, because $5.50 is greater than $5.
- Daniel donates $5. Will he get a bag? Explain how you know.
  No, because $5 is not greater than $5.
- Courtney donates $1.25. Will she get a bag? Explain how you know.
  No, because $1.25 is less than $5.
- Name 2 other amounts people could contribute and get a bag.
  solutions are any amounts greater than $5
- To get a bag, are the amounts greater than or less than $5?
  greater than $5
- Use the symbols > or < to show x is greater than $5.
  $x > 5$
- Explain how you know when any person should receive a free bag.
  When x, the amount donated, is greater than 5.

196 L20: Solving Inequalities

©Curriculum Associates, LLC Copying is not permitted.

ELL Support

- Point out that "greater than" is a mathematical way to say "more than." It does not refer to being better or more important, but simply a larger quantity.

Mathematical Discourse

- *How do you think inequalities are different from equations you've worked with before?*

  Students at this point may think that inequalities don't involve any operations. Listen for answers that talk about how the two sides of an inequality aren't equal, or don't balance, unlike the equations in the previous lesson.

- *How do you think inequality sentences could be useful?*

  Some students may think they are not, and mathematical inequality sentences aren't commonly used in simple real-world situations. However, some students may see that they are an efficient way to communicate meaning and could be helpful in problems that don't have one definite answer.

AT A GLANCE

Students learn about inequalities and their solutions. They review inequality symbols.

STEP BY STEP

- Read Find Out More as a class.
- Ask, *What does "infinitely many solutions" mean?* [It is impossible to list every solution individually because there is no end to how many there are.]
- Review the word *expressions* given in the table. You may want to especially focus on "is at least" and "is at most" because these can be the most challenging.

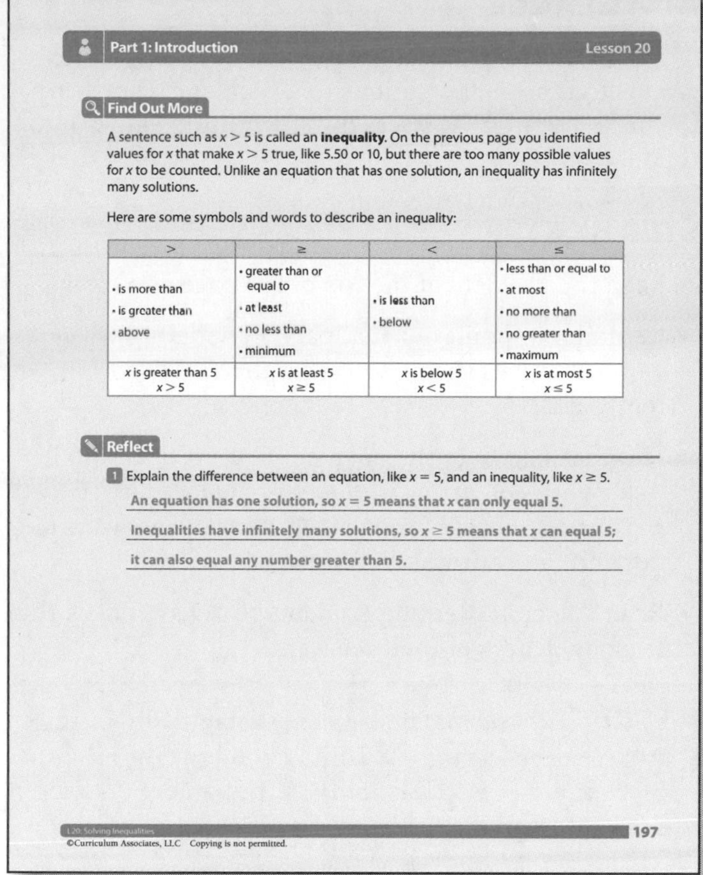

Part 1: Introduction Lesson 20

Find Out More

A sentence such as $x > 5$ is called an **inequality**. On the previous page you identified values for x that make $x > 5$ true, like 5.50 or 10, but there are too many possible values for x to be counted. Unlike an equation that has one solution, an inequality has infinitely many solutions.

Here are some symbols and words to describe an inequality:

$>$	$\geq$	$<$	$\leq$
• is more than • is greater than • above	• greater than or equal to • at least • no less than • minimum	• is less than • below	• less than or equal to • at most • no more than • no greater than • maximum
x is greater than 5 $x > 5$	x is at least 5 $x \geq 5$	x is below 5 $x < 5$	x is at most 5 $x \leq 5$

Reflect

1 Explain the difference between an equation, like $x = 5$, and an inequality, like $x \geq 5$.

An equation has one solution, so $x = 5$ means that x can only equal 5.

Inequalities have infinitely many solutions, so $x \geq 5$ means that x can equal 5; it can also equal any number greater than 5.

L20: Solving Inequalities 197

©Curriculum Associates, LLC Copying is not permitted.

ELL Support

English learners may be confused by the "small words" in the comparison phrases. Discuss each phrase. Have students repeat them and use them with examples. Have students copy and add to the chart in Find Out More for reference.

SMP Tip: The phrases in the chart let students communicate precisely when comparing quantities (*SMP 6*). Regularly call attention to students' use of the phrases in discussion and to their meaning in real-world situations.

Visual Model

Study unbalanced inequalities.

Materials: pan balance scale, lightweight opaque bag, several blocks

Before class, put 4 blocks in the bag labeled x. Place the bag in one pan of the balance scale. Ask students to direct you in putting blocks in the other pan to find the value of x. Write the inequality for each suggestion; for example, write $x > 1$ if they suggest 1 block. Continue until the value of x is known. Then write $x > 4$. Ask students to discuss how many values, including fractional values, there can be. Guide them to see that there are infinitely many. Then ask whether 2 or 0 could be solutions. Point out that while x can equal infinitely many numbers, not all numbers will be solutions to $x > 4$.

Real-World Connection

Ask students to think of real-world situations where multiple solutions can satisfy a constraint. The problem on page 196 is a good example where people who donated more than a certain amount get a reward. Budgets are usually constrained by being able to spend no more than a certain amount. Athletes might need to have at least a certain number of practices or grade-point average to be able to compete in a game. Students must have fewer than a certain number of absences to get credit for a class.

AT A GLANCE

Students learn how to use words, inequalities, and graphs to represent solutions to a problem. They learn to check graphical answers by substituting values into the inequality.

STEP BY STEP

- Read the problem at the top of the page as a class.
- In Model It, point out that part of modeling with words involves specifying what the variable represents.
- Make sure to note the open circle used in Graph It. Ask, *Why is an arrow used on this number line? Why not just a segment?* [to represent that the answers do not end but continue to infinity]
- Read Check It. Remind students to always check the reasonableness of their answers.

SMP Tip: Students become mathematically proficient by learning to think about whether their answers are reasonable (*SMP 1*). Tell students to use different methods to check answers.

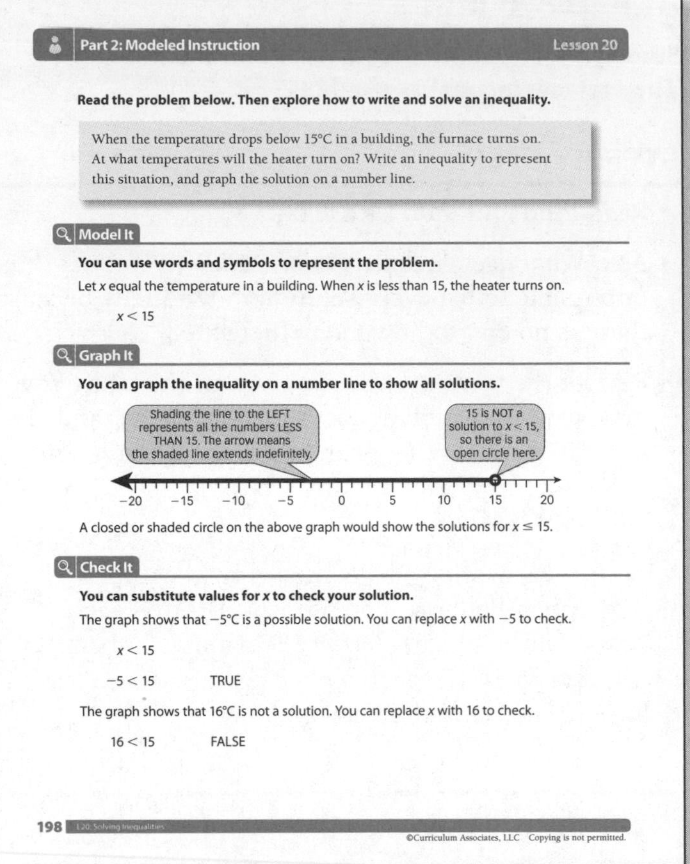

Part 2: Modeled Instruction Lesson 20

Read the problem below. Then explore how to write and solve an inequality.

When the temperature drops below 15°C in a building, the furnace turns on. At what temperatures will the heater turn on? Write an inequality to represent this situation, and graph the solution on a number line.

Model It

You can use words and symbols to represent the problem.

Let x equal the temperature in a building. When x is less than 15, the heater turns on.

$x < 15$

Graph It

You can graph the inequality on a number line to show all solutions.

A closed or shaded circle on the above graph would show the solutions for $x \leq 15$.

Check It

You can substitute values for x to check your solution.

The graph shows that −5°C is a possible solution. You can replace x with −5 to check.

$x < 15$

$-5 < 15$ TRUE

The graph shows that 16°C is not a solution. You can replace x with 16 to check.

$16 < 15$ FALSE

198 L20: Solving Inequalities ©Curriculum Associates, LLC Copying is not permitted.

Mathematical Discourse

- *How is this graphing similar to other graphing you have done? How is it different?*

  Students may note that they first find a number on a number line, something they have done before. Listen for answers that talk about using open circles and shading lines as being differences.

- *How would you explain the differences between graphing $x > 4$ and $x \geq 4$ to a student who missed this lesson?*

  Students will probably mention using open circles for $>$ and closed circles for $\geq$. Listen for them to talk about shading the number line and how to know which side to shade on. Listen for them to explain using an arrow and what that represents.

AT A GLANCE

Students revisit the problem on page 198. They discuss inequalities, how to represent them algebraically, and how to graph them.

STEP BY STEP

- Be sure students understand Connect It refers to the problem on page 198.
- Read Connect It as a class.
- Have students work through Try It on their own.

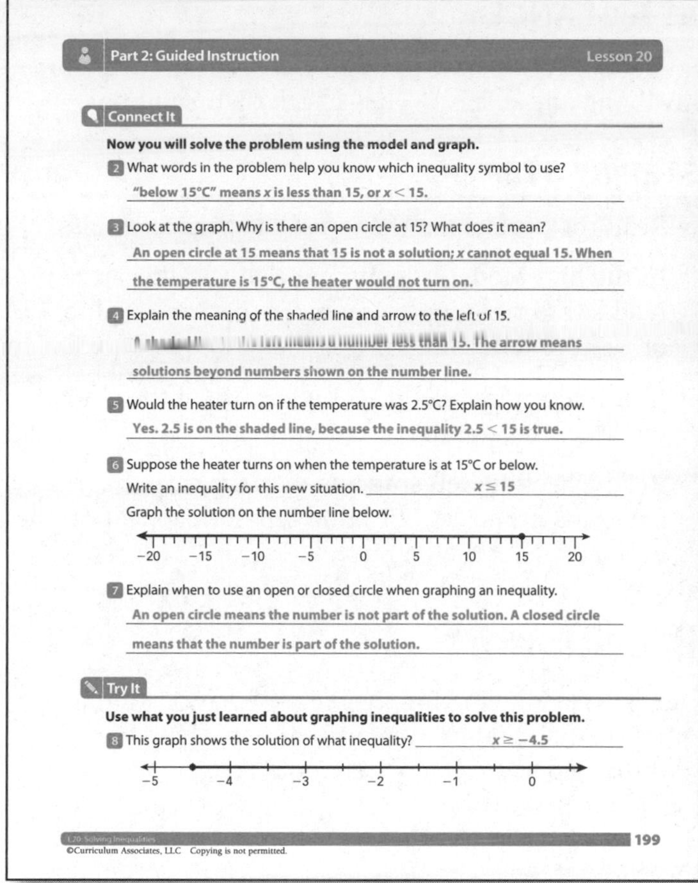

Part 2: Guided Instruction Lesson 20

Connect It

Now you will solve the problem using the model and graph.

2 What words in the problem help you know which inequality symbol to use?

"below 15°C" means x is less than 15, or $x < 15$.

3 Look at the graph. Why is there an open circle at 15? What does it mean?

An open circle at 15 means that 15 is not a solution; x cannot equal 15. When the temperature is 15°C, the heater would not turn on.

4 Explain the meaning of the shaded line and arrow to the left of 15.

[illegible] means a number less than 15. The arrow means solutions beyond numbers shown on the number line.

5 Would the heater turn on if the temperature was 2.5°C? Explain how you know.

Yes. 2.5 is on the shaded line, because the inequality $2.5 < 15$ is true.

6 Suppose the heater turns on when the temperature is at 15°C or below.

Write an inequality for this new situation. **$x \leq 15$**

Graph the solution on the number line below.

−20 −15 −10 −5 0 5 10 15 20

7 Explain when to use an open or closed circle when graphing an inequality.

An open circle means the number is not part of the solution. A closed circle means that the number is part of the solution.

Try It

Use what you just learned about graphing inequalities to solve this problem.

8 This graph shows the solution of what inequality? **$x \geq -4.5$**

−5 −4 −3 −2 −1 0

L20: Solving Inequalities 199

©Curriculum Associates, LLC Copying is not permitted.

Hands-On Activity

Graph an inequality.

Materials: masking tape, a large arrow made of poster board for each group

- Divide the class into groups of 4–6 students and direct each group to a separate space. Have each group model a number line on the floor using masking tape.
- Use a 10-foot strip for the line and use 4-inch strips to make tick marks about every foot from one end to the other. Label these from −5 to 5, perhaps using a longer strip for 0.
- Tell students they are going to model inequalities that you put on the board.
- One person is to model the boundary point. They are to either stand on it with arms to their sides for a $\geq$ or $\leq$ situation or stand just in front of it with their arms in a big circle over it for a $>$ or $<$ situation.
- The other students should line up as points on the side that satisfies the inequality, with the student farthest out holding an arrow pointed in the direction that the solutions continue.
- Display several inequalities, including both positive and negative values. Direct students to rotate their roles.

TRY IT SOLUTION

8 *Solution:* Check students' work. Values for x include anything greater than or equal to -4.5.

ERROR ALERT: Students who did not interpret the closed circle correctly do not understand the difference between $>$ and $\geq$.

AT A GLANCE

Students explore how to write and solve an inequality involving an "at least." They check their solutions.

STEP BY STEP

- Read the problem at the top of the page as a class.
- In the first Model It, point out that $x \geq 25$ can be read left to right, as "x is greater than or equal to 25," or right to left, as "25 is less than or equal to x."
- In the second Model It, point out use of the closed circle on the graph.
- Read Check It. Tell students to make sure that the solutions proposed (25.5 and 30) both appear on the correct side of the graph.

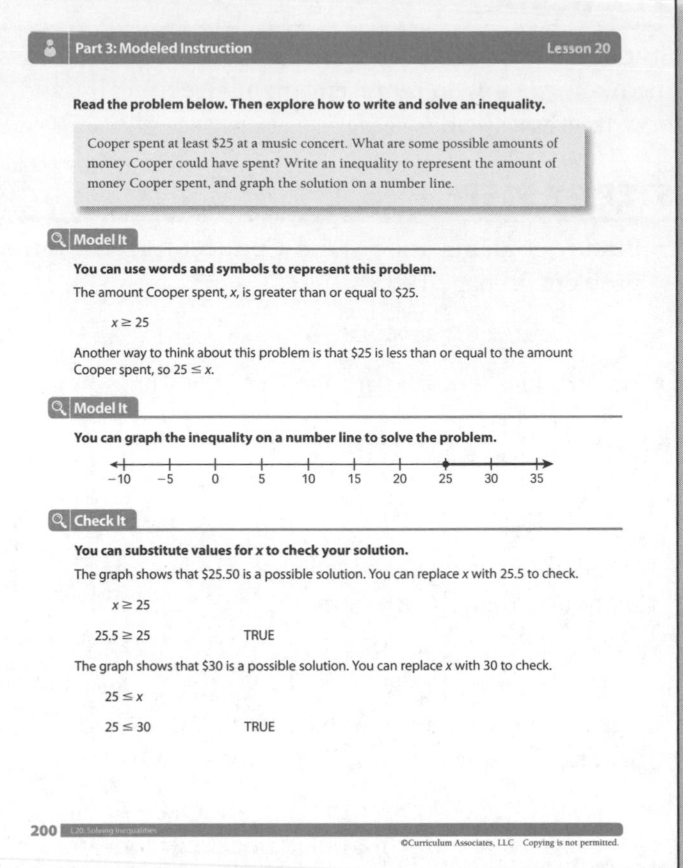

Part 3: Modeled Instruction Lesson 20

Read the problem below. Then explore how to write and solve an inequality.

Cooper spent at least $25 at a music concert. What are some possible amounts of money Cooper could have spent? Write an inequality to represent the amount of money Cooper spent, and graph the solution on a number line.

Model It

You can use words and symbols to represent this problem.

The amount Cooper spent, x, is greater than or equal to $25.

$x \geq 25$

Another way to think about this problem is that $25 is less than or equal to the amount Cooper spent, so $25 \leq x$.

Model It

You can graph the inequality on a number line to solve the problem.

Check It

You can substitute values for x to check your solution.

The graph shows that $25.50 is a possible solution. You can replace x with 25.5 to check.

$x \geq 25$

$25.5 \geq 25$ TRUE

The graph shows that $30 is a possible solution. You can replace x with 30 to check.

$25 \leq x$

$25 \leq 30$ TRUE

200 L20: Solving Inequalities

©Curriculum Associates, LLC Copying is not permitted.

ELL Support

Be careful about using the terms "correct" and "right" interchangeably in situations where the words "right" and "left" refer to direction or position.

SMP Tip: Students model the amount of money spent both symbolically and contextually (*SMP 4*). Point out the cue words "at least" and review other key word phrases frequently.

Mathematical Discourse

- *Which is easier for you to understand: the symbol inequality $x \geq 25$, or looking at the graph?*

  Students who are comfortable reasoning abstractly may prefer $x \geq 25$. They may think interpreting the inequality is faster and easier than drawing a graph. Students who are visual learners may prefer seeing which side of 25 is shaded on a graph.

- *How might you use a graph to represent a variable that must be bigger than 0 but less than 10?*

  Listen for students to talk about using open circles. Let students present their thinking visually on a whiteboard. While there is a definite standard for how to do this, you may want to let students just explore it for now.

AT A GLANCE

Students revisit the problem on page 200. They discuss meanings of inequality representations, both symbolically and graphically.

STEP BY STEP

- Point out that Connect It refers to the problem on page 200.
- Have students work through Try It on their own.

Concept Extension

Graph inequalities with two bounds.

- Tell students that there are problem situations where a range of solutions can be bounded on two ends. For example, a B grade might be given to a student whose percentage points are greater than or equal to 79.5 and less than 89.5. How do you represent this?
- First make a graph. Draw a section of a number line from about 75 to 95. Look at the boundary points.
- Ask, *Would 79.5 receive a B grade? How would you represent that on the graph?* [Yes; the problem said greater than or equal to. Put a closed circle there.]
- Ask, *Would 89.5 get a B?* [No. Put an open circle there.]
- Ask, *What other points would receive a B? How do we graph to show all the solutions?* [Test some values and find that values between the two boundary circles would be solutions. Shade the line between the circles.]
- Ask, *Without an arrow are there still infinitely many solutions?* [Yes, there are infinitely many decimal values that could receive a B grade.]
- If you have time, you may discuss how to represent this situation symbolically. Designate a variable, x, that represents the possible range of percentage points to receive a B grade. Working from left to right, translate the graph to an inequality, first in words, then symbols. 79.5 is less than or equal to x, which is less than 89.5. Or $79.5 \leq x < 89.5$.

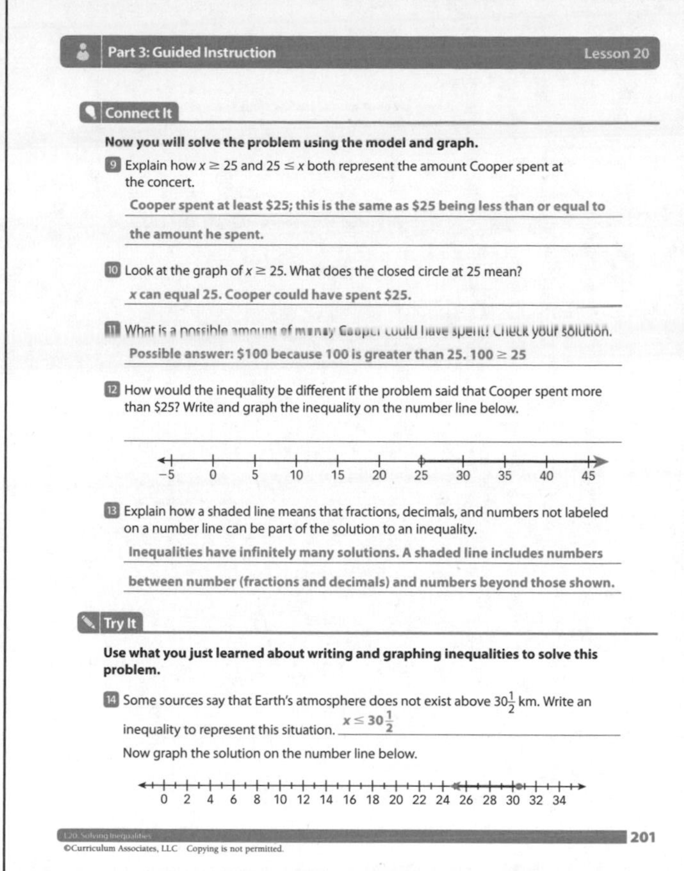

Part 3: Guided Instruction Lesson 20

Connect It

Now you will solve the problem using the model and graph.

9 Explain how $x \geq 25$ and $25 \leq x$ both represent the amount Cooper spent at the concert.

Cooper spent at least $25; this is the same as $25 being less than or equal to the amount he spent.

10 Look at the graph of $x \geq 25$. What does the closed circle at 25 mean?

***x* can equal 25. Cooper could have spent $25.**

11 What is a possible amount of money Cooper could have spent? Check your solution.

Possible answer: $100 because 100 is greater than 25. $100 \geq 25$

12 How would the inequality be different if the problem said that Cooper spent more than $25? Write and graph the inequality on the number line below.

13 Explain how a shaded line means that fractions, decimals, and numbers not labeled on a number line can be part of the solution to an inequality.

Inequalities have infinitely many solutions. A shaded line includes numbers between number (fractions and decimals) and numbers beyond those shown.

Try It

Use what you just learned about writing and graphing inequalities to solve this problem.

14 Some sources say that Earth's atmosphere does not exist above $30\frac{1}{2}$ km. Write an inequality to represent this situation. $x \leq 30\frac{1}{2}$

Now graph the solution on the number line below.

L20: Solving Inequalities 201

©Curriculum Associates, LLC Copying is not permitted.

TRY IT SOLUTION

14 *Solution:* x is the altitude above Earth's surface; $x \leq 30\frac{1}{2}$. Check students' work for the graph.

ERROR ALERT: Students who wrote $x < 30\frac{1}{2}$ may not understand that the cue words "not exist above" includes the value $30\frac{1}{2}$.

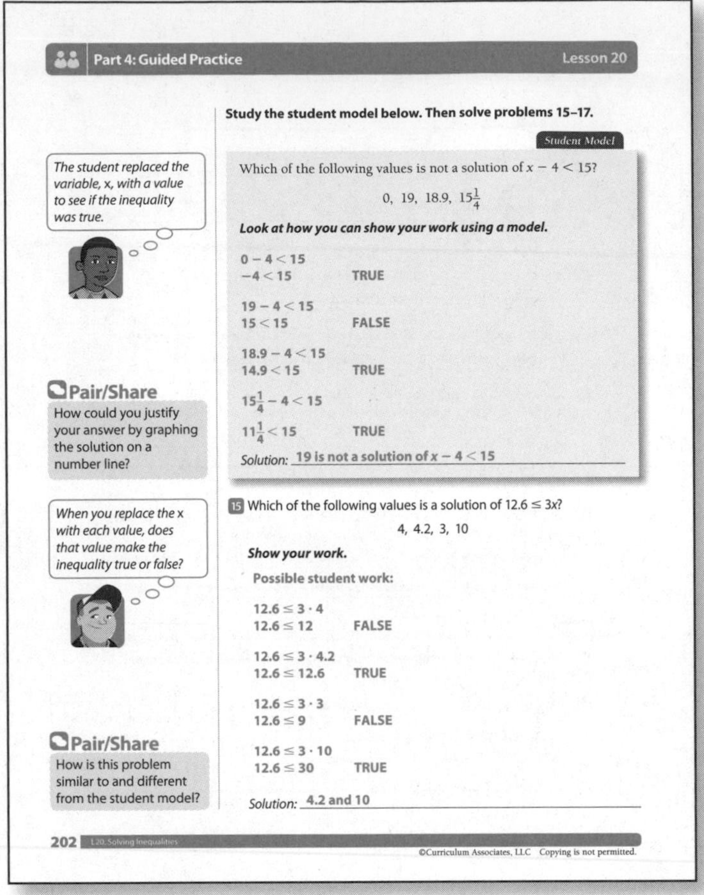

Part 4: Guided Practice Lesson 20

Study the student model below. Then solve problems 15–17.

Student Model

Which of the following values is not a solution of $x - 4 < 15$?

0, 19, 18.9, $15\frac{1}{4}$

Look at how you can show your work using a model.

$0 - 4 < 15$
$-4 < 15$ TRUE

$19 - 4 < 15$
$15 < 15$ FALSE

$18.9 - 4 < 15$
$14.9 < 15$ TRUE

$15\frac{1}{4} - 4 < 15$
$11\frac{1}{4} < 15$ TRUE

Solution: 19 is not a solution of $x - 4 < 15$

The student replaced the variable, x, with a value to see if the inequality was true.

Pair/Share
How could you justify your answer by graphing the solution on a number line?

15 Which of the following values is a solution of $12.6 \le 3x$?

4, 4.2, 3, 10

Show your work.

Possible student work:

$12.6 \le 3 \cdot 4$
$12.6 \le 12$ FALSE

$12.6 \le 3 \cdot 4.2$
$12.6 \le 12.6$ TRUE

$12.6 \le 3 \cdot 3$
$12.6 \le 9$ FALSE

$12.6 \le 3 \cdot 10$
$12.6 \le 30$ TRUE

Solution: 4.2 and 10

When you replace the x with each value, does that value make the inequality true or false?

Pair/Share
How is this problem similar to and different from the student model?

202 L20: Solving Inequalities ©Curriculum Associates, LLC Copying is not permitted.

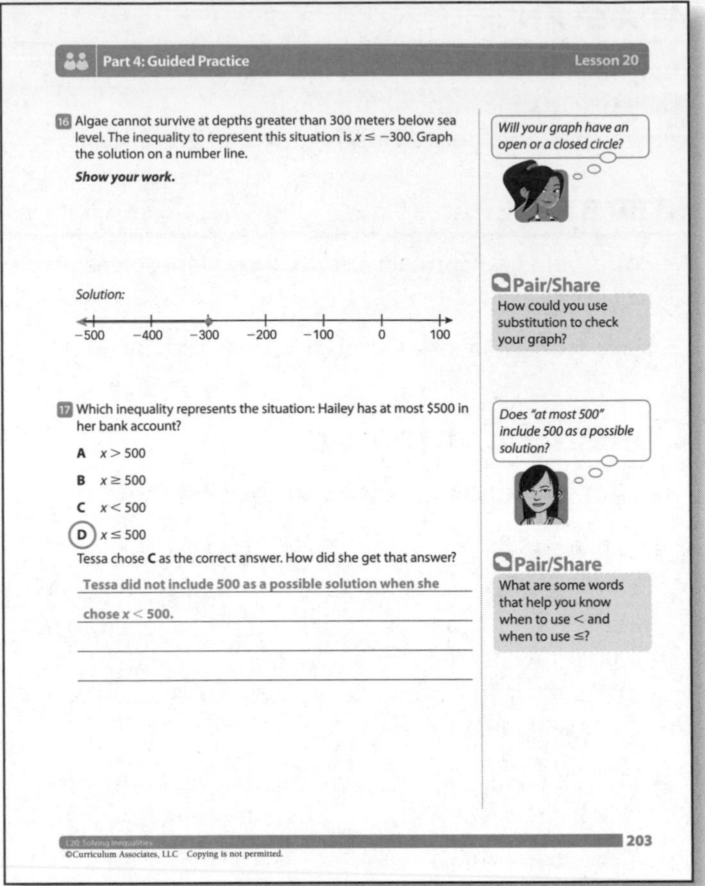

Part 4: Guided Practice Lesson 20

16 Algae cannot survive at depths greater than 300 meters below sea level. The inequality to represent this situation is $x \le -300$. Graph the solution on a number line.

Show your work.

Solution:

Will your graph have an open or a closed circle?

Pair/Share
How could you use substitution to check your graph?

17 Which inequality represents the situation: Hailey has at most $500 in her bank account?

A $x > 500$
B $x \ge 500$
C $x < 500$
(D) $x \le 500$

Tessa chose **C** as the correct answer. How did she get that answer?

Tessa did not include 500 as a possible solution when she chose $x < 500$.

Does "at most 500" include 500 as a possible solution?

Pair/Share
What are some words that help you know when to use < and when to use ≤?

L20: Solving Inequalities ©Curriculum Associates, LLC Copying is not permitted. 203

AT A GLANCE

Students work to solve problems involving inequalities represented symbolically and graphically.

STEP BY STEP

- Ask students to solve the problems individually.
- When students have completed each problem, have them Pair/Share to discuss their solutions with a partner or in a group.

SOLUTIONS

Ex Check each possible solution by substituting it for x in the inequality. Because 15 is not less than 15, 19 is not a solution.

15 *Solution:* 4.2 and 10 are solutions; Students could solve the problem by replacing each possible solution in the inequality to see which ones result in true statements. ***(DOK 1)***

16 *Solution:* See solution on student book page; Students could solve the problem by using a closed circle at $^-300$ and shading to the left. ***(DOK 1)***

17 *Solution:* **D**; Tessa could have $500 or less in her account.

Explain to students why the other two answer choices are not correct:

A is not correct because it would include values greater than $500.

B is not correct because it would include values of $500 or more. ***(DOK 3)***

Part 5: Common Core Practice Lesson 20

Solve the problems.

1 Which is a correct graph of $x \le -1\frac{1}{4}$?

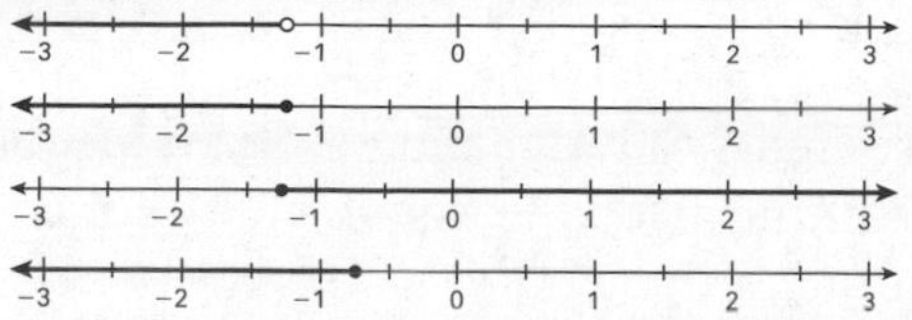

A
(B)
C
D

2 Mark cannot read traffic signs that are more than 50 meters away. Which inequality represents distances at which Mark cannot read signs?

(A) $x > 50$
B $x \ge 50$
C $x < 50$
D $x \le 50$

3 Look at the inequality $5x + 1 \ge 35$. Choose True or False for each statement.

		True	False
A	100 is not a solution because it is much greater than 35.	☐	☒
B	7.04 cannot be a solution because only whole numbers can be solutions.	☐	☒
C	$6\frac{4}{5}$ is not a solution because the expression on the left side cannot equal 35.	☐	☒
D	There are an infinite number of solutions.	☒	☐
E	34 is not a solution because it is less than 35.	☐	☒

Part 5: Common Core Practice Lesson 20

4 Which inequality does this graph represent?

Insert the appropriate inequality symbol to complete the statement.

<	
>	x (<) -2.5
≤	
≥	

5 Eric has practiced more than 40 hours with his band.

Write an inequality to express this situation. $x > 40$

On the graph below, graph Eric's situation.

Possible explanation: Eric could have practiced 50 hours.

6 Judah's family wants to ride the bumper boats at a water park.

- There are 4 children (c) and 2 adults (a) in Judah's family.
- The boats are safe if $40c + 120a \le 500$.

Can Judah's family ride the bumper boats safely? Explain.

Show your work.

Possible student work:

Is $40(4) + 120(2) \le 500$?

$160 + 240 \le 500$

$400 \le 500$ TRUE

Answer **Judah's family can ride the bumper boats safely.**

✓ **Self Check** ***Go back and see what you can check off on the Self Check on page 143.***

AT A GLANCE

Students use their knowledge of inequalities to solve problems that might appear on a mathematics test.

SOLUTIONS

1 *Solution:* **B**; The graph needs a closed circle at $-1\frac{1}{4}$ with shading to the left. ***(DOK 1)***

2 *Solution:* **A**; The words "more than" indicate a $>$ symbol. ***(DOK 2)***

3 *Solution:* A **False**; B **False**; C **False**; D **True**; E **False** ***(DOK 2)***

4 *Solution:* $<$; The point on the number line is located at $^-2.5$. A ray going to the left indicates $<$ or $\le$. The open point indicates $<$. ***(DOK 1)***

5 *Solution:* $x > 40$; See student book page above for possible student graph. ***(DOK 2)***

6 *Solution:* Yes; See student book page above for possible student work and explanation. ***(DOK 3)***

Assessment and Remediation

- Ask students to write and graph an inequality to represent the following situation: Martin has written at least 70 words of his essay. [$x \geq 70$; student number lines should have a closed circle at 70 and an arrow extending to the right.]
- For students who are struggling, use the chart below to guide remediation.
- After providing remediation, check students' understanding. Ask students to write and graph an inequality to represent the following situation: There are fewer than 30 students in the algebra class. [$x < 30$; student number lines should have an open circle at 30 and an arrow extending to the left.]

If the error is . . .	Students may . . .	To remediate . . .
$x > 70$	not understand that "at least" includes the given value as well as greater values.	Ask questions about specific values. Could he have written 120 words? Could he have written 70? Yes, 70 is at least 70. Help them to see that "at least" includes "more than" but also "equal to."
$x \leq 70, x < 70$	have difficulty translating words to symbols.	Remind students to test specific values in both the problem and the inequality they write. Is 80 words at least 70? It is, but if you put it in the inequality $80 \leq 70$, you see that isn't true.
$x \leq 70, x < 70$	confuse $<$ with $>$ and $\leq$ with $\geq$.	Review the meanings of the symbols and how to read them. Use some examples with specific numbers such as $3 < 7$ and $9 \geq 8$. Point out that the pointed end points to the smaller value while the larger, open end faces the larger value.
graph has an open circle at 70.	not understand the difference between closed and open circles.	Review how to plot points on a number line. Tell students that when an inequality is $\leq$ or $\geq$, it includes the number and the number must be plotted with a closed circle. An open circle excludes that value.
graph is shaded on the wrong side.	have difficulty translating symbols to the graph.	Remind students to check their answers. Tell them to pick a value in the section they've shaded and put it back in the inequality to test whether it works or not.

Hands-On Activity

Model inequalities on a floor number line.

Materials: approximately 2-foot long number line marked from $^-12$ to 12; black checkers or bingo markers; a small triangle to be used as an arrow head; two black circles with one-inch diameters, one with the inside cut out to make a ring.

Give students simple inequalities such as $x < 6$. Have students model the inequality on the number line. Use either the closed black circle or the ring to model the boundary point. Use checkers to plot several points that satisfy the inequality. Then place the triangle to indicate the direction the solutions continue in.

Alternatively, have students make a graph and then find the symbolic inequality.

Challenge Activity

Create word problems from a given inequality.

Ask students to write a real-world situation that is represented by the inequality $x > 35$, or for more difficulty, $^-5 \leq x \leq 30$. Have them graph their solutions.

Lesson 21 (Student Book pages 206–215)

Dependent and Independent Variables

LESSON OBJECTIVES

- Recognize that a change in the independent variable creates a change in the dependent variable.
- Make a table, graph, or equation to represent a problem context.
- Identify relationships between tables, graphs, and equations.
- Recognize when quantitative relationships between dependent and independent variables are linear.

PREREQUISITE SKILLS

- Recognize that variables can be replaced with numbers.
- Create a graph using ordered pairs from a set of data (e.g., from a table).
- Model values with charts, graphs, manipulatives, and story contexts.

VOCABULARY

dependent variable: a variable whose value depends on the values of one or more independent variables

independent variable: a variable whose value determines the value of other variables

THE LEARNING PROGRESSION

In elementary grades, students worked with and wrote simple equations with one operation and one variable. In Grade 6, they begin to study equations and the methods of solving them more in depth. They learn to state precisely what a variable represents and think more carefully about what values of that variable are reasonable. For example, *b* would represent the number of books ordered, as opposed to "books." They also understand that negative numbers would not make sense in this context, as there is no such thing as a "negative book."

Students are also beginning to understand how two variables can be related. In this lesson, they learn that the value of a dependent variable varies according to the value of the independent variable, setting a foundation for work with functions in future years. Students also work with tables and graphs to deepen their understanding of the relationship between varying quantities.

Ready ***Teacher Toolbox*** Teacher-Toolbox.com

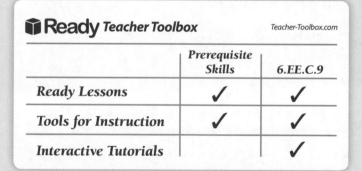

	Prerequisite Skills	*6.EE.C.9*
Ready Lessons	✓	✓
Tools for Instruction	✓	✓
Interactive Tutorials		✓

CCSS Focus

6.EE.C.9 Use variables to represent two quantities in a real-world problem that change in relationship to one another; write an equation to express one quantity, thought of as the dependent variable, in terms of the other quantity, thought of as the independent variable. Analyze the relationship between the dependent and independent variables using graphs and tables, and relate these to the equation. *For example, in a problem involving motion at constant speed, list and graph ordered pairs of distances and times, and write the equation $d = 65t$ to represent the relationship between distance and time.*

ADDITIONAL STANDARDS: 6.EE.B.6, *(see page A42 for full text)*

STANDARDS FOR MATHEMATICAL PRACTICE: ***SMP 1–4, 7, 8*** *(see page A9 for full text)*

AT A GLANCE

Students use a table of values to explore a relationship between two variables, total cost, and number of tickets purchased.

STEP BY STEP

- Tell students that this page models a way to talk about how different quantities are related.
- Have students read the problem at the top of the page.
- Work through Explore It as a class.
- Give students one minute to see if they can complete the table on their own. Then ask them to share their answers. Discuss their thought processes.
- Ask student pairs or groups to explain their answers for the remaining questions.
- Make sure students understand the multiplication relationship involved. Point out that we are not "just adding $8" to each succeeding row in one column.

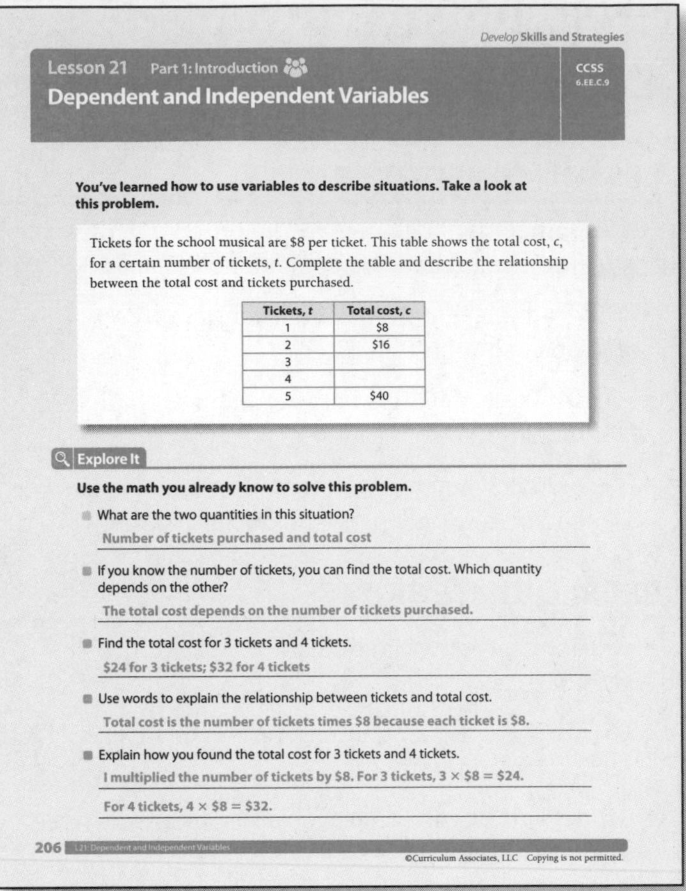

Develop **Skills and Strategies**

Lesson 21 Part 1: Introduction

Dependent and Independent Variables

CCSS 6.EE.C.9

You've learned how to use variables to describe situations. Take a look at this problem.

Tickets for the school musical are $8 per ticket. This table shows the total cost, *c*, for a certain number of tickets, *t*. Complete the table and describe the relationship between the total cost and tickets purchased.

Tickets, *t*	Total cost, *c*
1	$8
2	$16
3	
4	
5	$40

Explore It

Use the math you already know to solve this problem.

- What are the two quantities in this situation?
  Number of tickets purchased and total cost
- If you know the number of tickets, you can find the total cost. Which quantity depends on the other?
  The total cost depends on the number of tickets purchased.
- Find the total cost for 3 tickets and 4 tickets.
  $24 for 3 tickets; $32 for 4 tickets
- Use words to explain the relationship between tickets and total cost.
  Total cost is the number of tickets times $8 because each ticket is $8.
- Explain how you found the total cost for 3 tickets and 4 tickets.
  I multiplied the number of tickets by $8. For 3 tickets, 3 × $8 = $24.
  For 4 tickets, 4 × $8 = $32.

206 L21: Dependent and Independent Variables

©Curriculum Associates, LLC Copying is not permitted.

Hands-On Activity

Model the ticket sales.

Materials: colored paper, ruler, scissors, glue, sheet of paper

- Have students cut fifteen rectangles out of colored paper, each measuring 2 cm by 4 cm. Have students write the label "$8" along the length of each rectangle. These represent the tickets.
- Have students draw five vertical columns of equal width (greater than 2 cm) on their sheet of paper. Positioning the rectangles vertically, have students glue one in the first column, two in the second and so on, beginning at the bottom of each column.
- Have students number columns. Along the left edge of the paper, have students write the total cost of each column at the height of the column.
- Ask students what this picture might have in common with a graph. Lead students to see that the labels along the bottom and left edge could be used to form coordinate pairs on a graph.

Mathematical Discourse

- *Why might it be helpful to know the relationship between number of tickets purchased and total cost?*

  Listen for answers that talk about making calculations easier and faster. If you need to buy a large number of tickets, it would take a long time to add up the price of each ticket. It can be done much faster if you multiply.

- *How would you find the price for 6 tickets? 10 tickets?*

  Students may want to add $8 to $40 to find $48. This would be appropriate, but students should understand that they could find the cost for 10 tickets quickly by multiplying 10 by $8.

AT A GLANCE

Students explore equations with dependent and independent variables.

STEP BY STEP

- Read Find Out More as a class.
- You may want to use the equation to find the total cost for 2 tickets, to show that it produces the same value as was given in the table.
- Ask students to share their answers for Reflect. Ask, *What variable depends on the other one? How does it depend on it?* [The total cost depends on how many days you ate lunch because you get charged a certain amount for each lunch.]

ELL Support

Make sure students understand the term "variable" is a noun in this context. It does not refer to the changeable nature of an equation. Instead, it is the name for the letters that represent unknown quantities in an equation.

SMP Tip: Students decontextualize the problem situation when they represent it in equation form *(SMP 2)*. Help students contextualize their equation by asking questions like: What is the purpose of the 8 that is multiplied by t? What exactly do c and t represent?

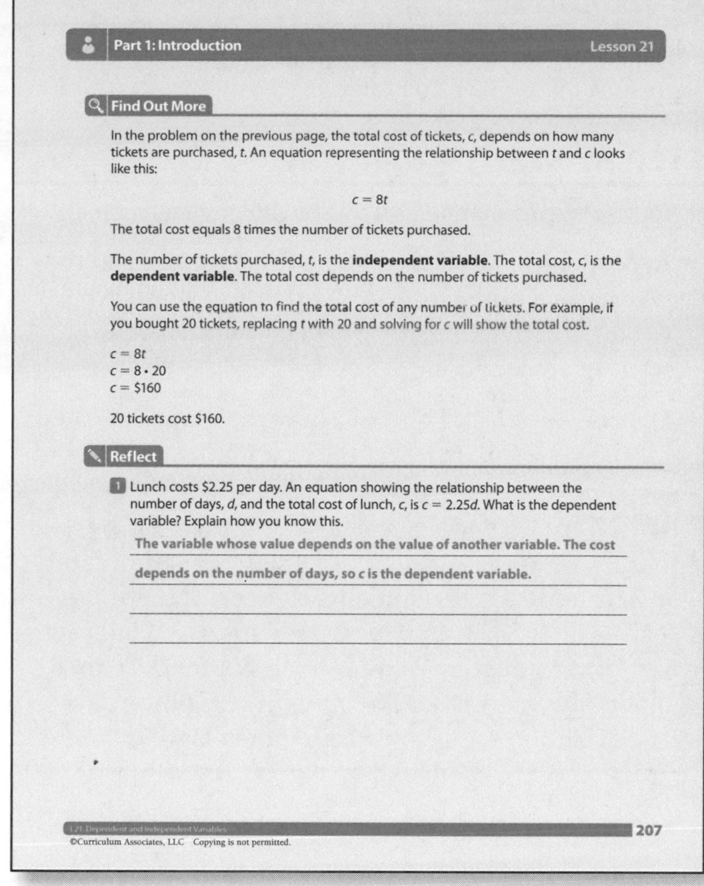

Part 1: Introduction Lesson 21

Find Out More

In the problem on the previous page, the total cost of tickets, c, depends on how many tickets are purchased, t. An equation representing the relationship between t and c looks like this:

$$c = 8t$$

The total cost equals 8 times the number of tickets purchased.

The number of tickets purchased, t, is the **independent variable**. The total cost, c, is the **dependent variable**. The total cost depends on the number of tickets purchased.

You can use the equation to find the total cost of any number of tickets. For example, if you bought 20 tickets, replacing t with 20 and solving for c will show the total cost.

$c = 8t$
$c = 8 \cdot 20$
$c = \$160$

20 tickets cost $160.

Reflect

1 Lunch costs $2.25 per day. An equation showing the relationship between the number of days, d, and the total cost of lunch, c, is $c = 2.25d$. What is the dependent variable? Explain how you know this.

The variable whose value depends on the value of another variable. The cost depends on the number of days, so c is the dependent variable.

L21: Dependent and Independent Variables 207
©Curriculum Associates, LLC Copying is not permitted.

Real-World Connection

Ask students to share situations where there is a direct relationship between two variables.

Examples: Libraries fine an amount for each day a book is overdue. Cars are rented by the number of days or weeks used. Apartments are usually rented by the month.

Have students think of non-financial situations.

Example: The number of students that can be transported, s, depends on the number of available buses, b. If a bus can hold 50 students, then $s = 50b$.

Example: If you want to have enough cookies for every person at a party to have 3, multiply the number of attendees by 3 to know how many cookies you need.

AT A GLANCE

Students use an equation and graphing to help represent data given in a table.

STEP BY STEP

- Read the problem at the top of the page as a class.
- In Model It, ask students how this is similar to the ticket price problem. Ask them to use words to explain the relationship between *c* and *m* before writing an equation.
- Discuss Graph It. Point out how the graph is scaled on the *y*-axis by labeling the tick marks by 10s.

SMP Tip: Students make sense of problems by finding ways to represent them with equations and graphs (*SMP 1*). Ask students to explain their reasoning in writing an equation and tell what each part of the equation represents. Ask them to think about how writing an equation and graphing data helps them to see the problem more clearly.

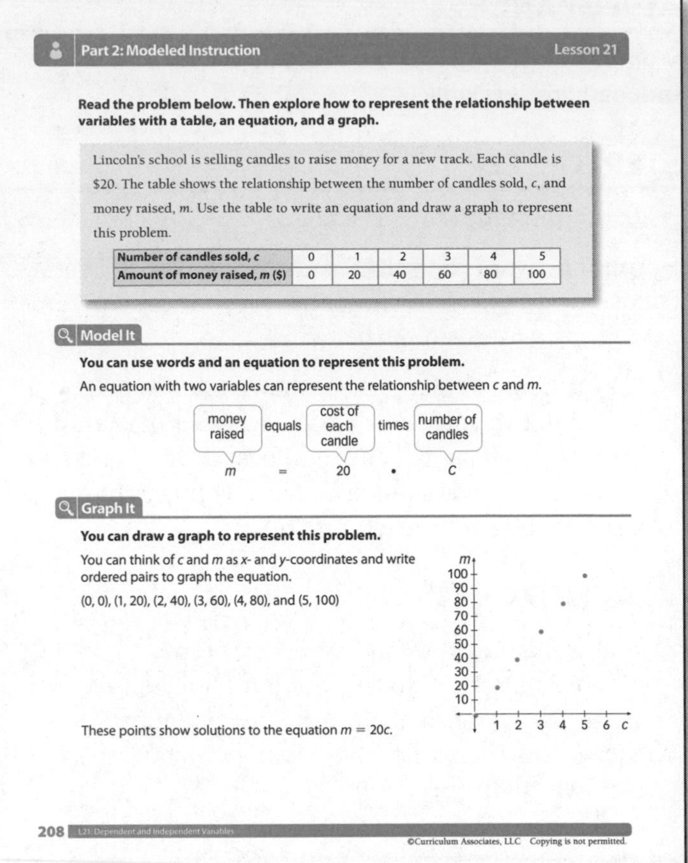

Part 2: Modeled Instruction Lesson 21

Read the problem below. Then explore how to represent the relationship between variables with a table, an equation, and a graph.

Lincoln's school is selling candles to raise money for a new track. Each candle is $20. The table shows the relationship between the number of candles sold, *c*, and money raised, *m*. Use the table to write an equation and draw a graph to represent this problem.

Number of candles sold, *c*	0	1	2	3	4	5
Amount of money raised, *m* ($)	0	20	40	60	80	100

Model It

You can use words and an equation to represent this problem.

An equation with two variables can represent the relationship between *c* and *m*.

money raised equals cost of each candle times number of candles

$m = 20 \cdot c$

Graph It

You can draw a graph to represent this problem.

You can think of *c* and *m* as *x*- and *y*-coordinates and write ordered pairs to graph the equation.

(0, 0), (1, 20), (2, 40), (3, 60), (4, 80), and (5, 100)

These points show solutions to the equation $m = 20c$.

208 L21: Dependent and Independent Variables ©Curriculum Associates, LLC Copying is not permitted.

Mathematical Discourse

- *How can a graph help you with problems like the one on page 208?*

  Students should understand that they can find a point on the graph and the related values of the two variables at that point. Help them to see how you could extend a graph (using a ruler) to find values farther out rather than putting values in a table.

- *Would you prefer to use an equation or a graph to represent this type of problem? Explain.*

  Some students may prefer to use an equation as it is generally more efficient. But the graphical representation may make it easier for some students to comprehend the relationship. Students may say that the form they prefer depends on whether they want to understand the overall relationship or determine values.

AT A GLANCE

Students revisit the problem on page 208. They explore how the table, graph, and equation are all related in describing the variable relationship.

STEP BY STEP

- Be sure to point out that the problems in Connect It refer to the problem on page 208.
- Have students work through Try It as a class or in small groups.

Concept Extension

Help students think about what values of variables make sense.

- Ask, *Would a value of 3.4 make sense for* c *in the problem on this page?* [No. You can only sell whole candles.]
- Tell students to think of situations where decimal or fractional values might make sense. [An example might be an insurance bill was canceled partway through a month, or a pro-rated charge for a karate class started partway through a month.]
- Tell students a certain cell plan charges 25 cents to make a connection and then charges 10 cents per minute. Say, *Find an equation that represents this situation in terms of total charge in cents,* c*, and the number of minutes used,* m. [$c = 25 + 10m$]
- Now tell students that the same company charges in halves of a minute, meaning that if you talk for 10 seconds, or 20, or 26, you will be charged for 30 seconds.
- Say: *A call lasts 3 minutes and 16 seconds. What would be the value for m?* [3.5]
- Tell students to find the charge for the call. [$c = 25 + 10(3.5) = 25 + 35 = 60$, so the call is $0.60.]

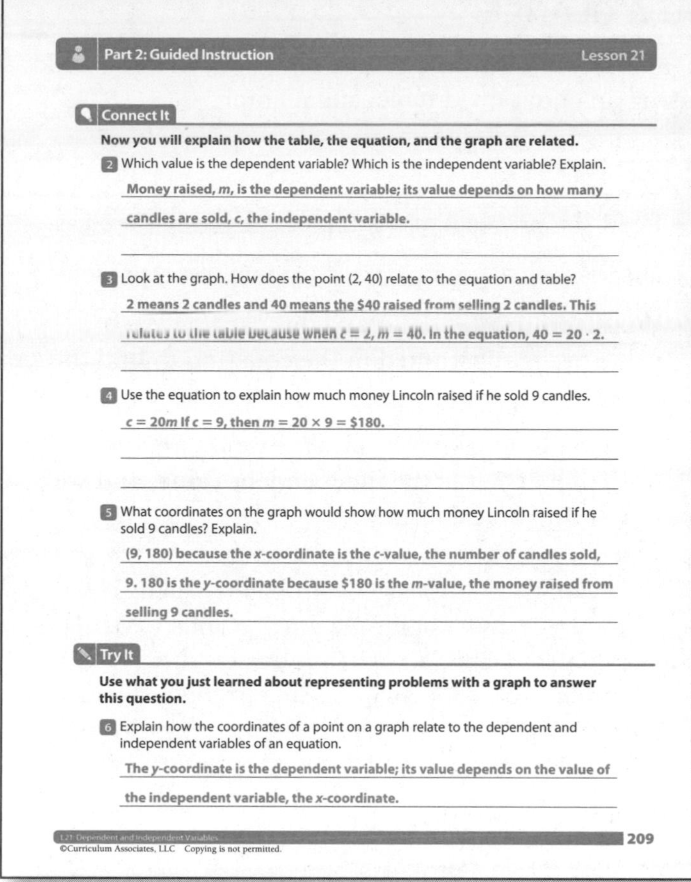

Part 2: Guided Instruction Lesson 21

Connect It

Now you will explain how the table, the equation, and the graph are related.

2 Which value is the dependent variable? Which is the independent variable? Explain.

Money raised, *m*, is the dependent variable; its value depends on how many candles are sold, *c*, the independent variable.

3 Look at the graph. How does the point (2, 40) relate to the equation and table?

2 means 2 candles and 40 means the $40 raised from selling 2 candles. This relates to the table because when $c = 2$, $m = 40$. In the equation, $40 = 20 \cdot 2$.

4 Use the equation to explain how much money Lincoln raised if he sold 9 candles.

$c = 20m$ If $c = 9$, then $m = 20 \times 9 = \$180$.

5 What coordinates on the graph would show how much money Lincoln raised if he sold 9 candles? Explain.

(9, 180) because the *x*-coordinate is the *c*-value, the number of candles sold, 9. 180 is the *y*-coordinate because $180 is the *m*-value, the money raised from selling 9 candles.

Try It

Use what you just learned about representing problems with a graph to answer this question.

6 Explain how the coordinates of a point on a graph relate to the dependent and independent variables of an equation.

The *y*-coordinate is the dependent variable; its value depends on the value of the independent variable, the *x*-coordinate.

L21: Dependent and Independent Variables 209
©Curriculum Associates, LLC Copying is not permitted.

TRY IT SOLUTION

6 *Solution:* Possible answer: The *y*-coordinate is the dependent variable; its value depends on the value of the independent variable, the *x*-coordinate.

AT A GLANCE

Students represent the cost of going to a skating rink using an equation, a table, and a graph.

STEP BY STEP

- Read the problem at the top of the page as a class.
- Discuss what each part of the equation represents.
- Work through Model It and discuss how each value of t is substituted in the equation to find the value for c.
- For Graph It, ask, *Why are the* t *values first in the ordered pairs?* [t is the independent value, and we graph that on the x-axis.]

SMP Tip: Students model problems when they make tables and when they draw graphs (*SMP 4*). Ask them to explain how they design their tables and what each coordinate means in the ordered pairs they are graphing.

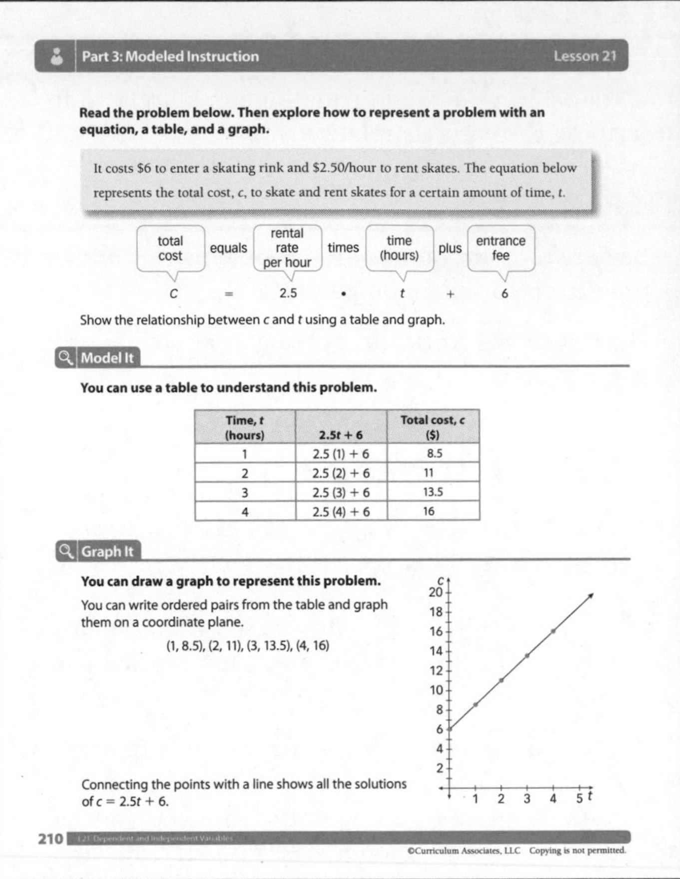
Part 3: Modeled Instruction Lesson 21

Read the problem below. Then explore how to represent a problem with an equation, a table, and a graph.

It costs \$6 to enter a skating rink and \$2.50/hour to rent skates. The equation below represents the total cost, c, to skate and rent skates for a certain amount of time, t.

total cost equals rental rate per hour times time (hours) plus entrance fee

$c = 2.5 \cdot t + 6$

Show the relationship between c and t using a table and graph.

Model It

You can use a table to understand this problem.

Time, t (hours)	$2.5t + 6$	Total cost, c (\$)
1	2.5 (1) + 6	8.5
2	2.5 (2) + 6	11
3	2.5 (3) + 6	13.5
4	2.5 (4) + 6	16

Graph It

You can draw a graph to represent this problem.

You can write ordered pairs from the table and graph them on a coordinate plane.

(1, 8.5), (2, 11), (3, 13.5), (4, 16)

Connecting the points with a line shows all the solutions of $c = 2.5t + 6$.

210 L21: Dependent and Independent Variables

©Curriculum Associates, LLC Copying is not permitted.

Concept Extension

Find the relationship from a table.

- Tell students there are times when real-world situations provide data without telling you what the rules of a relationship are.
- Give the following example: John buys tubes of oil paint at an art supply store. He cannot find a price sticker, but after several purchases, he has collected the data in this table.

Number of Tubes of Oil Paint, n	2	3	4	8
Total Cost, c (\$)	5	7.50	10	20

- He wants to buy 6 tubes, but needs to know how much it will cost.
- Give students 2 to 3 minutes to find a pattern in the table. Discuss the pattern as a class.
- Guide students to find the relationship $c = 2.5n$. Then ask students to find the cost of 6 tubes. [$c = 2.5(6) = \$15$]

Real-World Connection

Ask students to think of other situations like the one on this page where there may be a constant part in addition to a varying part.

Examples:

- A bowling alley may charge a flat rental fee for shoes, plus a charge for each game bowled.
- An event center may charge a cleaning deposit plus an hourly charge for the amount of time the center is rented.
- Assembly workers sometimes get paid an hourly rate, but get additional pay based on the number of items completed above a certain quota.

AT A GLANCE

Students revisit the problem on page 210. They review how the table, graph, and equation relate to each other and represent the variable relationship.

STEP BY STEP

- Read Connect It as a class. Be sure to point out that the problems refer to the problem on page 210.
- Ask, *Why is the total cost dependent on the hours you skate?* [You are charged per hour. The more hours you skate, the bigger the charge will be.]
- Ask, *What are some values of* t *that would be reasonable? For example, would* t = *24 make sense?* [No. The skating rink would be unlikely to let someone skate 24 hours at a time.]
- Ask, *What values of* c *would be reasonable?* [*c* can't be less than 6. It should most likely be less than \$31, as it would be unusual to skate more than 10 hours.]
- Read the problem in Try It.

SMP Tip: When students think about reasonable values in the equation, they make sense of the quantities in relationship to a particular problem (*SMP 2*). Help them build the habit of asking themselves, "Does it make sense in this problem?" as they solve equations and present their solutions.

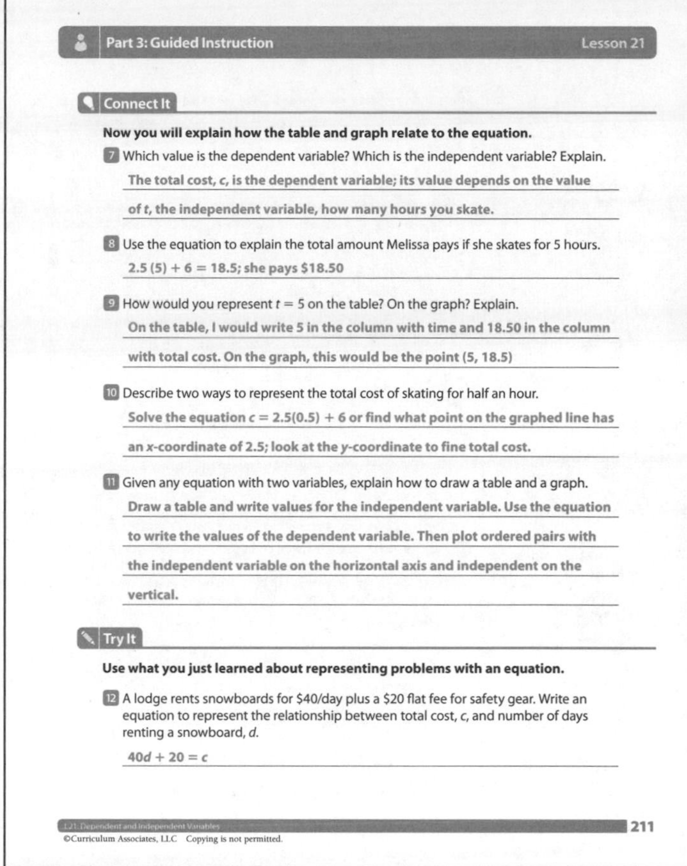

Part 3: Guided Instruction Lesson 21

Connect It

Now you will explain how the table and graph relate to the equation.

7 Which value is the dependent variable? Which is the independent variable? Explain.

The total cost, *c*, is the dependent variable; its value depends on the value of *t*, the independent variable, how many hours you skate.

8 Use the equation to explain the total amount Melissa pays if she skates for 5 hours.

$2.5(5) + 6 = 18.5$; she pays \$18.50

9 How would you represent $t = 5$ on the table? On the graph? Explain.

On the table, I would write 5 in the column with time and 18.50 in the column with total cost. On the graph, this would be the point (5, 18.5)

10 Describe two ways to represent the total cost of skating for half an hour.

Solve the equation $c = 2.5(0.5) + 6$ or find what point on the graphed line has an *x*-coordinate of 2.5; look at the *y*-coordinate to fine total cost.

11 Given any equation with two variables, explain how to draw a table and a graph.

Draw a table and write values for the independent variable. Use the equation to write the values of the dependent variable. Then plot ordered pairs with the independent variable on the horizontal axis and independent on the vertical.

Try It

Use what you just learned about representing problems with an equation.

12 A lodge rents snowboards for \$40/day plus a \$20 flat fee for safety gear. Write an equation to represent the relationship between total cost, *c*, and number of days renting a snowboard, *d*.

$40d + 20 = c$

L21: Dependent and Independent Variables 211

©Curriculum Associates, LLC Copying is not permitted.

TRY IT SOLUTION

12 *Solution:* $40d + 20 = c$

ERROR ALERT: Students who wrote $c = 20d + 40$ understand the form that the equation should have, but they do not understand its meaning. Students need to understand that a one-time cost should not be multiplied by anything and that the variable should be multiplied by whatever rate applies to it.

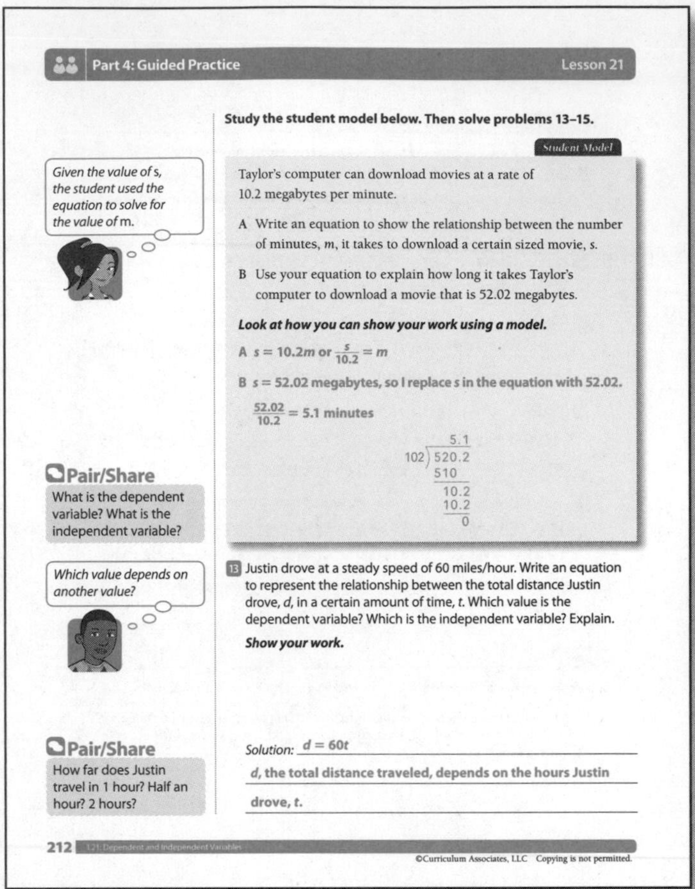

Part 4: Guided Practice Lesson 21

Study the student model below. Then solve problems 13–15.

Given the value of s, the student used the equation to solve for the value of m.

Student Model

Taylor's computer can download movies at a rate of 10.2 megabytes per minute.

A Write an equation to show the relationship between the number of minutes, m, it takes to download a certain sized movie, s.

B Use your equation to explain how long it takes Taylor's computer to download a movie that is 52.02 megabytes.

Look at how you can show your work using a model.

A $s = 10.2m$ or $\frac{s}{10.2} = m$

B $s = 52.02$ megabytes, so I replace s in the equation with 52.02.

$\frac{52.02}{10.2} = 5.1$ minutes

$$102\overline{)520.2} = 5.1;\ 510;\ 10.2;\ 10.2;\ 0$$

Pair/Share
What is the dependent variable? What is the independent variable?

Which value depends on another value?

13 Justin drove at a steady speed of 60 miles/hour. Write an equation to represent the relationship between the total distance Justin drove, d, in a certain amount of time, t. Which value is the dependent variable? Which is the independent variable? Explain.

Show your work.

Solution: $d = 60t$
d, the total distance traveled, depends on the hours Justin drove, t.

Pair/Share
How far does Justin travel in 1 hour? Half an hour? 2 hours?

212 L21: Dependent and Independent Variables ©Curriculum Associates, LLC Copying is not permitted.

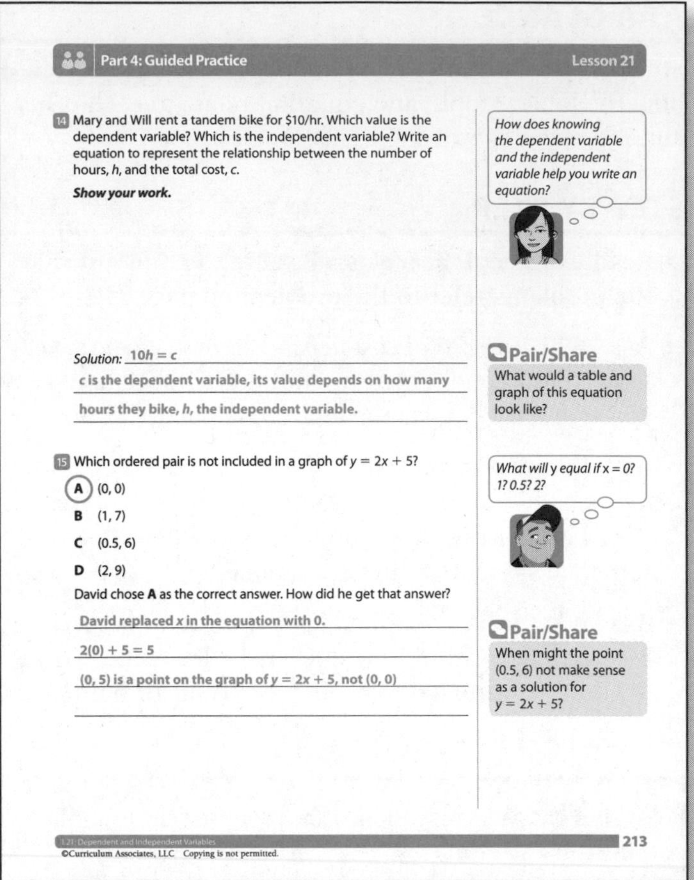

Part 4: Guided Practice Lesson 21

14 Mary and Will rent a tandem bike for $10/hr. Which value is the dependent variable? Which is the independent variable? Write an equation to represent the relationship between the number of hours, h, and the total cost, c.

Show your work.

How does knowing the dependent variable and the independent variable help you write an equation?

Solution: $10h = c$
c is the dependent variable, its value depends on how many hours they bike, h, the independent variable.

Pair/Share
What would a table and graph of this equation look like?

15 Which ordered pair is not included in a graph of $y = 2x + 5$?

(A) (0, 0)
B (1, 7)
C (0.5, 6)
D (2, 9)

David chose **A** as the correct answer. How did he get that answer?

David replaced x in the equation with 0.
$2(0) + 5 = 5$
$(0, 5)$ is a point on the graph of $y = 2x + 5$, not $(0, 0)$

What will y equal if x = 0? 1? 0.5? 2?

Pair/Share
When might the point (0.5, 6) not make sense as a solution for $y = 2x + 5$?

L21: Dependent and Independent Variables ©Curriculum Associates, LLC Copying is not permitted. 213

AT A GLANCE

Students model real-world problems involving dependent and independent variables.

STEP BY STEP

- Ask students to solve the problems individually and be sure to explain their thought process in writing.
- When students have completed each problem, have them Pair/Share to discuss their solutions with a partner or in a group.

SOLUTIONS

Ex **(A)** s = rate multiplied by m

(B) substitutes 52.02 for s to get $\frac{52.02}{10.2} = 5.1$ min.

13 *Solution:* $d = 60t$; d, the total distance traveled, depends on the hours Justin drove, t. ***(DOK 2)***

14 *Solution:* $10h = c$; c is the dependent variable, and its value depends on how many hours they bike, h, the independent variable. ***(DOK 1)***

15 *Solution:* **A**; David replaced x in the equation with 0. $2(0) + 5 = 5$. $(0, 5)$ is a point on the graph of $y = 2x + 5$, not $(0, 0)$

Explain to students why the other answer choices are not correct:

B, C, and **D** are not correct because the given x values replaced in the equation would result in the corresponding y values for each answer choice. ***(DOK 3)***

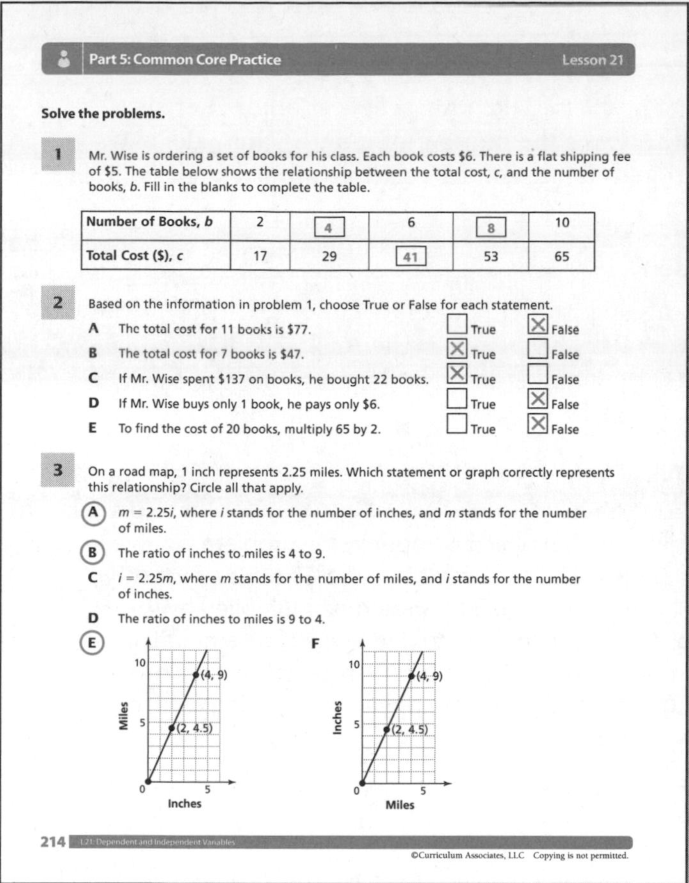

Part 5: Common Core Practice Lesson 21

Solve the problems.

1 Mr. Wise is ordering a set of books for his class. Each book costs $6. There is a flat shipping fee of $5. The table below shows the relationship between the total cost, *c*, and the number of books, *b*. Fill in the blanks to complete the table.

Number of Books, *b*	2	4	6	8	10
Total Cost ($), *c*	17	29	41	53	65

2 Based on the information in problem 1, choose True or False for each statement.

A The total cost for 11 books is $77. ☐ True ☒ False

B The total cost for 7 books is $47. ☒ True ☐ False

C If Mr. Wise spent $137 on books, he bought 22 books. ☒ True ☐ False

D If Mr. Wise buys only 1 book, he pays only $6. ☐ True ☒ False

E To find the cost of 20 books, multiply 65 by 2. ☐ True ☒ False

3 On a road map, 1 inch represents 2.25 miles. Which statement or graph correctly represents this relationship? Circle all that apply.

(A) $m = 2.25i$, where i stands for the number of inches, and m stands for the number of miles.

(B) The ratio of inches to miles is 4 to 9.

C $i = 2.25m$, where m stands for the number of miles, and i stands for the number of inches.

D The ratio of inches to miles is 9 to 4.

(E) F

214 L21: Dependent and Independent Variables

©Curriculum Associates, LLC Copying is not permitted.

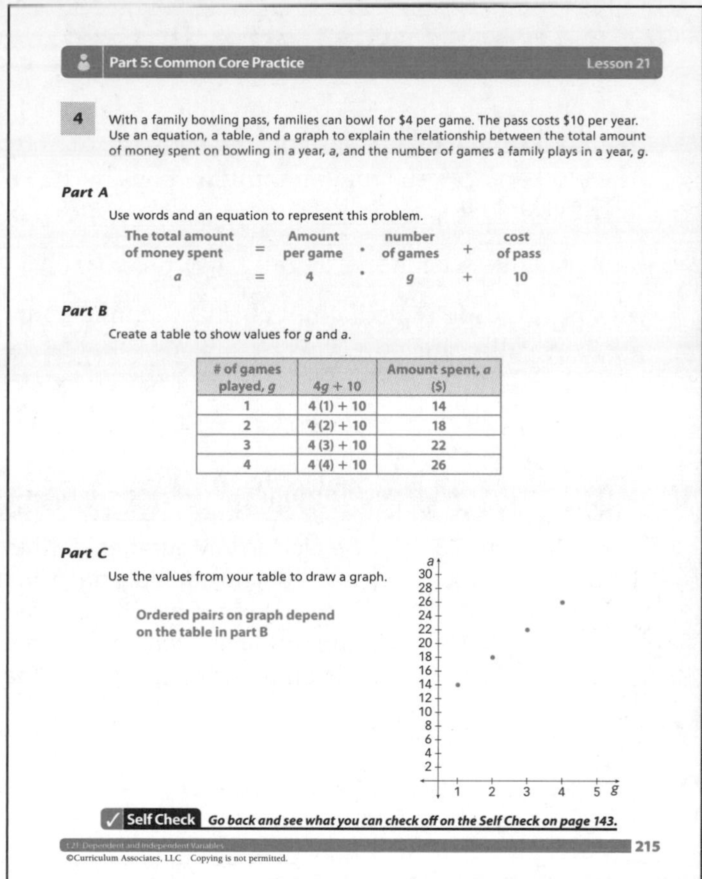

Part 5: Common Core Practice Lesson 21

4 With a family bowling pass, families can bowl for $4 per game. The pass costs $10 per year. Use an equation, a table, and a graph to explain the relationship between the total amount of money spent on bowling in a year, *a*, and the number of games a family plays in a year, *g*.

Part A

Use words and an equation to represent this problem.

The total amount of money spent	=	Amount per game	•	number of games	+	cost of pass
a	=	4	•	*g*	+	10

Part B

Create a table to show values for *g* and *a*.

# of games played, *g*	4*g* + 10	Amount spent, *a* ($)
1	4 (1) + 10	14
2	4 (2) + 10	18
3	4 (3) + 10	22
4	4 (4) + 10	26

Part C

Use the values from your table to draw a graph.

Ordered pairs on graph depend on the table in part B

✓ Self Check *Go back and see what you can check off on the Self Check on page 143.*

L21: Dependent and Independent Variables 215

©Curriculum Associates, LLC Copying is not permitted.

AT A GLANCE

Students use graphs, equations, and models to solve problems that might appear on a mathematics test.

SOLUTIONS

1 *Solution:* See student book page above for correct solution; Either find the unit rate or use proportions to find the missing numbers. ***(DOK 1)***

2 *Solution:* A **False**; B **True**; C **True**; D **False**; E **False** ***(DOK 2)***

3 *Solution:* **A**; If 1 inch represents 2.25 miles, then you can multiply the number of inches by 2.25 to find the total number of miles.

B; Multiply both 1 inch and 2.25 miles by 4 to get a ratio of 4:9.

E; The line on the graph represents the equation $m = 2.25i$, which is the relationship between inches and miles in the problem. ***(DOK 2)***

4 *Part A Solution:* $a = 4g + 10$; The total amount of money spent, *a*, equals the amount per game ($4) multiplied by the number of games, *g*, plus the cost of the pass ($10).

Part B Solution: See student book page above for possible student table.

Part C Solution: See student book page above for possible student graph. ***(DOK 3)***

Assessment and Remediation

- Ask students to find an equation that models the following problem: Jake joins a soccer club. There is a registration fee of $35 dollars, and a charge of $60 a month. If *m* is the number of months that Jake plays in the club and *c* is the total amount he pays, write an equation to represent the relationship between *c* and *m* [$c = 60m + 35$].
- For students who are struggling, use the chart below to guide remediation.
- After providing remediation, check students' understanding. Ask students to model another problem. Sarah gets a $5 allowance every week. She also gets $0.25 for every day she takes out the trash. Write an equation to represent the relationship between her allowance, *a*, and the number of days she takes out the trash, *d*. [$a = 0.25d + 5$]

If the error is . . .	Students may . . .	To remediate . . .
$c = 35m$, $m = 35c$, or $m = 60c$	be picking any number in the problem, multiplying it by one of the variables, and setting it equal to the other variable.	help students pick out which number in the problem is a rate that will change based on something else. There is a **monthly** fee of $60, which means that 60 should be multiplied by the number of months. Help them to find a one-time amount, if there is one. Explain that in this problem, because it is a one-time registration fee, it is not multiplied by anything, but added to find the total payment.
$m = 60c + 35$ or $c = 35m + 60$	know the form the equation should have, but not understand the role of the constant values.	see help in row above.

Hands-On Activity

Create an advertisement.

Materials: Poster board, graph paper, ruler, and markers

Have students create an advertisement for a fitness center. They need to promote the savings of a one-year membership over 12 separate monthly payments by including a table and graph illustrating the cost comparison.

Challenge Activity

Tell students to find an equation to represent the following problem:

Sarah orders clay for her pottery studio from a website. She is unable to find their price list, but after several orders she collects the data in this table.

Number of Blocks of Clay, *n*	1	2	3	4	6
Total Cost, *c* ($)	13	16	19	22	28

She wants to order 9 blocks of clay, but needs to know how much it will cost.

If it proves too difficult, tell students Sarah found out the site charged a flat shipping fee of $10. Guide students to find the relationship $c = 3n + 10$. Then ask students to find the cost of 9 blocks. [$3(9) + 10 = \$37$]

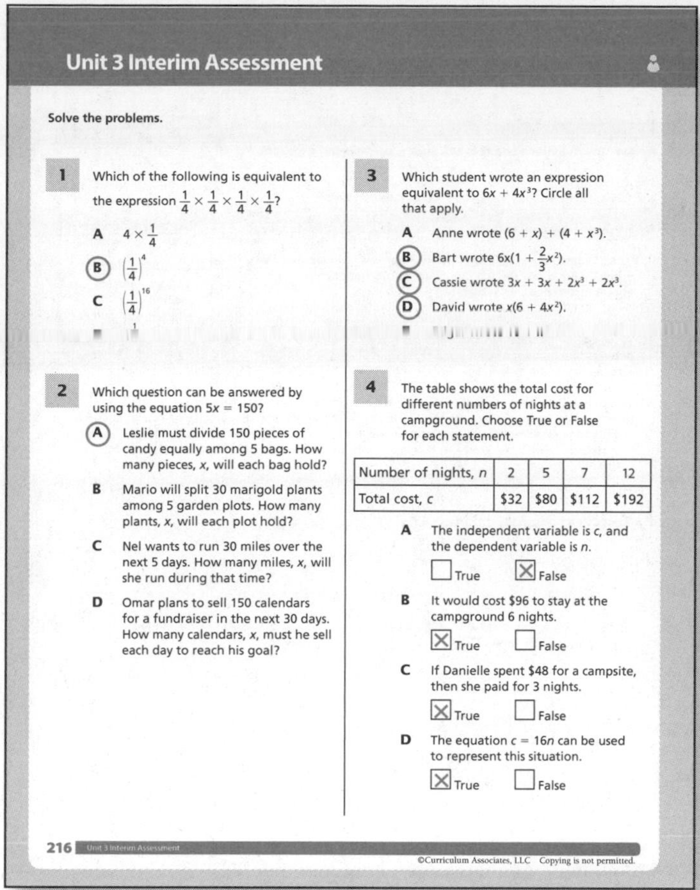

Unit 3 Interim Assessment

Solve the problems.

1 Which of the following is equivalent to the expression $\frac{1}{4} \times \frac{1}{4} \times \frac{1}{4} \times \frac{1}{4}$?

A $4 \times \frac{1}{4}$

(B) $\left(\frac{1}{4}\right)^4$

C $\left(\frac{1}{4}\right)^{16}$

D [illegible]

2 Which question can be answered by using the equation $5x = 150$?

(A) Leslie must divide 150 pieces of candy equally among 5 bags. How many pieces, x, will each bag hold?

B Mario will split 30 marigold plants among 5 garden plots. How many plants, x, will each plot hold?

C Nel wants to run 30 miles over the next 5 days. How many miles, x, will she run during that time?

D Omar plans to sell 150 calendars for a fundraiser in the next 30 days. How many calendars, x, must he sell each day to reach his goal?

3 Which student wrote an expression equivalent to $6x + 4x^3$? Circle all that apply.

A Anne wrote $(6 + x) + (4 + x^3)$.

(B) Bart wrote $6x(1 + \frac{2}{3}x^2)$.

(C) Cassie wrote $3x + 3x + 2x^3 + 2x^3$.

(D) David wrote $x(6 + 4x^2)$.

E [illegible]

4 The table shows the total cost for different numbers of nights at a campground. Choose True or False for each statement.

Number of nights, n	2	5	7	12
Total cost, c	\$32	\$80	\$112	\$192

A The independent variable is c, and the dependent variable is n.
☐ True ☒ False

B It would cost \$96 to stay at the campground 6 nights.
☒ True ☐ False

C If Danielle spent \$48 for a campsite, then she paid for 3 nights.
☒ True ☐ False

D The equation $c = 16n$ can be used to represent this situation.
☒ True ☐ False

216 Unit 3 Interim Assessment ©Curriculum Associates, LLC Copying is not permitted.

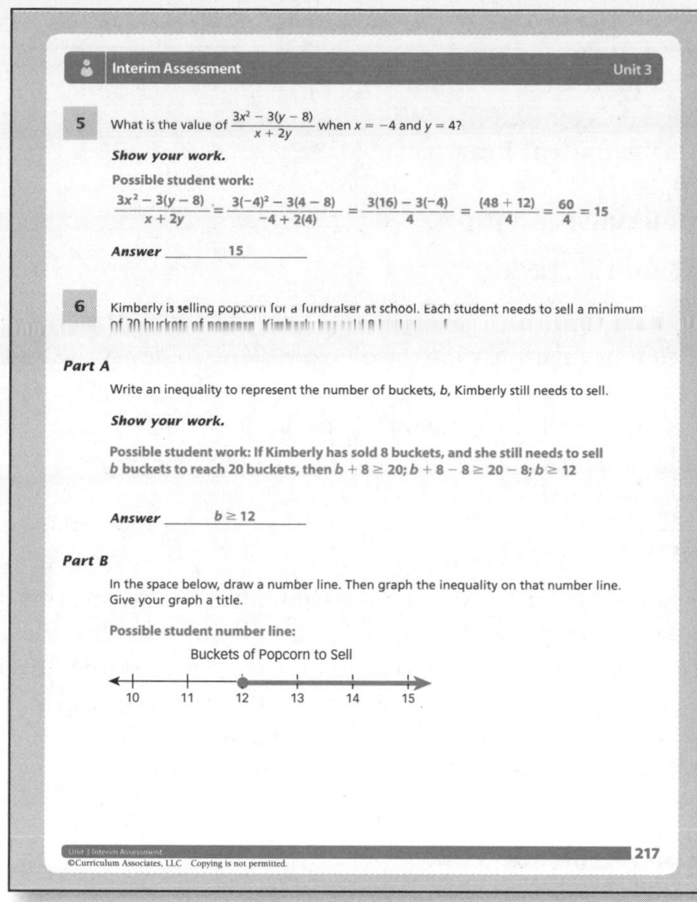

Interim Assessment Unit 3

5 What is the value of $\frac{3x^2 - 3(y - 8)}{x + 2y}$ when $x = -4$ and $y = 4$?

Show your work.

Possible student work:
$\frac{3x^2 - 3(y - 8)}{x + 2y} = \frac{3(-4)^2 - 3(4 - 8)}{-4 + 2(4)} = \frac{3(16) - 3(-4)}{4} = \frac{(48 + 12)}{4} = \frac{60}{4} = 15$

Answer 15

6 Kimberly is selling popcorn for a fundraiser at school. Each student needs to sell a minimum of 20 buckets of popcorn. [illegible]

Part A

Write an inequality to represent the number of buckets, b, Kimberly still needs to sell.

Show your work.

Possible student work: If Kimberly has sold 8 buckets, and she still needs to sell b buckets to reach 20 buckets, then $b + 8 \geq 20$; $b + 8 - 8 \geq 20 - 8$; $b \geq 12$

Answer $b \geq 12$

Part B

In the space below, draw a number line. Then graph the inequality on that number line. Give your graph a title.

Possible student number line:

Unit 3 Interim Assessment ©Curriculum Associates, LLC Copying is not permitted. 217

SCORING GUIDE AND ANSWER ANALYSIS

1 *Solution:* **B**; The fraction $\frac{1}{4}$ multiplied by itself 4 times produces an exponent of 4: Hence, $\left(\frac{1}{4}\right)^4$. ***(DOK 1)***

2 *Solution:* **A**; $5x = 150$ is the related multiplication equation for $150 \div 5 = x$. ***(DOK 2)***

3 *Solution:* **B**; Factor out $6x$ from the given expression.

C; Divide both terms of the given expression by 2 and add them.

D; Factor out x from the given expression. ***(DOK 2)***

4 *Solution:* A **False**; B **True**; C **True**; D **True** ***(DOK 2)***

5 *Solution:* 15; See student book page above for possible student work. ***(DOK 1)***

6 *Part A Solution:* $b \geq 12$; See student book page above for possible student work.

Part B Solution: Draw a number line and graph $b \geq 12$. See student book page above for possible student work. ***(DOK 2)***

PERFORMANCE TASK SAMPLE RESPONSE

Common Core Standards: 6.EE.A.2a, 6.EE.A.2b, 6.EE.A.2c, 6.EE.B.7, 6.EE.C.9
Mathematical Practices: SMP 1, 2, 3, 4, 6, 7, 8
DOK: 3
Materials: grid paper

About the Task

To complete this task, students analyze and represent different relationships to solve problems. They write and evaluate expressions and write and graph equations. The task also calls for students to evaluate the different relationships and use reasoning to suggest a profitable business plan.

Getting Started

Read the problem aloud with students. Ask students to identify what Shawn's costs are in making each bracelet. Invite students to share the expressions they wrote for Part A and explain the meaning of the numbers and symbols that they used. You might also want them to identify the constant, coefficient, and variable in the expression. ***(SMP 6)***

Completing the Task

Students should realize that the expression they write for Part A is used to find the answer to Part B. Have students compare the costs to make the two bracelets.

In Part C, students write equations and make graphs. You might suggest that they also make tables of values to help with the graphs. Challenge students to describe the connections between each of the representations they use. ***(SMP 4)***

Part D provides students the opportunity to explore different options for making bracelets and make a suggestion that makes sense to them. The main focus is on mathematical reasoning, but there are other real-world factors that might affect the decision. For example, students might suggest making all Charmer bracelets because Shawn is more likely to sell more items at a lower price. Others might suggest making more of the Sparkler since the profit is larger. Encourage students to share their recommendations and allow others to critique reasoning. ***(SMP 3)***

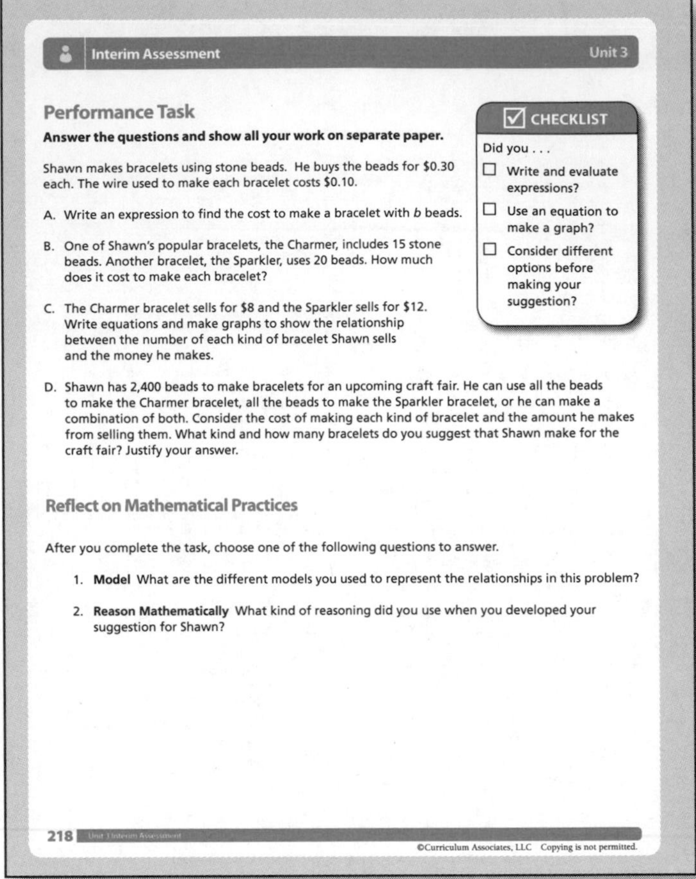

Interim Assessment Unit 3

Performance Task

Answer the questions and show all your work on separate paper.

Shawn makes bracelets using stone beads. He buys the beads for $0.30 each. The wire used to make each bracelet costs $0.10.

A. Write an expression to find the cost to make a bracelet with *b* beads.

B. One of Shawn's popular bracelets, the Charmer, includes 15 stone beads. Another bracelet, the Sparkler, uses 20 beads. How much does it cost to make each bracelet?

C. The Charmer bracelet sells for $8 and the Sparkler sells for $12. Write equations and make graphs to show the relationship between the number of each kind of bracelet Shawn sells and the money he makes.

D. Shawn has 2,400 beads to make bracelets for an upcoming craft fair. He can use all the beads to make the Charmer bracelet, all the beads to make the Sparkler bracelet, or he can make a combination of both. Consider the cost of making each kind of bracelet and the amount he makes from selling them. What kind and how many bracelets do you suggest that Shawn make for the craft fair? Justify your answer.

CHECKLIST

Did you . . .

- ☐ Write and evaluate expressions?
- ☐ Use an equation to make a graph?
- ☐ Consider different options before making your suggestion?

Reflect on Mathematical Practices

After you complete the task, choose one of the following questions to answer.

1. **Model** What are the different models you used to represent the relationships in this problem?
2. **Reason Mathematically** What kind of reasoning did you use when you developed your suggestion for Shawn?

218 Unit 3 Interim Assessment

©Curriculum Associates, LLC Copying is not permitted.

Extension

If some students have more time to spend on this problem, you can have them solve this extension:

A bracelet costs $9.10 to make. How many beads are used to make the bracelet?

PERFORMANCE TASK SAMPLE RESPONSES AND RUBRIC

4-Point Solution

A. $0.1 + 0.3b$

B. Charmer: $0.1 + (0.3 \times 15) = \$4.60$
Sparkler: $0.1 + (0.3 \times 20) = \$6.10$

C. Charmer $m = 8b$ Sparkler $m = 12b$

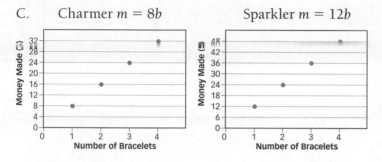

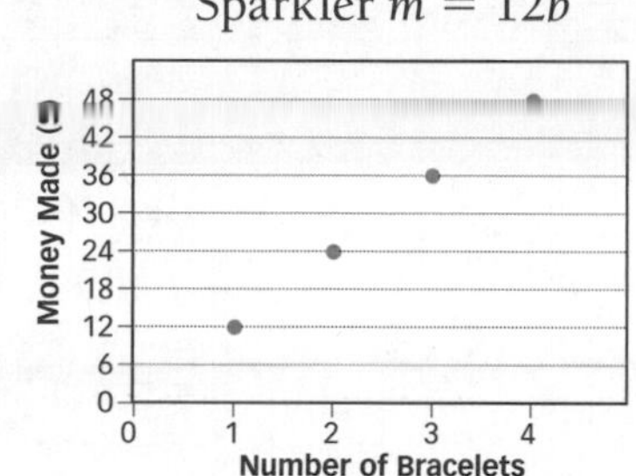

D. **The Charmer:** It sells for \$8 and costs \$4.60 to make. Shawn makes \$8.00 − \$4.60, or \$3.40 on each bracelet sold. With 2,400 beads, he could make 2,400 ÷ 15, or 160 bracelets, and 160 × \$3.40 = \$544. Shawn could make \$544 if he makes and sells 160 Charmer bracelets.

The Sparkler: It sells for \$12 and costs \$6.10 to make. Shawn makes \$12.00 − \$6.10, or \$5.90 on each bracelet sold. With 2,400 beads, he could make 2,400 ÷ 20, or 120 bracelets, and 120 × \$5.90 = \$708. Shawn could make \$708 if he makes and sells 120 Sparkler bracelets.

I think Shawn should make some of each kind of bracelet. Some people might be concerned about price and want to buy the Charmer. Others might like the look of the bracelet that has more stones and not be worried about the price. I would suggest that he make 100 Charmer and 45 Sparkler bracelets.

Charmer: 100 bracelets × 15 beads = 1,500 beads and 100 × \$3.40 = \$340.00

Sparkler: 45 bracelets × 20 beads = 900 beads and 45 × \$5.90 = \$265.50

He would use 2,400 beads and make \$605.50 if he sells all the bracelets.

REFLECT ON MATHEMATICAL PRACTICES

1. Look for responses that include expressions, equations, tables and graphs. ***(SMP 4)***
2. Look for the understanding that the selling price minus the cost equals the money made for selling each bracelet. ***(SMP 2)***

SCORING RUBRIC

4 points The student has completed all parts of the problem. All expressions, equations and graphs are accurate, and all calculations are correct. The recommendation follows sound reasoning.

3 points The student has completed all parts of the problem. The expressions, equations and graphs are accurate, but there may be a few minor computation errors. The recommendation follows sound reasoning.

2 points The student attempted all parts of the problem. Some of the expressions, equations, and graphs are accurate and there are some computation errors. The student justifies the recommendation, but it may not be completely reasonable.

1 point The student has not completed all parts of the problems. There are several errors with expressions, equations, graphs, and calculations. The student makes a recommendation, but does not justify it.

SOLUTION TO THE EXTENSION

$0.1 + 0.3b = 9.10$
$0.3b = 9$
$b = 30$

Which lessons are students building upon?

Grade 4, Lesson 26
Perimeter and Area
4.MD.A.3

Grade 5, Lesson 14
Multiply Fractions Using an Area Model
5.NF.B.4b

Grade 5, Lesson 29
Graph Points in the Coordinate Plane
5.G.A.2

Grade 4, Lesson 26
Perimeter and Area
4.MD.A.3

Grade 6, Lesson 22
Area of Polygons
6.G.A.1

Grade 5, Lesson 24
Understand Volume
5.MD.C.3a, 5.MD.C.3b

Grade 5, Lesson 25
Find Volume Using Unit Cubes
5.MD.C.4

Grade 5, Lesson 26
Find Volume Using Formulas
5.MD.C.5a, 5.MD.C.5b

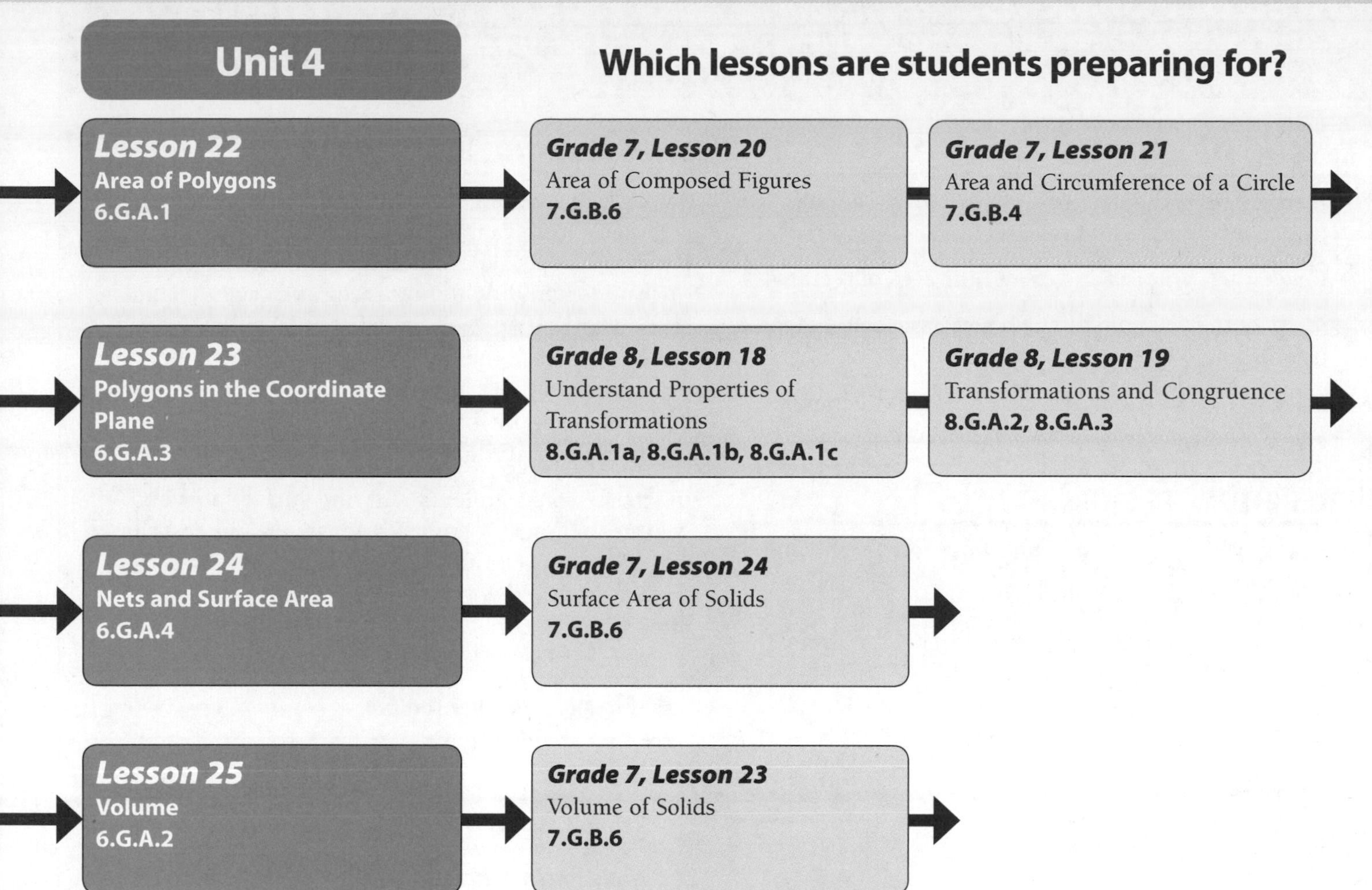
Unit 4
Which lessons are students preparing for?
Lesson 22
Area of Polygons
6.G.A.1
Grade 7, Lesson 20
Area of Composed Figures
7.G.B.6
Grade 7, Lesson 21
Area and Circumference of a Circle
7.G.B.4
Lesson 23
Polygons in the Coordinate Plane
6.G.A.3
Grade 8, Lesson 18
Understand Properties of Transformations
8.G.A.1a, 8.G.A.1b, 8.G.A.1c
Grade 8, Lesson 19
Transformations and Congruence
8.G.A.2, 8.G.A.3
Lesson 24
Nets and Surface Area
6.G.A.4
Grade 7, Lesson 24
Surface Area of Solids
7.G.B.6
Lesson 25
Volume
6.G.A.2
Grade 7, Lesson 23
Volume of Solids
7.G.B.6

Lesson 22 (Student Book pages 220–229)

Area of Polygons

LESSON OBJECTIVES

- Identify special quadrilaterals (squares, rhombi, trapezoids, parallelograms, rectangles, and kites).
- Relate the area of triangles and the area of rectangles.
- Identify the relationship between bases and heights in polygons.
- Decompose and compose polygons into rectangles and triangles to find the area.

PREREQUISITE SKILLS

- Recognize that perpendicular lines form right angles.
- Define and identify polygons.
- Recognize that area is measured in square units.
- Determine the area of rectangles.
- Compose and decompose polygons.

VOCABULARY

There is no new vocabulary.

THE LEARNING PROGRESSION

In Grade 4, students apply the area formula for rectangles to solve real-world and mathematical problems. In Grade 6, students build on and extend their understanding to find the area of right triangles, other triangles, special quadrilaterals, and polygons. They decompose these shapes and rearrange them in order to relate their area to the area of rectangles. They develop and apply formulas for finding the area of triangles and parallelograms.

In later lessons, students will find surface area and volume. In Grade 7, students construct and describe geometric figures and solve problems involving area, surface area, and volume of two- and three-dimensional figures.

Ready ***Teacher Toolbox*** Teacher-Toolbox.com

	Prerequisite Skills	6.G.A.1
Ready Lessons	✓	✓
Tools for Instruction		
Interactive Tutorials	✓	✓

CCSS Focus

6.G.A.1 Find the area of right triangles, other triangles, special quadrilaterals, and polygons by composing into rectangles or decomposing into triangles and other shapes; apply these techniques in the context of solving real-world and mathematical problems.

ADDITIONAL STANDARDS: ***6.EE.A.2c, 6.EE.B.6*** *(see page A42 for full text)*

STANDARDS FOR MATHEMATICAL PRACTICE CODES: ***SMP 1–7*** *(see page A9 for full text)*

AT A GLANCE

Students read a word problem and answer a series of questions to explore finding the area of a parallelogram.

STEP BY STEP

- Tell students that this page models using what you know about rectangles and triangles to find the area of a parallelogram by breaking it into familiar triangles and rectangles.
- Have students read the problem at the top of the page. Point out that the word *parallelogram* often refers only to figures like the yellow ones in the stained glass window—a quadrilateral with two pairs of parallel lines and angle measurements that are not 90 degrees. Students may recall that *any* quadrilateral with two pairs of parallel lines, including rectangles, squares, and rhombi, are parallelograms.
- Work through Explore It as a class.
- Students might not understand why multiplying the base and the height gives the area of a rectangle. Use grid paper to demonstrate if needed. An 8 by 4 rectangle drawn on grid paper would be 32 squares. $8 \times 4 = 32$.
- Ask student pairs or groups to explain their answers for how they would find the area of a parallelogram.

SMP Tip: Students compose and decompose two- and three-dimensional figures to solve real world problems involving area and volume (*SMP 7*). Be sure to give students opportunities to explore the area of shapes by decomposing them and composing them into more familiar shapes.

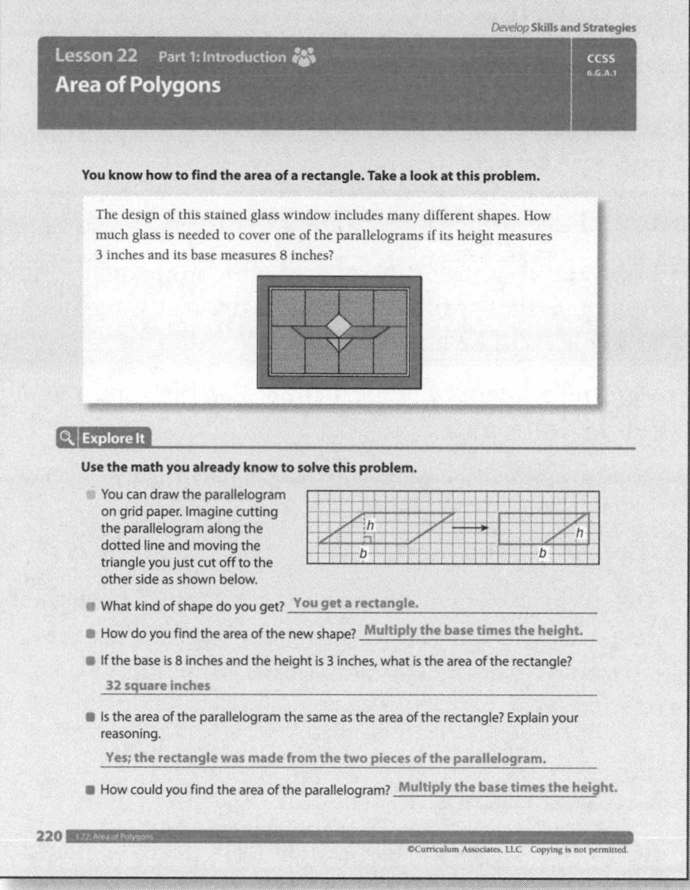

Develop Skills and Strategies

Lesson 22 Part 1: Introduction CCSS 6.G.A.1

Area of Polygons

You know how to find the area of a rectangle. Take a look at this problem.

The design of this stained glass window includes many different shapes. How much glass is needed to cover one of the parallelograms if its height measures 3 inches and its base measures 8 inches?

Explore It

Use the math you already know to solve this problem.

- You can draw the parallelogram on grid paper. Imagine cutting the parallelogram along the dotted line and moving the triangle you just cut off to the other side as shown below.
- What kind of shape do you get? You get a rectangle.
- How do you find the area of the new shape? Multiply the base times the height.
- If the base is 8 inches and the height is 3 inches, what is the area of the rectangle? 32 square inches
- Is the area of the parallelogram the same as the area of the rectangle? Explain your reasoning. Yes; the rectangle was made from the two pieces of the parallelogram.
- How could you find the area of the parallelogram? Multiply the base times the height.

220 L22: Area of Polygons ©Curriculum Associates, LLC Copying is not permitted.

Mathematical Discourse

- *What do you already know about area and the area of rectangles?*

  Listen to see that students understand the concept of area and that area is measured in square units. Students should recall that the area of a rectangle is found by multiplying the base by the height or length by width. Students might be familiar with other area formulas. Probe further by asking whether students can add on to an explanation or have questions about area.

AT A GLANCE

Students explore finding the area of a triangle using what they know about finding the area of a rectangle.

STEP BY STEP

- Read Find Out More as a class.
- Point out that it doesn't matter which diagonal in the rectangle that students choose—the resulting triangles will be equivalent.
- Remind students that perpendicular lines meet at a 90-degree angle.
- Students may become confused when they read that the height can sometimes be drawn outside the triangle. Be sure to provide several examples.
- Discuss the Reflect directive. As students share their responses, ask others whether they agree, disagree, or want to ask questions to better understand the response.

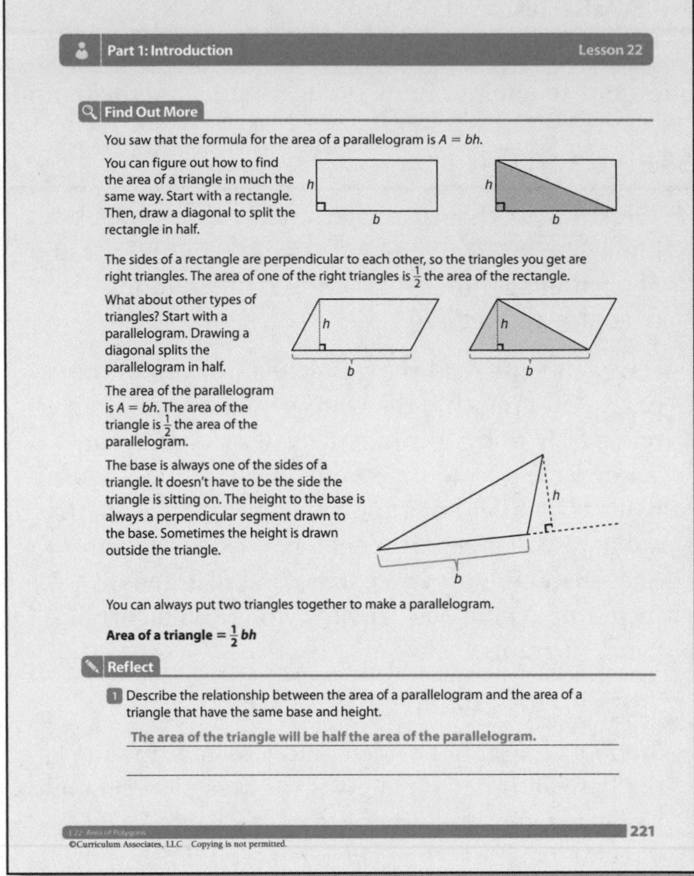
Part 1: Introduction Lesson 22

Find Out More

You saw that the formula for the area of a parallelogram is $A = bh$.

You can figure out how to find the area of a triangle in much the same way. Start with a rectangle. Then, draw a diagonal to split the rectangle in half.

The sides of a rectangle are perpendicular to each other, so the triangles you get are right triangles. The area of one of the right triangles is $\frac{1}{2}$ the area of the rectangle.

What about other types of triangles? Start with a parallelogram. Drawing a diagonal splits the parallelogram in half.

The area of the parallelogram is $A = bh$. The area of the triangle is $\frac{1}{2}$ the area of the parallelogram.

The base is always one of the sides of a triangle. It doesn't have to be the side the triangle is sitting on. The height to the base is always a perpendicular segment drawn to the base. Sometimes the height is drawn outside the triangle.

You can always put two triangles together to make a parallelogram.

Area of a triangle = $\frac{1}{2}bh$

Reflect

1 Describe the relationship between the area of a parallelogram and the area of a triangle that have the same base and height.

The area of the triangle will be half the area of the parallelogram.

L22: Area of Polygons 221

©Curriculum Associates, LLC Copying is not permitted.

ELL Support

Review the terms *diagonal*, *right triangle*, *base*, *height* and *perpendicular.* Have students draw two or more triangles and label them with the vocabulary for reference.

Real-World Connection

Ask students to think of and share everyday places or situations where they might need to find the area of a polygon.

Examples: painting a surface, creating a cover, creating a garden, construction

AT A GLANCE

Students read a word problem and then explore how to find the area of a figure by decomposing the figure into triangles and parallelograms.

STEP BY STEP

- Read the problem at the top of the page as a class.
- Read Picture It. Have a volunteer explain why you would divide the figure into two triangles and four parallelograms.
- Direct students to look at the parallelogram and triangle in Model It.
- Ask students to discuss with a partner how they know that the height of each figure is 3 cm and how they would find the given lengths of the bases.
- Read Solve It. Discuss why it would be beneficial to know the formulas for finding the area of a triangle or parallelogram.

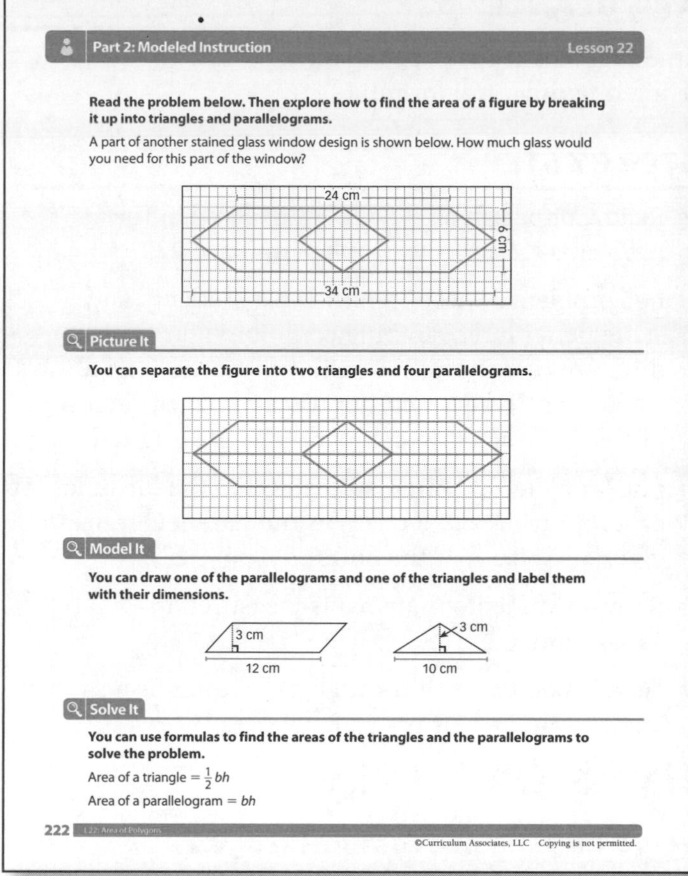

Part 2: Modeled Instruction Lesson 22

Read the problem below. Then explore how to find the area of a figure by breaking it up into triangles and parallelograms.

A part of another stained glass window design is shown below. How much glass would you need for this part of the window?

Picture It

You can separate the figure into two triangles and four parallelograms.

Model It

You can draw one of the parallelograms and one of the triangles and label them with their dimensions.

Solve It

You can use formulas to find the areas of the triangles and the parallelograms to solve the problem.

Area of a triangle $= \frac{1}{2}bh$

Area of a parallelogram $= bh$

222 L22: Area of Polygons

©Curriculum Associates, LLC Copying is not permitted.

ELL Support

Formulas use letters to represent certain items or measurements. Review with your ELL students the capital and lowercase letters used in formulas.

SMP Tip: Students look for and use structure as they decompose geometric figures into their component triangles or rectangles (*SMP 7*). Whenever appropriate, encourage students to look for more than one way to decompose regular and irregular figures.

Mathematical Discourse

- *We divided the figure in the problem on this page into four parallelograms and two triangles to find the area. Can you think of another way to find the area?*

  Some students may recognize that it can also be divided into a large rectangle with two triangles on the ends. Encourage a variety of answers. Have students draw sketches or use the illustration to demonstrate their ideas.

AT A GLANCE

Students revisit the problem on page 222 and solve using drawings and formulas.

STEP BY STEP

- Read Connect It as a class. Point out that the problems refer to the problem on page 222.
- For problem 3, keep in mind that students may struggle with recognizing common figures in different orientations. Remind them they can always trace a figure onto another piece of paper, then turn or flip the tracing to compare it to the original.
- For problem 4, remind students that the formulas for calculating area of a triangle and parallelogram are given in Solve It at the bottom of page 222.
- Remind students that area is measured in square units.
- Have students work through Try It and discuss their answers with their partner.

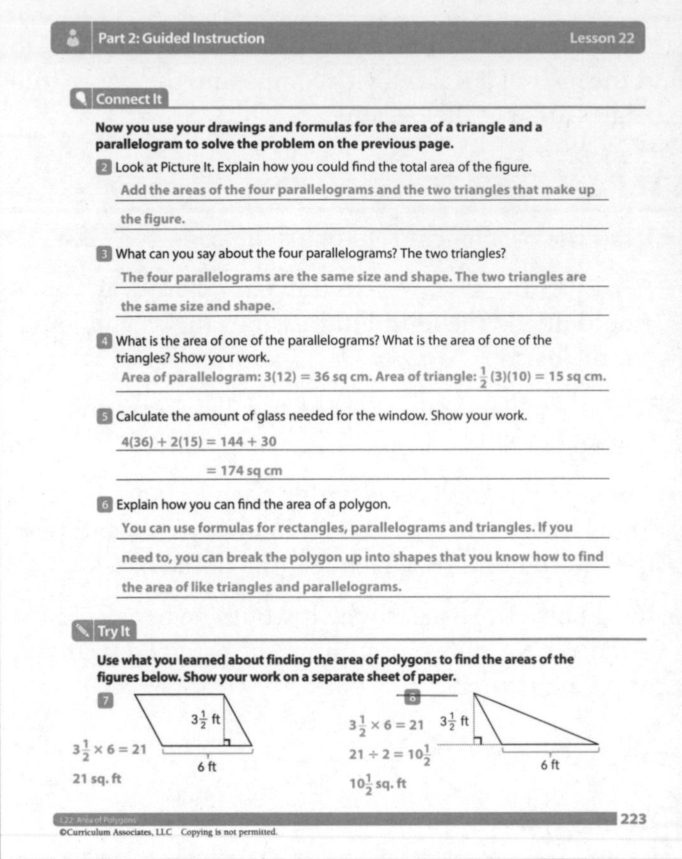

Part 2: Guided Instruction Lesson 22

Connect It

Now you use your drawings and formulas for the area of a triangle and a parallelogram to solve the problem on the previous page.

2 Look at Picture It. Explain how you could find the total area of the figure.
Add the areas of the four parallelograms and the two triangles that make up the figure.

3 What can you say about the four parallelograms? The two triangles?
The four parallelograms are the same size and shape. The two triangles are the same size and shape.

4 What is the area of one of the parallelograms? What is the area of one of the triangles? Show your work.
Area of parallelogram: 3(12) = 36 sq cm. Area of triangle: $\frac{1}{2}$(3)(10) = 15 sq cm.

5 Calculate the amount of glass needed for the window. Show your work.
4(36) + 2(15) = 144 + 30
= 174 sq cm

6 Explain how you can find the area of a polygon.
You can use formulas for rectangles, parallelograms and triangles. If you need to, you can break the polygon up into shapes that you know how to find the area of like triangles and parallelograms.

Try It

Use what you learned about finding the area of polygons to find the areas of the figures below. Show your work on a separate sheet of paper.

7 $3\frac{1}{2}$ ft, 6 ft
$3\frac{1}{2} \times 6 = 21$
21 sq. ft

8 $3\frac{1}{2}$ ft, 6 ft
$3\frac{1}{2} \times 6 = 21$
$21 \div 2 = 10\frac{1}{2}$
$10\frac{1}{2}$ sq. ft

L22: Area of Polygons 223
©Curriculum Associates, LLC Copying is not permitted.

TRY IT SOLUTIONS

7 *Solution:* 21 sq ft; Students might multiply 6 ft $\times 3\frac{1}{2}$ ft

8 *Solution:* $10\frac{1}{2}$ sq ft; Students might multiply $\frac{1}{2} \times 6$ ft $\times 3\frac{1}{2}$ ft.

ERROR ALERT: Students who wrote 21 sq ft for 8 forgot to multiply by $\frac{1}{2}$.

Hands-On Activity

Find the area of a composite figure.

Materials: grid paper, ruler, pencil

- Ask students to recreate on grid paper the figure modeled in the problem on page 222. Each square on the grid paper should represent 1 cm in the figure and be within a 34 × 6 block space.
- Point out to students they can extend the lines of the figure to make it a rectangle.
- Ask students to find the area of the rectangle. [34 cm × 6 cm = 204 cm^2]
- Guide students to realize they can subtract the area of the drawn-in triangles to find the area of the figure.
- Guide students to discover that each of the four triangles has a base of 5 cm and a height of 3 cm. [34 − 24 = 10. 10 ÷ 2 = 5. 6 ÷ 2 = 3]
- Ask students to find the area of one of the triangles using the formula. $\left[\frac{1}{2} \times 5 \times 3 = 7\frac{1}{2}\right]$
- Students then subtract $7\frac{1}{2}$ four times, or multiply it by 4 and then subtract. [204 cm^2 − 30 cm^2 = 174 cm^2]

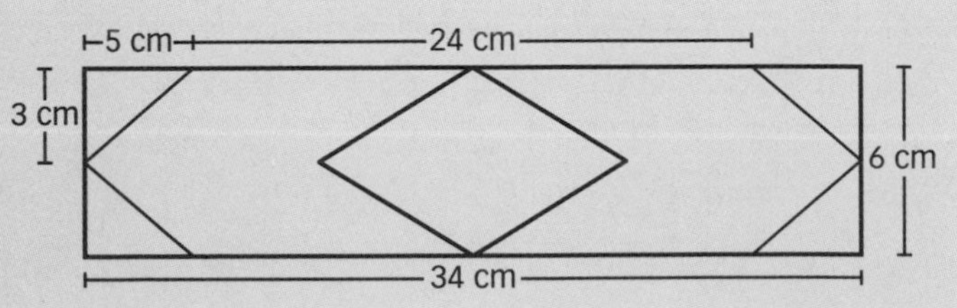

AT A GLANCE

Students read a word problem and explore a method for finding the area of a trapezoid.

STEP BY STEP

- Read the problem at the top of the page as a class.
- Read Picture It.
- Direct students to look at the trapezoid in Model It.
- Ask a volunteer to explain why you would separate the trapezoid into two triangles and one rectangle.
- Read Solve It. Discuss why it would be beneficial to know the formulas for finding the area of a triangle or rectangle.

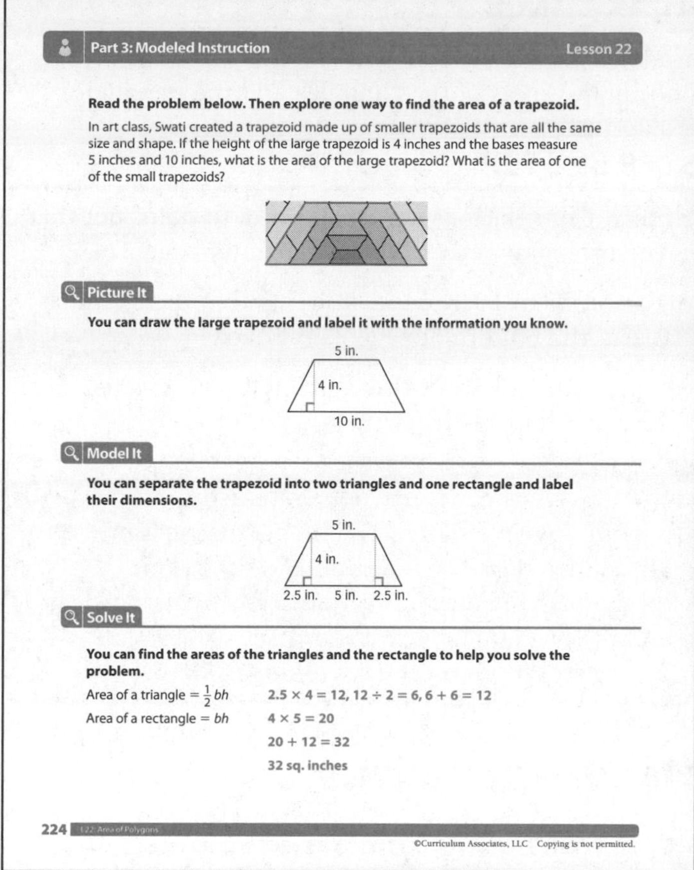
Part 3: Modeled Instruction Lesson 22

Read the problem below. Then explore one way to find the area of a trapezoid.

In art class, Swati created a trapezoid made up of smaller trapezoids that are all the same size and shape. If the height of the large trapezoid is 4 inches and the bases measure 5 inches and 10 inches, what is the area of the large trapezoid? What is the area of one of the small trapezoids?

Picture It

You can draw the large trapezoid and label it with the information you know.

Model It

You can separate the trapezoid into two triangles and one rectangle and label their dimensions.

Solve It

You can find the areas of the triangles and the rectangle to help you solve the problem.

Area of a triangle = $\frac{1}{2}bh$ — **$2.5 \times 4 = 12, 12 \div 2 = 6, 6 + 6 = 12$**

Area of a rectangle = bh — **$4 \times 5 = 20$**

$20 + 12 = 32$

32 sq. inches

224 L22: Area of Polygons

©Curriculum Associates, LLC Copying is not permitted.

Mathematical Discourse

- *Can you think of another way to find the area of the large trapezoid?*

  Students may decompose the figure into a parallelogram ($b = 5$ and $h = 4$) and a triangle (also $b = 5$ and $h = 4$). Have them show this way to decompose the trapezoid and explain how they figured the dimensions. Other students may have experience with using the formula for finding the area of a trapezoid.

- *Which method for finding the area of a trapezoid do you think is the best to use? Why?*

  Students may prefer to use a parallelogram and a triangle because it involves finding the area of only two figures. Students may prefer using the rectangle and two triangles because they are more comfortable using a rectangle than a parallelogram.

AT A GLANCE

Students revisit the problem on page 224 and solve by finding the areas of the triangles and the rectangle.

STEP BY STEP

- Read Connect It as a class. Be sure to point out that the problems refer to the problem on page 224.
- For problem 10, remind students that the formulas are at the bottom of page 224 if needed.
- Have students work through Try It and discuss their answers with their partner.

SMP Tip: Encourage students to use appropriate terminology when referring to geometric figures. Students in Grade 6 continue to refine their mathematical communication skills by using clear and precise language in their discussions with others and in their own reasoning (*SMP 6*).

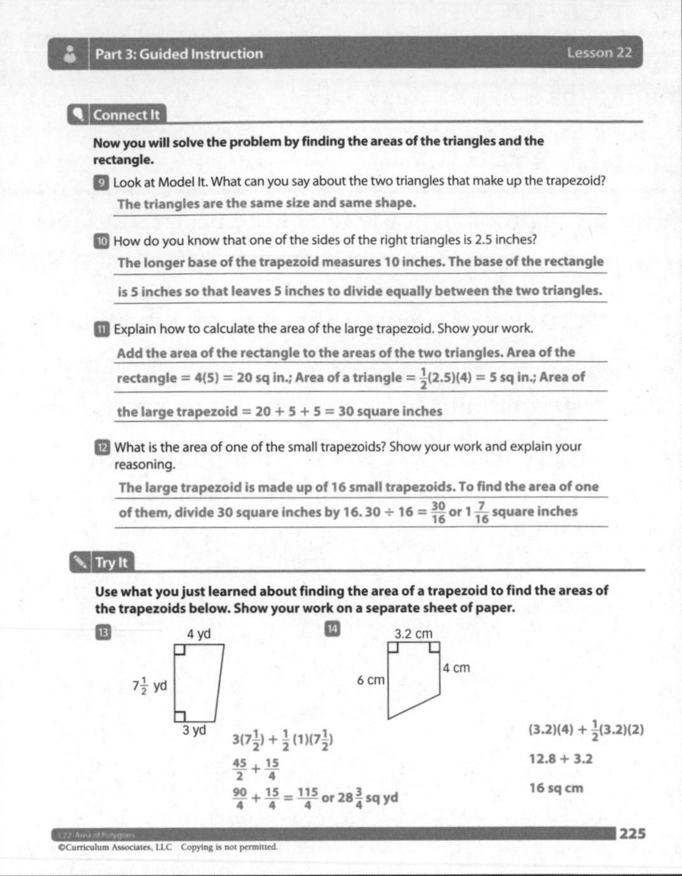

Part 3: Guided Instruction Lesson 22

Connect It

Now you will solve the problem by finding the areas of the triangles and the rectangle.

9 Look at Model It. What can you say about the two triangles that make up the trapezoid?

The triangles are the same size and same shape.

10 How do you know that one of the sides of the right triangles is 2.5 inches?

The longer base of the trapezoid measures 10 inches. The base of the rectangle is 5 inches so that leaves 5 inches to divide equally between the two triangles.

11 Explain how to calculate the area of the large trapezoid. Show your work.

Add the area of the rectangle to the areas of the two triangles. Area of the rectangle = 4(5) = 20 sq in.; Area of a triangle = $\frac{1}{2}$(2.5)(4) = 5 sq in.; Area of the large trapezoid = 20 + 5 + 5 = 30 square inches

12 What is the area of one of the small trapezoids? Show your work and explain your reasoning.

The large trapezoid is made up of 16 small trapezoids. To find the area of one of them, divide 30 square inches by 16. 30 ÷ 16 = $\frac{30}{16}$ or $1\frac{7}{16}$ square inches

Try It

Use what you just learned about finding the area of a trapezoid to find the areas of the trapezoids below. Show your work on a separate sheet of paper.

13

$3(7\frac{1}{2}) + \frac{1}{2}(1)(7\frac{1}{2})$

$\frac{45}{2} + \frac{15}{4}$

$\frac{90}{4} + \frac{15}{4} = \frac{115}{4}$ or $28\frac{3}{4}$ sq yd

14

$(3.2)(4) + \frac{1}{2}(3.2)(2)$

12.8 + 3.2

16 sq cm

L22: Area of Polygons 225

©Curriculum Associates, LLC Copying is not permitted.

Hands-On Activity

Compose figures from pattern blocks.

Materials: pattern blocks

- Give students 16 trapezoids from a pattern block kit.
- Tell them to recreate the large trapezoid pictured in the problem on page 224.
- Encourage them to manipulate and move the trapezoids to form figures that are more familiar to them to find the area.
- They may "trade" the trapezoid blocks for triangles or other pieces from the kit as needed to decompose the shape. Be sure that they are conducting "equal trades," e.g., 3 triangles = 1 trapezoid.

TRY IT SOLUTIONS

13 *Solution:* $26\frac{1}{4}$ sq yd; Students may divide the figure into a rectangle and a triangle.

The area of the rectangle would be $3\left(7\frac{1}{2}\right) = 22\frac{1}{2}$.

The area of the triangle would be $\frac{1}{2}(1)\left(7\frac{1}{2}\right) = 3\frac{3}{4}$.

$22\frac{1}{2} + 3\frac{3}{4} = 26\frac{1}{4}$

ERROR ALERT: Students who wrote 30 sq yd forgot to multiply by $\frac{1}{2}$ when finding the area of the triangle.

14 *Solution:* 16 sq cm; Students may divide the figure into a rectangle and a triangle.

$(3.2)(4) + \frac{1}{2}(3.2)(2)$

$12.8 + 3.2 = 16$ sq cm

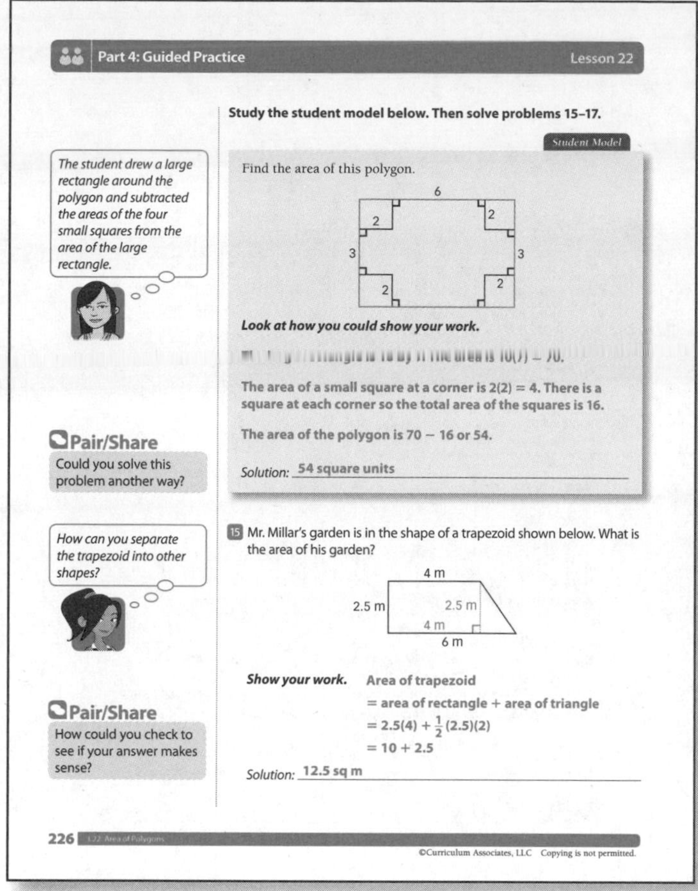

Part 4: Guided Practice Lesson 22

Study the student model below. Then solve problems 15–17.

Student Model

The student drew a large rectangle around the polygon and subtracted the areas of the four small squares from the area of the large rectangle.

Find the area of this polygon.

Look at how you could show your work.

[illegible]

The area of a small square at a corner is 2(2) = 4. There is a square at each corner so the total area of the squares is 16.

The area of the polygon is 70 − 16 or 54.

Solution: **54 square units**

Pair/Share

Could you solve this problem another way?

How can you separate the trapezoid into other shapes?

15 Mr. Millar's garden is in the shape of a trapezoid shown below. What is the area of his garden?

Show your work. **Area of trapezoid**

= area of rectangle + area of triangle

$= 2.5(4) + \frac{1}{2}(2.5)(2)$

= 10 + 2.5

Solution: **12.5 sq m**

Pair/Share

How could you check to see if your answer makes sense?

226 L22: Area of Polygons ©Curriculum Associates, LLC Copying is not permitted.

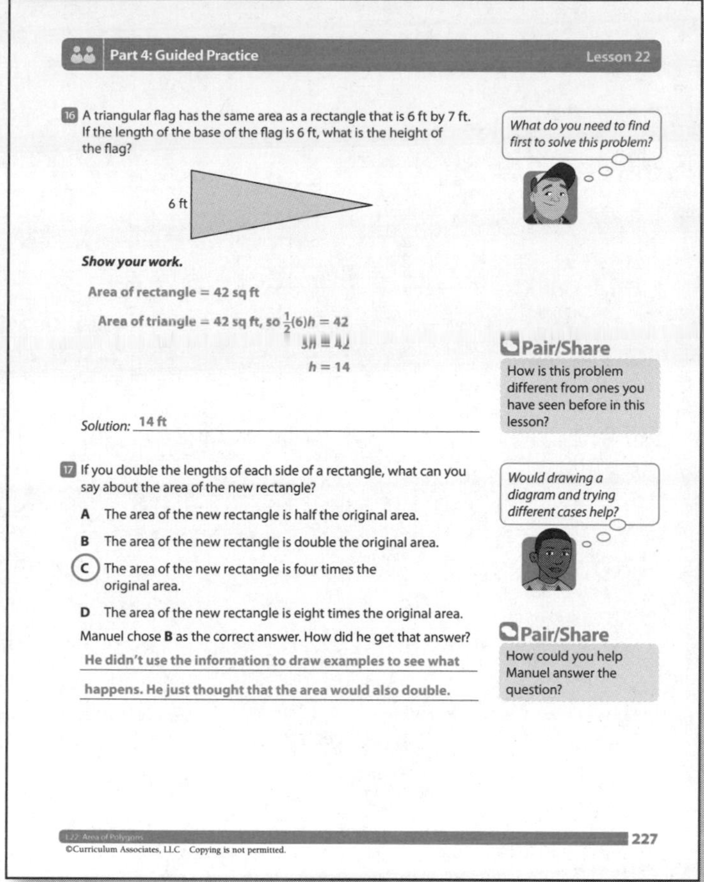

Part 4: Guided Practice Lesson 22

16 A triangular flag has the same area as a rectangle that is 6 ft by 7 ft. If the length of the base of the flag is 6 ft, what is the height of the flag?

What do you need to find first to solve this problem?

Show your work.

Area of rectangle = 42 sq ft

Area of triangle = 42 sq ft, so $\frac{1}{2}(6)h = 42$

$3h = 42$

$h = 14$

Solution: **14 ft**

Pair/Share

How is this problem different from ones you have seen before in this lesson?

17 If you double the lengths of each side of a rectangle, what can you say about the area of the new rectangle?

Would drawing a diagram and trying different cases help?

A The area of the new rectangle is half the original area.

B The area of the new rectangle is double the original area.

(C) The area of the new rectangle is four times the original area.

D The area of the new rectangle is eight times the original area.

Manuel chose **B** as the correct answer. How did he get that answer?

He didn't use the information to draw examples to see what happens. He just thought that the area would also double.

Pair/Share

How could you help Manuel answer the question?

L22: Area of Polygons ©Curriculum Associates, LLC Copying is not permitted. 227

AT A GLANCE

Students study a model of finding the area of a polygon by decomposing it into simpler shapes. Then they solve problems in which they decompose complex shapes into simpler shapes.

STEP BY STEP

- Ask students to solve the problems individually.
- When students have completed each problem, have them Pair/Share to discuss their solutions with a partner or in a group.

SOLUTIONS

Ex One way to find the area of this polygon is to draw a large rectangle around the polygon and subtract the areas of the four small squares from the area of the large rectangle.

15 *Solution:* 12.5 sq m; Students could solve the problem by finding and adding the areas of the rectangle (10 sq m) and triangle (2.5 sq m). ***(DOK 1)***

16 *Solution:* 14 ft; Students could solve the problem by using the formula for area of a triangle: $A = \frac{1}{2}bh$. ***(DOK 2)***

17 *Solution:* **C**; Students could solve the problem by drawing examples to see what happens.

Explain to students why the other two answer choices are not correct.

A is not correct because increasing the side lengths can't cause a decrease in area.

D is not correct because that's what happens to the volume of a rectangular prism when sides are doubled. ***(DOK 3)***

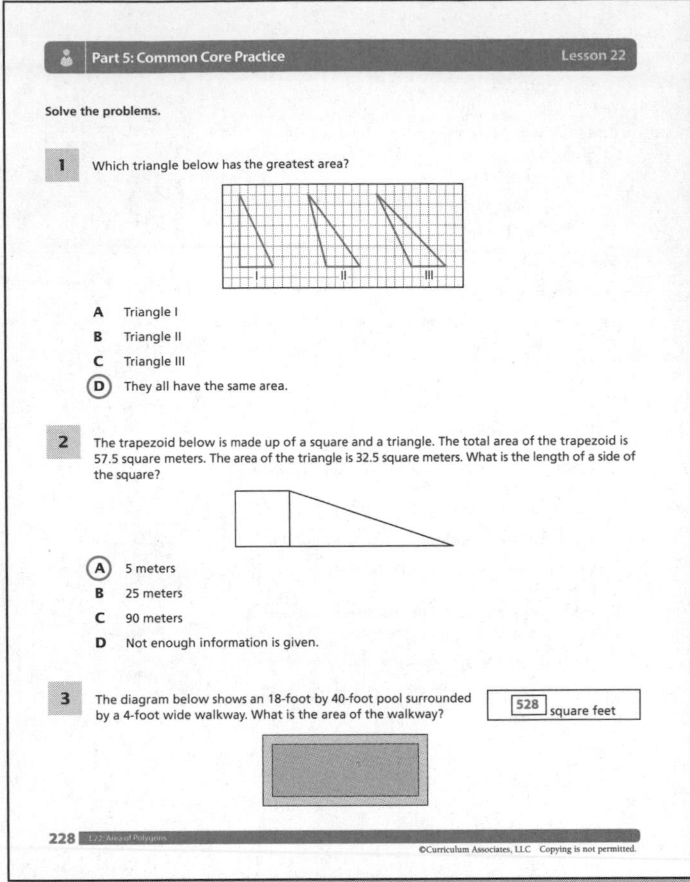

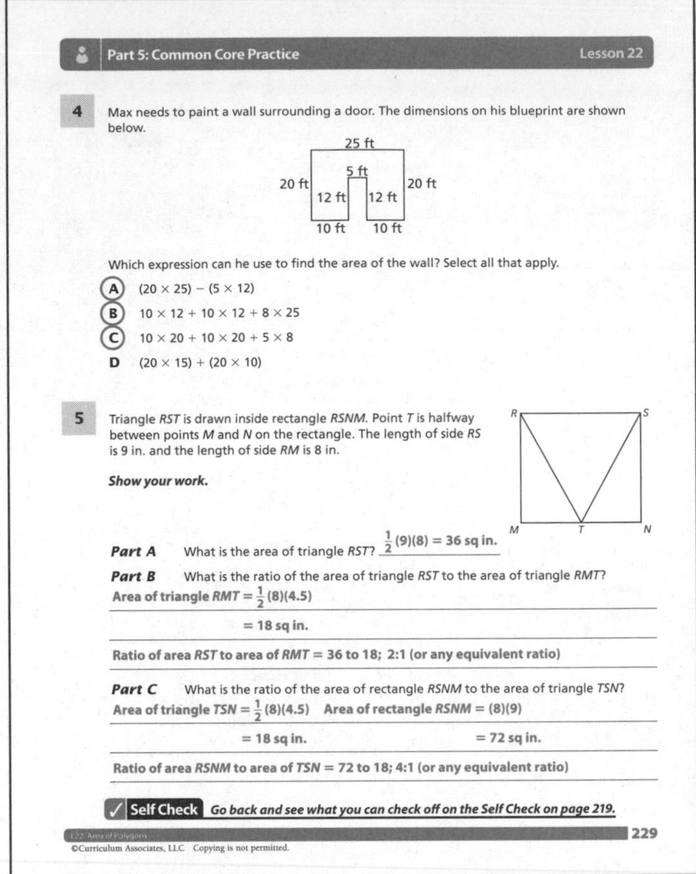

AT A GLANCE

Students compose and decompose figures to solve word problems involving area that might appear on a mathematics test.

SOLUTIONS

1 *Solution:* **D**; Students count the squares to determine the height and base and discover that each triangle has the same dimensions: base = 4, height = 7. ***(DOK 2)***

2 *Solution:* **A**; Students should subtract the area of the triangle from the total area. (57.5 − 32.5 = 25) The remaining figure is a square, so they can find the square root to find a side length. ***(DOK 2)***

3 *Solution:* **528**; Students should find the area of the pool, including the walkway (48 × 26 = 1,248) and subtract the area of the pool (40 × 18 = 720). ***(DOK 2)***

4 *Solution:* **A**; Find the area of the 20 ft by 25 ft rectangle. Find the area of the 5 ft by 12 ft rectangle that's not part of the figure. Subtract the area of the small rectangle from the area of the large rectangle.

B; Break apart the figure into three rectangles, find the area of each, and then add the areas.

C; Break apart the figure into three rectangles, find the area of each, and then add the areas. ***(DOK 2)***

5 *Part A Solution:* 36 square inches; See student book page above for possible student work.

Part B Solution: 36 to 18; or 2:1 (or an equivalent ratio); See student book page above for possible student work.

Part C Solution: 72 to 18, or 4:1 (or an equivalent ratio); See student book page above for possible work. ***(DOK 3)***

Assessment and Remediation

- Ask students to find the area of a trapezoid with a height of 6 in. and bases of 10 in. and 8 in. [54 sq in.]
- For students who are struggling, use the chart below to guide remediation.
- After providing remediation, check students' understanding. Ask students to find the area of a trapezoid with a height of 5 in. and bases of 10 in. and 6 in. [40 sq in.]
- If a student is still having difficulty, use ***Ready Instruction*, *Level 4*,** Lesson 26.

If the error is . . .	Students may . . .	To remediate . . .
60 sq in.	have forgotten to multiply by $\frac{1}{2}$ when finding the area of the triangles.	Remind them to multiply $\frac{1}{2}bh$ when finding the area of a triangle.
480 sq in.	have multiplied together the 3 dimensions given.	Remind them to use a formula or decompose the figure into simpler shapes. Ask students to model the problem on grid paper.
240 sq in.	have multiplied $\frac{1}{2}$ by the 6 in. × 10 in. × 8 in.	Remind students that they can use the formula $\frac{1}{2}bh$ when finding the area of a triangle. Since this is not a triangle, they must decompose the trapezoid into a rectangle and two triangles or a parallelogram and a triangle. Find the area of the shapes and find the sum of the areas.

Hands-On Activity

Find area of composite figures for points.

Materials: Grid paper, pencil, ruler

- Divide students up into groups of 2–4.
- Direct teams to draw a composite figure. They can use squares, rhombi, trapezoids, parallelograms, rectangles, and kites. Each team should find the area of their own figure on a separate sheet of paper and hold on to that sheet for the entire game.
- Ask teams to exchange figures and find the area of the figure they receive. Teams who find the correct areas receive 1 point.
- Play continues until all teams have found the area of the other teams' figures. The team with the most points wins.

Challenge Activity

Estimate areas of states.

- Provide students with a map of the United States that includes a mileage key.
- Challenge students to use a grid to estimate the area of various states and of the country. For example, Nevada closely represents the shape of a rectangle and a triangle composed together.

Lesson 23 (Student Book pages 230–239)

Polygons in the Coordinate Plane

LESSON OBJECTIVES

- Understand that a line segment from one coordinate pair to another represents a distance.
- Understand that if two coordinates have the same *x*- or *y*-value they are on the same line.
- Find the distance between two points on the coordinate plane.
- Plot points in all four quadrants of the Cartesian coordinate plane.
- Plot a polygon in the Cartesian coordinate plane with given coordinates.

PREREQUISITE SKILLS

- Understand and plot ordered pairs (x, y).
- Recognize that a coordinate plane has 4 quadrants.

VOCABULARY

polygon: a closed plane figure whose sides are line segments that intersect only at their endpoints

THE LEARNING PROGRESSION

Students have worked previously with finding area and perimeter of triangles and special quadrilaterals. Students have also plotted points in the coordinate plane.

In this lesson, students are expected to draw polygons in the coordinate plane when given coordinates for the vertices. They are also expected to use coordinates to find the length of a side joining points that have the same first coordinate or the same second coordinate. Later, students will find the surface area of three-dimensional figures using nets.

Ready *Teacher Toolbox* Teacher-Toolbox.com

	Prerequisite Skills	6.G.A.3
Ready Lessons	✓	✓
Tools for Instruction		✓
Interactive Tutorials	✓	✓

CCSS Focus

6.G.A.3 Draw polygons in the coordinate plane given coordinates for the vertices; use coordinates to find the length of a side joining points with the same first coordinate or the same second coordinate. Apply these techniques in the context of solving real-world and mathematical problems.

STANDARDS FOR MATHEMATICAL PRACTICE: *SMP 1, 2, 4, 5, 7 (see page A9 for full text)*

AT A GLANCE

Students read a word problem and answer a series of questions to analyze plane figures in the coordinate plane.

STEP BY STEP

- Tell students that this page models finding the distance between two points on the coordinate plane.
- Have students read the problem at the top of the page.
- Work through Explore It as a class.
- Review key vocabulary such as *x*-axis, *y*-axis, coordinate plane, origin, and ordered pair.
- Remind students that the first coordinate is the *x*-coordinate. The *x*-coordinate indicates how many spaces to the right (if positive) or to the left (if negative) they should move from the origin.
- Remind students that the second coordinate is the *y*-coordinate. The *y*-coordinate indicates how many spaces up (if positive) or down (if negative) they should then move.
- Ask student pairs or groups to explain their answers for how you could find which route is longer.

SMP Tip: In this lesson, students learn that the coordinate plane may be a helpful tool for representing geometric figures or calculating perimeter. Mathematically proficient students consider available tools when solving a mathematical problem and decide when a certain tool might be helpful (*SMP 5*).

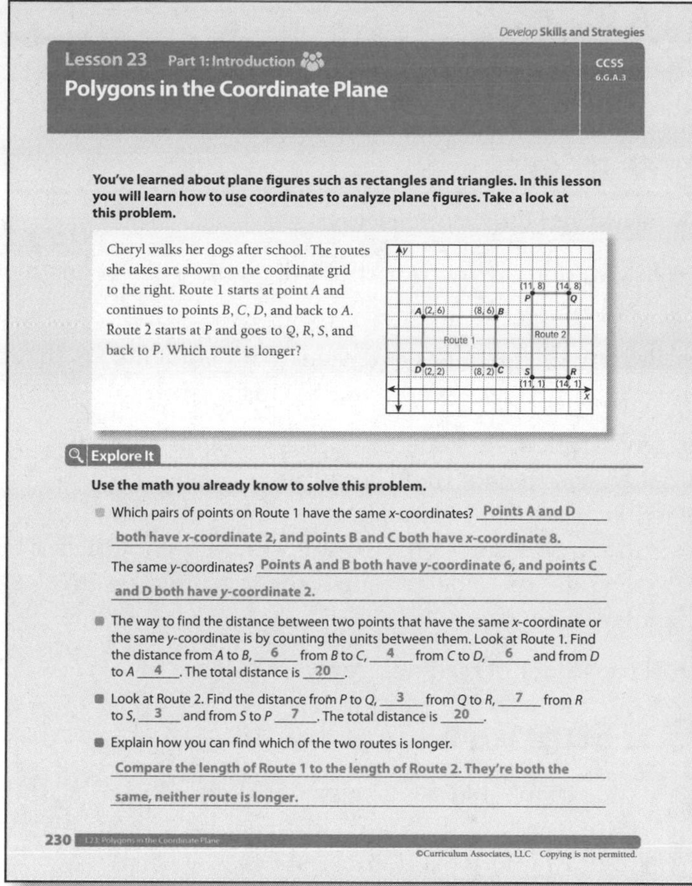

Develop Skills and Strategies

Lesson 23 Part 1: Introduction CCSS 6.G.A.3

Polygons in the Coordinate Plane

You've learned about plane figures such as rectangles and triangles. In this lesson you will learn how to use coordinates to analyze plane figures. Take a look at this problem.

Cheryl walks her dogs after school. The routes she takes are shown on the coordinate grid to the right. Route 1 starts at point *A* and continues to points *B*, *C*, *D*, and back to *A*. Route 2 starts at *P* and goes to *Q*, *R*, *S*, and back to *P*. Which route is longer?

Explore It

Use the math you already know to solve this problem.

- Which pairs of points on Route 1 have the same *x*-coordinates? Points A and D both have *x*-coordinate 2, and points B and C both have *x*-coordinate 8.

  The same *y*-coordinates? Points A and B both have *y*-coordinate 6, and points C and D both have *y*-coordinate 2.
- The way to find the distance between two points that have the same *x*-coordinate or the same *y*-coordinate is by counting the units between them. Look at Route 1. Find the distance from *A* to *B*, 6 from *B* to *C*, 4 from *C* to *D*, 6 and from *D* to *A* 4. The total distance is 20.
- Look at Route 2. Find the distance from *P* to *Q*, 3 from *Q* to *R*, 7 from *R* to *S*, 3 and from *S* to *P* 7. The total distance is 20.
- Explain how you can find which of the two routes is longer.

  Compare the length of Route 1 to the length of Route 2. They're both the same, neither route is longer.

230 L23: Polygons in the Coordinate Plane ©Curriculum Associates, LLC Copying is not permitted.

Mathematical Discourse

- *As you worked through the Explore It questions, you found the distance between two points that have the same* x- *or* y-*coordinate by counting the units between them. Can you think of another way to find the distance between two points with the same* x- *or* y-*coordinate?*

  Students may recognize that they can subtract the *y*-coordinates if they have the same *x*-coordinate or can subtract the *x*-coordinates if they have the same *y*-coordinate.
- *Geometry uses many terms with very specific meanings. Which terms on this page do you recognize? Can you explain or draw a sketch to show what they mean?*

  Students should be able to identify several terms and either describe or illustrate them accurately. Probe vague answers to determine whether there is a deeper understanding.

AT A GLANCE

Students review concepts and vocabulary helpful for investigating polygons on a coordinate plane.

STEP BY STEP

- Read Find Out More as a class.
- Ask students why they think the length of a segment is always positive.
- Review the term *absolute value* with students, as they will apply the concept later in this lesson.
- Give students several examples and non-examples of polygons to help them recall their previous work with polygons. Non-examples may include figures with curved sides or with sides that do not touch. Ask students to determine if the given figures are polygons or not polygons.
- Have students read and reply to Reflect.

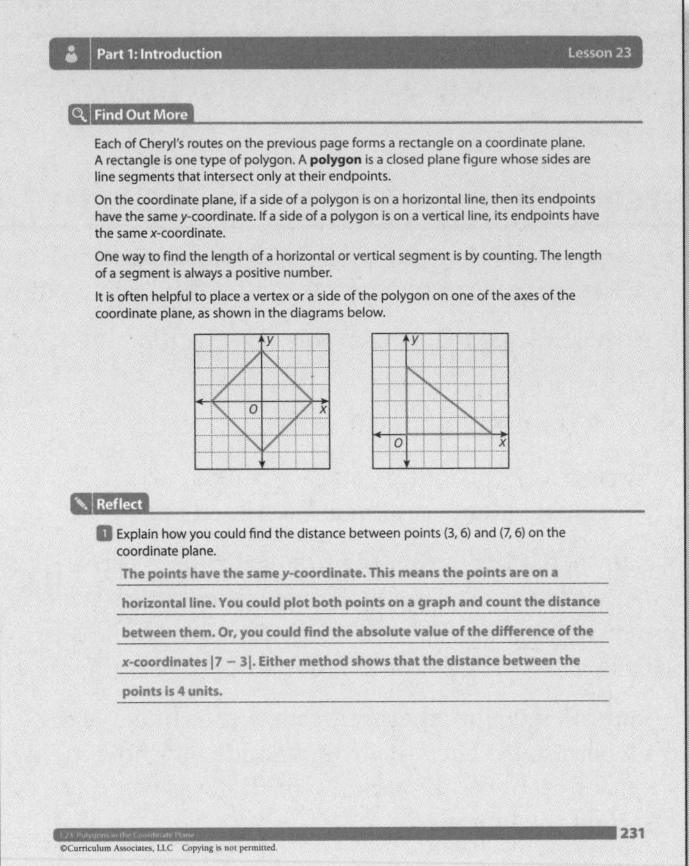

Part 1: Introduction Lesson 23

Find Out More

Each of Cheryl's routes on the previous page forms a rectangle on a coordinate plane. A rectangle is one type of polygon. A **polygon** is a closed plane figure whose sides are line segments that intersect only at their endpoints.

On the coordinate plane, if a side of a polygon is on a horizontal line, then its endpoints have the same *y*-coordinate. If a side of a polygon is on a vertical line, its endpoints have the same *x*-coordinate.

One way to find the length of a horizontal or vertical segment is by counting. The length of a segment is always a positive number.

It is often helpful to place a vertex or a side of the polygon on one of the axes of the coordinate plane, as shown in the diagrams below.

Reflect

1 Explain how you could find the distance between points (3, 6) and (7, 6) on the coordinate plane.

The points have the same *y*-coordinate. This means the points are on a horizontal line. You could plot both points on a graph and count the distance between them. Or, you could find the absolute value of the difference of the *x*-coordinates $|7 - 3|$. Either method shows that the distance between the points is 4 units.

L23: Polygons in the Coordinate Plane 231
©Curriculum Associates, LLC Copying is not permitted.

ELL Support

Provide graph paper. Have students make a coordinate plane and 2 to 3 different polygons. Help them draw and label to illustrate these terms: *polygon, rectangle, coordinate plane, endpoints, sides, segment, vertex, axis, horizontal,* and *vertical*. It may help to connect *horizontal* with the word *horizon*. Point out that the plural of *axis* is *axes*, which looks but does not sound like the English word for a tool for chopping wood.

Hands-On Activity

Follow directions on a coordinate plane.

- Set up a situation in your classroom where a student can move unobstructed from one location to another by following a series of two commands.
- Point out that every step is like moving along a coordinate plane. The first step is in the direction of the *x*-coordinate; the second step is in the direction of the *y*-coordinate.
- Tell the student where to stand to start. Have the class take turns giving the student two commands to move the student to a new location.
- Students may only use four directions: left, right, forward, and backward.

Real-World Connection

Ask students to share real-life circumstances in which they need to calculate the distance between two points or when it might be helpful to use a coordinate plane. If necessary, start the discussion by saying that maps and some video games are based on a coordinate plane. Have students explain or show the connection.

Examples: building a fence, putting up baseboards in a room, reading a map for an outdoor activity such as hiking

AT A GLANCE

Students read a problem and then use what they know about rectangles and coordinates to find missing coordinates and dimensions.

STEP BY STEP

- Read the problem at the top of the page as a class.
- Be sure to listen for appropriate mathematical terminology (*SMP 6*) as you go through Graph It and Model It with your students.

SMP Tip: Students need many opportunities to connect and explain the connections between different representations (*SMP 4*). After students graph the problem on this page, ask them to explain why sketching the rectangle is a good strategy for solving the problem.

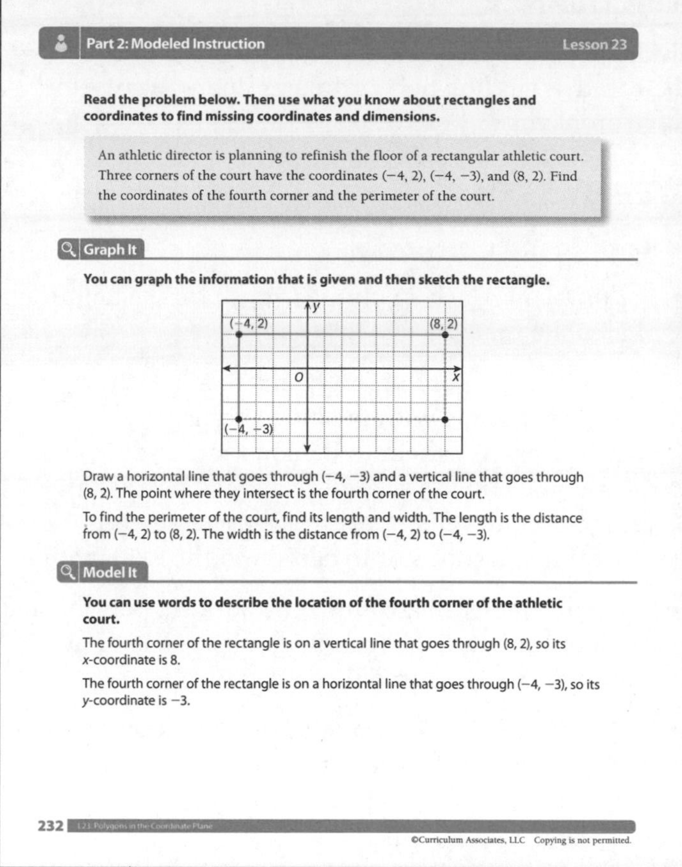

Part 2: Modeled Instruction Lesson 23

Read the problem below. Then use what you know about rectangles and coordinates to find missing coordinates and dimensions.

An athletic director is planning to refinish the floor of a rectangular athletic court. Three corners of the court have the coordinates (−4, 2), (−4, −3), and (8, 2). Find the coordinates of the fourth corner and the perimeter of the court.

Graph It

You can graph the information that is given and then sketch the rectangle.

Draw a horizontal line that goes through (−4, −3) and a vertical line that goes through (8, 2). The point where they intersect is the fourth corner of the court.

To find the perimeter of the court, find its length and width. The length is the distance from (−4, 2) to (8, 2). The width is the distance from (−4, 2) to (−4, −3).

Model It

You can use words to describe the location of the fourth corner of the athletic court.

The fourth corner of the rectangle is on a vertical line that goes through (8, 2), so its *x*-coordinate is 8.

The fourth corner of the rectangle is on a horizontal line that goes through (−4, −3), so its *y*-coordinate is −3.

232 L23: Polygons in the Coordinate Plane

©Curriculum Associates, LLC Copying is not permitted.

Mathematical Discourse

- *Look at the graph in the Model It. If someone said that one corner of the rectangle is on a vertical line that goes through (2, 8) what would you say?*

  Students should recognize that the ordered pair given is inverted; it should be (8, 2).

- *If your classmates had trouble remembering whether the x- or y-coordinate comes first in an ordered pair, how would you help them remember?*

  Students might suggest that *x* comes before *y* in the alphabet, so *x* always comes first.

- *How are the streets of your town similar to the coordinate plane? How are they different?*

  Similar: The coordinate plane and many towns (or parts of towns) form a grid. Different: Town maps generally use north, south, east, and west instead of positive or negative numbers to show direction.

AT A GLANCE

Students revisit the problem on page 232 and use their understanding of coordinates and polygons to solve problems.

STEP BY STEP

- Read Connect It as a class.
- For problem 3, ask a volunteer to share the definition of *absolute value*.
- As students respond to problems 3 and 4, show another rectangle with positive and negative coordinates. Ask them to demonstrate and explain the methods on the second rectangle, particularly using absolute value. Encourage others to ask clarifying questions or to add on to the explanation.
- For problem 5, ask a volunteer to draw a polygon and use it to illustrate the meanings of *perimeter* and *area*, which are commonly confused.
- Have students work through Try It and then discuss their answers with their partner.

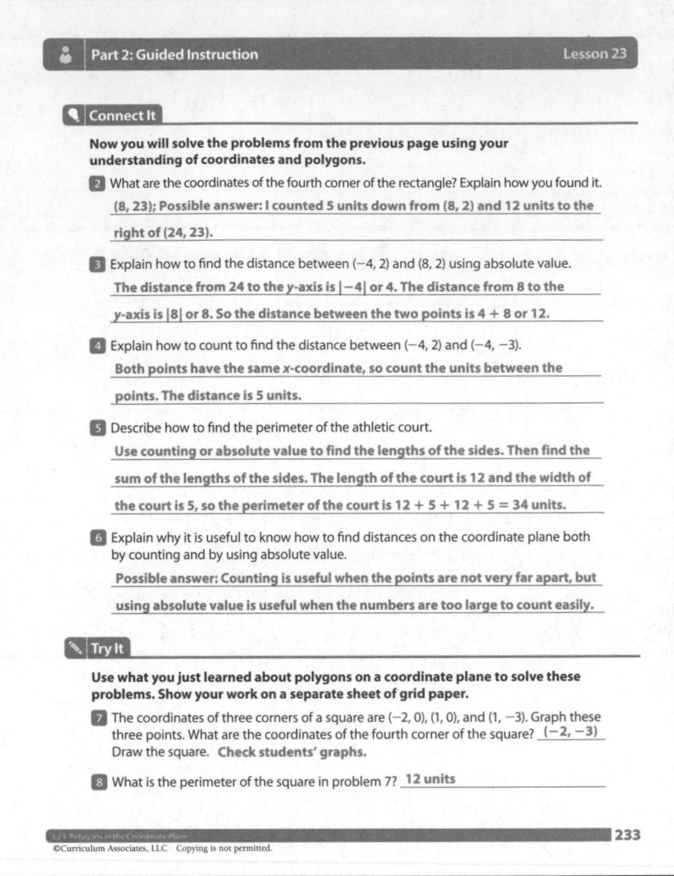

Part 2: Guided Instruction Lesson 23

Connect It

Now you will solve the problems from the previous page using your understanding of coordinates and polygons.

2 What are the coordinates of the fourth corner of the rectangle? Explain how you found it.
(8, 23); Possible answer: I counted 5 units down from (8, 2) and 12 units to the right of (24, 23).

3 Explain how to find the distance between (−4, 2) and (8, 2) using absolute value.
The distance from 24 to the *y*-axis is |−4| or 4. The distance from 8 to the *y*-axis is |8| or 8. So the distance between the two points is 4 + 8 or 12.

4 Explain how to count to find the distance between (−4, 2) and (−4, −3).
Both points have the same *x*-coordinate, so count the units between the points. The distance is 5 units.

5 Describe how to find the perimeter of the athletic court.
Use counting or absolute value to find the lengths of the sides. Then find the sum of the lengths of the sides. The length of the court is 12 and the width of the court is 5, so the perimeter of the court is 12 + 5 + 12 + 5 = 34 units.

6 Explain why it is useful to know how to find distances on the coordinate plane both by counting and by using absolute value.
Possible answer: Counting is useful when the points are not very far apart, but using absolute value is useful when the numbers are too large to count easily.

Try It

Use what you just learned about polygons on a coordinate plane to solve these problems. Show your work on a separate sheet of grid paper.

7 The coordinates of three corners of a square are (−2, 0), (1, 0), and (1, −3). Graph these three points. What are the coordinates of the fourth corner of the square? **(−2, −3)** Draw the square. **Check students' graphs.**

8 What is the perimeter of the square in problem 7? **12 units**

L23: Polygons in the Coordinate Plane 233

©Curriculum Associates, LLC Copying is not permitted.

Hands-On Activity

Use Geoboards to create polygons.

Materials: geoboards, rubber bands

- Distribute a geoboard and at least 10 rubber bands to each student. Have each student create four quadrants on geoboards by connecting the middle pegs to form axes. Label the top and side with coordinates.
- Ask students to use the remaining rubber bands to create polygons on their geoboard.
- Have students hold up their geoboards. Scan the class to assess understanding. This would be a good time to review special quadrilaterals, triangles, and other polygons.
- Pair up students. Have all students make a rectangle on their geoboards and calculate the rectangle's perimeter both by counting and using absolute value.
- Have students in each pair swap their geoboards and calculate the perimeter of their partner's rectangle.

TRY IT SOLUTIONS

7 *Solution:* (−2, −3); check students' grid paper to see if they drew a square; Students may draw a square on the coordinate plane to find the missing coordinate.

8 *Solution:* 12 units; Students may count the units around the square on the graph they drew for problem 7.

ERROR ALERT: Students who wrote 9 square units found the square's area instead of its perimeter. Remind students that perimeter is the distance around a figure.

AT A GLANCE

Students read a word problem and then explore how to find the area of a polygon on a coordinate plane.

STEP BY STEP

- Read the problem at the top of the page as a class.
- Ask students to read aloud the sections of the problem that let them identify the shape, without a diagram. Ask: *Could you identify the polygon if you knew it had four vertices? Five?*
- For Solve It, point out that the commutative and associative properties of multiplication allow us to multiply the factors in any order and we choose the order that is easiest for us. Discuss different ways to multiply $\frac{1}{2}$, 8, and 3 and which way students prefer.

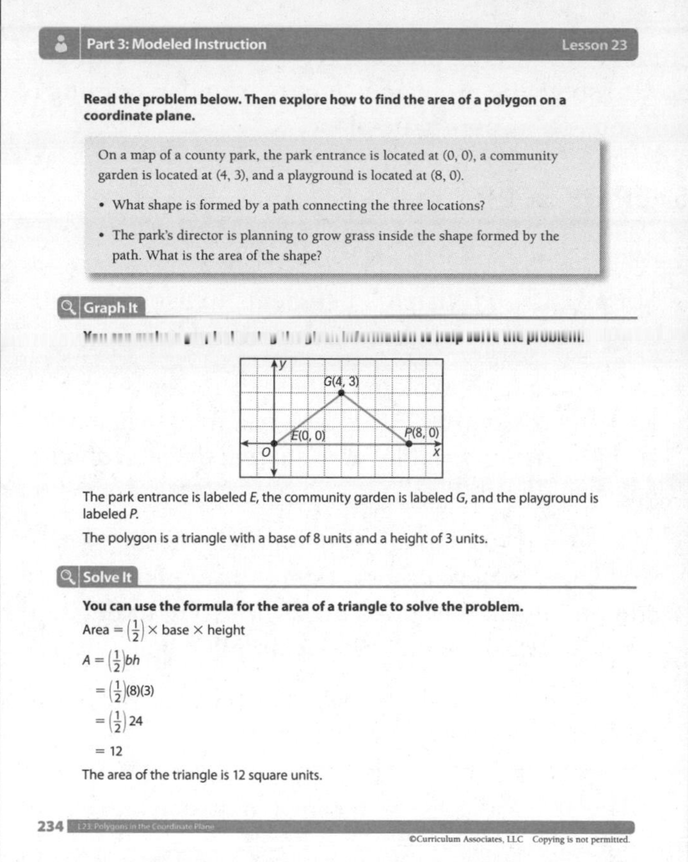

Part 3: Modeled Instruction Lesson 23

Read the problem below. Then explore how to find the area of a polygon on a coordinate plane.

On a map of a county park, the park entrance is located at (0, 0), a community garden is located at (4, 3), and a playground is located at (8, 0).

- What shape is formed by a path connecting the three locations?
- The park's director is planning to grow grass inside the shape formed by the path. What is the area of the shape?

Graph It

You can [illegible] information to help solve the problem.

The park entrance is labeled *E*, the community garden is labeled *G*, and the playground is labeled *P*.

The polygon is a triangle with a base of 8 units and a height of 3 units.

Solve It

You can use the formula for the area of a triangle to solve the problem.

Area $= \left(\frac{1}{2}\right) \times$ base $\times$ height

$A = \left(\frac{1}{2}\right)bh$

$= \left(\frac{1}{2}\right)(8)(3)$

$= \left(\frac{1}{2}\right)24$

$= 12$

The area of the triangle is 12 square units.

234 L23: Polygons in the Coordinate Plane

Mathematical Discourse

- *The polygon in Graph It is a triangle. Can you think of other terms to identify the polygon?*

  Answers may include *obtuse triangle*, *isosceles triangle*, and *obtuse isosceles triangle*.

- *What makes a triangle obtuse? Isosceles? What are some other classifications for triangles?*

  Obtuse triangles have an angle greater than 90 degrees; an isosceles triangle has two equivalent sides. Other classifications may include equilateral, right, acute, or scalene.

- *When using the area formula, you have to multiply $\frac{1}{2}$ by the base by the height. Why do we multiply by $\frac{1}{2}$?*

  Students may remember from Lesson 22 that two equivalent triangles together make a parallelogram. Because one triangle is half a parallelogram, you can multiply $\frac{1}{2}bh$ to find the area of the triangle.

AT A GLANCE

Students revisit the problem on page 234 and explain how to solve the problem using their understanding of polygons on a coordinate plane.

STEP BY STEP

- Read Connect It as a class.
- For problem 11, listen for students to use the word *congruent* when describing the triangles.
- Ask students to explain in their own words why Kristina divided *EGP* into two triangles. Then ask: *Would Kristina's method work to find the area of other polygons?* [yes]
- Ask several students to explain their responses to problem 13. Have others restate the explanations, add on, or ask questions until the group understands why the area is not a negative number.
- Have students work through the Try It problems and discuss their answers with a partner.

SMP Tip: Students reason abstractly when they discuss the meaning of the coordinate values (*SMP 2*).

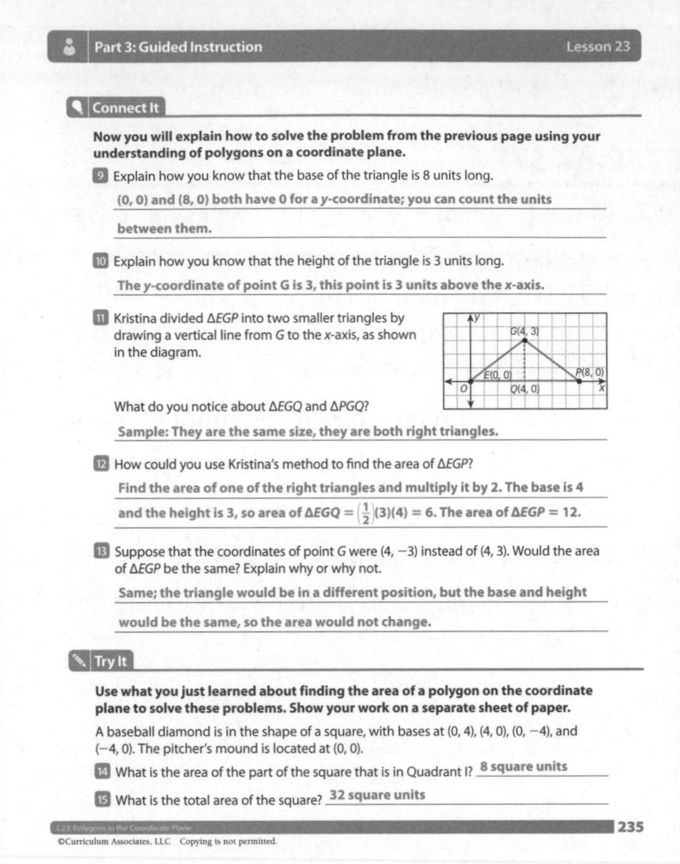

Part 3: Guided Instruction Lesson 23

Connect It

Now you will explain how to solve the problem from the previous page using your understanding of polygons on a coordinate plane.

9 Explain how you know that the base of the triangle is 8 units long.

(0, 0) and (8, 0) both have 0 for a *y*-coordinate; you can count the units between them.

10 Explain how you know that the height of the triangle is 3 units long.

The *y*-coordinate of point G is 3, this point is 3 units above the *x*-axis.

11 Kristina divided ΔEGP into two smaller triangles by drawing a vertical line from *G* to the *x*-axis, as shown in the diagram.

What do you notice about ΔEGQ and ΔPGQ?

Sample: They are the same size, they are both right triangles.

12 How could you use Kristina's method to find the area of ΔEGP?

Find the area of one of the right triangles and multiply it by 2. The base is 4 and the height is 3, so area of $\Delta EGQ = \left(\frac{1}{2}\right)(3)(4) = 6$. The area of $\Delta EGP = 12$.

13 Suppose that the coordinates of point *G* were (4, −3) instead of (4, 3). Would the area of ΔEGP be the same? Explain why or why not.

Same; the triangle would be in a different position, but the base and height would be the same, so the area would not change.

Try It

Use what you just learned about finding the area of a polygon on the coordinate plane to solve these problems. Show your work on a separate sheet of paper.

A baseball diamond is in the shape of a square, with bases at (0, 4), (4, 0), (0, −4), and (−4, 0). The pitcher's mound is located at (0, 0).

14 What is the area of the part of the square that is in Quadrant I? **8 square units**

15 What is the total area of the square? **32 square units**

L23: Polygons in the Coordinate Plane 235

©Curriculum Associates, LLC Copying is not permitted.

TRY IT SOLUTIONS

14 *Solution:* 8 square units; Students may draw the square on the coordinate plane.

ERROR ALERT: Students who wrote 16 square units forgot to multiply by $\frac{1}{2}$ when finding the area of the triangle. Students who consistently forget would benefit from more time working with cutting a parallelogram into half to find the area of the triangle.

15 *Solution:* 32 square units; Students may realize that because the area of the triangle is 8 and there are 4 triangles altogether, they can multiply 8 and 4 to find the area.

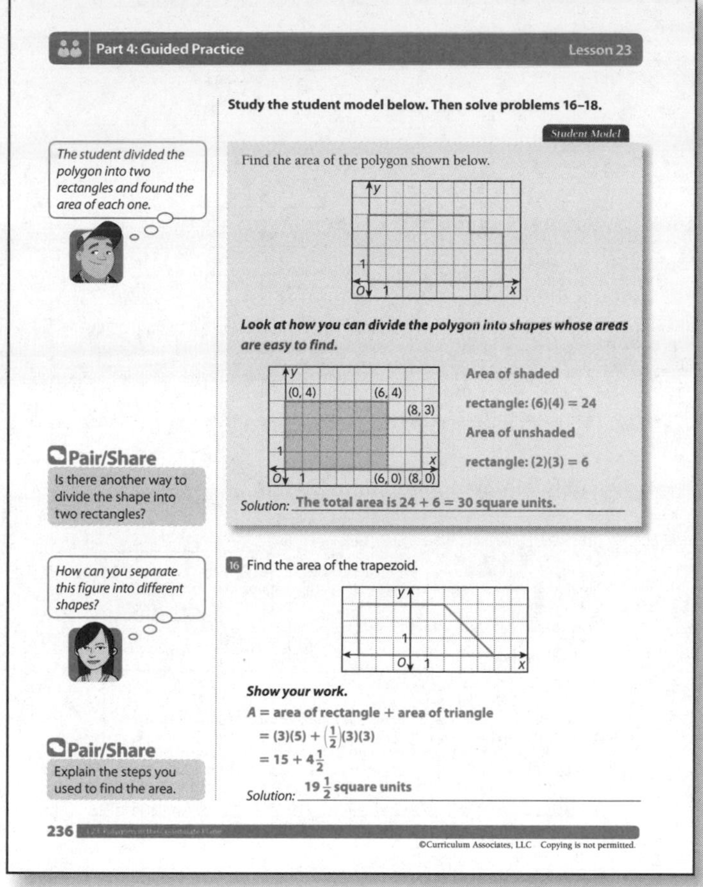

Part 4: Guided Practice Lesson 23

Study the student model below. Then solve problems 16–18.

Student Model

Find the area of the polygon shown below.

Look at how you can divide the polygon into shapes whose areas are easy to find.

(0, 4) (6, 4) (8, 3) (6, 0) (8, 0)

Area of shaded rectangle: (6)(4) = 24

Area of unshaded rectangle: (2)(3) = 6

Solution: The total area is 24 + 6 = 30 square units.

The student divided the polygon into two rectangles and found the area of each one.

Pair/Share Is there another way to divide the shape into two rectangles?

16 Find the area of the trapezoid.

How can you separate this figure into different shapes?

Show your work.

A = area of rectangle + area of triangle

$= (3)(5) + (\frac{1}{2})(3)(3)$

$= 15 + 4\frac{1}{2}$

Solution: $19\frac{1}{2}$ square units

Pair/Share Explain the steps you used to find the area.

236 L23: Polygons in the Coordinate Plane ©Curriculum Associates, LLC Copying is not permitted.

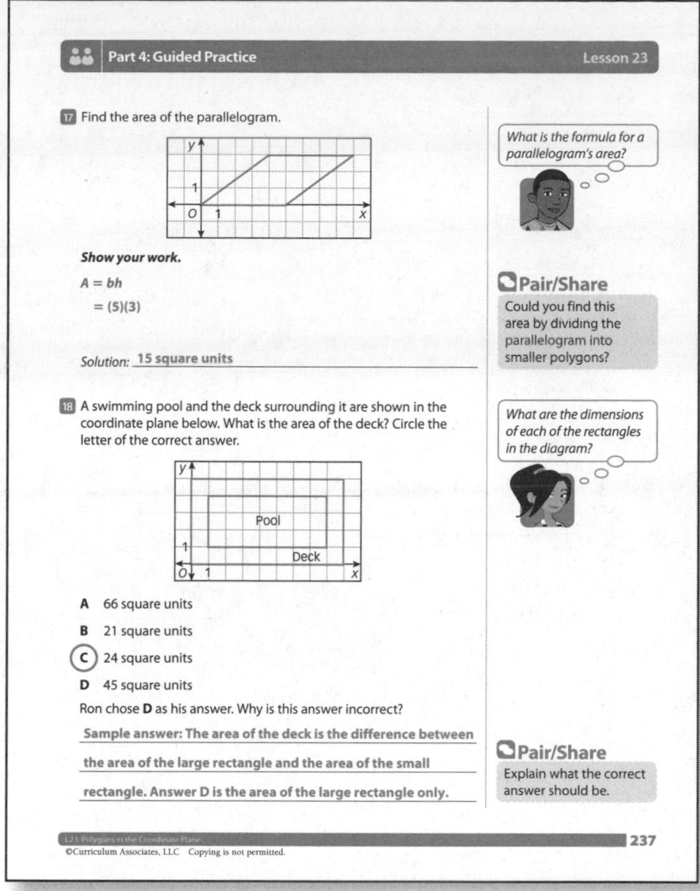

Part 4: Guided Practice Lesson 23

17 Find the area of the parallelogram.

What is the formula for a parallelogram's area?

Show your work.

$A = bh$

$= (5)(3)$

Solution: 15 square units

Pair/Share Could you find this area by dividing the parallelogram into smaller polygons?

18 A swimming pool and the deck surrounding it are shown in the coordinate plane below. What is the area of the deck? Circle the letter of the correct answer.

What are the dimensions of each of the rectangles in the diagram?

Pool

Deck

A 66 square units

B 21 square units

(C) 24 square units

D 45 square units

Ron chose **D** as his answer. Why is this answer incorrect?

Sample answer: The area of the deck is the difference between the area of the large rectangle and the area of the small rectangle. Answer D is the area of the large rectangle only.

Pair/Share Explain what the correct answer should be.

L23: Polygons in the Coordinate Plane ©Curriculum Associates, LLC Copying is not permitted. 237

AT A GLANCE

Students study a model and then use it solve problems involving polygons in the coordinate plane.

STEP BY STEP

- Ask students to solve the problems individually.
- When students have completed each problem, have them Pair/Share to discuss their solutions with a partner or in a group.

SOLUTIONS

Ex Polygon is divided into simpler shapes. Total area is 24 + 6 = 30 square units.

16 *Solution:* $19\frac{1}{2}$ square units; Students could decompose the trapezoid into a rectangle and a triangle, find the area of each, and add them to find the total area of the trapezoid. ***(DOK 1)***

17 *Solution:* 15 square units; Students could solve the problem by using the area formula for a parallelogram, $A = bh$. ***(DOK 1)***

18 *Solution:* **C**; Ron found the area of the large rectangle.

Explain to students why the other two answer choices are not correct:

A is not correct because it is the area of the large rectangle plus the area of the small rectangle.

B is not correct because it is the area of the small rectangle (pool). ***(DOK 3)***

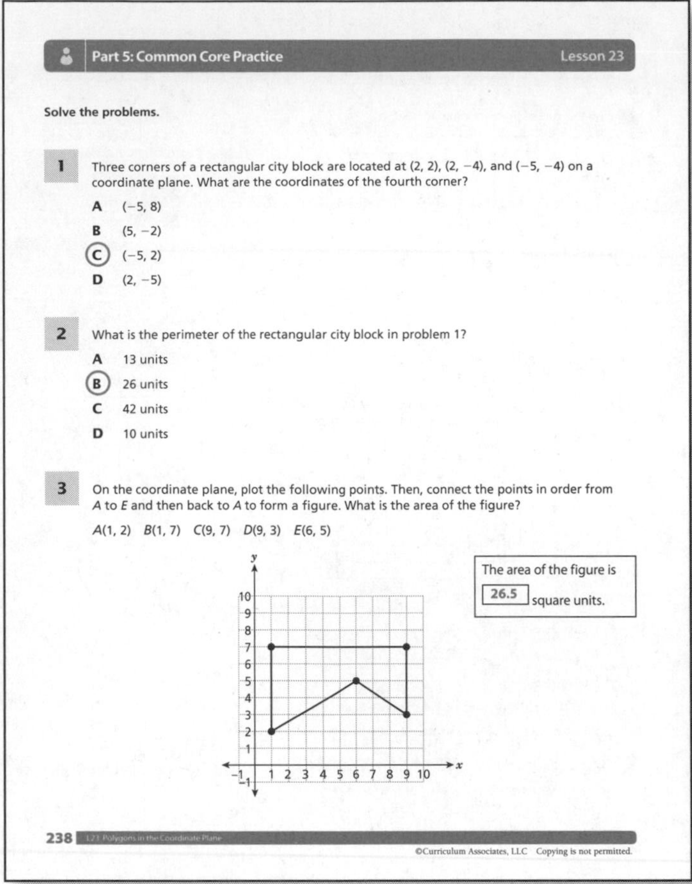
Part 5: Common Core Practice Lesson 23

Solve the problems.

1 Three corners of a rectangular city block are located at (2, 2), (2, −4), and (−5, −4) on a coordinate plane. What are the coordinates of the fourth corner?

A (−5, 8)
B (5, −2)
Ⓒ (−5, 2)
D (2, −5)

2 What is the perimeter of the rectangular city block in problem 1?

A 13 units
Ⓑ 26 units
C 42 units
D 10 units

3 On the coordinate plane, plot the following points. Then, connect the points in order from *A* to *E* and then back to *A* to form a figure. What is the area of the figure?

A(1, 2) *B*(1, 7) *C*(9, 7) *D*(9, 3) *E*(6, 5)

The area of the figure is 26.5 square units.

238 L23: Polygons in the Coordinate Plane ©Curriculum Associates, LLC Copying is not permitted.

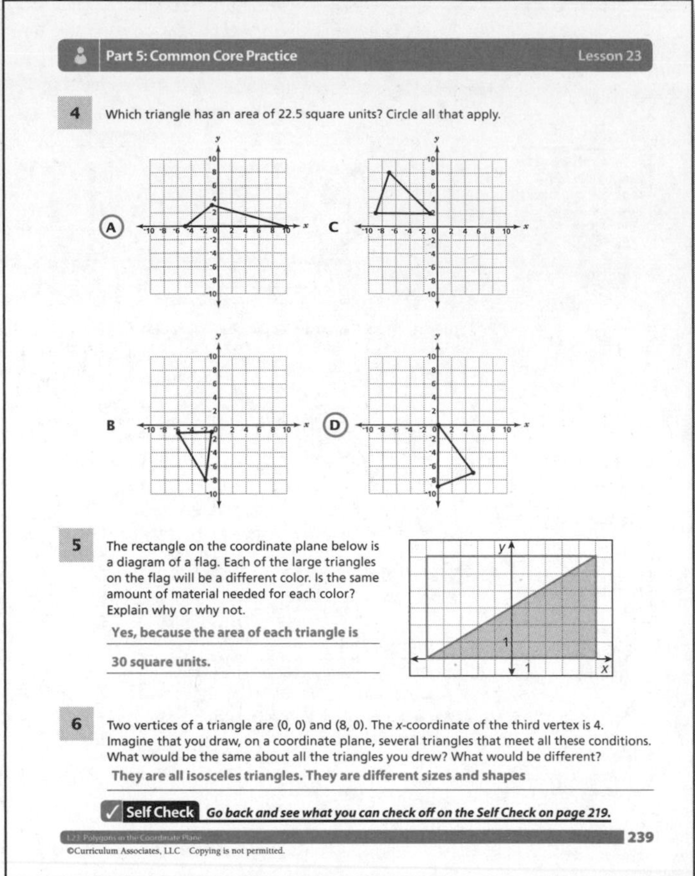
Part 5: Common Core Practice Lesson 23

4 Which triangle has an area of 22.5 square units? Circle all that apply.

Ⓐ C B Ⓓ

5 The rectangle on the coordinate plane below is a diagram of a flag. Each of the large triangles on the flag will be a different color. Is the same amount of material needed for each color? Explain why or why not.

Yes, because the area of each triangle is 30 square units.

6 Two vertices of a triangle are (0, 0) and (8, 0). The *x*-coordinate of the third vertex is 4. Imagine that you draw, on a coordinate plane, several triangles that meet all these conditions. What would be the same about all the triangles you drew? What would be different?

They are all isosceles triangles. They are different sizes and shapes

✓ Self Check *Go back and see what you can check off on the Self Check on page 219.*

L23: Polygons in the Coordinate Plane ©Curriculum Associates, LLC Copying is not permitted. 239

AT A GLANCE

Students use a coordinate plane to solve problems involving area and perimeter that might appear on a mathematics test.

SOLUTIONS

1 *Solution:* **C**; Students could plot the points in the coordinate plane, and then count to find the 4th point. ***(DOK 2)***

2 *Solution:* **B**; Students use the coordinates of the ordered pairs to find the side lengths of the rectangle to be 6, 7, 6, and 7. Add the side lengths to find the perimeter. ***(DOK 2)***

3 *Solution:* **26.5**; Break apart the figure into two trapezoids or a rectangle and two triangles. Find the area of each figure and add to find the total area. ***(DOK 2)***

4 *Solution:* **A**; The height is 3, and the base length is 15. Substitute these values into the area formula to get an area of 22.5.

D; The height is 5, and the base length is 9. Substitute these values into the area formula to get an area of 22.5. ***(DOK 2)***

5 *Solution:* Yes, because the area of each triangle is 30 square units. ***(DOK 3)***

6 *Solution:* Sample response: They are all isosceles triangles. They are different sizes and shapes. ***(DOK 3)***

Assessment and Remediation

- Ask students to find the perimeter of a rectangle with points (3, 3), (3, −4), and (−7, −4). [34 units]
- For students who are struggling, use the chart below to guide remediation.
- After providing remediation, check students' understanding. Ask students to find the perimeter of a rectangle with points (−5, 1), (2, 1), and (2, −3). [22 units]
- If a student is still having difficulty, use ***Ready Instruction, Level 6,*** Lesson 14.

If the error is . . .	Students may . . .	To remediate . . .
70	have correctly found the missing vertex but found area instead of perimeter.	Remind students that perimeter is the distance around. They should add the length of each of the sides.
17	have found the length of the two sides between the three given points but did not find the missing coordinate or sides.	Remind students that they must have all four sides of a rectangle to find its perimeter. Help students count on the coordinate plane to find the missing coordinate and sides.
35	have used the three coordinates given to form a triangle and found the area of the triangle.	Remind students to draw a picture and underline key information in a problem. Point out that they were to find the perimeter of a rectangle.

Hands-On Activity

Physically move on a coordinate plane.

Materials: floor-sized coordinate plane

- The coordinate plane could be made with painter's tape or an old sheet on which you have drawn *x*- and *y*-axes. Be sure it ranges from at least −10 to 10 on both axes.
- Give students the coordinates (9, 2), (9, −2), (−1, −2), and (−1, 2).
- Ask them to walk the coordinate plane to find the perimeter. [28 units] Then, ask them to determine the area. [40 square units]
- Continue as needed with additional figures and allow students to physically move on the coordinate plane.

Challenge Activity

Design a garden.

- Tell students that they have been chosen to design a garden for the school. You have already bought a border that could go around a 48 unit perimeter.
- Ask students to come up with at least three different gardens with a perimeter of 48 units.
- After they have completed this task tell them that they must also create a cover to protect the garden from frost.
- The smaller the area is, the cheaper the cost of protecting the garden. Which of their gardens has the smallest area?

Lesson 24 (Student Book pages 240–251)

Nets and Surface Area

LESSON OBJECTIVES

- Recognize that surfaces of three-dimensional shapes are composed of two-dimensional faces (polygons).
- Use a net to represent a 3-D figure (polyhedron).
- Use a net to find the surface area of a polyhedron made up of rectangles and triangles.

PREREQUISITE SKILLS

- Understand that polygons can be decomposed.
- Understand that area is measured in square units.
- Find the area of a rectangle and of a triangle.

VOCABULARY

base: the face of a geometric figure from which the height can be measured

net: a flat, "unfolded" representation of a prism or pyramid

surface area: the sum of the areas of the faces of a figure

triangular prism: a three-dimensional figure that has two parallel triangular faces that are the same size and shape

pyramid: a three-dimensional figure whose base is a polygon and whose other faces are triangles

THE LEARNING PROGRESSION

From elementary school, students have had repeated experience working with shapes. They compose and decompose shapes, identify and classify shapes by their defining attributes, recognize and describe sub-categories of shapes in the case of quadrilaterals, and find perimeter, area, and volume.

In this lesson, students learn to find the surface area of pyramids and prisms by decomposing them into two-dimensional nets and finding the area of each part.

In Grade 7, students build on their knowledge of surface area and use formulas to solve more complex problems. They find areas of rectangular and triangular prisms when faces are composed of more than one shape.

Ready *Teacher Toolbox* Teacher-Toolbox.com

	Prerequisite Skills	*6.G.A.4*
Ready Lessons		✓
Tools for Instruction		✓✓
Interactive Tutorials	✓	✓

CCSS Focus

6.G.A.4 Represent three-dimensional figures using nets made up of rectangles and triangles, and use the nets to find the surface area of these figures. Apply these techniques in the context of solving real-world and mathematical problems.

ADDITIONAL STANDARDS: ***6.G.A.1*** *(see page A42 for full text)*

STANDARDS FOR MATHEMATICAL PRACTICE: ***SMP 7, 8*** *(see page A9 for full text)*

AT A GLANCE

Students find the surface area of a rectangular prism by unfolding the three-dimensional prism and then finding and adding the areas of the six faces.

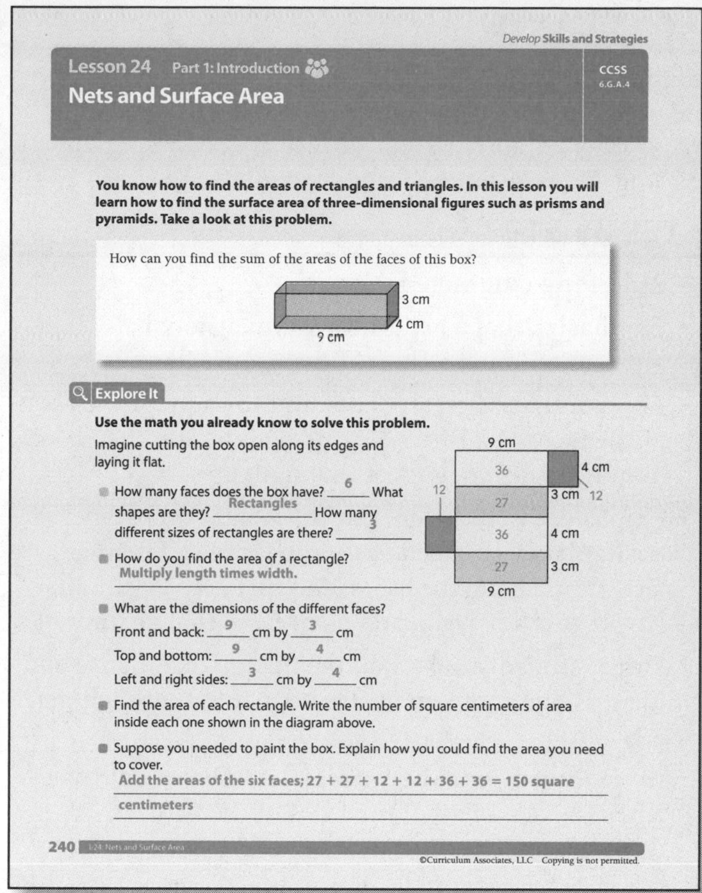
Develop **Skills and Strategies**

Lesson 24 Part 1: Introduction

Nets and Surface Area

CCSS 6.G.A.4

You know how to find the areas of rectangles and triangles. In this lesson you will learn how to find the surface area of three-dimensional figures such as prisms and pyramids. Take a look at this problem.

How can you find the sum of the areas of the faces of this box?

Explore It

Use the math you already know to solve this problem.

Imagine cutting the box open along its edges and laying it flat.

- How many faces does the box have? **6** What shapes are they? **Rectangles** How many different sizes of rectangles are there? **3**
- How do you find the area of a rectangle? **Multiply length times width.**
- What are the dimensions of the different faces?
  Front and back: **9** cm by **3** cm
  Top and bottom: **9** cm by **4** cm
  Left and right sides: **3** cm by **4** cm
- Find the area of each rectangle. Write the number of square centimeters of area inside each one shown in the diagram above.
- Suppose you needed to paint the box. Explain how you could find the area you need to cover. **Add the areas of the six faces; 27 + 27 + 12 + 12 + 36 + 36 = 150 square centimeters**

240 L24: Nets and Surface Area

STEP BY STEP

- Tell students that this page models finding the total area of a rectangular prism by first unfolding it and breaking it down into two-dimensional rectangles.
- Have students read the problem at the top of the page.
- Explain to students that a *face* is a two-dimensional polygon.
- Work through Explore It as a class.
- Ask, *If you cut open the box and lay it flat, can you tell what the prism is made up of? What shape is each face of the prism?* [a rectangle]
- Point out that the net has three pairs of rectangles, and the rectangles in each pair have the same dimensions.
- Ask a volunteer to explain how to find the area of a rectangle.
- Guide students to see that each face of the prism has a corresponding face of the same dimensions.
- Ask volunteers to explain their solution to the last problem on page 240.

ELL Support

Use models of geometric solids to show students the meanings of *edge, face,* and *prism*. Help students relate each polygon of the net with a face of the prism. Point out that the *sides* of the polygon become the *edges* of the prism.

SMP Tip: Students use spatial reasoning to unfold the three-dimensional rectangular prism and recognize that it is made up of six rectangles. Encourage students to look for and make use of structure by seeing objects (e.g., three-dimensional prisms) as being composed of several shapes (*SMP 7*).

Mathematical Discourse

- *What are some rectangular prisms you find in your surroundings?*

  Student answers will vary. Listen for answers such as buildings, packages, moving boxes. You might need to prompt students to think about everyday places inside their homes, school, or communities.

- *Why would we want to know the surface area of a real-life rectangular prism? What would we do with the information?*

  Encourage students to think about activities such as painting, wrapping, or other reasons to cover real-life prisms. Remind them that surface area is the total area of all of the rectangles of a rectangular prism.

AT A GLANCE

Students examine how three-dimensional figures can be unfolded into two-dimensional flat surfaces called nets. They explore finding surface area of a figure by adding the areas of the faces shown in the net.

STEP BY STEP

- Read Find Out More as a class.
- Emphasize that a *net* is a two-dimensional representation of a three-dimensional figure.
- Explain that when students find the sum of the areas of the faces of a three-dimensional figure, they have found the *surface area* of that figure.
- Emphasize that a *triangular prism* has two parallel triangular faces called *bases* and three rectangular faces connecting the bases, and that a *pyramid* has a *base* that is a polygon and other faces that are triangles.
- Direct students to look at the net for each figure and identify the component shapes making up each net.
- Help students find the corresponding faces of each three-dimensional figure on its net. Point out that a net is made of all of the faces of the three-dimensional figure.
- Read and discuss Reflect as a class.

SMP Tip: Understanding and using geometric vocabulary is one way that students attend to precision when discussing and writing about shapes. (*SMP 6*) Use the words regularly in class and make clear your expectation that students use the appropriate terms.

ELL Support

- Visualize and classify the new terms in this lesson using a graphic organizer: *rectangular prism, triangular prism, pyramid, net, base, surface area.* Note: the term goes in the center oval.

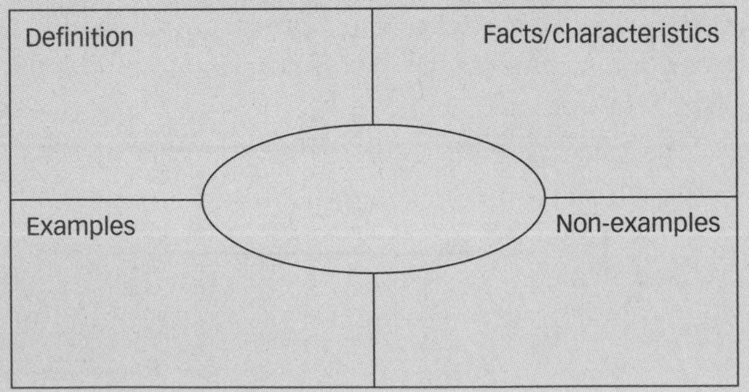

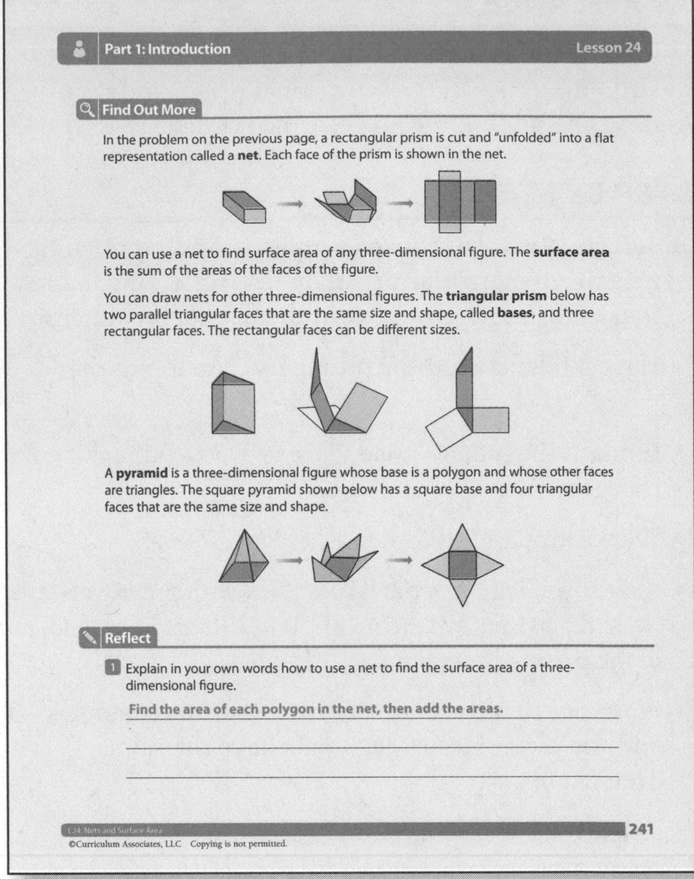

Part 1: Introduction — Lesson 24

Find Out More

In the problem on the previous page, a rectangular prism is cut and "unfolded" into a flat representation called a **net**. Each face of the prism is shown in the net.

You can use a net to find surface area of any three-dimensional figure. The **surface area** is the sum of the areas of the faces of the figure.

You can draw nets for other three-dimensional figures. The **triangular prism** below has two parallel triangular faces that are the same size and shape, called **bases**, and three rectangular faces. The rectangular faces can be different sizes.

A **pyramid** is a three-dimensional figure whose base is a polygon and whose other faces are triangles. The square pyramid shown below has a square base and four triangular faces that are the same size and shape.

Reflect

1 Explain in your own words how to use a net to find the surface area of a three-dimensional figure.

Find the area of each polygon in the net, then add the areas.

L24: Nets and Surface Area 241
©Curriculum Associates, LLC Copying is not permitted.

Real-World Connection

- *Read the following text to students. Then have them answer the following question related to this situation:*

  "Sabrina constructed a three-dimensional pyramid from a cardboard cut-out which Carlos accidentally stepped on and crushed. Carlos picked up the flat two-dimensional figure and said, 'Look, your three-dimensional figure is now two-dimensional, so it must be a net.' Sabrina looked at the flat piece of cardboard and disagreed."

- *What are some arguments Sabrina could have used to prove her point?*

  Listen for students to explain that the flat figure is just a crushed or stepped-on three-dimensional object, not an "unfolded" version of the object that displays its faces. Listen for terms such as *unfolded, polygons, two-dimensional, faces,* and *three-dimensional.*

AT A GLANCE

Students read a word problem and examine a rectangular prism and its net to explore how to find the surface area of a rectangular prism. They also examine a table used to organize the needed data.

STEP BY STEP

- Read the problem at the top of the page as a class. Have a volunteer explain the connection between the amount of leather needed and the surface area of the box.
- Read Picture It. Point out that the net shows each of the corresponding rectangular faces of the box with matching dimensions.
- Read Model It. Ask, *How can a table help you find the surface area of the box?* [Students may mention that a table helps them keep track of the values for length, width, and height; helps them keep track of when they have found the areas of both faces in each pair; and helps them keep the area of each face in a single column, leading to easy summation at the end.]
- Have pairs of students work together to point to the sides of the box and find the matching rectangles in the net and in the table.

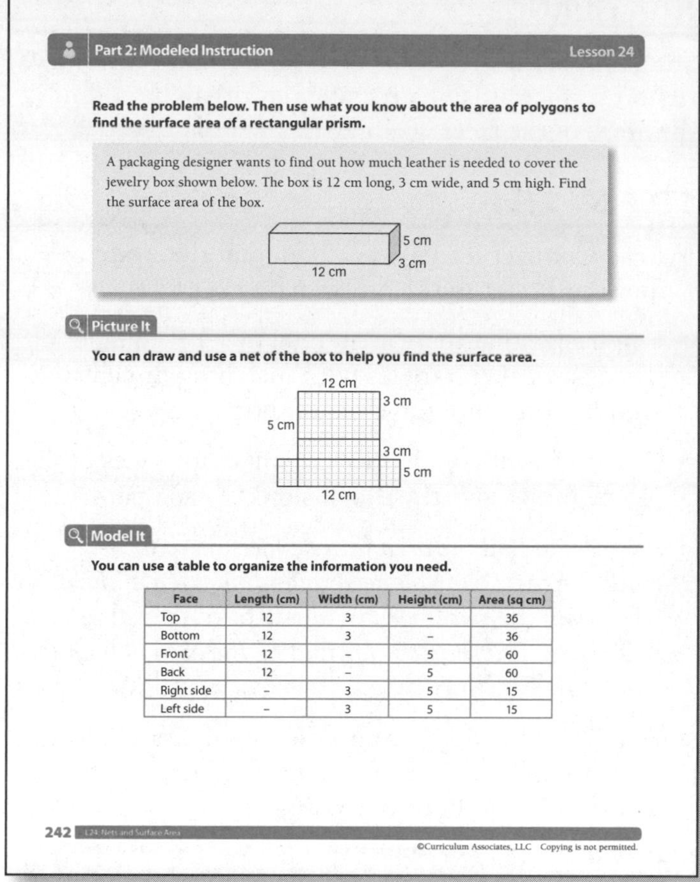

Part 2: Modeled Instruction Lesson 24

Read the problem below. Then use what you know about the area of polygons to find the surface area of a rectangular prism.

A packaging designer wants to find out how much leather is needed to cover the jewelry box shown below. The box is 12 cm long, 3 cm wide, and 5 cm high. Find the surface area of the box.

Picture It

You can draw and use a net of the box to help you find the surface area.

Model It

You can use a table to organize the information you need.

Face	Length (cm)	Width (cm)	Height (cm)	Area (sq cm)
Top	12	3	–	36
Bottom	12	3	–	36
Front	12	–	5	60
Back	12	–	5	60
Right side	–	3	5	15
Left side	–	3	5	15

242 L24: Nets and Surface Area

©Curriculum Associates, LLC Copying is not permitted.

Hands-On Activity

Create a rectangular prism from its net.

Materials: teacher-drawn net for each student, scissors, tape

- Prepare an enlarged copy of the net on student page 242 for each student.
- Tell students to cut out the net only around the outside lines.
- Tell students to fold on each line that is inside the net. They should fold all the same way—either outward or inward.
- Let students tape the faces together.

Mathematical Discourse

- *Page 242 shows a sketch of a prism and its net. How are they different? Which do you find most helpful for thinking about the surface area? Why?*

  Students' preferences will vary, but discussion might note that the labeled sketch is easier to draw and gives information concisely, but it may not be as helpful as the net for seeing all of the faces.

- *What do we lose when we unfold a three-dimensional figure into a two-dimensional net? What do we gain?*

  Encourage students to use their own words to describe what happens to the figure. Listen for them to say that the figure's original shape is lost if the third dimension is lost. However, we gain an understanding of the shapes that make up its surface and a new way for understanding and calculating its surface area.

AT A GLANCE

Students revisit the problem on page 242 to learn how to find surface area of a rectangular prism by adding the areas of the faces.

STEP BY STEP

- Read Connect It as a class. Point out that the questions refer to the problem on page 242.
- Emphasize that there are a total of six rectangles or three pairs of rectangles with matching dimensions and that these are the faces of the prism.
- Guide students to identify the matching faces of the prism and to give the dimensions of each pair.
- Ask, *If you find the area for one face of a pair of matching faces, do you need to find the area of the other face?* [No, the two faces in a pair have the same area.] Ask, *What is a shortcut for finding the area of both faces in a pair?* [Multiply by 2.]
- Have students do Try It on their own. Encourage them to use a table to organize their data. Then discuss the solutions as a class.

SMP Tip: When students recognize that there are pairs of faces with matching dimensions, they realize they can calculate the area and multiply by 2 instead of repeating the area calculation. Encourage students to notice if calculations are repeated and to look for general methods and for shortcuts (*SMP 8*).

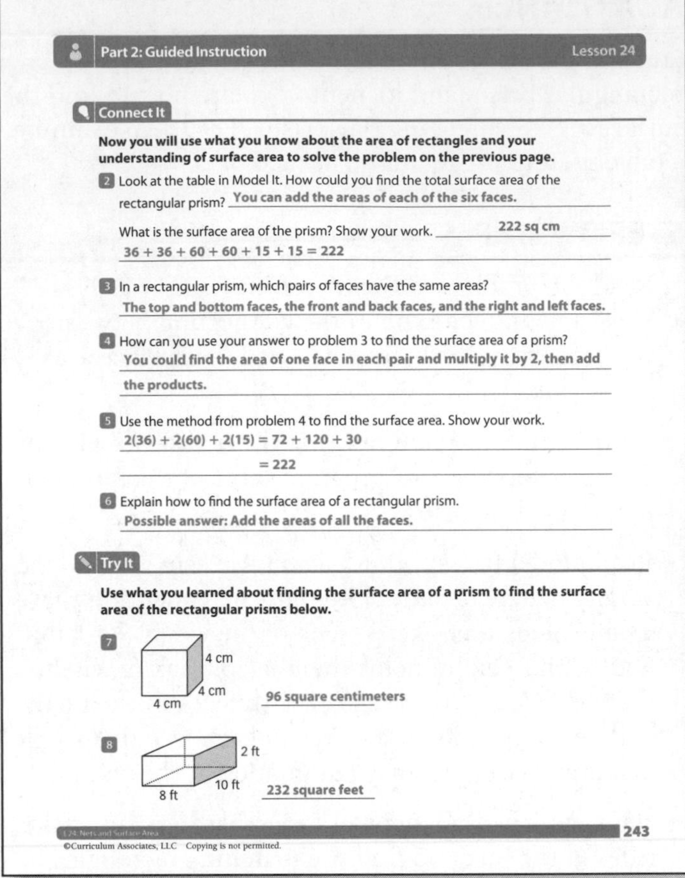

Part 2: Guided Instruction Lesson 24

Connect It

Now you will use what you know about the area of rectangles and your understanding of surface area to solve the problem on the previous page.

2 Look at the table in Model It. How could you find the total surface area of the rectangular prism? **You can add the areas of each of the six faces.**

What is the surface area of the prism? Show your work. **222 sq cm**

36 + 36 + 60 + 60 + 15 + 15 = 222

3 In a rectangular prism, which pairs of faces have the same areas?

The top and bottom faces, the front and back faces, and the right and left faces.

4 How can you use your answer to problem 3 to find the surface area of a prism?

You could find the area of one face in each pair and multiply it by 2, then add the products.

5 Use the method from problem 4 to find the surface area. Show your work.

2(36) + 2(60) + 2(15) = 72 + 120 + 30

= 222

6 Explain how to find the surface area of a rectangular prism.

Possible answer: Add the areas of all the faces.

Try It

Use what you learned about finding the surface area of a prism to find the surface area of the rectangular prisms below.

7 4 cm, 4 cm, 4 cm **96 square centimeters**

8 2 ft, 10 ft, 8 ft **232 square feet**

L24: Nets and Surface Area 243

©Curriculum Associates, LLC Copying is not permitted.

TRY IT SOLUTIONS

7 *Solution:* 96 square centimeters; Students may recognize that the prism is made up of six 4-by-4 squares. They can find the area of one face (4 cm × 4 cm = 16 sq cm) and multiply this by 6 to get 96 sq cm.

ERROR ALERT: Students who wrote 64 may have found the volume of the cube rather than the surface area.

8 *Solution:* 232 square feet; Students may determine that there are three pairs of rectangles with matching dimensions and solve:

$$2(8 \times 2) + 2(2 \times 10) + 2(8 \times 10) = 232.$$

Hands-On Activity

Identify rectangular prisms in the classroom.

- Have students walk around the classroom and write down examples of rectangular prisms. [books, tissue boxes, table tops, and AV equipment such as recorders or laptops]
- Have students describe the matching faces of those objects in their own words or mathematical terms (e.g., front/back, top/bottom, right/left).
- If time permits, let students measure the dimensions of the rectangular prisms and find the surface areas of the objects.

AT A GLANCE

Students read a word problem and examine a triangular prism and its net to explore how to find the surface area of a triangular prism. They also examine a table used to organize the needed data.

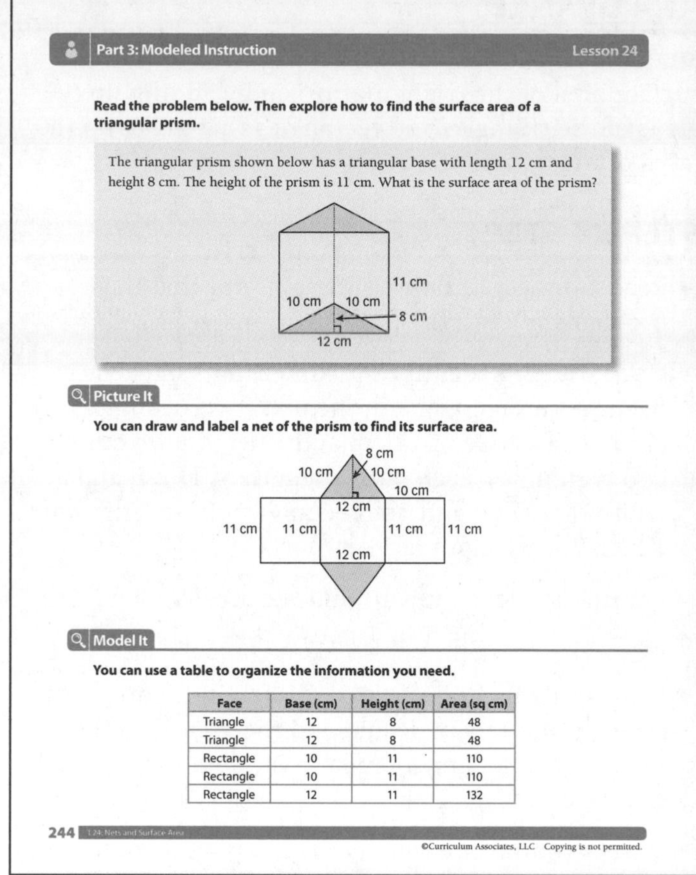

Part 3: Modeled Instruction Lesson 24

Read the problem below. Then explore how to find the surface area of a triangular prism.

The triangular prism shown below has a triangular base with length 12 cm and height 8 cm. The height of the prism is 11 cm. What is the surface area of the prism?

Picture It

You can draw and label a net of the prism to find its surface area.

Model It

You can use a table to organize the information you need.

Face	Base (cm)	Height (cm)	Area (sq cm)
Triangle	12	8	48
Triangle	12	8	48
Rectangle	10	11	110
Rectangle	10	11	110
Rectangle	12	11	132

244 L24: Nets and Surface Area

©Curriculum Associates, LLC Copying is not permitted.

STEP BY STEP

- Read the problem at the top of the page.
- Ask, *How do you think finding the surface area for this triangular prism will be different from finding the surface area of a rectangular prism?* [The shapes will be different: The triangular prism will be made of rectangles and triangles.]
- Read Picture It. Ask, *What are the different shapes in this figure? How many of each face are there?* [two triangular faces and three rectangular faces]
- Ask students to identify which faces have the same dimensions. [The triangles have the same dimensions, base = 12 cm and h = 8 cm. Two of the rectangles are 11 cm × 10 cm.]
- Ask, *Do you think you will use the same formula to find the areas of the faces of the triangular prism that you used for the rectangular prism?* [No. Only the formula for area of a rectangle was used.]
- Ask, *What formulas will you use to find the areas of the faces of the triangular prism?* [the formula for the area of a rectangle and the formula for area of a triangle]
- Read Model It. Point out the two kinds and numbers of shapes given in the table: one pair of triangles, one pair of identical rectangles, and one unique rectangle.

AT A GLANCE

Students revisit the problem on page 244 to find the surface area of the triangular prism by adding up the areas of the triangles and rectangles that make up the faces of the figure.

STEP BY STEP

- Read Connect It. Be sure to point out that the problems refer to the problem on page 244.
- Have students identify the dimensions of each triangle and rectangle in the net. [two triangles, each with a base of 12 cm and a height of 8 cm; two rectangles, each with a length of 11 cm and a width of 10 cm; and one rectangle with a length of 12 cm and a height of 11 cm]
- Remind students how to find the area of a triangle using the formula $A = \frac{1}{2}bh$.
- Have students find the area of each individual triangle and rectangle and add the areas together. Encourage them to compare their data to the data in the table on page 244.
- Have a volunteer explain to the class how to find the surface area of any triangular prism. [Find the area of each face and add the areas.]
- Have pairs of students work through the Try It problems. Encourage them to make tables to organize their data. Ask volunteer pairs to share with the class what they did to solve the problems.

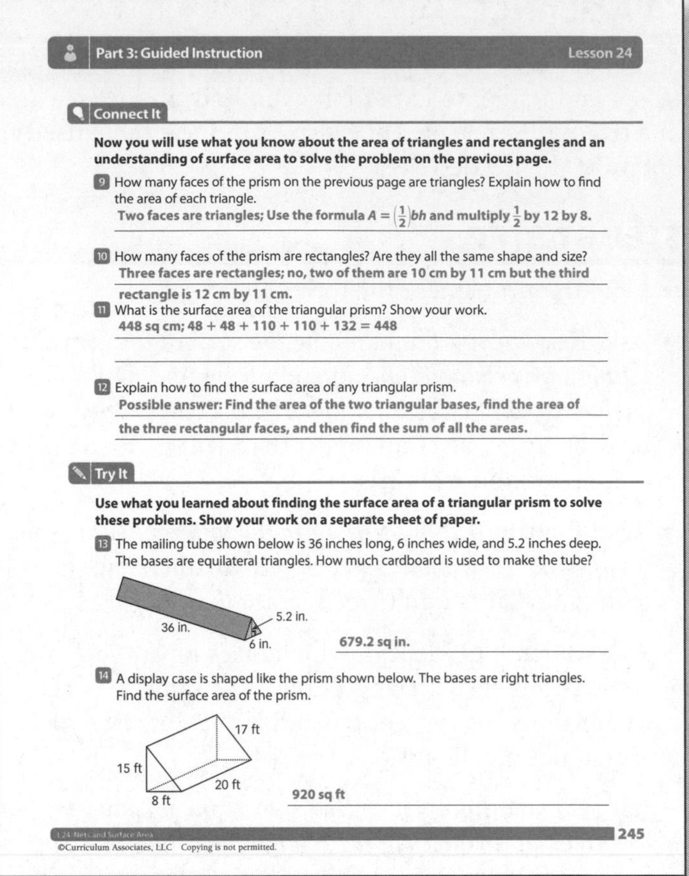

Part 3: Guided Instruction Lesson 24

Connect It

Now you will use what you know about the area of triangles and rectangles and an understanding of surface area to solve the problem on the previous page.

9 How many faces of the prism on the previous page are triangles? Explain how to find the area of each triangle.
Two faces are triangles; Use the formula $A = \left(\frac{1}{2}\right)bh$ and multiply $\frac{1}{2}$ by 12 by 8.

10 How many faces of the prism are rectangles? Are they all the same shape and size?
Three faces are rectangles; no, two of them are 10 cm by 11 cm but the third rectangle is 12 cm by 11 cm.

11 What is the surface area of the triangular prism? Show your work.
448 sq cm; 48 + 48 + 110 + 110 + 132 = 448

12 Explain how to find the surface area of any triangular prism.
Possible answer: Find the area of the two triangular bases, find the area of the three rectangular faces, and then find the sum of all the areas.

Try It

Use what you learned about finding the surface area of a triangular prism to solve these problems. Show your work on a separate sheet of paper.

13 The mailing tube shown below is 36 inches long, 6 inches wide, and 5.2 inches deep. The bases are equilateral triangles. How much cardboard is used to make the tube?

679.2 sq in.

14 A display case is shaped like the prism shown below. The bases are right triangles. Find the surface area of the prism.

920 sq ft

L24: Nets and Surface Area 245
©Curriculum Associates, LLC Copying is not permitted.

TRY IT SOLUTIONS

13 *Solution:* 679.2 sq in. Students may find the surface area of the three rectangular sides by multiplying $36 \times 6 \times 3 = 648$. Then they find the surface area of the two triangular sides by multiplying $\frac{1}{2} \times 6 \times 5.2 \times 2 = 31.2$. Add 648 and 31.2 to get 679.2.

14 *Solution:* 920 sq ft; Students may break the triangular prism into triangle pairs with base = 8 ft and height = 15 ft and three rectangles of dimensions 20 ft × 17 ft, 20 ft × 15 ft, and 8 ft × 20 ft. Then they would add the areas: $120 + 340 + 300 + 160 = 920$ sq ft

ERROR ALERT: Students who wrote 860 sq ft found the area of only one triangle.

AT A GLANCE

Students read a word problem and examine a pyramid and its net to explore how to find the surface area of a pyramid. They also examine a table used to organize the needed data.

STEP BY STEP

- Read the problem at the top of the page as a class.
- Emphasize that a *pyramid* is different than a rectangular or triangular prism.
- Read Picture It as a class.
- Ask, *What polygon makes up the base of the pyramid?* [a square] Ask, *What is the length of one side of the square?* [6 in.]
- Ask, *What other polygons are contained in the net? How many of each are there?* [triangles; four]
- Ask, *How does the net of a square pyramid differ from the net of a triangular prism?* [The net of a triangular prism is made of two triangle faces and three rectangles. The net of a square pyramid is made up of four triangular faces and a base that is a square.]
- Read Model It. Help students match the faces among the sketch, the net, and the table.

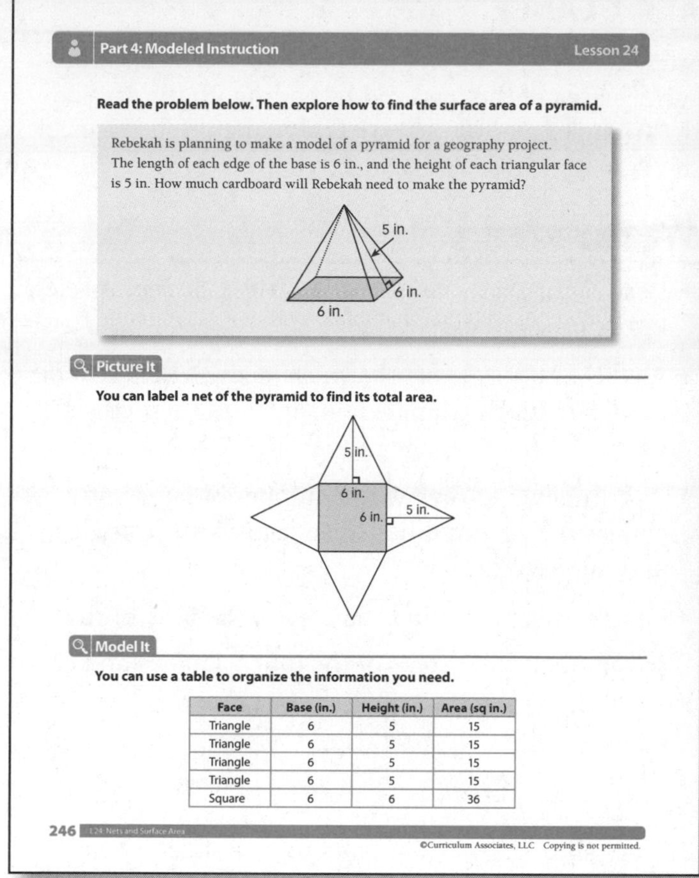

Part 4: Modeled Instruction Lesson 24

Read the problem below. Then explore how to find the surface area of a pyramid.

Rebekah is planning to make a model of a pyramid for a geography project. The length of each edge of the base is 6 in., and the height of each triangular face is 5 in. How much cardboard will Rebekah need to make the pyramid?

Picture It

You can label a net of the pyramid to find its total area.

Model It

You can use a table to organize the information you need.

Face	Base (in.)	Height (in.)	Area (sq in.)
Triangle	6	5	15
Triangle	6	5	15
Triangle	6	5	15
Triangle	6	5	15
Square	6	6	36

246 L24: Nets and Surface Area

©Curriculum Associates, LLC Copying is not permitted.

Concept Extension

Name the three-dimensional figure described.

Materials: sets of three large index cards with the words *rectangular prism* on one, *triangular prism* on one, and *pyramid* on one

- Give each student a set of the three cards.
- Tell students you will read clues and they will hold up the card having the name of the figure you describe. Examples:

  My faces are one rectangular base and four triangles. [pyramid]

  I am made up of two parallel triangles and three rectangles. [triangular prism]

  To find my surface area you need only one formula: $A = l \times w$. [rectangular prism]

AT A GLANCE

Students revisit the problem on page 246 to find the surface area of the pyramid by adding up the areas of the triangles and the square that make up the faces of the figure.

STEP BY STEP

- Read Connect It. Point out that the Connect It refers to the problem on page 246.
- Ask, *How does the net shown on page 246 fold into the pyramid?* [Each triangle folds up, and their edges meet.]
- Ask students to review the number of faces and shapes the pyramid has. [five faces: four triangles and one square]
- Guide students to find the area of the base of the pyramid and the areas of the four triangles and add them together to get the surface area. [Base: $6 \times 6 = 36$; $(4)\frac{1}{2}(6)(5) = 60$; $36 + 60 = 96$; Surface Area $= 96$ sq in.]
- Have students work in pairs to complete Try It. Encourage them to use a table to organize their data. Caution students to look carefully at the dimensions of the base in problem 21. When students have solved the problems, ask volunteers to share with the class how they solved them.

Concept Extension

Make different nets for the same rectangular prism.

Materials: graph paper, pencil, scissors, tape

- Form students into groups of 4 to 6 students.
- Tell students that they will sketch a rectangular prism that has six equal-size squares for faces. They may choose the dimensions and units.
- Working as a group or individually (but checking with other members), each student will draw a *different* net for this rectangular prism.
- Have students fold and tape the net to make the rectangular prism (cube).

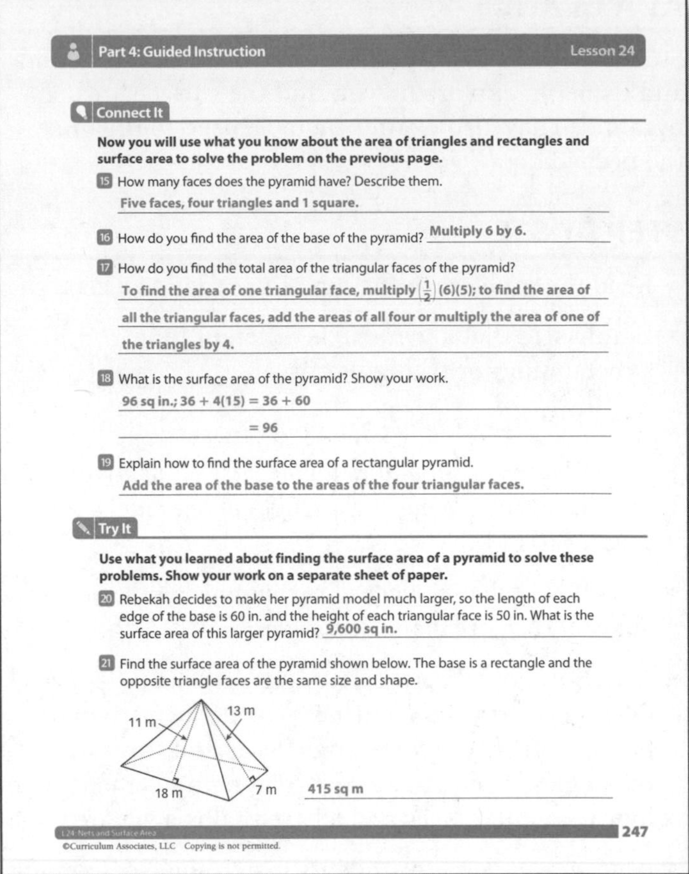

Part 4: Guided Instruction Lesson 24

Connect It

Now you will use what you know about the area of triangles and rectangles and surface area to solve the problem on the previous page.

15 How many faces does the pyramid have? Describe them.
Five faces, four triangles and 1 square.

16 How do you find the area of the base of the pyramid? **Multiply 6 by 6.**

17 How do you find the total area of the triangular faces of the pyramid?
To find the area of one triangular face, multiply $\left(\frac{1}{2}\right)(6)(5)$; to find the area of all the triangular faces, add the areas of all four or multiply the area of one of the triangles by 4.

18 What is the surface area of the pyramid? Show your work.
96 sq in.; $36 + 4(15) = 36 + 60$
$= 96$

19 Explain how to find the surface area of a rectangular pyramid.
Add the area of the base to the areas of the four triangular faces.

Try It

Use what you learned about finding the surface area of a pyramid to solve these problems. Show your work on a separate sheet of paper.

20 Rebekah decides to make her pyramid model much larger, so the length of each edge of the base is 60 in. and the height of each triangular face is 50 in. What is the surface area of this larger pyramid? **9,600 sq in.**

21 Find the surface area of the pyramid shown below. The base is a rectangle and the opposite triangle faces are the same size and shape.

415 sq m

L24: Nets and Surface Area 247
©Curriculum Associates, LLC Copying is not permitted.

TRY IT SOLUTIONS

20 *Solution:* 9,600 square inches; Students might find the area of the square base: $60 \times 60 = 3{,}600$. They might also find the area of one triangle, $A = \frac{1}{2}(60)(50) = 1{,}500$, and multiply by 4: $4 \times 1{,}500 = 6{,}000$. Then they add the areas: $3{,}600 + 6{,}000 = 9{,}600$.

ERROR ALERT: Students who wrote 8,500 sq in. may have confused the dimensions and found the area of the base as 50 in. $\times$ 50 in. $= 2{,}500$ sq in.

21 *Solution:* 415 sq m; Students may find the area of the rectangular base, $18 \times 7 = 126$. They may find the area of one triangle, $\frac{1}{2}(18)(11) = 99$, and multiply by 2: $2 \times 99 = 198$; then find and double the area of a different triangle: $2\left(\frac{1}{2}\right)(7)(13) = 91$. Then they would add the areas: $126 + 198 + 91 = 415$.

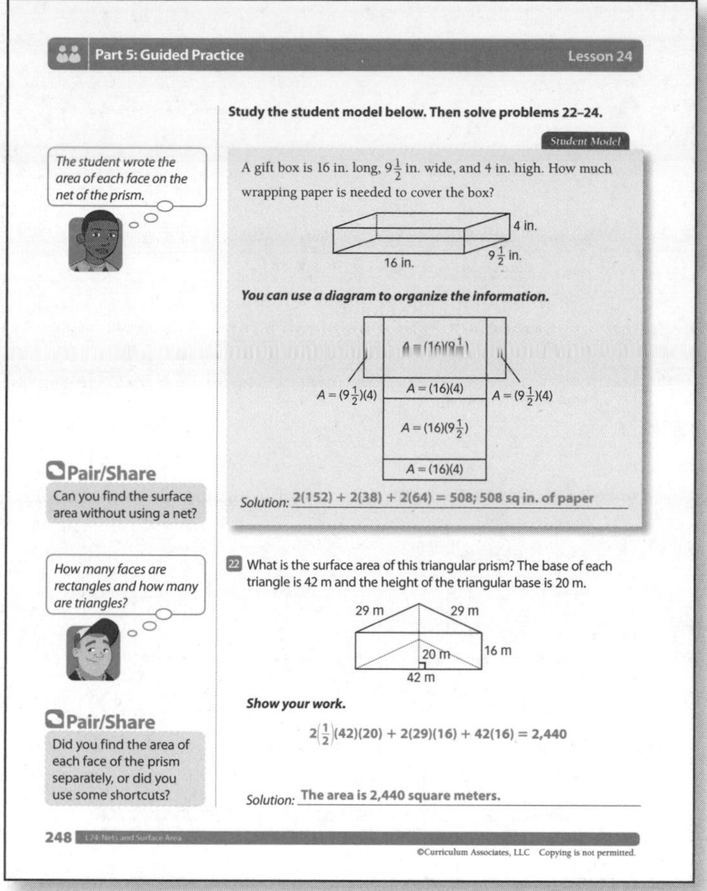

Study the student model below. Then solve problems 22–24.

Student Model

A gift box is 16 in. long, $9\frac{1}{2}$ in. wide, and 4 in. high. How much wrapping paper is needed to cover the box?

You can use a diagram to organize the information.

Solution: **2(152) + 2(38) + 2(64) = 508; 508 sq in. of paper**

The student wrote the area of each face on the net of the prism.

Pair/Share
Can you find the surface area without using a net?

22 What is the surface area of this triangular prism? The base of each triangle is 42 m and the height of the triangular base is 20 m.

Show your work.

$2\left(\frac{1}{2}\right)(42)(20) + 2(29)(16) + 42(16) = 2,440$

Solution: **The area is 2,440 square meters.**

How many faces are rectangles and how many are triangles?

Pair/Share
Did you find the area of each face of the prism separately, or did you use some shortcuts?

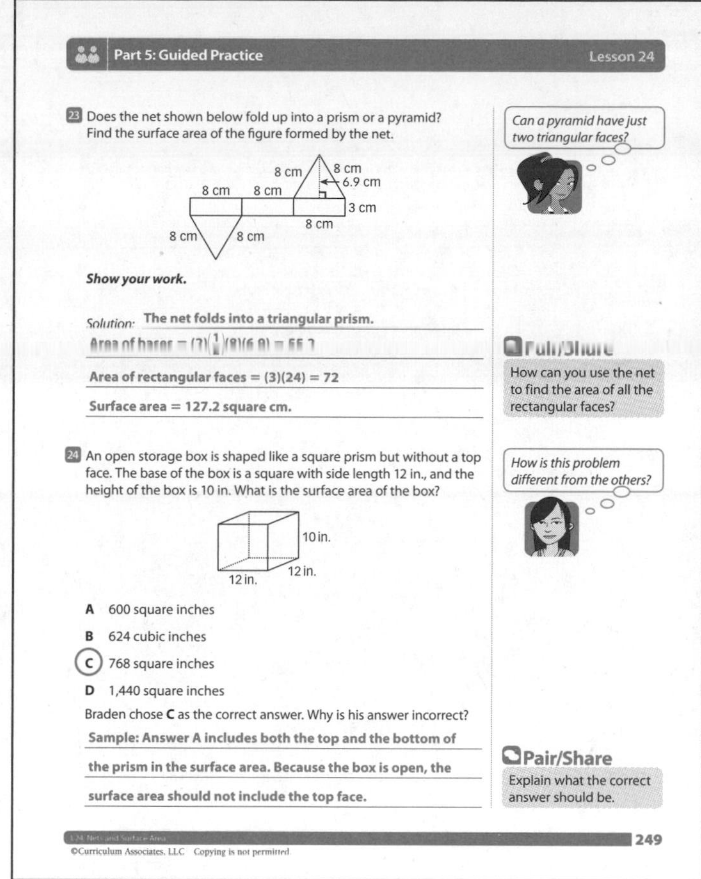

23 Does the net shown below fold up into a prism or a pyramid? Find the surface area of the figure formed by the net.

Show your work.

Solution: **The net folds into a triangular prism.**

Area of bases = $(2)\left(\frac{1}{2}\right)(8)(6.9) = 55.2$

Area of rectangular faces = (3)(24) = 72

Surface area = 127.2 square cm.

Can a pyramid have just two triangular faces?

Pair/Share
How can you use the net to find the area of all the rectangular faces?

24 An open storage box is shaped like a square prism but without a top face. The base of the box is a square with side length 12 in., and the height of the box is 10 in. What is the surface area of the box?

A 600 square inches

B 624 cubic inches

(C) 768 square inches

D 1,440 square inches

Braden chose **C** as the correct answer. Why is his answer incorrect?

Sample: Answer A includes both the top and the bottom of the prism in the surface area. Because the box is open, the surface area should not include the top face.

How is this problem different from the others?

Pair/Share
Explain what the correct answer should be.

AT A GLANCE

Students use models and nets to solve word problems involving finding the surface area of rectangular prisms and triangular prisms.

STEP BY STEP

- Ask students to solve the problems individually and to show their work.
- When students have completed each problem, have them Pair/Share to discuss their solutions with a partner or in a group.

SOLUTIONS

Ex *Solution:* Students could also make a table.

22 *Solution:* 2,440 sq m; Students may find the area of one base triangle, $\frac{1}{2}$ (42)(20), then multiply this by 2 to find the total area of the base triangles, 840 sq m. Find the area of two rectangles: $2 \times 29 \times 16 = 928$. Find the area of the last rectangle: $16 \times 42 = 672$. Add up the areas. ***(DOK 1)***

23 *Solution:* 127.2 square cm. See possible student work above. ***(DOK 1)***

24 *Solution:* **B**; Students must see the box has no top. Explain to students why the other two answer choices are not correct:

B is not correct because the area of the base was multiplied by the height, producing the volume.

D is not correct because the surface area was calculated with all faces having the same area of 10 in. × 10 in. and then multiplied by 6 faces. ***(DOK 3)***

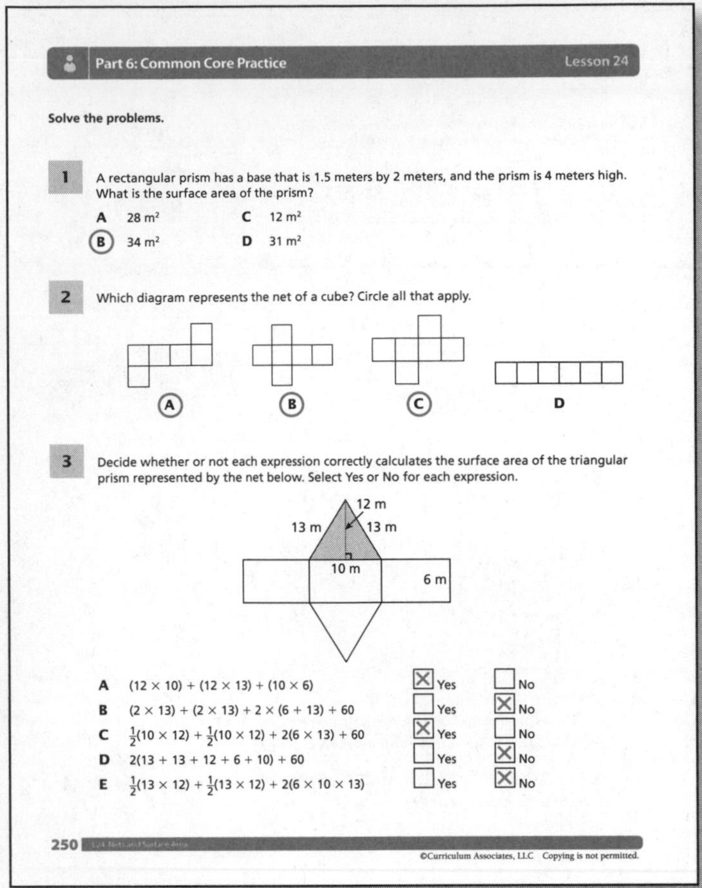
Part 6: Common Core Practice Lesson 24

Solve the problems.

1 A rectangular prism has a base that is 1.5 meters by 2 meters, and the prism is 4 meters high. What is the surface area of the prism?

A 28 m^2 C 12 m^2

(B) 34 m^2 D 31 m^2

2 Which diagram represents the net of a cube? Circle all that apply.

(A) (B) (C) D

3 Decide whether or not each expression correctly calculates the surface area of the triangular prism represented by the net below. Select Yes or No for each expression.

12 m, 13 m, 13 m, 10 m, 6 m

	Expression	Yes	No
A	$(12 \times 10) + (12 \times 13) + (10 \times 6)$	☒ Yes	☐ No
B	$(2 \times 13) + (2 \times 13) + 2 \times (6 + 13) + 60$	☐ Yes	☒ No
C	$\frac{1}{2}(10 \times 12) + \frac{1}{2}(10 \times 12) + 2(6 \times 13) + 60$	☒ Yes	☐ No
D	$2(13 + 13 + 12 + 6 + 10) + 60$	☐ Yes	☒ No
E	$\frac{1}{2}(13 \times 12) + \frac{1}{2}(13 \times 12) + 2(6 \times 10 \times 13)$	☐ Yes	☒ No

250 L24: Nets and Surface Area ©Curriculum Associates, LLC Copying is not permitted.

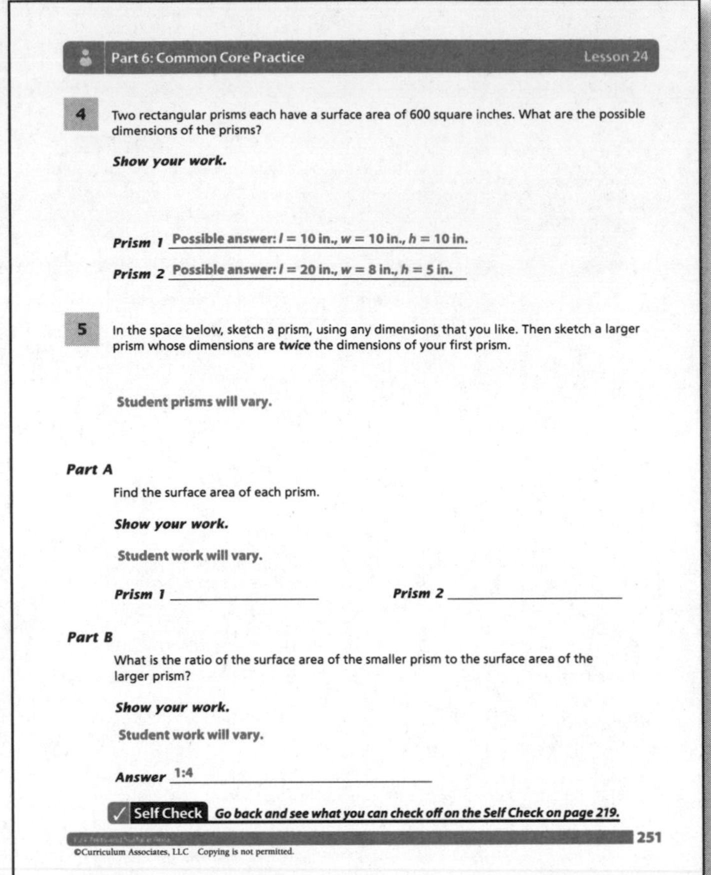
Part 6: Common Core Practice Lesson 24

4 Two rectangular prisms each have a surface area of 600 square inches. What are the possible dimensions of the prisms?

Show your work.

Prism 1 Possible answer: $l = 10$ in., $w = 10$ in., $h = 10$ in.

Prism 2 Possible answer: $l = 20$ in., $w = 8$ in., $h = 5$ in.

5 In the space below, sketch a prism, using any dimensions that you like. Then sketch a larger prism whose dimensions are *twice* the dimensions of your first prism.

Student prisms will vary.

Part A

Find the surface area of each prism.

Show your work.

Student work will vary.

Prism 1 ____________ *Prism 2* ____________

Part B

What is the ratio of the surface area of the smaller prism to the surface area of the larger prism?

Show your work.

Student work will vary.

Answer 1:4

✓ Self Check *Go back and see what you can check off on the Self Check on page 219.*

L24: Nets and Surface Area 251 ©Curriculum Associates, LLC Copying is not permitted.

AT A GLANCE

Students solve problems involving nets and surface areas of three-dimensional figures that might appear on a mathematics test.

SOLUTIONS

1 *Solution:* **B**; Find the dimensions of each pair of matching faces. Multiply each pair's area by 2. Add the areas.
$(2)(1.5)(2) + (2)(1.5)(4) + (2)(2)(4) = 34$ ***(DOK 1)***

2 *Solution:* **A**; **B**; **C**; These nets all fold into a cube. ***(DOK 1)***

3 *Solution:* A **Yes**; B **No**; C **Yes**; D **No**; E **No** ***(DOK 2)***

4 *Solution:* Possible solutions: a cube with edge length 10 in.; a rectangular prism with length 15 in., width 6 in., height 10 in.; another rectangular prism with length 20 in., width 8 in., and height 5 in. ***(DOK 3)***

5 *Solution Part A:* All prisms will vary, although the larger prism must have dimensions twice that of the smaller prism.

Solution Part B: The ratio of the surface area of the small prism to that of the large prism is 1:4. ***(DOK 3)***

Assessment and Remediation

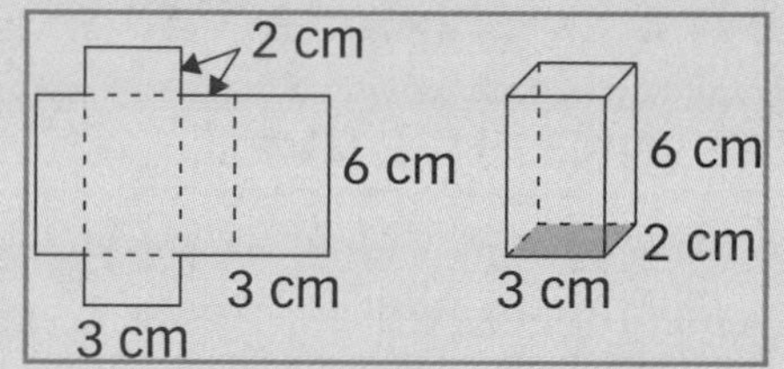

- Draw the rectangular prism and its net shown to the right. Ask students to determine what type of three-dimensional figure is represented. Then, ask them to find the surface area. [rectangular prism; 72 sq cm]
- For students who are struggling, use the chart below to guide remediation.
- After providing remediation, check students' understanding. Draw a different rectangular prism and net. Ask students to create a table of the dimensions and areas of all the faces and then total the areas to find the surface area. The table in Model It on page 242 can be used as a guide.

If the error is . . .	Students may . . .	To remediate . . .
the student did not correctly identify the figure as a rectangular prism.	not be able to distinguish between the different three-dimensional figures and their nets.	Have students review the three-dimensional diagrams and two-dimensional nets for rectangular prisms, triangular prisms, and pyramids, and label each correctly.
36 sq cm	not have multiplied the area of each single rectangle that has a pair by 2; or found volume.	Help students practice decomposing three-dimensional figures into nets and breaking down nets into individual polygons to calculate areas. Encourage students to use a table to list all the faces and areas.
any value other than 72 sq cm	not have used area formula correctly.	Help students review the steps for finding the surface area of a rectangular prism. [Determine the dimensions of each of the three pairs of faces, find the area of each face and multiply by 2, and add up the areas to find the surface area.]

Hands-On Activity

Make a table of data for finding surface area.

Materials: teacher-prepared table for each student

Create a table for students to complete. Make the column headings "Net," "Name of 3D Figure," "Number of Rectangles," "Number of Triangles," and "Formulas I Will Use to Find the Surface Area." In the first row, in the Net column, make a line drawing of a net of a rectangular prism, triangular prism, or pyramid. (Do not label dimensions or anything else on the net.) Leave the rest of the row blank for students to fill in their information about the particular net. Repeat with the second row using a different net, and so on. When students have completed the table, discuss their tables with the class.

Challenge Activity

Draw different rectangular prisms having the same surface area.

Challenge students to sketch two different rectangular prisms that have the same surface area. Tell them to label the prisms and sketch and label their nets. Then have students exchange drawings and have the other student find the surface area of both prisms and compare the surface areas.

Lesson 25 (Student Book pages 252–261)

Volume

LESSON OBJECTIVES

- Measuring with fractional units requires relating volume to multiplication with fractions.
- Use these formulas: $V = lwh$ and $V = Bh$.
- Prove that the volume formula works by creating diagrams of prisms with unit fraction edge lengths and showing how unit fraction cubes pack them.

PREREQUISITE SKILLS

- Volume is measured with cubic units.
- Ability to multiply fractions.
- Finding the area of polygons, including those with unit fraction edge lengths.
- Substitution for values in formulas.
- Finding volume of prisms with whole-unit side lengths.
- Use of physical models with whole-unit side lengths.
- Find volume using a unit cube model.

VOCABULARY

There is no new vocabulary.

THE LEARNING PROGRESSION

In Grade 5, students studied volume by decomposing three-dimensional prisms into layers of rows and columns. Composition and decomposition of shapes is used throughout geometry from Grade 6 to high school and beyond as students become more sophisticated in applying strategies and formulas for areas and volumes to the solution of real-world and mathematical problems.

This lesson extends students' understanding of how to find the volume of a right rectangular prism to include prisms with fractional edge lengths. Students decompose a cube, packing it with unit cubes of the appropriate unit fraction edge lengths and showing that the volume is the same as the product of the edge lengths of the prism.

Ready ***Teacher Toolbox*** Teacher-Toolbox.com

	Prerequisite Skills	6.G.A.2
Ready Lessons	✓	✓
Tools for Instruction		✓✓
Interactive Tutorials		✓

CCSS Focus

6.G.A.2 Find the volume of a right rectangular prism with fractional edge lengths by packing it with unit cubes of the appropriate unit fraction edge lengths, and show that the volume is the same as would be found by multiplying the edge lengths of the prism. Apply the formulas $V = lwh$ and $V = bh$ to find volumes of right rectangular prisms with fractional edge lengths in the context of solving real-world and mathematical problems.

ADDITIONAL STANDARDS: ***6.EE.A.2c*** *(see page A42 for full text)*

STANDARDS FOR MATHEMATICAL PRACTICE: ***SMP 1, 4*** *(see page A9 for full text)*

AT A GLANCE

Students read a word problem and answer a series of questions designed to help them determine the volume of unit cubes packed into a larger cube.

STEP BY STEP

- Tell students that this page models breaking down a large cube into small cubes and finding the volume of a small cube.
- Have students read the problem at the top of the page.
- Work through Explore It as a class.
- Ask, *What is the volume of the large cube whose edge measures 1 yard?* [1 cubic yard] Say, *Tell me how you found that.* [by multiplying the length, width, and height of the cube] Remind students that volume is always expressed in cubic units.
- Guide students to see that dividing each edge of the large cube into three equal parts measuring 1 foot produces 3 cubes along each edge, 9 cubes in each layer and—because there are 3 layers—a total of 27 small cubes in the large cube.
- Ask, *What fraction represents 1 of the 27 cubes?* [$\frac{1}{27}$]
- Ask, *If the volume of large cube is 1 cubic yard and a small cube is $\frac{1}{27}$ of this amount, how can we express the volume of each smaller cube?* [$\frac{1}{27}$ cubic yard]
- Ask, *Does the volume of the large cube change when its volume is expressed as 27 unit cubes instead of 1 cubic yard?* [The volume does not change; a cube with edges 1 yard long holds 27 cubes with edges $\frac{1}{3}$ yard long.]

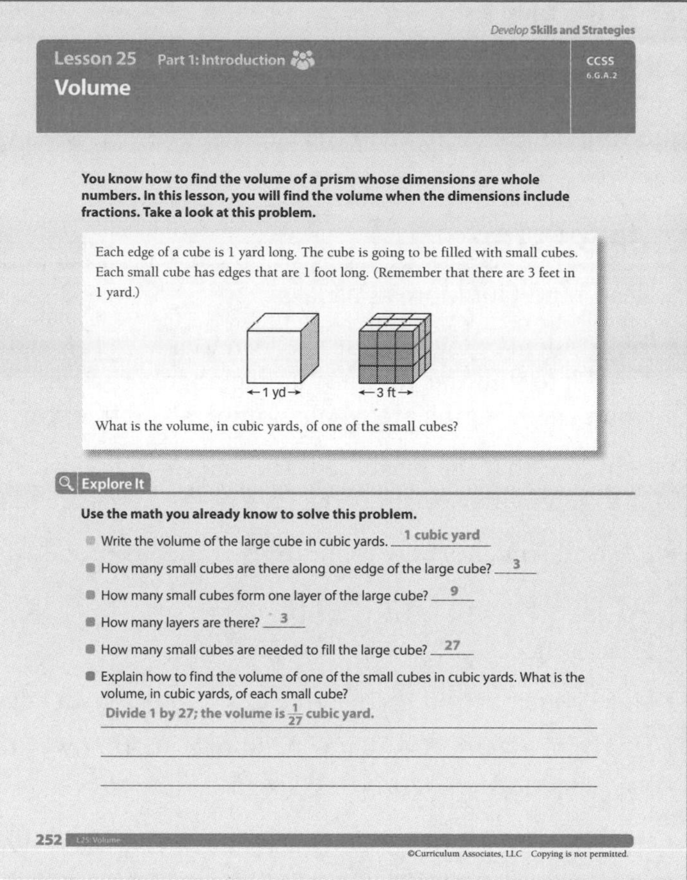
Develop Skills and Strategies

Lesson 25 Part 1: Introduction CCSS 6.G.A.2

Volume

You know how to find the volume of a prism whose dimensions are whole numbers. In this lesson, you will find the volume when the dimensions include fractions. Take a look at this problem.

Each edge of a cube is 1 yard long. The cube is going to be filled with small cubes. Each small cube has edges that are 1 foot long. (Remember that there are 3 feet in 1 yard.)

What is the volume, in cubic yards, of one of the small cubes?

Explore It

Use the math you already know to solve this problem.

- Write the volume of the large cube in cubic yards. 1 cubic yard
- How many small cubes are there along one edge of the large cube? 3
- How many small cubes form one layer of the large cube? 9
- How many layers are there? 3
- How many small cubes are needed to fill the large cube? 27
- Explain how to find the volume of one of the small cubes in cubic yards. What is the volume, in cubic yards, of each small cube? Divide 1 by 27; the volume is $\frac{1}{27}$ cubic yard.

252 L25: Volume ©Curriculum Associates, LLC Copying is not permitted.

Mathematical Discourse

- *What does the saying "a picture is worth a thousand words" mean?*

  This is a common saying. Get students thinking that pictures can sometimes do a better job of explaining a concept than words can.

- *Why is this phrase appropriate for the exercise we just did?*

  The picture helped explain volume.

- *Can you think of any other math concept where a picture did a good or better job of explaining the concept than words, symbols, or formulas did?*

  Students may recall any concept they learned from kindergarten through Grade 5 in which diagrams were used. This engages prior knowledge.

AT A GLANCE

Students explore how the volume of a cube can be found by multiplying or by decomposing the large cube into unit cubes, even when the edge lengths are fractional.

STEP BY STEP

- Read Find Out More as a class.
- Tell students they can use the formulas $V = lwh$ and $V = Bh$ to find the volume of a rectangular prism when edge lengths are whole numbers and fractions.
- Point out that the product of the length and width of a rectangular prism is the area of the base B.
- Remind students how to multiply fractions properly. For example, $\left(\frac{a}{b}\right) \times \left(\frac{c}{d}\right) = \left(\frac{ac}{bd}\right)$
- Read Reflect.
- Have students find the volume of a cube with an edge length of $\frac{1}{4}$ yard. Ask if anyone knows another way to describe the expression $\frac{1}{4} \times \frac{1}{4} \times \frac{1}{4}$.
- Ask, *In what ways is finding the volume of a prism with fractional edge lengths different from finding the volume when edge lengths are whole numbers? How is it the same?*

SMP Tip: When students compare the volume found by multiplying with the volume found by decomposing the large cube into unit cubes, they have interpreted their mathematical results in the context of the model and reflected on whether these results make sense (*SMP 4*).

ELL Support

Geometry lessons generally involve mathematical language, making them a special challenge for ELL students. Use a Freyer Model graphic organizer to help students with the academic vocabulary in the lesson.

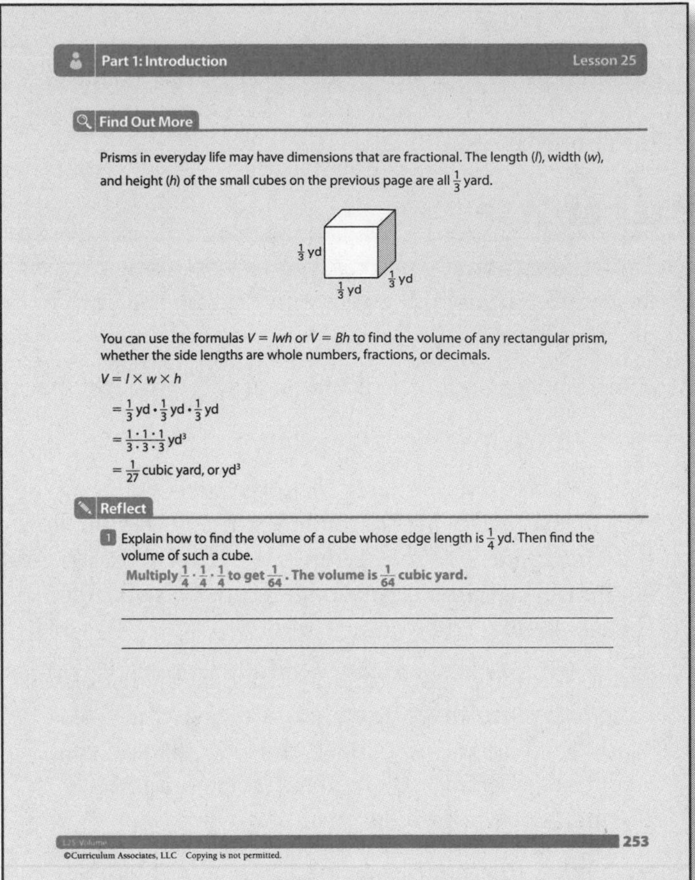

Part 1: Introduction Lesson 25

Find Out More

Prisms in everyday life may have dimensions that are fractional. The length (l), width (w), and height (h) of the small cubes on the previous page are all $\frac{1}{3}$ yard.

You can use the formulas $V = lwh$ or $V = Bh$ to find the volume of any rectangular prism, whether the side lengths are whole numbers, fractions, or decimals.

$V = l \times w \times h$

$= \frac{1}{3}\text{ yd} \cdot \frac{1}{3}\text{ yd} \cdot \frac{1}{3}\text{ yd}$

$= \frac{1 \cdot 1 \cdot 1}{3 \cdot 3 \cdot 3}\text{ yd}^3$

$= \frac{1}{27}$ cubic yard, or yd^3

Reflect

1 Explain how to find the volume of a cube whose edge length is $\frac{1}{4}$ yd. Then find the volume of such a cube.

Multiply $\frac{1}{4} \cdot \frac{1}{4} \cdot \frac{1}{4}$ to get $\frac{1}{64}$. The volume is $\frac{1}{64}$ cubic yard.

L25: Volume 253

Real-World Connection

Encourage students to name examples of cubes found in everyday life.

Examples: building blocks, swimming pools, storage containers, moving boxes, rooms in a house

Ask, *When would we be interested in knowing the volume of a real-life cube or the volume of contents of the real-life cube?* [Volume capacity of a moving box or mailing box (how much can I put in there), storage capacity, volume of water to fill a pool.]

AT A GLANCE

Students explore how the volume of a cube can be found by multiplying or by decomposing the large cube into unit cubes, even when the edge lengths are fractional.

STEP BY STEP

- Read the problem at the top of the page as a class.
- Read Picture It.
- Ask students whether they think it would be easier to find the volume of the sandbox or the sand. Have them explain their answers.
- Encourage students to discuss the difference between operations with whole numbers and with fractions or mixed numbers.
- Read Model It.
- Encourage students to discuss how the sandbox problem differs from the packed prism with 27 small cubes from the earlier example. Lead students to recognize that in the prism each layer had the same number of cubes (9) while the sandbox has two full layers and a half layer.

SMP Tip: Using a diagram to help conceptualize and solve a problem is an important tool for problem solving. Regularly ask students to draw a sketch or diagram to understand the situation in word problems or to find a solution strategy (*SMP 1*).

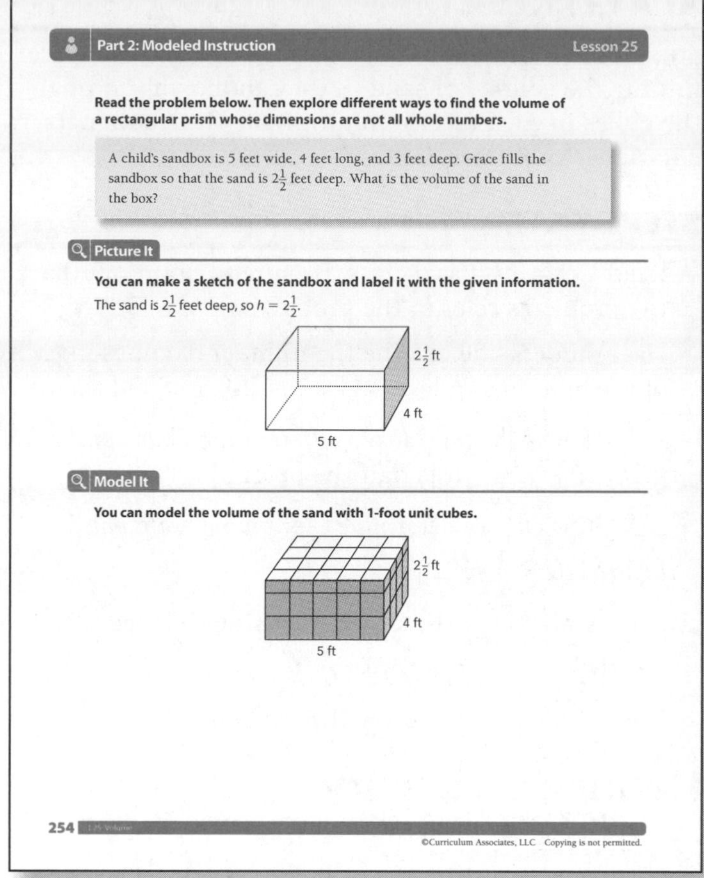
Part 2: Modeled Instruction Lesson 25

Read the problem below. Then explore different ways to find the volume of a rectangular prism whose dimensions are not all whole numbers.

A child's sandbox is 5 feet wide, 4 feet long, and 3 feet deep. Grace fills the sandbox so that the sand is $2\frac{1}{2}$ feet deep. What is the volume of the sand in the box?

Picture It

You can make a sketch of the sandbox and label it with the given information.

The sand is $2\frac{1}{2}$ feet deep, so $h = 2\frac{1}{2}$.

$2\frac{1}{2}$ ft

4 ft

5 ft

Model It

You can model the volume of the sand with 1-foot unit cubes.

$2\frac{1}{2}$ ft

4 ft

5 ft

254 L25: Volume

©Curriculum Associates, LLC Copying is not permitted.

Mathematical Discourse

- *Do you prefer working with whole numbers or fractions? Why?*

  Most students will prefer whole numbers to fractions because whole numbers are easier to work with. Encourage students to support their answers with specific examples.

- *If most of us prefer working with whole numbers, why do we even bother with fractions? Why not just ignore fractions entirely?*

  Get students to see that we cannot avoid fractions because they exist in the real world. Fractional edges of real-life prisms, percents as fractions, fractional amounts of any measure (pounds, cups, and feet)—we are always working with these quantities, like it or not.

AT A GLANCE

Students revisit the problem on page 254 and compare finding the volume of sand in the sandbox by adding the cubes in each layer to multiplying the fractional edge lengths of the sand fill.

STEP BY STEP

- Read Connect It as a class. Be sure to point out that the problems refer to the problem on page 254.
- Have students determine the number of cubes in each of the bottom two layers ($4 \cdot 5 = 20$) and add them.
- Ask, *How is the third layer different than each of the first two layers?* [It is half the height.]
- Ask, *How can we determine the volume of the third layer?* [$20 \times \frac{1}{2} = 10$]
- Have students find the volume using the formula $V = lwh$. [$5 \cdot 4 \cdot \frac{5}{2} = 50$]
- Have students do the Try It problems.

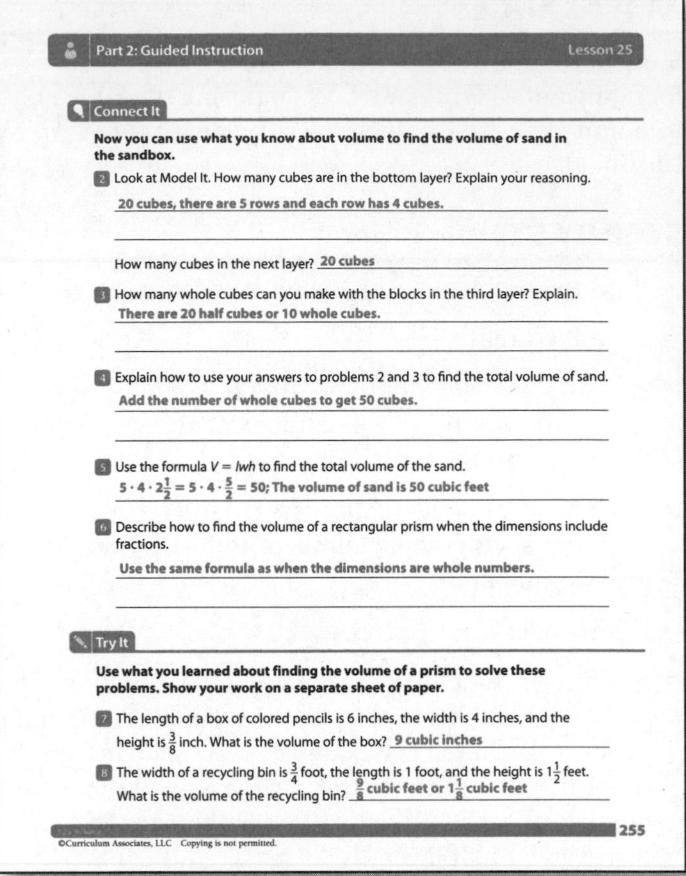

Part 2: Guided Instruction Lesson 25

Connect It

Now you can use what you know about volume to find the volume of sand in the sandbox.

2 Look at Model It. How many cubes are in the bottom layer? Explain your reasoning.
20 cubes, there are 5 rows and each row has 4 cubes.

How many cubes in the next layer? **20 cubes**

3 How many whole cubes can you make with the blocks in the third layer? Explain.
There are 20 half cubes or 10 whole cubes.

4 Explain how to use your answers to problems 2 and 3 to find the total volume of sand.
Add the number of whole cubes to get 50 cubes.

5 Use the formula $V = lwh$ to find the total volume of the sand.
$5 \cdot 4 \cdot 2\frac{1}{2} = 5 \cdot 4 \cdot \frac{5}{2} = 50$; The volume of sand is 50 cubic feet

6 Describe how to find the volume of a rectangular prism when the dimensions include fractions.
Use the same formula as when the dimensions are whole numbers.

Try It

Use what you learned about finding the volume of a prism to solve these problems. Show your work on a separate sheet of paper.

7 The length of a box of colored pencils is 6 inches, the width is 4 inches, and the height is $\frac{3}{8}$ inch. What is the volume of the box? **9 cubic inches**

8 The width of a recycling bin is $\frac{3}{4}$ foot, the length is 1 foot, and the height is $1\frac{1}{2}$ feet. What is the volume of the recycling bin? **$\frac{9}{8}$ cubic feet or $1\frac{1}{8}$ cubic feet**

255

©Curriculum Associates, LLC Copying is not permitted.

TRY IT SOLUTIONS

7 *Solution:* 9 cubic inches; Students may multiply the dimensions $6 \cdot 4 \cdot \frac{3}{8}$ to get 9 cubic inches. Students may multiply but not simplify to get $\frac{72}{8}$ cubic inches.

8 *Solution:* $\frac{9}{8}$ cubic feet or $1\frac{1}{8}$ cubic feet; Students may multiply $\frac{3}{4} \cdot 1 \cdot \frac{3}{2}$ to get $\frac{9}{8}$ cubic inches.

ERROR ALERT: Students who wrote $\frac{3}{8}$ cubic feet may not have converted the mixed number into an improper fraction and instead multiplied $\frac{3}{4} \cdot 1 \cdot 1 \cdot \frac{1}{2}$.

Hands-On Activity

Fooled by the box!

Materials: a variety of common grocery items; a blank piece of paper, pencil, ruler

- Break students into groups. Give each group three grocery items, such as a rice box, a sugar box, and a cereal box.
- Create a four-column table and label the columns: "Product Name," "Product Type," "Package Volume (cubic in.)," "Content Volume (cubic in.)."
- Have students measure the dimensions of each package. Then have them calculate and record each volume in the table.
- Next, have students open each package and carefully measure the height of the contents and calculate and record the content volume.
- Have students discuss whether the packaging is misleading. Discuss whether they have noticed this with other foods or drinks.

AT A GLANCE

Students read the problem and answer questions designed to extend their understanding of how to find a missing fractional dimension of a prism given its volume and two of its other dimensions.

STEP BY STEP

- Read the problem and Picture It as a class.
- Ask, *How does this problem look different from the ones we've been doing? Hint: What information are you given and what are you being asked to solve?* [We are given volume and the base ($l \cdot w$). We are asked to solve for height, h. In earlier problems, we were given the dimensions and multiplied them to find volume.]
- Read Model It. Then have students read the two formulas for volume and ask how they differ. You may want to write both formulas on the board and circle $l \cdot w$ in the first formula and B in the second formula. After doing that, ask students what values replace the variables.
- Guide students to see that the two formulas in Model It are equivalent expressions ($B = l \cdot w$).
- Explain that solving this problem requires the use of algebra, i.e., solving equations with one variable.

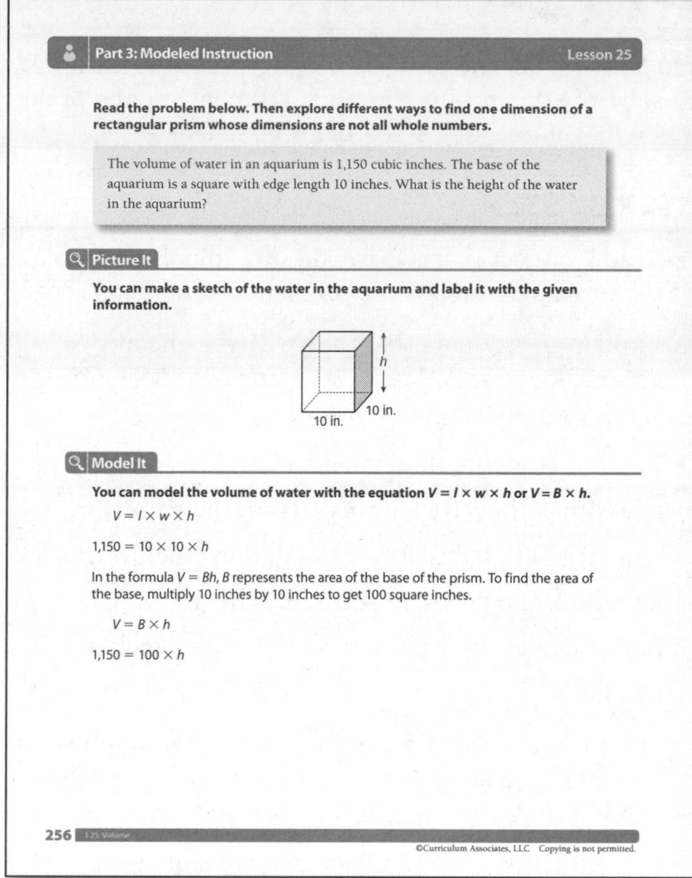
Part 3: Modeled Instruction Lesson 25

Read the problem below. Then explore different ways to find one dimension of a rectangular prism whose dimensions are not all whole numbers.

The volume of water in an aquarium is 1,150 cubic inches. The base of the aquarium is a square with edge length 10 inches. What is the height of the water in the aquarium?

Picture It

You can make a sketch of the water in the aquarium and label it with the given information.

Model It

You can model the volume of water with the equation $V = l \times w \times h$ or $V = B \times h$.

$V = l \times w \times h$

$1{,}150 = 10 \times 10 \times h$

In the formula $V = Bh$, B represents the area of the base of the prism. To find the area of the base, multiply 10 inches by 10 inches to get 100 square inches.

$V = B \times h$

$1{,}150 = 100 \times h$

256 L25: Volume
©Curriculum Associates, LLC Copying is not permitted.

ELL Support

- Provide students with a graphic organizer for the term "base" and have them write the definition(s) of "base."
- List mathematical concepts and formulas where the term "base" is used, such as:
  - The formula for the volume of a prism is $V = B \cdot h$
  - An exponent has a base: $\text{Base}^{\text{Exponent}}$
  - The formula for the area of a triangle is $A = \frac{1}{2}bh$
  - Other Parallelogram Area Formulas

SMP Tip: When students recognize the way this problem differs from the prior problems, stepping back for an overview and shifting perspective, they are able to develop the appropriate problem solving processes to find the missing height. In doing so they discern between different structures of algebraic expressions *(SMP 1)*.

Mathematical Discourse

- *Can you think of an example where we could use $V = B \cdot h$ but not $V = l \cdot w \cdot h$?*

  We could be given $B = 20$ and not know what the values of l and w are. The values of l and w could be 4 and 5, 10 and 2, or 20 and 1.

- *Can you think of any other examples where we have two different formulas to calculate the same value?*

  Perimeter of Rectangle: $P = l + l + w + w$ or $P = 2l + 2w$

  Area of a Square: $A = s \times s$ or $A = s^2$

  Listen for responses that may describe different ways to do a particular calculation that may not be a formula.

AT A GLANCE

Students revisit the problem on page 256 and learn how to solve for the missing fractional dimension of a prism given its volume and two other dimensions.

STEP BY STEP

- Read Connect It as a class. Be sure to point out that the problems refer to the problem on page 256.
- Explain to students that they will use one of two volume formulas ($V = l \cdot w \cdot h$ and $V = B \cdot h$) to solve for a missing dimension.
- Remind students that when solving one-variable equations, they are looking to find the value for the variable that makes the equation true. In this situation, they need to solve for h by dividing both sides of the equation by 100. The formula becomes $\frac{V}{B} = h$.
- Point out to students that instead of height you could be looking to solve for length or width. The problem-solving steps are the same in all situations.
- Tell students, *Compare the process of finding the volume of the sand in the sandbox to finding the height of the water in the aquarium. Explain how the processes are different.* [When we found the volume of the sand, we multiplied the dimensions. When we found the height of the aquarium, we set up the equation and then divided the volume by the base to find height.]

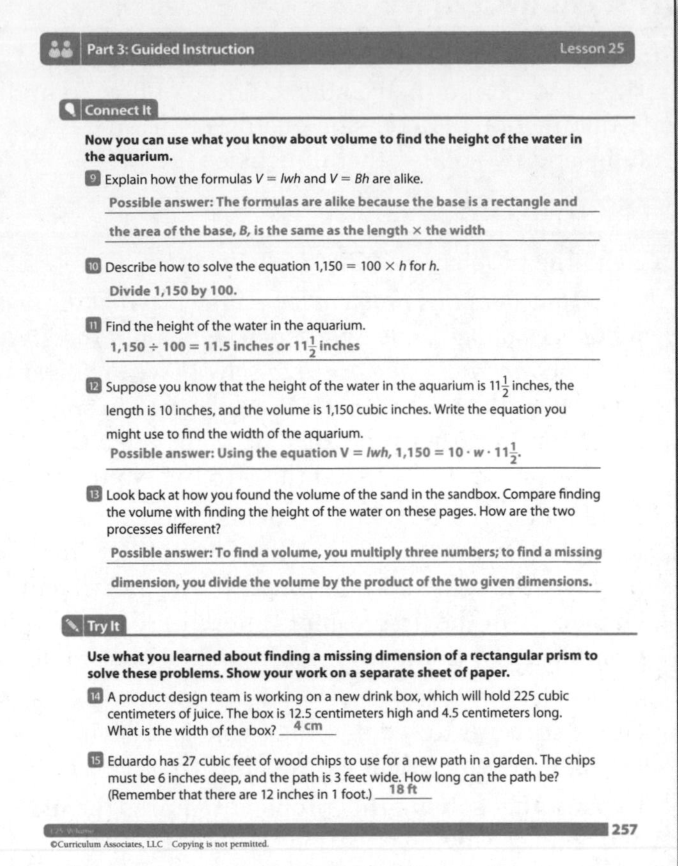
Part 3: Guided Instruction Lesson 25

Connect It

Now you can use what you know about volume to find the height of the water in the aquarium.

9 Explain how the formulas $V = lwh$ and $V = Bh$ are alike.
Possible answer: The formulas are alike because the base is a rectangle and the area of the base, B, is the same as the length × the width

10 Describe how to solve the equation $1,150 = 100 \times h$ for h.
Divide 1,150 by 100.

11 Find the height of the water in the aquarium.
$1,150 \div 100 = 11.5$ inches or $11\frac{1}{2}$ inches

12 Suppose you know that the height of the water in the aquarium is $11\frac{1}{2}$ inches, the length is 10 inches, and the volume is 1,150 cubic inches. Write the equation you might use to find the width of the aquarium.
Possible answer: Using the equation $V = lwh$, $1,150 = 10 \cdot w \cdot 11\frac{1}{2}$.

13 Look back at how you found the volume of the sand in the sandbox. Compare finding the volume with finding the height of the water on these pages. How are the two processes different?
Possible answer: To find a volume, you multiply three numbers; to find a missing dimension, you divide the volume by the product of the two given dimensions.

Try It

Use what you learned about finding a missing dimension of a rectangular prism to solve these problems. Show your work on a separate sheet of paper.

14 A product design team is working on a new drink box, which will hold 225 cubic centimeters of juice. The box is 12.5 centimeters high and 4.5 centimeters long. What is the width of the box? **4 cm**

15 Eduardo has 27 cubic feet of wood chips to use for a new path in a garden. The chips must be 6 inches deep, and the path is 3 feet wide. How long can the path be? (Remember that there are 12 inches in 1 foot.) **18 ft**

L25: Volume 257

©Curriculum Associates, LLC Copying is not permitted.

TRY IT SOLUTIONS

14 *Solution:* 4 cm; Students may solve using the formula $V = l \cdot w \cdot h$ substituting into the formula $V = 255$, $l = 4.5$, $h = 12.5$ to find $w = 4$.

15 *Solution:* 18 ft; Students may solve using the formula $V = l \cdot w \cdot h$ substituting into the formula $V = 27$, $w = 3$, $h = \frac{1}{2}$ to find $l = 18$.

ERROR ALERT: Students who wrote 1.5 ft did not convert 6 inches to $\frac{1}{2}$ ft to make units consistent.

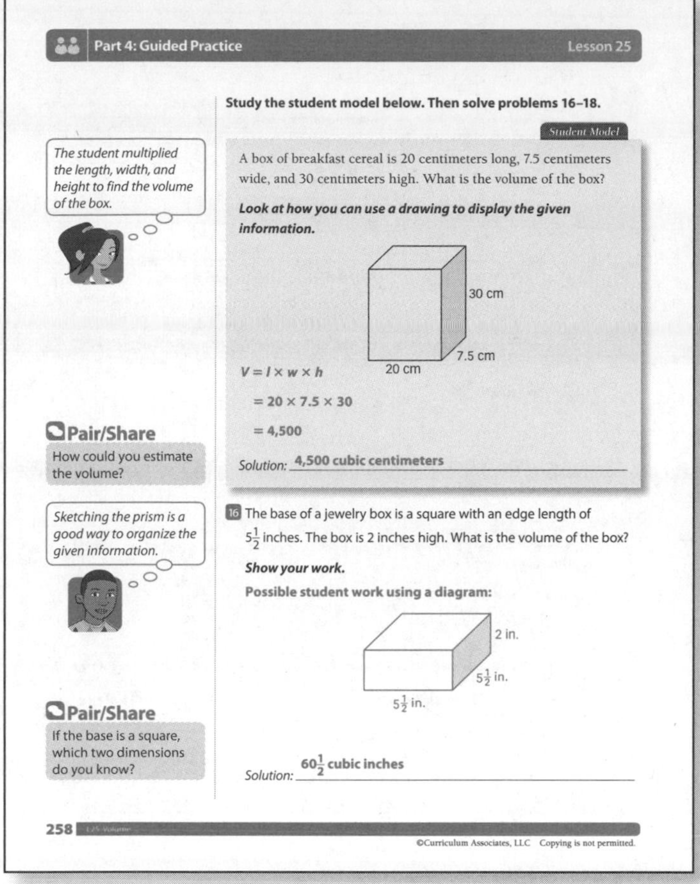

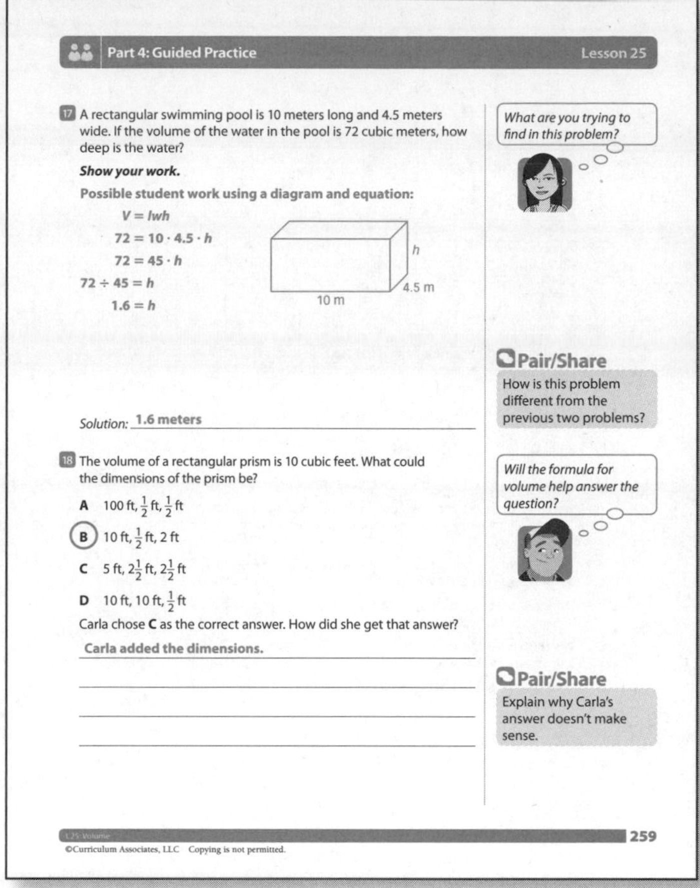

AT A GLANCE

Students solve a set of volume problems involving fractional dimensions by applying the volume formula.

STEP BY STEP

- Ask students to solve the problems individually.
- When students have completed each problem, have them Pair/Share to discuss their solutions with a partner or in a group.

SOLUTIONS

Ex Solution: 4,500 cubic centimeters; Students could solve the problem by multiplying $l \cdot w \cdot h$ as follows: $20 \cdot 7.5 \cdot 30$.

16 *Solution:* $\frac{121}{2}$ or $60\frac{1}{2}$ cubic inches; Students could solve the problem by multiplying $l \cdot w \cdot h$ as follows: $2 \cdot \frac{11}{2} \cdot \frac{11}{2}$. ***(DOK 1)***

17 *Solution:* 1.6 meters; Students could solve the problem by solving the equation $72 = 10 \cdot 4.5 \cdot h$. ***(DOK 1)***

18 *Solution:* **B**; Carla added the dimensions, which is an incorrect method.

Explain to students why the other two answer choices are not correct.

A is not correct because multiplying these values produces a volume of 25 cubic feet.

D is not correct because multiplying these values produces a volume of 50 cubic feet. ***(DOK 3)***

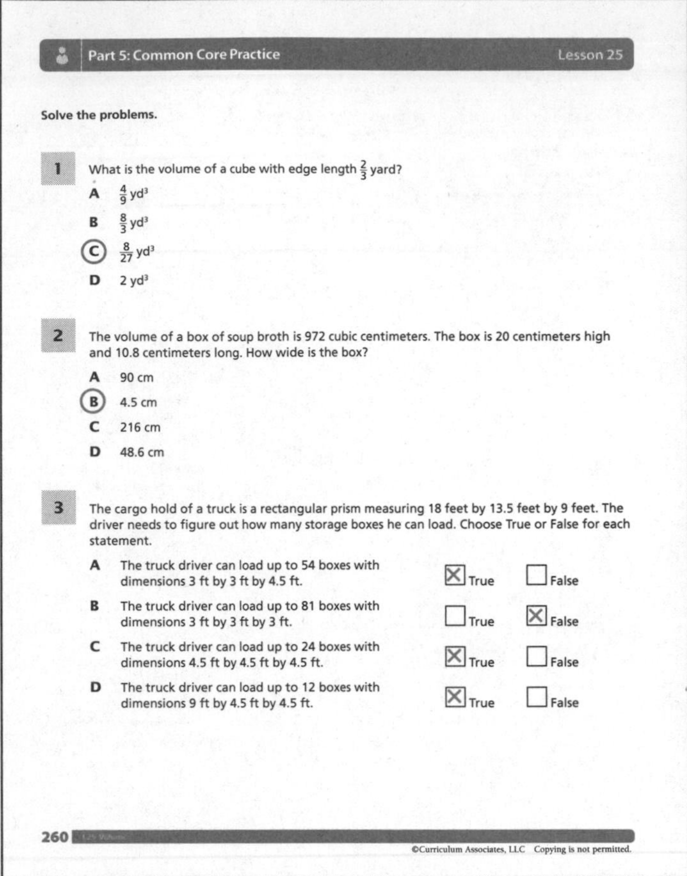

Part 5: Common Core Practice Lesson 25

Solve the problems.

1 What is the volume of a cube with edge length $\frac{2}{3}$ yard?

A $\frac{4}{9}$ yd³

B $\frac{8}{3}$ yd³

(C) $\frac{8}{27}$ yd³

D 2 yd³

2 The volume of a box of soup broth is 972 cubic centimeters. The box is 20 centimeters high and 10.8 centimeters long. How wide is the box?

A 90 cm

(B) 4.5 cm

C 216 cm

D 48.6 cm

3 The cargo hold of a truck is a rectangular prism measuring 18 feet by 13.5 feet by 9 feet. The driver needs to figure out how many storage boxes he can load. Choose True or False for each statement.

	Statement	True	False
A	The truck driver can load up to 54 boxes with dimensions 3 ft by 3 ft by 4.5 ft.	☒	☐
B	The truck driver can load up to 81 boxes with dimensions 3 ft by 3 ft by 3 ft.	☐	☒
C	The truck driver can load up to 24 boxes with dimensions 4.5 ft by 4.5 ft by 4.5 ft.	☒	☐
D	The truck driver can load up to 12 boxes with dimensions 9 ft by 4.5 ft by 4.5 ft.	☒	☐

260 L25: Volume ©Curriculum Associates, LLC Copying is not permitted.

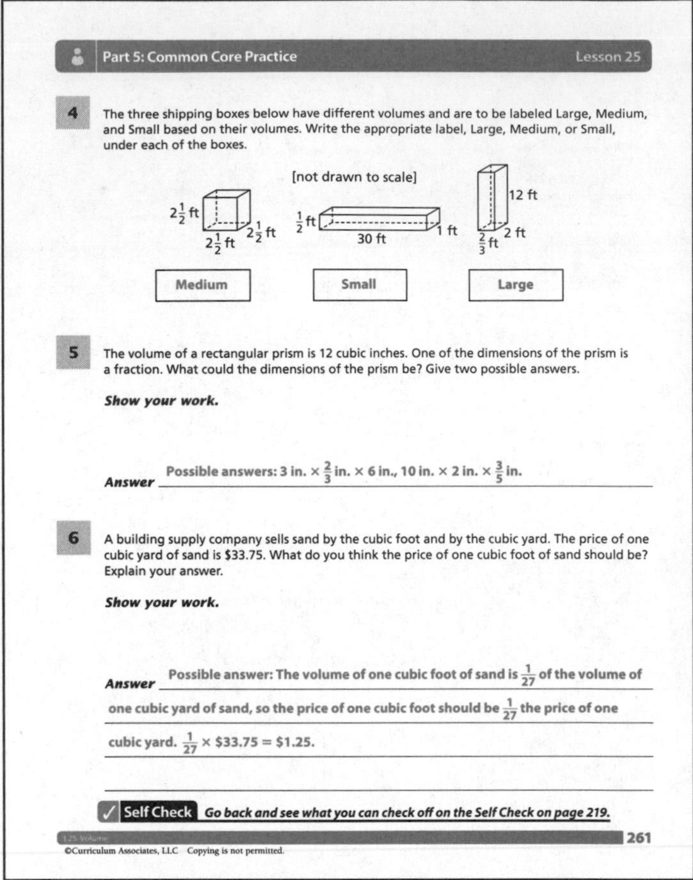

Part 5: Common Core Practice Lesson 25

4 The three shipping boxes below have different volumes and are to be labeled Large, Medium, and Small based on their volumes. Write the appropriate label, Large, Medium, or Small, under each of the boxes.

Medium Small Large

5 The volume of a rectangular prism is 12 cubic inches. One of the dimensions of the prism is a fraction. What could the dimensions of the prism be? Give two possible answers.

Show your work.

Answer Possible answers: 3 in. × $\frac{2}{3}$ in. × 6 in., 10 in. × 2 in. × $\frac{3}{5}$ in.

6 A building supply company sells sand by the cubic foot and by the cubic yard. The price of one cubic yard of sand is $33.75. What do you think the price of one cubic foot of sand should be? Explain your answer.

Show your work.

Answer Possible answer: The volume of one cubic foot of sand is $\frac{1}{27}$ of the volume of one cubic yard of sand, so the price of one cubic foot should be $\frac{1}{27}$ the price of one cubic yard. $\frac{1}{27}$ × $33.75 = $1.25.

✓ Self Check *Go back and see what you can check off on the Self Check on page 219.*

L25: Volume ©Curriculum Associates, LLC Copying is not permitted. 261

AT A GLANCE

Students solve a set of volume problems involving fractional dimensions that might appear on a mathematics test.

SOLUTIONS

1 *Solution:* **C**; Multiply $\frac{2}{3} \cdot \frac{2}{3} \cdot \frac{2}{3}$. ***(DOK 1)***

2 *Solution:* **B**; Set up the equation $972 = 20 \cdot 10.8 \cdot w$. Next, divide both sides by 216 to solve for *w*. ***(DOK 2)***

3 *Solution:* A **True**; B **False**; C **True**; D **True** ***(DOK 2)***

4 *Solution:* Medium, Small, Large (from left to right); Multiply the length, width, and height of each prism to find the volume. The volume, from left to right, are 15.625 ft³, 15 ft³, and 16 ft³. ***(DOK 1)***

5 *Solution:* Answers will vary. Find three numbers with a product of 12, at least one of which is a fraction.

Sample solutions: $3 \cdot \frac{2}{3} \cdot 6$ or $10 \cdot 2 \cdot \frac{3}{5}$. ***(DOK 3)***

6 *Solution:* Answers will vary. Sample solution: Because the volume of one cubic foot of sand is $\frac{1}{27}$ of the volume of one cubic yard of sand, the price of one cubic foot should be $\frac{1}{27}$ the price of one cubic yard. Price of one cubic foot $= \frac{1}{27} \times \$33.75 = \$1.25$. ***(DOK 3)***

Assessment and Remediation

- Ask students to find the height of a prism with dimensions $V = 36$ cu ft, $w = 48$ in., and $l = 1\frac{1}{2}$ ft.[6 ft]
- For students who are struggling, use the chart below to guide remediation.
- After providing remediation, check students' understanding. Ask students to explain their thinking in finding the height of a prism with dimensions $V = 24$ cu in., $l = 2$ in., and $w = 3$ in. [4 in.]
- If a student is still having difficulty, use ***Ready Instruction, Level 5,*** Lessons 24–27.

If the error is . . .	Students may . . .	To remediate . . .
$\frac{1}{2}$ ft	not have converted 48 inches to 4 feet.	Have students practice doing word problems with mixed-unit measures to be able to identify instances where unit conversions need to be done. Stress that when working with measures, units need to be consistent.
30 ft	have subtracted 6 from 36 (rather than divide by 6) to solve for *h*.	Review the steps for solving one-step equations.
Any other answer.	have multiplied $4 \cdot 1.5$ incorrectly or divided $36 \div 6$ incorrectly.	Have students practice solving one-step equations requiring the operations of multiplication and division.

Hands-On Activity

Use connecting cubes to model volume.

Materials: 30 connecting cubes per group

- Organize students in small groups and distribute connecting cubes. Have students make 6 towers of 5 cubes each. Then, have them place the towers together to make a rectangular prism.
- Have students examine their rectangular prism. Ask, *What is the length? What is the width? What is the height? How many cubes did you use to make the rectangular prism?*
- Record the dimensions on the board. Write the volume formula $V = Bh = (l \times w) \times h$. Fill in the values for each variable and show that multiplying the dimensions yields the total number of cubes used.
- Repeat with other rectangular prism models.

Challenge Activity

Which truck can fill the pools?

- Tell students that two water trucks pull up to the town swimming pool the week before Memorial Day to fill the big pool and the kiddie pool.
- The dimensions of the big pool are 40 ft long, 20 ft wide, and 4 ft deep. The kiddie pool is 25 ft long, 15 ft wide, and 18 in. deep.
- The dimensions of the water container on the first truck are 30 ft long, 8 ft wide, and 14 ft high.
- The dimensions of the water container on the other truck are 25 ft long, 6 ft wide, and 20 ft high.
- If both trucks are filled to capacity, would either truck hold enough water to fill *both* pools to 6 inches below the top? If not, how much water would be needed from the other truck?

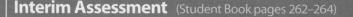

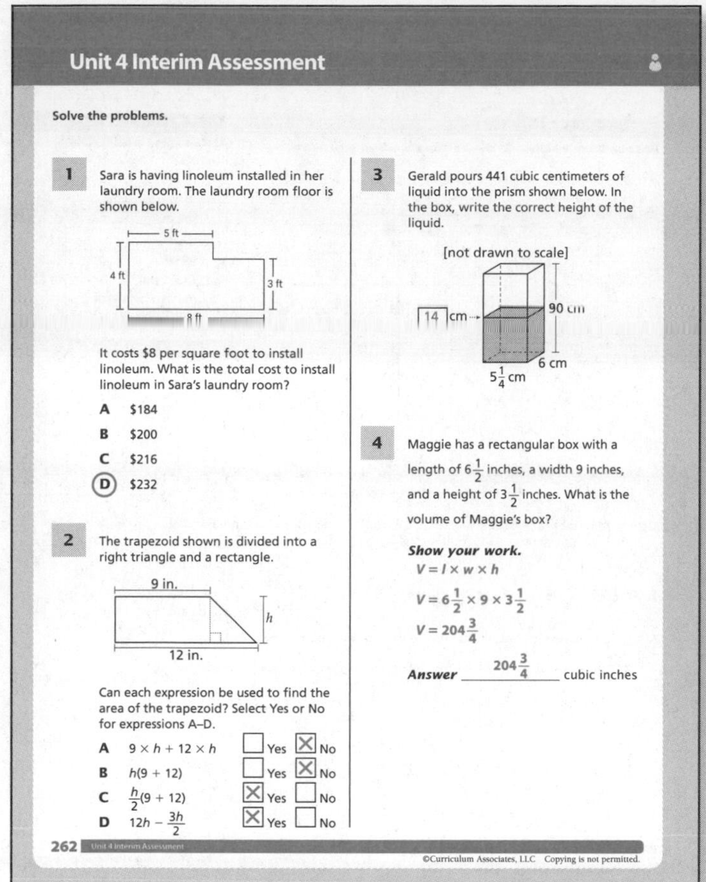

Unit 4 Interim Assessment

Solve the problems.

1 Sara is having linoleum installed in her laundry room. The laundry room floor is shown below.

It costs \$8 per square foot to install linoleum. What is the total cost to install linoleum in Sara's laundry room?

A \$184

B \$200

C \$216

(D) \$232

2 The trapezoid shown is divided into a right triangle and a rectangle.

Can each expression be used to find the area of the trapezoid? Select Yes or No for expressions A–D.

A	$9 \times h + 12 \times h$	☐ Yes	☒ No
B	$h(9 + 12)$	☐ Yes	☒ No
C	$\frac{h}{2}(9 + 12)$	☒ Yes	☐ No
D	$12h - \frac{3h}{2}$	☒ Yes	☐ No

3 Gerald pours 441 cubic centimeters of liquid into the prism shown below. In the box, write the correct height of the liquid.

4 Maggie has a rectangular box with a length of $6\frac{1}{2}$ inches, a width 9 inches, and a height of $3\frac{1}{2}$ inches. What is the volume of Maggie's box?

Show your work.

$V = l \times w \times h$

$V = 6\frac{1}{2} \times 9 \times 3\frac{1}{2}$

$V = 204\frac{3}{4}$

Answer $204\frac{3}{4}$ cubic inches

262 Unit 4 Interim Assessment

©Curriculum Associates, LLC Copying is not permitted.

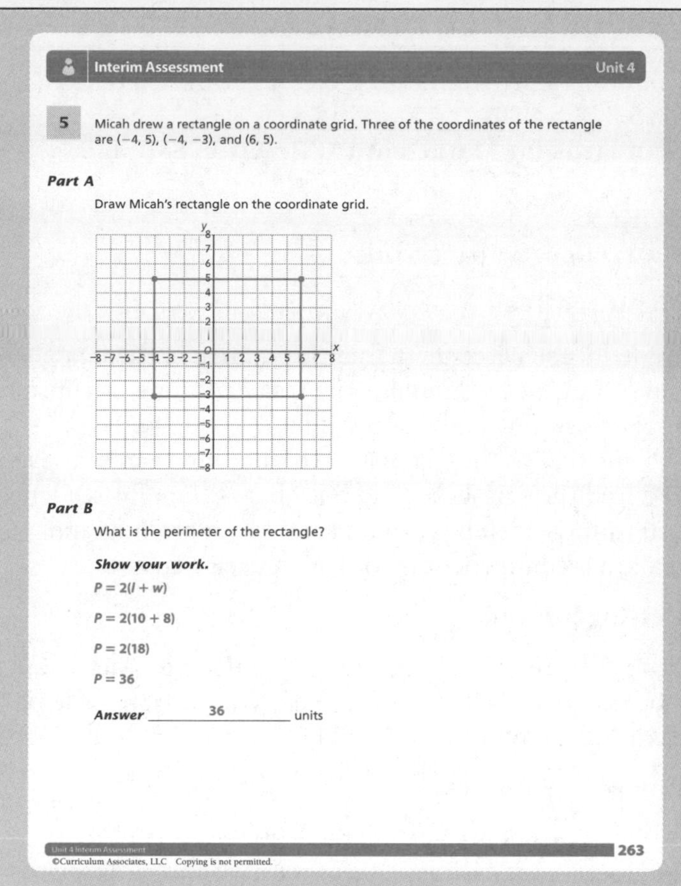

Interim Assessment Unit 4

5 Micah drew a rectangle on a coordinate grid. Three of the coordinates of the rectangle are (−4, 5), (−4, −3), and (6, 5).

Part A

Draw Micah's rectangle on the coordinate grid.

Part B

What is the perimeter of the rectangle?

Show your work.

$P = 2(l + w)$

$P = 2(10 + 8)$

$P = 2(18)$

$P = 36$

Answer 36 units

Unit 4 Interim Assessment 263

©Curriculum Associates, LLC Copying is not permitted.

SCORING GUIDE AND ANSWER ANALYSIS

1 *Solution:* **D**; First divide the shape into two rectangles: $4 \times 5 = 20$ ft², and $3 \times 3 = 9$ ft². Add those areas to get 29 ft². ***(DOK 2)***

2 *Solution:* A **No**; B **No**; C **Yes**; D **Yes** ***(DOK 2)***

3 *Solution:* **14**; Divide the volume, 441, by the product of $5\frac{1}{4}$ and 6. ***(DOK 2)***

4 *Solution:* $204\frac{3}{4}$ in.³, or 204.75 in.³ The volume of a rectangular prism is length × width × height, so $6\frac{1}{2} \times 9 \times 3\frac{1}{2} = 204\frac{3}{4}$. ***(DOK 1)***

5 *Part A Solution:*
See student book page above for drawing on grid; Points should be plotted at (−4, 5), (−4, −3), (6, 5), and (6, −3).

Part B Solution: 36; See student book page above for possible student work. ***(DOK 2)***

PERFORMANCE TASK TEACHER NOTES

Common Core Standards: 6.G.A.2, 6.G.A.4, 6.RP.A.3a, 6.NS.B.3, 6.NS.B.4
Standards for Mathematical Practice: SMP 1, 2, 4, 5, 6, 7
DOK: 3
Materials: grid paper, ruler

About the Task

Students use percents to find the volume of the box given the volume of the granola. The task calls for students to apply reasoning and computation to create two box designs that fit the calculated volume and then draw nets and find the surface area of both boxes. Finally, students determine which box would cost less to produce and make a recommendation of which design to use.

Getting Started

Read the problem aloud with students. For part A, ask students if the volume of the box will be more or less than the volume of the granola and why. ***(SMP 2)***

Completing the Task

In Part B, students need to determine two different combinations of dimensions that have the required volume. For students who are struggling, ask them to think about three factors that generate the desired product. Some students may find a factor tree useful. You may wish to challenge some students to find dimensions that include fractions. ***(SMP 4)***

As students draw the nets and give the dimensions of the two different box designs, discuss how the grid and the net can be used as a tool for finding surface area. Ask students to describe the connection between the net model and a constructed box. ***(SMP 4, 5)***

In Part C, students determine which of their boxes will cost less to make. Guide students to understand the connection between the surface area of the box and the amount of material needed to construct it. Invite students to give their recommendations of which box design to use, including the reasoning behind their choices. ***(SMP 2)***

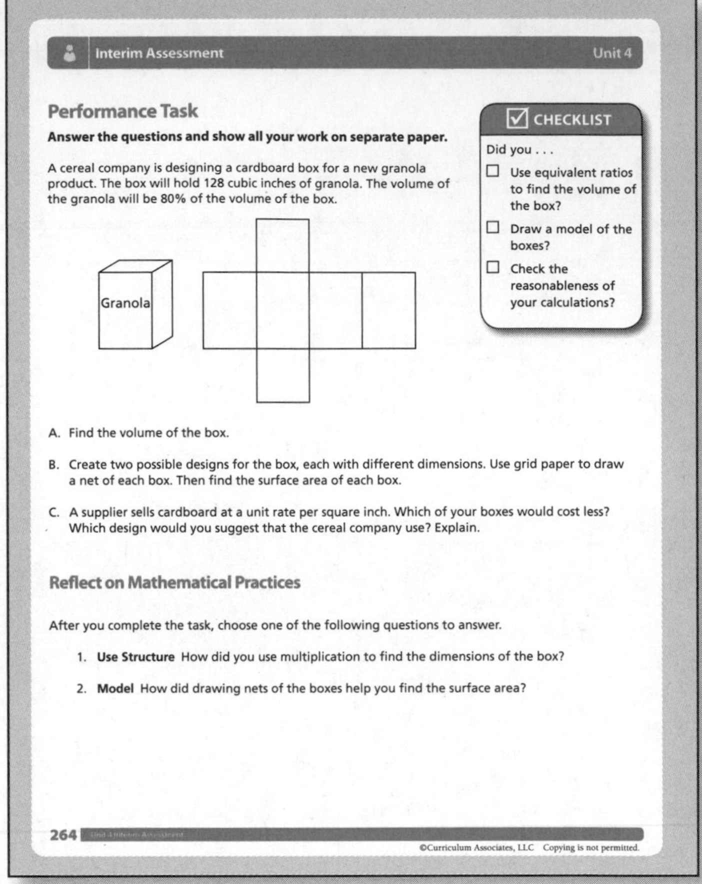
Interim Assessment Unit 4

Performance Task

Answer the questions and show all your work on separate paper.

A cereal company is designing a cardboard box for a new granola product. The box will hold 128 cubic inches of granola. The volume of the granola will be 80% of the volume of the box.

CHECKLIST
Did you . . .
- ☐ Use equivalent ratios to find the volume of the box?
- ☐ Draw a model of the boxes?
- ☐ Check the reasonableness of your calculations?

A. Find the volume of the box.

B. Create two possible designs for the box, each with different dimensions. Use grid paper to draw a net of each box. Then find the surface area of each box.

C. A supplier sells cardboard at a unit rate per square inch. Which of your boxes would cost less? Which design would you suggest that the cereal company use? Explain.

Reflect on Mathematical Practices

After you complete the task, choose one of the following questions to answer.

1. **Use Structure** How did you use multiplication to find the dimensions of the box?
2. **Model** How did drawing nets of the boxes help you find the surface area?

264 Unit 4 Interim Assessment
©Curriculum Associates, LLC Copying is not permitted.

Extension

If some students have more time to spend on this problem, you can have them solve this extension:

Would the dimensions $\frac{1}{2}$ inch × 10 inches × 32 inches work for the design of the box? Would you recommend that the company use such a box? Explain.

PERFORMANCE TASK SAMPLE RESPONSES AND RUBRIC

4-Point Solution

A. The volume of granola, 128 cubic inches, is 80% of the volume of the box. Use the ratio $\frac{128}{80}$ and find an equivalent ratio, where the second term is 100.

Volume of granola	16	128	160
Volume of box	10	80	100

The volume of the box is 160 cubic inches.

B. Use factors to find possible dimensions:
4 in. × 4 in. × 10 in. = 160 sq in.

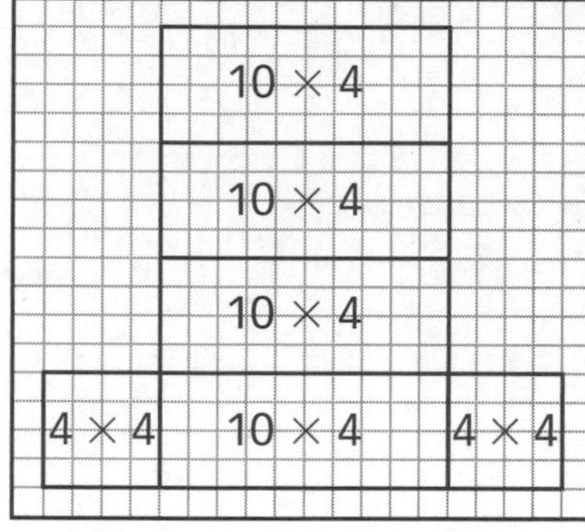

Surface area of 4 × 4 × 10 box:

(40 × 4) + (16 × 2)

160 + 32 = 192

2 in. × 8 in. × 10 in. = 160 sq in.

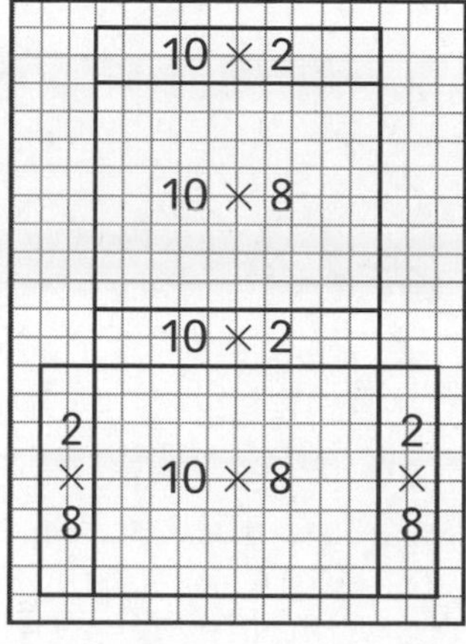

Surface area of 2 × 8 × 10 box:

(20 × 2) + (80 × 2) + (16 × 2)

40 + 160 + 32 = 232

C. The 4 × 4 × 10 box has a smaller surface area, so it would cost less than the 2 × 8 × 10 box. To save money, I would suggest that the company use the 4 × 4 × 10 box.

REFLECT ON MATHEMATICAL PRACTICES

1. Look for an understanding that you need to find three factors whose product is 160. ***(SMP 7)***
2. Look for an understanding that drawing and labeling the dimensions of a net of a rectangular prism gives you all the information you need to find the surface area. ***(SMP 4)***

SCORING RUBRIC

4 points The student's response is accurate and complete. The diagrams show two different nets that have a volume of 160 square inches. The surface area calculations are correct and the student makes a reasonable recommendation of which box to use.

3 points The student's calculation for the volume of the box is correct. The nets and surface area calculations are mostly accurate, but there may be a few minor errors. The student's recommendation is reasonable.

2 points The student attempted all parts of this problem, but there are errors in the calculations of volume or surface area. The diagrams may be incomplete or inaccurate. The student is able to partially justify the recommendation.

1 point The diagram and the calculations contain errors and are incomplete. The student is not able to make a reasonable recommendation.

SOLUTION TO THE EXTENSION

The volume of a box $\frac{1}{2}$ inch × 10 inches × 32 inches is 160 square inches, so it would work for the problem. I would not recommend using this design since $\frac{1}{2}$ inch is very small and 32 inches is long. The box would be an odd shape and would probably not fit well on a shelf.

Unit 5: Statistics and Probability

Which lessons are students building upon?

Grade 5, Lesson 23
Make Line Plots and Interpret Data
5.MD.B.2

Grade 5, Lesson 23
Make Line Plots and Interpret Data
5.MD.B.2

Grade 5, Lesson 23
Make Line Plots and Interpret Data
5.MD.B.2

Grade 6, Lesson 27
Measures of Center and Variability
6.SP.A.2, 6.SP.A.3

Grade 5, Lesson 23
Make Line Plots and Interpret Data
5.MD.B.2

Grade 6, Lesson 27
Measures of Center and Variability
6.SP.A.2, 6.SP.A.3

Grade 6, Lesson 28
Display Data on Dot Plots, Histograms, and Box Plots
6.SP.B.4

Unit 5

Which lessons are students preparing for?

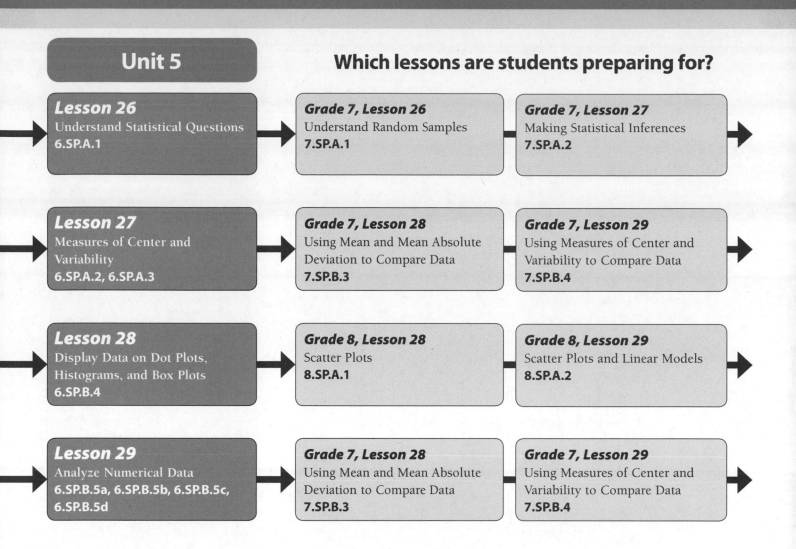

Unit 5		
Lesson 26 Understand Statistical Questions **6.SP.A.1**	**Grade 7, Lesson 26** Understand Random Samples **7.SP.A.1**	**Grade 7, Lesson 27** Making Statistical Inferences **7.SP.A.2**
Lesson 27 Measures of Center and Variability **6.SP.A.2, 6.SP.A.3**	**Grade 7, Lesson 28** Using Mean and Mean Absolute Deviation to Compare Data **7.SP.B.3**	**Grade 7, Lesson 29** Using Measures of Center and Variability to Compare Data **7.SP.B.4**
Lesson 28 Display Data on Dot Plots, Histograms, and Box Plots **6.SP.B.4**	**Grade 8, Lesson 28** Scatter Plots **8.SP.A.1**	**Grade 8, Lesson 29** Scatter Plots and Linear Models **8.SP.A.2**
Lesson 29 Analyze Numerical Data **6.SP.B.5a, 6.SP.B.5b, 6.SP.B.5c, 6.SP.B.5d**	**Grade 7, Lesson 28** Using Mean and Mean Absolute Deviation to Compare Data **7.SP.B.3**	**Grade 7, Lesson 29** Using Measures of Center and Variability to Compare Data **7.SP.B.4**

Lesson 26 (Student Book pages 266–271)

Understand Statistical Questions

LESSON OBJECTIVES

- Understand that data generated from statistical questions will vary.
- Recognize that responses to statistical questions have variations that can be used to draw conclusions about the data set.
- Identify the difference between a statistical and non-statistical question.
- Write simple statistical questions.
- Create models that represent the anticipated data from statistical questions such as charts and tables.

PREREQUISITE SKILLS

- Know the difference between a statement and a question.
- Be able to formulate a question.
- Know how to set up and use charts and tables for representing data.

VOCABULARY

statistical questions: questions with answers involving a mass of numerical data

THE LEARNING PROGRESSION

Understanding of statistical variability is fundamental to future studies in statistics and to everyday decision-making based on data. This lesson teaches students that statistical investigations begin with a question and that answers to such questions always involve variability in the data collected to answer them. Students are guided to distinguish statistical questions from non-statistical questions and to compare the variability of different statistical questions.

In Grade 6, students build on the knowledge and experiences developed in earlier grades. They develop a deeper understanding of variability and more precise descriptions of data distributions using numerical measures of center and spread and terms such as cluster, peak, gap, symmetry, skew, and outlier.

In Grade 7, students move from concentrating on analysis of data to production of data, understanding that good answers to statistical questions depend upon a good plan for collecting data relevant to the questions of interest.

Ready ***Teacher Toolbox*** Teacher-Toolbox.com

	Prerequisite Skills	6.SP.A.1
Ready Lessons		✓
Tools for Instruction		✓
Interactive Tutorials		

CCSS Focus

6.SP.A.1 Recognize a statistical question as one that anticipates variability in the data related to the question and accounts for it in the answers. *For example, "How old am I?" is not a statistical question, but "How old are the students in my school?" is a statistical question because one anticipates variability in students' ages.*

STANDARDS FOR MATHEMATICAL PRACTICE: ***SMP 1, 3, 6*** *(see page A9 for full text)*

AT A GLANCE

Students explore the difference between statistical and non-statistical questions. Students learn that statistical questions have variability. i.e., a variety of answers, while non-statistical questions have exact answers.

STEP BY STEP

- Introduce the question at the top of the page.
- Explain to students that one of the ways we can find out more about something is to ask the same statistical question to a group of people and use the answers to make a prediction or draw a conclusion about a larger group to which these people belong.
- Explain that when we ask a statistical question we expect to get a variety of answers instead of the exact same answers.
- Reinforce the idea that this variety of answers, called variability, is the difference between statistical and non-statistical questions.
- Read Think with students. Remind students that they should circle only the questions where there could be different answers from different people or at different times. Only those questions solicit data with some degree of variability.
- Have two or three students answer the second and third questions as a way to demonstrate how those questions solicit a variety of answers. Such variety is what makes these questions statistical questions.

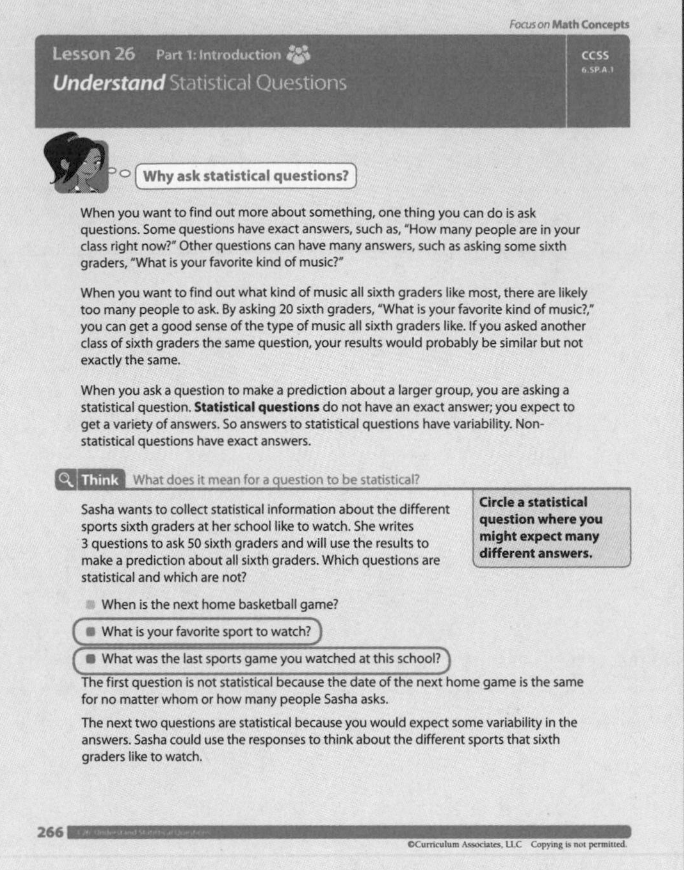

Focus on **Math Concepts**

Lesson 26 Part 1: Introduction

Understand Statistical Questions

CCSS 6.SP.A.1

Why ask statistical questions?

When you want to find out more about something, one thing you can do is ask questions. Some questions have exact answers, such as, "How many people are in your class right now?" Other questions can have many answers, such as asking some sixth graders, "What is your favorite kind of music?"

When you want to find out what kind of music all sixth graders like most, there are likely too many people to ask. By asking 20 sixth graders, "What is your favorite kind of music?," you can get a good sense of the type of music all sixth graders like. If you asked another class of sixth graders the same question, your results would probably be similar but not exactly the same.

When you ask a question to make a prediction about a larger group, you are asking a statistical question. **Statistical questions** do not have an exact answer; you expect to get a variety of answers. So answers to statistical questions have variability. Non-statistical questions have exact answers.

Think What does it mean for a question to be statistical?

Sasha wants to collect statistical information about the different sports sixth graders at her school like to watch. She writes 3 questions to ask 50 sixth graders and will use the results to make a prediction about all sixth graders. Which questions are statistical and which are not?

Circle a statistical question where you might expect many different answers.

- When is the next home basketball game?
- What is your favorite sport to watch?
- What was the last sports game you watched at this school?

The first question is not statistical because the date of the next home game is the same for no matter whom or how many people Sasha asks.

The next two questions are statistical because you would expect some variability in the answers. Sasha could use the responses to think about the different sports that sixth graders like to watch.

266

ELL Support

Have students do a cloze activity using the following terms: *variability*, *variety*, *vary*, and *variable*.

- A ____________________ is a symbol usually represented by a letter that stands for a value that may vary. [variable]
- What makes a statistical question different from a non-statistical question is ____________________. [variability]
- Non-statistical questions have answers that do not ____________________. [vary]
- When we ask a statistical question we expect to get a ____________________ of answers. [variety]

Mathematical Discourse

- *Can you think of a career you would like to be in some day where you would ask a statistical question to learn more about something?*

  Examples: People do research in the sciences and medicine; athletes use statistics for performance measures (e.g., earned run averages in baseball); market research to design products. Accept other reasonable responses.

- *What is one statistical question you could ask to help you in the career you described?*

  Answers will vary. Encourage students to think about what information or data they would work with in such a career. Ask students what questions they can ask to learn that information.

AT A GLANCE

Students explore how to write an effective statistical question. Students identify statistical questions that are too general or too specific.

STEP BY STEP

- Read Think with students.
- Emphasize to students that Sasha is interested in knowing what *school* sports sixth graders like to watch the most.
- Tell students that they will consider the effectiveness of Sasha's questions from page 266, given what she is interested in learning about sixth graders.
- Point out that Sasha can phrase her statistical question in more than one way, but that questions need to be carefully worded so that they are neither too general nor too specific. Tell students that one goal in devising a statistical question is to produce varying answers.
- Have students read and respond to the Reflect directive.

SMP Tip: When students identify questions as too general or too specific, they attend to precision by relating statistical questions to anticipated variability in the data (*SMP 6*).

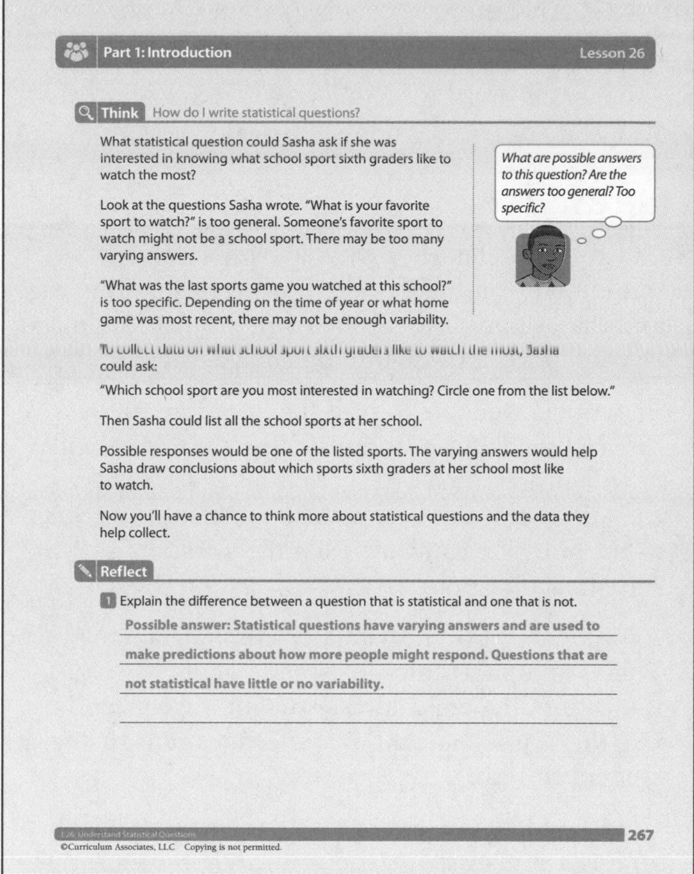

Part 1: Introduction Lesson 26

Think How do I write statistical questions?

What statistical question could Sasha ask if she was interested in knowing what school sport sixth graders like to watch the most?

Look at the questions Sasha wrote. "What is your favorite sport to watch?" is too general. Someone's favorite sport to watch might not be a school sport. There may be too many varying answers.

"What was the last sports game you watched at this school?" is too specific. Depending on the time of year or what home game was most recent, there may not be enough variability.

What are possible answers to this question? Are the answers too general? Too specific?

To collect data on what school sport sixth graders like to watch the most, Sasha could ask:

"Which school sport are you most interested in watching? Circle one from the list below."

Then Sasha could list all the school sports at her school.

Possible responses would be one of the listed sports. The varying answers would help Sasha draw conclusions about which sports sixth graders at her school most like to watch.

Now you'll have a chance to think more about statistical questions and the data they help collect.

Reflect

1 Explain the difference between a question that is statistical and one that is not.

Possible answer: Statistical questions have varying answers and are used to make predictions about how more people might respond. Questions that are not statistical have little or no variability.

L26: Understand Statistical Questions 267
©Curriculum Associates, LLC Copying is not permitted.

Mathematical Discourse

- *Describe in your own words how a statistical question can affect how accurately you can describe or predict something.*

  Listen for students to explain that a good question that allows for variability in the responses helps the questioner understand or predict something about a group. If the question is too specific or too general, that quality affects how accurate the prediction is.

- *In the real world, what are some effects of making a bad prediction? What are some effects of bad predictions in science, medicine, business?*

  Answers will vary. Bad predictions lead to an inaccurate understanding of a situation. Such lack of understanding can lead to incorrect courses of action.

Concept Extension

Rank questions in order of variability.

- Present to students three statistical questions that could be asked of a group of sixth graders. You can make up your own or use the following:

  How many brothers and sisters do you have?
  How many books did you read last school year?
  How many extracurricular activities do you do (sports, music, dance, and theater)?

- Have students rank the questions in order of greatest to least variability (i.e., which question would solicit the greatest variety of responses? The least?) [There is no single correct answer. Have students explain the rationale for their order, which will likely be based on their own personal experience or observations.]

AT A GLANCE

Students determine whether questions are statistical or non-statistical and explain their reasoning. Students write a statistical and a non-statistical question.

STEP BY STEP

- Tell students that they will have time to work individually on the Explore It problems on this page and then share their responses in groups. You may choose to work through problem 2 as a class.
- Encourage students to read the questions and ask themselves, *Is there an exact answer to this question, or will answers vary?* [If there is an exact answer, the question is not a statistical question. If answers to the question can vary, then the question is a statistical question.]
- As students work individually, circulate among them. This is an opportunity to assess student understanding and address student misconceptions. Use the Mathematical Discourse questions to engage student thinking.
- Guide students to distinguish between statistical and non-statistical questions for the problems. Ask students to volunteer their answers and encourage them to think aloud and explain their reasoning to the class.
- Reinforce the idea that if the answer to the question varies, it is a statistical question. Answers to statistical questions let the questioner make predictions about the larger group to which the responders belong.
- Take note of students who are still having difficulty. Wait to see if their understanding progresses as they work in their groups during the next part of the lesson.

STUDENT MISCONCEPTION ALERT: Suppose you ask a group of sixth graders, *How many U.S. senators are there?* You might get a variety of answers because students don't know the exact answer. Students may confuse this sort of variety with statistical variety.

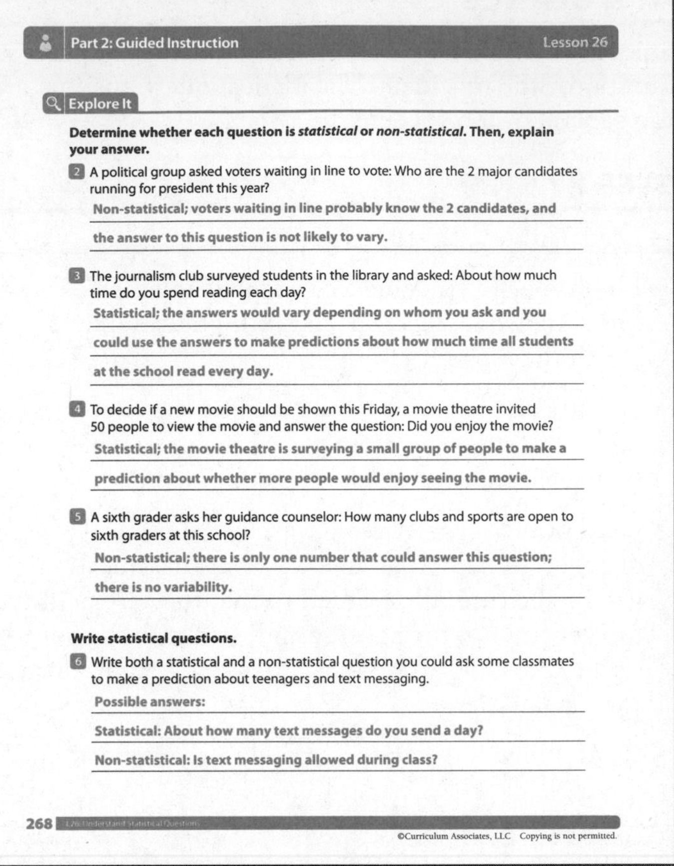

Part 2: Guided Instruction Lesson 26

Explore It

Determine whether each question is *statistical* or *non-statistical*. Then, explain your answer.

2 A political group asked voters waiting in line to vote: Who are the 2 major candidates running for president this year?

Non-statistical; voters waiting in line probably know the 2 candidates, and the answer to this question is not likely to vary.

3 The journalism club surveyed students in the library and asked: About how much time do you spend reading each day?

Statistical; the answers would vary depending on whom you ask and you could use the answers to make predictions about how much time all students at the school read every day.

4 To decide if a new movie should be shown this Friday, a movie theatre invited 50 people to view the movie and answer the question: Did you enjoy the movie?

Statistical; the movie theatre is surveying a small group of people to make a prediction about whether more people would enjoy seeing the movie.

5 A sixth grader asks her guidance counselor: How many clubs and sports are open to sixth graders at this school?

Non-statistical; there is only one number that could answer this question; there is no variability.

Write statistical questions.

6 Write both a statistical and a non-statistical question you could ask some classmates to make a prediction about teenagers and text messaging.

Possible answers:

Statistical: About how many text messages do you send a day?

Non-statistical: Is text messaging allowed during class?

268 L26: Understand Statistical Questions

©Curriculum Associates, LLC Copying is not permitted.

Mathematical Discourse

- *When our answer to a math problem is not a number that we can plug back into an equation to check, how do we "check" our answer?*

  Listen for students to explain how they judge whether an answer is correct or incorrect when they can't plug a number back into an equation. Listen for students to explain how they reason, use logic, reread the question, and so on as ways to check the reasonableness of an answer.

- *What are the ways you have checked some of your answers in this lesson so far?*

  Listen for students to explain how they decide whether a question is statistical or non-statistical. Encourage students to break down their reasoning into steps such as (1) recall the definition of a statistical question, (2) reread the question, and (3) evaluate the question against our definition.

AT A GLANCE

Students revisit the problems from page 268 and give examples of how statistical questions have variability. Students make changes to the wording of non-statistical questions to make them statistical questions.

STEP BY STEP

- Organize students into pairs or groups. Work through problem 7 as a class. Remind students that problem 7 refers to page 268.
- Encourage students to explain how the statistical questions from page 268 have variability. Also have students explain the ways in which the non-statistical questions lack variability.
- Have student groups work through Try It Another Way.

SMP Tip: When students give examples that show how the statistical questions have variability and the non-statistical questions lack variability, they demonstrate they understand and can use stated assumptions, definitions, and previously established results in constructing arguments (*SMP 3*).

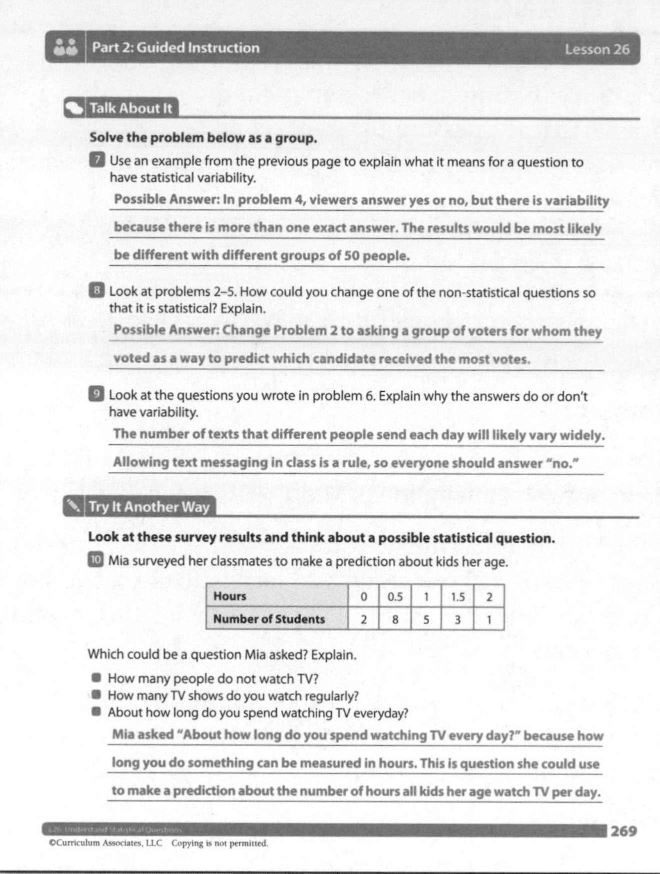

Part 2: Guided Instruction Lesson 26

Talk About It

Solve the problem below as a group.

7 Use an example from the previous page to explain what it means for a question to have statistical variability.

Possible Answer: In problem 4, viewers answer yes or no, but there is variability because there is more than one exact answer. The results would be most likely be different with different groups of 50 people.

8 Look at problems 2–5. How could you change one of the non-statistical questions so that it is statistical? Explain.

Possible Answer: Change Problem 2 to asking a group of voters for whom they voted as a way to predict which candidate received the most votes.

9 Look at the questions you wrote in problem 6. Explain why the answers do or don't have variability.

The number of texts that different people send each day will likely vary widely. Allowing text messaging in class is a rule, so everyone should answer "no."

Try It Another Way

Look at these survey results and think about a possible statistical question.

10 Mia surveyed her classmates to make a prediction about kids her age.

Hours	0	0.5	1	1.5	2
Number of Students	2	8	5	3	1

Which could be a question Mia asked? Explain.

- How many people do not watch TV?
- How many TV shows do you watch regularly?
- About how long do you spend watching TV everyday?

Mia asked "About how long do you spend watching TV every day?" because how long you do something can be measured in hours. This is question she could use to make a prediction about the number of hours all kids her age watch TV per day.

L26: Understand Statistical Questions 269

©Curriculum Associates, LLC Copying is not permitted.

Hands-On Activity

Materials: strips of paper, scissors, markers

- Put students into pairs or small groups. Tell them that they will write down each of the following question stems on two strips of paper.

  What are . . . , How many . . . , When do . . .

- Next, for each question stem, they are to write an ending that will create a statistical question and a non-statistical question. (You may want to give them examples such as *How many books are on the book shelf in this classroom? How many books have you read this year?*)
- Discuss each question stem as a class. Have one person from each group read the group's questions for that stem. Discuss why each question is or is not a statistical question.

AT A GLANCE

Students demonstrate their understanding of how variability distinguishes a statistical question from a non-statistical question by answering a series of questions. Students compare the variability of statistical questions.

STEP BY STEP

- Discuss each Connect It problem as a class using the discussion points outlined below.

Compare:

- You may choose to have students work in pairs to encourage sharing ideas and justifications.
- For quick assessment, you can read the first question and ask for a show of hands—statistical question or non-statistical question. Do the same for the second question.
- Ask a student to volunteer to explain how he/she knew that the first question is statistical and the second is non-statistical.

Analyze:

- The second problem focuses on the idea that certain statistical questions are better than others because they solicit answers that help you make better predictions or draw conclusions based on your original question.
- Read the problem together as a class. Ask students to continue to work in pairs to discuss and write their responses to the question.
- Begin the discussion by asking: *What does the problem tell us that we are trying to learn about by asking a question? Be specific.*

Predict:

- This discussion gives students an opportunity to predict which question will produce a greater variety of answers.
- Discuss the possible answers for the first question. [Answers will be yes or no.]
- Discuss the possible answers to the second question. Emphasize the variety of answers to this question versus the first one.

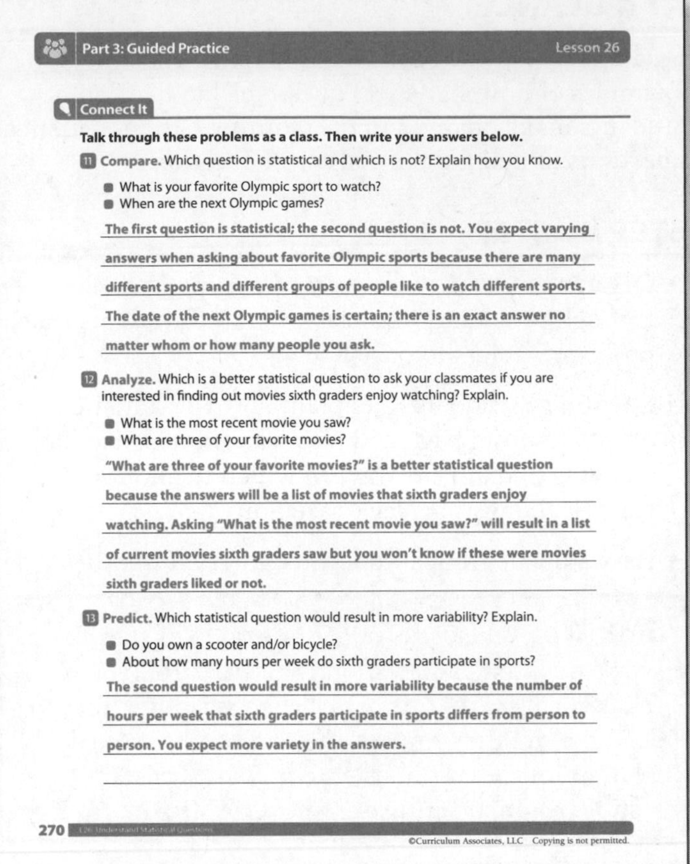

Connect It

Talk through these problems as a class. Then write your answers below.

11 **Compare.** Which question is statistical and which is not? Explain how you know.

- What is your favorite Olympic sport to watch?
- When are the next Olympic games?

The first question is statistical; the second question is not. You expect varying answers when asking about favorite Olympic sports because there are many different sports and different groups of people like to watch different sports. The date of the next Olympic games is certain; there is an exact answer no matter whom or how many people you ask.

12 **Analyze.** Which is a better statistical question to ask your classmates if you are interested in finding out movies sixth graders enjoy watching? Explain.

- What is the most recent movie you saw?
- What are three of your favorite movies?

"What are three of your favorite movies?" is a better statistical question because the answers will be a list of movies that sixth graders enjoy watching. Asking "What is the most recent movie you saw?" will result in a list of current movies sixth graders saw but you won't know if these were movies sixth graders liked or not.

13 **Predict.** Which statistical question would result in more variability? Explain.

- Do you own a scooter and/or bicycle?
- About how many hours per week do sixth graders participate in sports?

The second question would result in more variability because the number of hours per week that sixth graders participate in sports differs from person to person. You expect more variety in the answers.

SMP Tip: As students advance through a series of increasingly difficult questions relating statistical questions to variability, they are making sense of problems and persevering in solving them (*SMP 1*).

AT A GLANCE

Students write two statistical questions and analyze variability in the answers. Students ask a question, record the answers in a line plot, and explain variability of answers.

STEP BY STEP

- Direct students to complete the Put It Together task on their own.
- Explain to students that their questions should be carefully worded to get a variety of responses. Allow them to make predictions or draw conclusions based on what they are interested in learning about their classmates.
- As students work on their own, give additional support, if needed.
- Have students ask classmates one of their questions and record the answers on a line plot.
- Have students write down their responses to the questions about the variability of given responses and predicted variability.

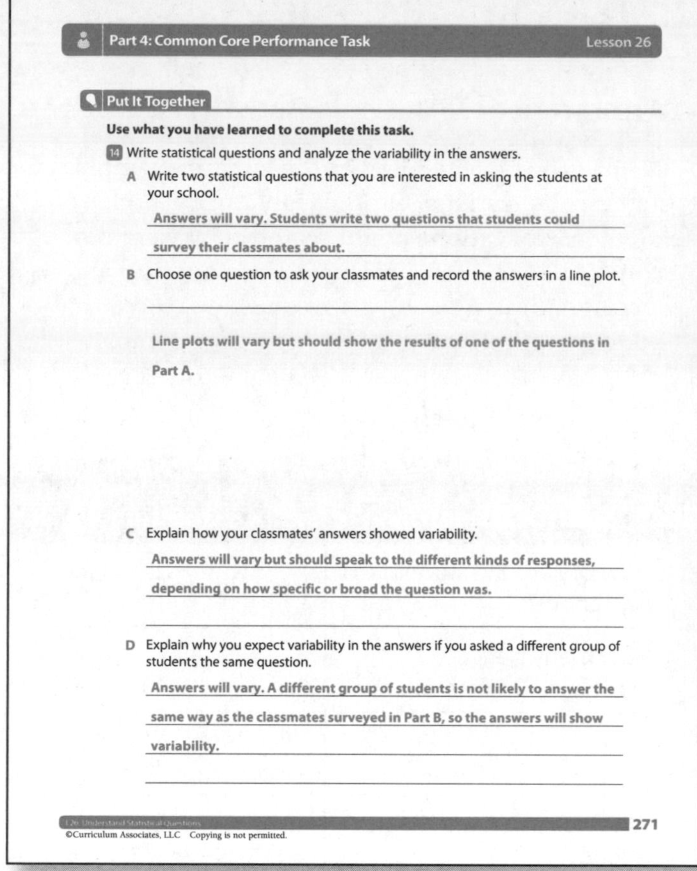

Part 4: Common Core Performance Task Lesson 26

Put It Together

Use what you have learned to complete this task.

14 Write statistical questions and analyze the variability in the answers.

A Write two statistical questions that you are interested in asking the students at your school.

Answers will vary. Students write two questions that students could survey their classmates about.

B Choose one question to ask your classmates and record the answers in a line plot.

Line plots will vary but should show the results of one of the questions in Part A.

C Explain how your classmates' answers showed variability.

Answers will vary but should speak to the different kinds of responses, depending on how specific or broad the question was.

D Explain why you expect variability in the answers if you asked a different group of students the same question.

Answers will vary. A different group of students is not likely to answer the same way as the classmates surveyed in Part B, so the answers will show variability.

L26: Understand Statistical Questions 271

©Curriculum Associates, LLC Copying is not permitted.

SCORING RUBRICS

See student facsimile page for possible student answers.

A

Points	Expectations
2	The question demonstrates the student's mathematical understanding of how to devise a good statistical question that has variability.
1	One or both questions lacked variability or were too general or specific based on what the student wanted to learn about classmates.
0	Student did not write the questions or showed little effort or understanding of variability.

B

Points	Expectations
2	Student records answers in an organized line plot.
1	Student records answers but line plot is incorrectly drawn.
0	There is no line plot or plot does not represent data collected.

C

Points	Expectations
2	Student's explanation about answers is clear, correct, and demonstrates a good understanding of the concept of variability.
1	Student attempts to explain answers but lacks clarity understanding about the concept of variability.
0	Student does not respond to the question or does not address the key point about variability.

D

Points	Expectations
2	Student's response demonstrates a good understanding of how asking different groups increases variability.
1	Student's response shows minimal understanding of how variability is affected by asking additional groups.
0	Student does not respond or shows a lack of understanding of the concept of variability.

Intervention Activity

Write statistical and non-statistical questions.

Display the table below. On the left are examples of statistical questions. On the right are examples of how these questions might read if they were non-statistical. The first row shows the statistical and its corresponding non-statistical question. Have students complete the table. After they complete the table, have them explain why they wrote the question as they did.

Statistical Question	Non-Statistical Question
How old are the students in my school?	How old am I?
How many pets do students in my school own?	
	What is my math test score?
When do sixth graders go to bed?	
	What is my best friend's favorite ice cream flavor?
What is the height of the girls in my grade?	
	What is my favorite type of music?

On-Level Activity

Write and analyze questions with variability.

Tell students that they will write three different questions—one non-statistical and two statistical. Then tell students that one statistical question should produce data with more variability than the other statistical question.

Tell students the following:

1 Write a non-statistical question.

2 Explain why this question does not have variability.

3 Write your first statistical question.

4 Explain how this question has variability.

5 Write your second statistical question.

6 Explain how this question has variability.

7 Explain how one statistical question has more variability than the other statistical question.

Challenge Activity

Create problems to match data.

At the right is a line plot for data that were collected in response to a statistical question. Answer the following questions related to the line plot.

1 Write two statistical questions that could have been asked to produce the data.

2 How many people responded to the question?

3 Pick a question from problem 1 (above) to answer these questions: Why would someone be interested in asking this question? What could that person do with the data they collect from that question?

		x		
		x	x	
	x	x	x	
	x	x	x	x
x	x	x	x	x
x	x	x	x	x
Below 65	66–69	70–79	80–89	90–100

Lesson 27 (Student Book pages 272–283)

Measures of Center and Variability

LESSON OBJECTIVES

- Understand that data distribution can be viewed by its center (mean, median, and mode), spread (range), and overall shape, and it can be analyzed by its distribution.
- Understand that the mean, median, and mode of a set of numerical data are measures of center of that set of data.
- Understand that the range of a set of numerical data is a measure of how the data varies.

PREREQUISITE SKILLS

- Understand statistical questions and data collection.
- Understand that graphs and tables organize data.

VOCABULARY

cluster: a group of data points that crowd near each other

skewed left: when most of the data points on a graph are clustered near higher values

skewed right: when most of the data points on a graph are clustered near lower values

symmetrical graphs: graphs that show the same number of data points above and below a middle point

peak: what forms when many data points are at one value

outlier: a data point far away from the other data points; it doesn't quite fit with the rest of the data points

median: the middle number in an ordered set of numbers

mode: the most common number in a set of numbers

range: the variation of data points between the least and greatest values

mean absolute deviation (MAD): the average distance of each data point from the mean

THE LEARNING PROGRESSION

Understanding, analyzing, and displaying data are skills that are increasingly important for college and career readiness.

Students have created and interpreted different data displays in earlier grades. In Grade 6, they begin working with statistical measures of center and variability. In earlier lessons, students learned that statistical data can vary. In this lesson, students will learn to explain variability and measures of spread in data. In later lessons, students will display data in graphs and summarize and describe distributions.

Ready *Teacher Toolbox* — Teacher-Toolbox.com

	Prerequisite Skills	*6.SP.A.2 6.SP.A.3*
Ready Lessons		✓
Tools for Instruction		✓
Interactive Tutorials		✓

CCSS Focus

6.SP.A.2 Understand that a set of data collected to answer a statistical question has a distribution which can be described by its center, spread, and overall shape.

6.SP.A.3 Recognize that a measure of center for a numerical data set summarizes all of its values with a single number, while a measure of variation describes how its values vary with a single number.

ADDITIONAL STANDARDS: ***6.SP.B.5*** *(see page A42 for full text)*

STANDARDS FOR MATHEMATICAL PRACTICE: ***SMP 2, 4–7*** *(see page A9 for full text)*

AT A GLANCE

Students read a word problem and explore how to explain variability in data.

STEP BY STEP

- Tell students that this page models variability in data.
- Have students read the problem at the top of the page.
- Work through Explore It as a class.
- Ask student pairs or groups to explain their answers for the final Explore It question.

SMP Tip: Students in Grade 6 use measures of center, variability, and data displays to draw inferences about and make comparisons between data sets (*SMP 4*). Students need multiple opportunities to make and explain connections between different representations.

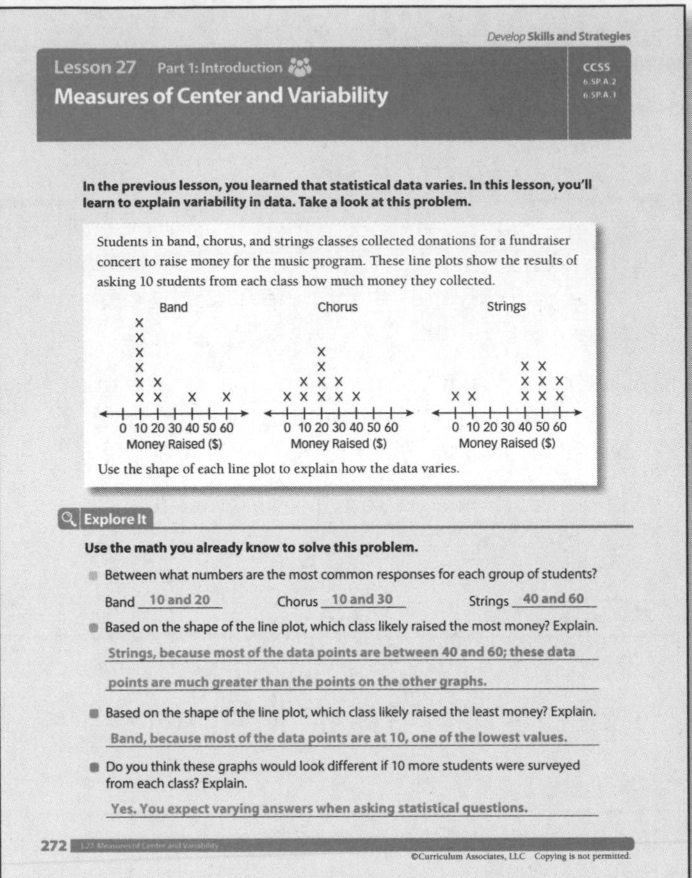

Develop Skills and Strategies

Lesson 27 Part 1: Introduction

Measures of Center and Variability

CCSS 6.SP.A.2 6.SP.A.1

In the previous lesson, you learned that statistical data varies. In this lesson, you'll learn to explain variability in data. Take a look at this problem.

Students in band, chorus, and strings classes collected donations for a fundraiser concert to raise money for the music program. These line plots show the results of asking 10 students from each class how much money they collected.

Use the shape of each line plot to explain how the data varies.

Explore It

Use the math you already know to solve this problem.

- Between what numbers are the most common responses for each group of students?
  Band 10 and 20 Chorus 10 and 30 Strings 40 and 60
- Based on the shape of the line plot, which class likely raised the most money? Explain.
  Strings, because most of the data points are between 40 and 60; these data points are much greater than the points on the other graphs.
- Based on the shape of the line plot, which class likely raised the least money? Explain.
  Band, because most of the data points are at 10, one of the lowest values.
- Do you think these graphs would look different if 10 more students were surveyed from each class? Explain.
  Yes. You expect varying answers when asking statistical questions.

272 L27: Measures of Center and Variability

©Curriculum Associates, LLC Copying is not permitted.

Mathematical Discourse

- *Previously we learned that statistical data varies. Explain to your partner what that means.*

  Students may talk about variation and how it describes the spread of the values in a data set. Data are the values produced in response to a statistical question.

- *How do you know if a question is statistical?*

  A statistical question is one that collects information that addresses differences in a population.

AT A GLANCE

Students look at line plots and explore concepts of variability in data.

STEP BY STEP

- Read Find Out More as a class.
- Ask students to think of some ways to help them remember the vocabulary. For example, an outlier is a data point far from the other data points. You could think of it as being "outside."
- Have students read and reply to the Reflect question.

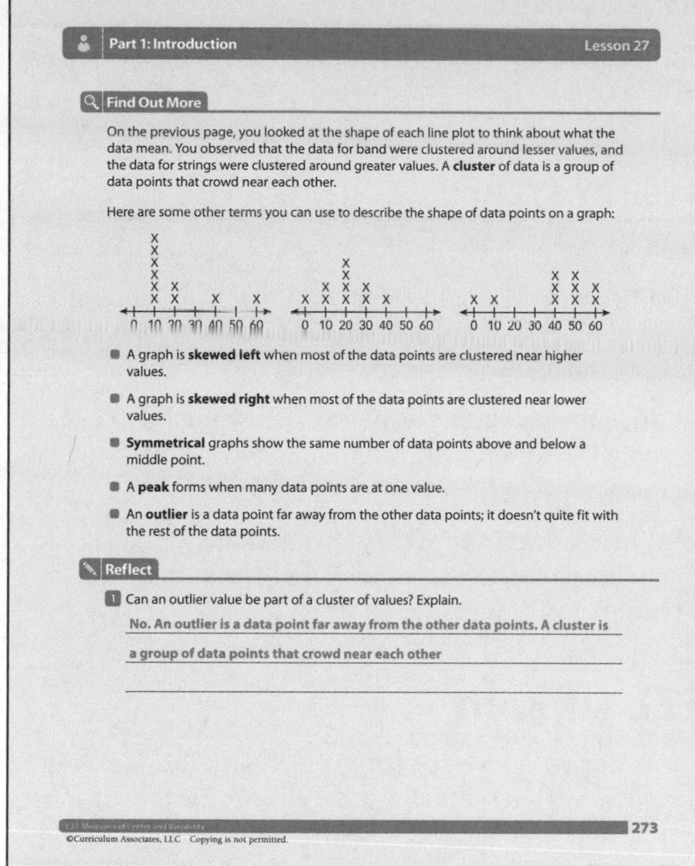

Part 1: Introduction Lesson 27

Find Out More

On the previous page, you looked at the shape of each line plot to think about what the data mean. You observed that the data for band were clustered around lesser values, and the data for strings were clustered around greater values. A **cluster** of data is a group of data points that crowd near each other.

Here are some other terms you can use to describe the shape of data points on a graph:

- A graph is **skewed left** when most of the data points are clustered near higher values.
- A graph is **skewed right** when most of the data points are clustered near lower values.
- **Symmetrical** graphs show the same number of data points above and below a middle point.
- A **peak** forms when many data points are at one value.
- An **outlier** is a data point far away from the other data points; it doesn't quite fit with the rest of the data points.

Reflect

1 Can an outlier value be part of a cluster of values? Explain.

No. An outlier is a data point far away from the other data points. A cluster is a group of data points that crowd near each other

L27: Measures of Center and Variability 273

©Curriculum Associates, LLC Copying is not permitted.

ELL Support

- Review the meanings of *skewed, symmetrical, peak*, and *outlier.* Use visual examples and verbal explanations.
- Explain that *skewed* refers to a slant more toward one direction.
- Show students geometric shapes or other objects that are *symmetrical*.
- Point out that a stack of data points at one value comes to a *peak*, or a high point, similar to a mountain peak.
- Break apart the term *outlier* into *out*, which means "apart" or "away from," and *lier*, which in this case means "placed" or "put."
- Have students draw line plots with several data points to practice displaying shapes to illustrate each term.

SMP Tip: Students consider available tools when solving a mathematical problem and decide when certain tools might be useful (*SMP 5*). Number lines might be used to create line plots, dot plots, histograms, and box plots to visually compare the center and variability of data.

Real-World Connection

Scientists collect and organize data about animal populations to make predictions. Ask students to think of other real-world examples in which data collection might be useful for making predictions.

Examples: report cards, city populations, daily temperatures, illness outbreaks, obesity rates

AT A GLANCE

Students read a word problem and then explore how to describe the center of a data set using the mean, or average.

STEP BY STEP

- Read the problem at the top of the page as a class.
- When talking about the first Model It, be sure to encourage students to cross out each ($) symbol as they move it so they don't accidently count one twice.
- After the symbols are moved, ask students to use the model to find how much money the average student raised.
- When talking about the second Model It, be sure to emphasize that you are dividing the sum by the number of values.

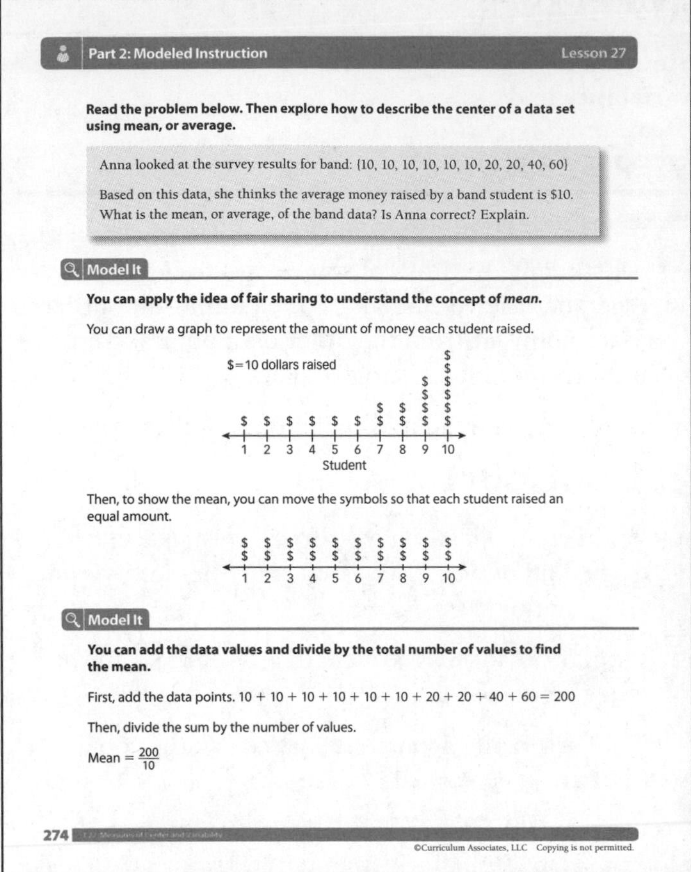

Part 2: Modeled Instruction Lesson 27

Read the problem below. Then explore how to describe the center of a data set using mean, or average.

Anna looked at the survey results for band: {10, 10, 10, 10, 10, 10, 20, 20, 40, 60}

Based on this data, she thinks the average money raised by a band student is $10. What is the mean, or average, of the band data? Is Anna correct? Explain.

Model It

You can apply the idea of fair sharing to understand the concept of *mean*.

You can draw a graph to represent the amount of money each student raised.

Then, to show the mean, you can move the symbols so that each student raised an equal amount.

Model It

You can add the data values and divide by the total number of values to find the mean.

First, add the data points. $10 + 10 + 10 + 10 + 10 + 10 + 20 + 20 + 40 + 60 = 200$

Then, divide the sum by the number of values.

Mean $= \frac{200}{10}$

274 L27: Measures of Center and Variability

©Curriculum Associates, LLC Copying is not permitted.

ELL Support

It is important to check for understanding. ELL students often will not ask for help for fear of calling attention to themselves. Ask students to narrate the process they use to solve a problem.

Visual Model

Use counters to find the mean of a set of data.

Materials: counters, data sets

Write the following list on the board: 3, 7, 1, 3, 6. Give students the following instructions:

- Use counters to make stacks that match the data.
- Now move some of the counters so that all 5 stacks have an equivalent number of counters.
- Ask: *How many counters are in each stack?* [4]. The set of data can be described by the number 4. It is the mean, or average of the data set.

Repeat the activity as needed with the following data sets: (3, 4, 2, 5, 1, 3); (6, 7, 4, 3); (7, 8, 4, 11, 5).

Challenge students to collect their own data by surveying classmates and then use the counters to find the mean.

AT A GLANCE

Students revisit the problem on page 274 and solve it, explaining how the mean describes the center of the data set.

STEP BY STEP

- Discuss each Connect It problem as a class.
- You may choose to have students work in pairs or small groups to encourage sharing ideas.
- Ask students to complete the Try It problems and then share their answers with a partner or small group.

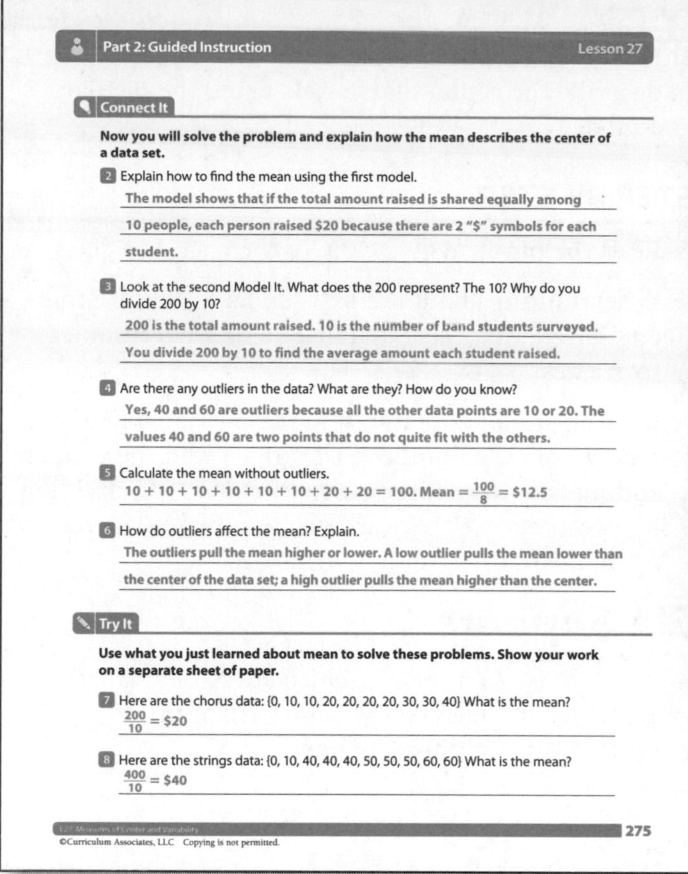

Part 2: Guided Instruction Lesson 27

Connect It

Now you will solve the problem and explain how the mean describes the center of a data set.

2 Explain how to find the mean using the first model.

The model shows that if the total amount raised is shared equally among 10 people, each person raised \$20 because there are 2 "\$" symbols for each student.

3 Look at the second Model It. What does the 200 represent? The 10? Why do you divide 200 by 10?

200 is the total amount raised. 10 is the number of band students surveyed. You divide 200 by 10 to find the average amount each student raised.

4 Are there any outliers in the data? What are they? How do you know?

Yes, 40 and 60 are outliers because all the other data points are 10 or 20. The values 40 and 60 are two points that do not quite fit with the others.

5 Calculate the mean without outliers.

$10 + 10 + 10 + 10 + 10 + 10 + 20 + 20 = 100$. Mean = $\frac{100}{8}$ = \$12.5

6 How do outliers affect the mean? Explain.

The outliers pull the mean higher or lower. A low outlier pulls the mean lower than the center of the data set; a high outlier pulls the mean higher than the center.

Try It

Use what you just learned about mean to solve these problems. Show your work on a separate sheet of paper.

7 Here are the chorus data: {0, 10, 10, 20, 20, 20, 20, 30, 30, 40} What is the mean?

$\frac{200}{10}$ = \$20

8 Here are the strings data: {0, 10, 40, 40, 40, 50, 50, 50, 60, 60} What is the mean?

$\frac{400}{10}$ = \$40

L27: Measures of Center and Variability 275

©Curriculum Associates, LLC Copying is not permitted.

TRY IT SOLUTIONS

7 *Solution:* \$20; Students may use a line plot to display the data and then evenly distribute the symbols to find the mean.

8 *Solution:* \$40; Students may find the sum (400) and then divide by 10 to find the mean.

ERROR ALERT: Students who wrote \$44.4 divided by 9 instead of by 10. They might have done this because they didn't count the 0 in the data set as a number. Remind students that they must count each number given in the data set when determining the mean.

AT A GLANCE

Students read a word problem and then explore how to describe the center of data sets using the median and mode.

STEP BY STEP

- Read the problem at the top of the page as a class.
- When talking about the first Model It, be sure to emphasize that the data must be ordered from least to greatest.
- Remind students that to find the median when there are two middle numbers, they must find the mean by adding the two numbers together and then dividing by two (because there are two numbers). The result is the median.

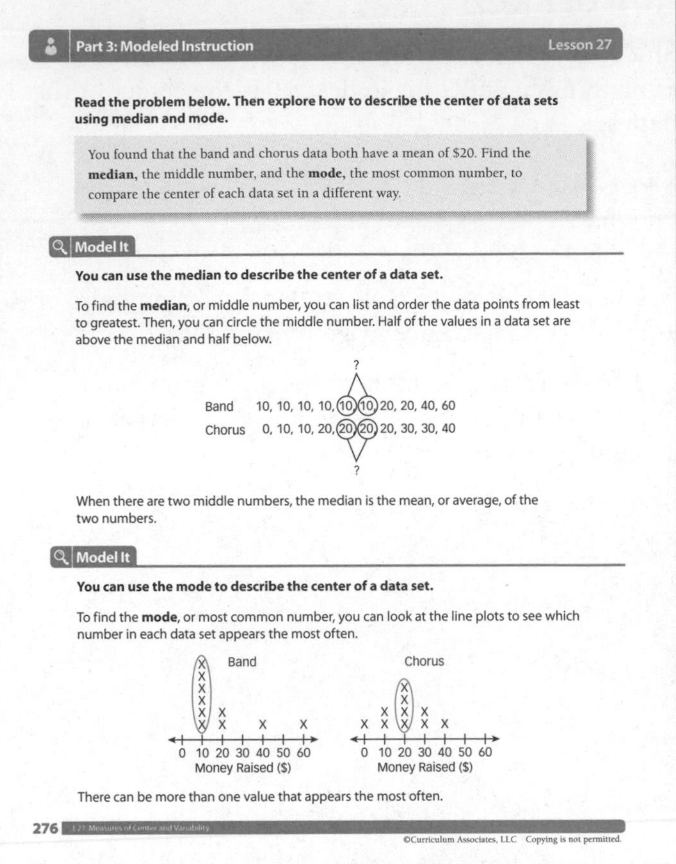

Part 3: Modeled Instruction Lesson 27

Read the problem below. Then explore how to describe the center of data sets using median and mode.

You found that the band and chorus data both have a mean of $20. Find the **median,** the middle number, and the **mode,** the most common number, to compare the center of each data set in a different way.

Model It

You can use the median to describe the center of a data set.

To find the **median,** or middle number, you can list and order the data points from least to greatest. Then, you can circle the middle number. Half of the values in a data set are above the median and half below.

When there are two middle numbers, the median is the mean, or average, of the two numbers.

Model It

You can use the mode to describe the center of a data set.

To find the **mode,** or most common number, you can look at the line plots to see which number in each data set appears the most often.

There can be more than one value that appears the most often.

276 L27: Measures of Center and Variability

©Curriculum Associates, LLC Copying is not permitted.

ELL Support

Relate the word *median* to the median of an interstate. Students can visualize the median splitting the highway into halves.

Concept Extension

Find the median.

Materials: small squares of scrap paper, pencil

Students who incorrectly calculate median often forget to order the numbers from least to greatest. Display this data set: (5, 4, 2, 7, 9, 4, 3, 7, 9, 8, 0). Then give students the following instructions:

- Write each number on a separate slip of paper.
- Order the numbers from least to greatest.
- Find the median by splitting the data set into two halves and moving the papers away from each other. [The median is 5.]
- Take away the 0 from your data set. Now you have ten numbers in the data set. To find the median when a data set has an even number of numbers, you must find the mean of the two numbers in the middle. What two numbers are in the middle? [The two numbers in the middle are 5 and 7.]
- Add 5 to 7, and then divide by 2 to find the median. [$5 + 7 = 12$. $\frac{12}{2} = 6$]

Mathematical Discourse

- *Discuss with a partner why finding median or mode would be useful to a convenience-store owner.*

  Students might discuss that finding the most commonly sold item would be beneficial for stocking shelves at a convenience store. The median might be useful for determining what the average customer might be spending.

- *What other examples can you think of where finding median or mode would be useful?*

  Answers will vary. Students may suggest that median and mode are especially useful for data sets with outliers. This will be covered in Lesson 29.

AT A GLANCE

Students revisit the problem on page 276 and solve using the models. Students will explain how the median and mode describe the center of the data set.

STEP BY STEP

- Discuss each Connect It problem as a class.
- You may choose to have students work in pairs or small groups to encourage sharing ideas.
- Remind students that outliers can have a large effect on the mean.
- Ask students to complete the Try It problem and then share their answers with a partner or small group.

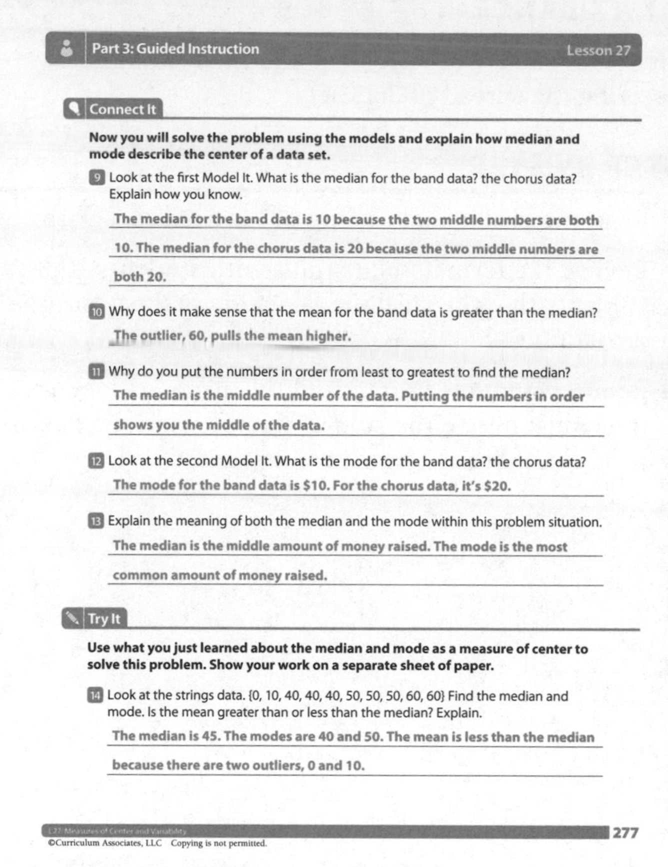

Part 3: Guided Instruction Lesson 27

Connect It

Now you will solve the problem using the models and explain how median and mode describe the center of a data set.

9 Look at the first Model It. What is the median for the band data? the chorus data? Explain how you know.

The median for the band data is 10 because the two middle numbers are both 10. The median for the chorus data is 20 because the two middle numbers are both 20.

10 Why does it make sense that the mean for the band data is greater than the median?

The outlier, 60, pulls the mean higher.

11 Why do you put the numbers in order from least to greatest to find the median?

The median is the middle number of the data. Putting the numbers in order shows you the middle of the data.

12 Look at the second Model It. What is the mode for the band data? the chorus data?

The mode for the band data is $10. For the chorus data, it's $20.

13 Explain the meaning of both the median and the mode within this problem situation.

The median is the middle amount of money raised. The mode is the most common amount of money raised.

Try It

Use what you just learned about the median and mode as a measure of center to solve this problem. Show your work on a separate sheet of paper.

14 Look at the strings data. {0, 10, 40, 40, 40, 50, 50, 50, 60, 60} Find the median and mode. Is the mean greater than or less than the median? Explain.

The median is 45. The modes are 40 and 50. The mean is less than the median because there are two outliers, 0 and 10.

L27: Measures of Center and Variability 277

©Curriculum Associates, LLC Copying is not permitted.

TRY IT SOLUTION

14 *Solution:* The median is 45. The modes are 40 and 50. The mean is less than the median; Students may explain that the mean is less than the median because there are two outliers, 0 and 10. They are lower values and pull the mean (average) lower.

ERROR ALERT: Students who wrote that the median was 9 added the two values in the middle together: 40 + 50 = 90. Then, instead of dividing by 2 to find the median they divided by 10, the number of numbers in the data set.

AT A GLANCE

Students read a word problem and then explore how to describe the spread of data sets.

STEP BY STEP

- Read the problem at the top of the page as a class.
- Review the term *absolute value* with students. Tell students that the absolute deviation is the positive deviation.
- Remind students that to find the mean, or average, they must divide the sum of the values in the data set by the number of terms in the data set.

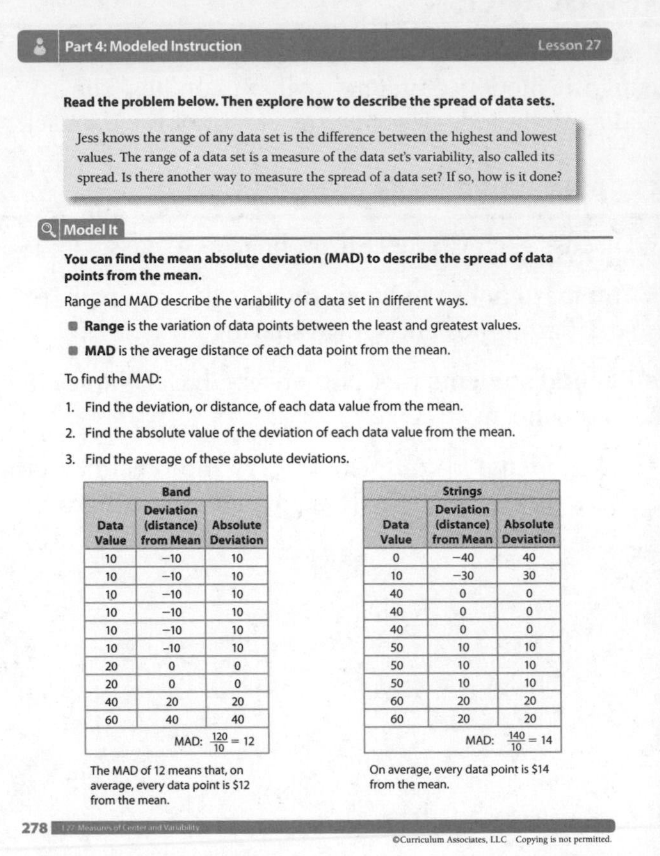

Read the problem below. Then explore how to describe the spread of data sets.

Jess knows the range of any data set is the difference between the highest and lowest values. The range of a data set is a measure of the data set's variability, also called its spread. Is there another way to measure the spread of a data set? If so, how is it done?

Model It

You can find the mean absolute deviation (MAD) to describe the spread of data points from the mean.

Range and MAD describe the variability of a data set in different ways.

- **Range** is the variation of data points between the least and greatest values.
- **MAD** is the average distance of each data point from the mean.

To find the MAD:

1. Find the deviation, or distance, of each data value from the mean.
2. Find the absolute value of the deviation of each data value from the mean.
3. Find the average of these absolute deviations.

Band		
Data Value	Deviation (distance) from Mean	Absolute Deviation
10	−10	10
10	−10	10
10	−10	10
10	−10	10
10	−10	10
10	−10	10
20	0	0
20	0	0
40	20	20
60	40	40
	MAD:	$\frac{120}{10} = 12$

The MAD of 12 means that, on average, every data point is $12 from the mean.

Strings		
Data Value	Deviation (distance) from Mean	Absolute Deviation
0	−40	40
10	−30	30
40	0	0
40	0	0
40	0	0
50	10	10
50	10	10
50	10	10
60	20	20
60	20	20
	MAD:	$\frac{140}{10} = 14$

On average, every data point is $14 from the mean.

Mathematical Discourse

- *Explain how to find Mean Absolute Deviation in your own words.*

  Listen for students' explanations that they must first find the mean of a data set, then find the absolute deviation of each data value from the mean, and then find the mean of the absolute deviations.

- *How would you explain MAD to a student who was absent?*

  Same as above, but they might discuss using a table to keep the data organized.

AT A GLANCE

Students revisit the problem on page 278 and solve using the model. Students describe the spread of data sets.

STEP BY STEP

- Discuss each Connect It problem as a class.
- You may choose to have students work in pairs or small groups to encourage sharing ideas.
- Ask students to recall what MAD stands for. [Mean Absolute Deviation]
- Ask students to complete the Try It problem and then share their answers with a partner or small group.

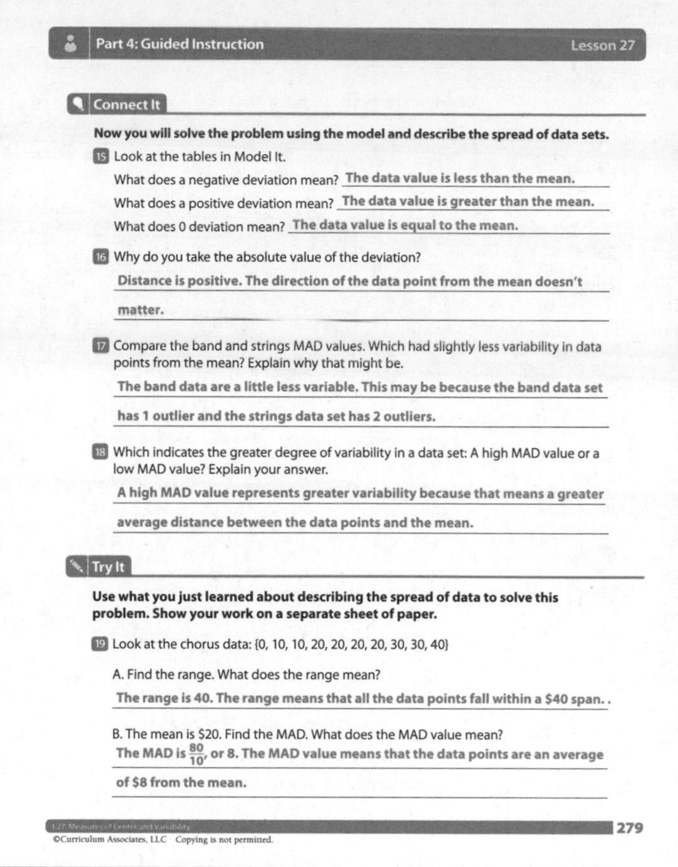

Part 4: Guided Instruction Lesson 27

Connect It

Now you will solve the problem using the model and describe the spread of data sets.

15 Look at the tables in Model It.

What does a negative deviation mean? **The data value is less than the mean.**

What does a positive deviation mean? **The data value is greater than the mean.**

What does 0 deviation mean? **The data value is equal to the mean.**

16 Why do you take the absolute value of the deviation?

Distance is positive. The direction of the data point from the mean doesn't matter.

17 Compare the band and strings MAD values. Which had slightly less variability in data points from the mean? Explain why that might be.

The band data are a little less variable. This may be because the band data set has 1 outlier and the strings data set has 2 outliers.

18 Which indicates the greater degree of variability in a data set: A high MAD value or a low MAD value? Explain your answer.

A high MAD value represents greater variability because that means a greater average distance between the data points and the mean.

Try It

Use what you just learned about describing the spread of data to solve this problem. Show your work on a separate sheet of paper.

19 Look at the chorus data: {0, 10, 10, 20, 20, 20, 20, 30, 30, 40}

A. Find the range. What does the range mean?

The range is 40. The range means that all the data points fall within a $40 span..

B. The mean is $20. Find the MAD. What does the MAD value mean?

The MAD is $\frac{80}{10}$, or 8. The MAD value means that the data points are an average of $8 from the mean.

L27: Measures of Center and Variability 279

©Curriculum Associates, LLC Copying is not permitted.

TRY IT SOLUTIONS

19A *Solution:* The range is 40; Students may explain that the range means that all the data points fall within a $40 span. Students find range by subtracting the lowest value from the highest value.

19B *Solution:* The MAD is 8; Students may create a table to find the absolute deviation for each data point, find the sum (80) and then divide by 10 to find the MAD.

ERROR ALERT: Students who wrote 0 forgot to find the absolute deviation. The sum of the deviations is 0; 0 divided by 10 is 0.

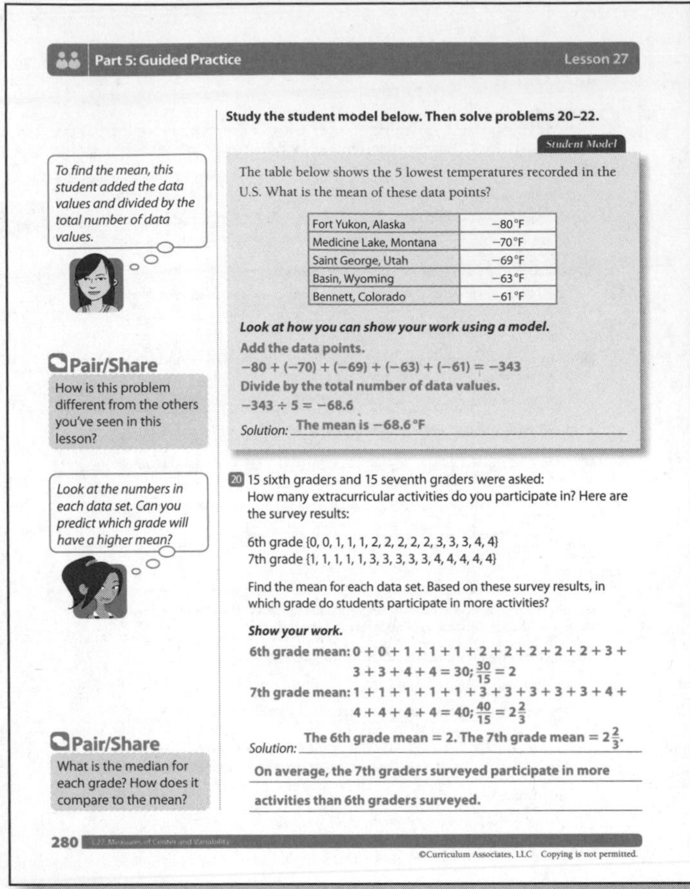

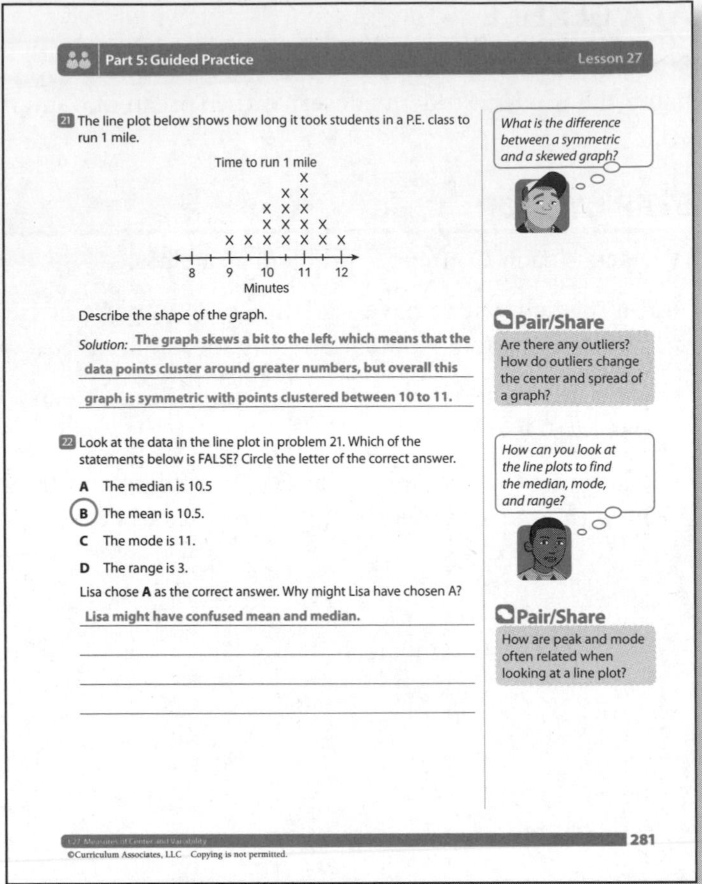

AT A GLANCE

Students study a model and then solve similar problems.

STEP BY STEP

- Ask students to solve the problems individually.
- When students have completed each problem, have them Pair/Share to discuss their solutions with a partner or in a group.

SOLUTIONS

Ex Adding the data points and dividing by the total number of data values is shown as one way to solve the problem.

20 *Solution:* 6th grade mean = 2, 7th grade mean = $2\frac{2}{3}$; 7th grade students participate in more activities. Students could solve the problem by finding the sum of each data set and dividing by 15. ***(DOK 1)***

21 *Solution:* The graph is skewed left (i.e., there are more data points around the greater values), but overall the graph is symmetric with points clustered between 10 and 11. ***(DOK 1)***

22 *Solution:* **B**; Lisa may not have looked for a false statement; Students could solve the problem by finding the mean, median, mode, and range.

Explain to students why the other answer choices are not correct:

C is not correct because the most data points are listed at 11, so 11 is the mode.

D is not correct because the range is 12 − 9 = 3. ***(DOK 3)***

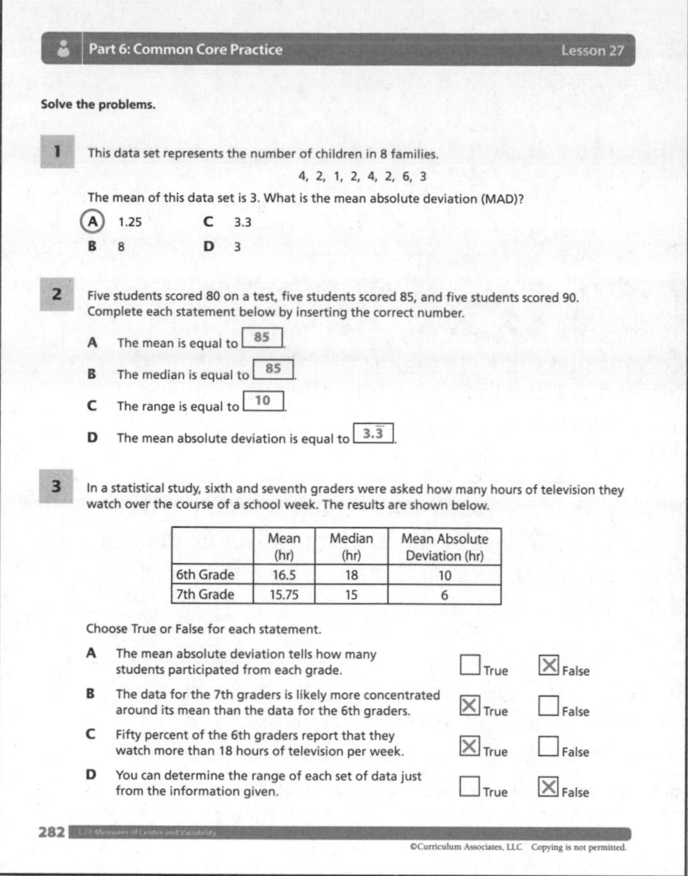

Part 6: Common Core Practice Lesson 27

Solve the problems.

1 This data set represents the number of children in 8 families.

4, 2, 1, 2, 4, 2, 6, 3

The mean of this data set is 3. What is the mean absolute deviation (MAD)?

Ⓐ 1.25
B 8
C 3.3
D 3

2 Five students scored 80 on a test, five students scored 85, and five students scored 90. Complete each statement below by inserting the correct number.

A The mean is equal to 85.
B The median is equal to 85.
C The range is equal to 10.
D The mean absolute deviation is equal to $3.\overline{3}$.

3 In a statistical study, sixth and seventh graders were asked how many hours of television they watch over the course of a school week. The results are shown below.

	Mean (hr)	Median (hr)	Mean Absolute Deviation (hr)
6th Grade	16.5	18	10
7th Grade	15.75	15	6

Choose True or False for each statement.

A The mean absolute deviation tells how many students participated from each grade. ☐ True ☒ False
B The data for the 7th graders is likely more concentrated around its mean than the data for the 6th graders. ☒ True ☐ False
C Fifty percent of the 6th graders report that they watch more than 18 hours of television per week. ☒ True ☐ False
D You can determine the range of each set of data just from the information given. ☐ True ☒ False

282 L27: Measures of Center and Variability ©Curriculum Associates, LLC Copying is not permitted.

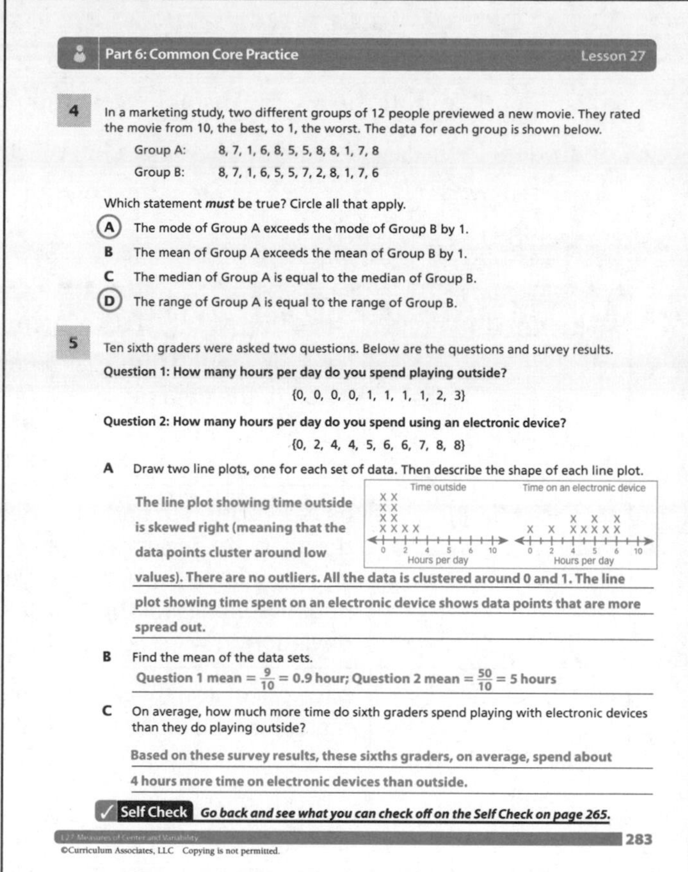

Part 6: Common Core Practice Lesson 27

4 In a marketing study, two different groups of 12 people previewed a new movie. They rated the movie from 10, the best, to 1, the worst. The data for each group is shown below.

Group A: 8, 7, 1, 6, 8, 5, 5, 8, 8, 1, 7, 8
Group B: 8, 7, 1, 6, 5, 5, 7, 2, 8, 1, 7, 6

Which statement *must* be true? Circle all that apply.

Ⓐ The mode of Group A exceeds the mode of Group B by 1.
B The mean of Group A exceeds the mean of Group B by 1.
C The median of Group A is equal to the median of Group B.
Ⓓ The range of Group A is equal to the range of Group B.

5 Ten sixth graders were asked two questions. Below are the questions and survey results.

Question 1: How many hours per day do you spend playing outside?

{0, 0, 0, 0, 1, 1, 1, 1, 2, 3}

Question 2: How many hours per day do you spend using an electronic device?

{0, 2, 4, 4, 5, 6, 6, 7, 8, 8}

A Draw two line plots, one for each set of data. Then describe the shape of each line plot.

The line plot showing time outside is skewed right (meaning that the data points cluster around low values). There are no outliers. All the data is clustered around 0 and 1. The line plot showing time spent on an electronic device shows data points that are more spread out.

B Find the mean of the data sets.

Question 1 mean = $\frac{9}{10}$ = 0.9 hour; Question 2 mean = $\frac{50}{10}$ = 5 hours

C On average, how much more time do sixth graders spend playing with electronic devices than they do playing outside?

Based on these survey results, these sixths graders, on average, spend about 4 hours more time on electronic devices than outside.

✓ Self Check *Go back and see what you can check off on the Self Check on page 265.*

L27: Measures of Center and Variability ©Curriculum Associates, LLC Copying is not permitted. 283

AT A GLANCE

Students solve word problems dealing with measures of center and variability that might appear on a mathematics test.

SOLUTIONS

1 *Solution:* **A**; Find the sum of the absolute deviations (10) then divide by 8. ***(DOK 1)***

2 *Solution:* mean is 85; Multiply 5 by 80, 5 by 85, and 5 by 90. Add the products and divide by 15.

median is 85, Find the middle number in the data set.

range is 10, Subtract the highest score, 90, from the lowest score, 80.

mean absolute deviation is $3.\overline{3}$; Find the distance each value is from the mean. Add the values and divide by 15. ***(DOK 1)***

3 *Solution:* A **False**; B **True**; C **True**; D **False** ***(DOK 2)***

4 *Solution:* **A**; Compare the mode of Group A, 8, to the mode of Group B, 7.

D; Compare the range of Group A, 7, to the range of Group B, 7. ***(DOK 2)***

5 *Part A Solution*: See student book page above for possible line plots and descriptions.

Part B Solution: Question 1 mean: 0.9 hour
Question 2 mean: 5 hours

Part C Solution: See student book page above for possible answer. ***(DOK 3)***

Assessment and Remediation

- Ask students to find the Mean Absolute Deviation of this data set: 5, 3, 2, 4, 1, 9. [2]
- For students who are struggling, use the chart below to guide remediation.
- After providing remediation, check students' understanding. Ask students to find the MAD of the following data set: 3, 13, 11, 5. [4]

If the error is . . .	Students may . . .	To remediate . . .
6	have only found the mean of the data set.	Remind students that there are multiple steps to finding the MAD. First they must find the mean, then the absolute deviation from the mean for each data value. Then they need to find the average of these absolute deviations.
0	have forgotten to find the absolute deviation and calculated the negative values for the deviation.	Remind students that there are multiple steps to finding the MAD. First they must find the mean, then the absolute deviation from the mean for each data value. Then they need to find the average of these absolute deviations.
3.5	have calculated the median of the data set.	Remind students that there are multiple steps to finding the MAD. First they must find the mean, then the absolute deviation from the mean for each data value. Then they need to find the average of these absolute deviations.

Hands-On Activity

Play a data game.

Materials: Six number cubes, paper, and pencil

Put students in groups of 2. Ask students to roll 6 number cubes at one time.

Before calculating, students should decide whether they will find the median, mode, mean, or MAD. Each player calculates his or her chosen data measure using paper and pencil. The student finding the highest value earns a point.

Challenge Activity

Find the missing data.

Give students the following table and challenge them to find the missing information.

The MAD of the following data set is 2, and the sum of the data values is 36. Find the mean and fill in the missing data. [The mean is 6.]

Data Value	Deviation from Mean	Absolute Deviation
3	−3	**?**
4	**?**	2
?	−1	1
7	1	1
8	2	2
9	3	3
	MAD	$\frac{?}{6} = 2$

Lesson 28 (Student Book pages 284–295)

Display Data on Dot Plots, Histograms, and Box Plots

LESSON OBJECTIVES

- Create dot plots, histograms, and box plots, including labeling and scaling axes appropriately.
- Know when data are best represented on dot plots, histograms, or box plots.
- Describe the overall pattern of data, determine variability, and identify striking deviations from the overall pattern.

PREREQUISITE SKILLS

- Choose appropriate and consistent scale and interval for a given data set.
- Accurately plot a set of numerical data in a dot plot.
- Calculate the median and range of a data set.

VOCABULARY

lower quartile: the middle number between the minimum and the median in an ordered set of numbers

upper quartile: the middle number between the median and the maximum in an ordered set of numbers

box plot: a 5-number summary that includes the minimum, the lower quartile, the median, the upper quartile, and the maximum

interquartile range (IQR): the difference between the upper quartile and lower quartile

THE LEARNING PROGRESSION

Skill in data display and analysis are important in our information-filled world. We use data to evaluate product reviews, understand and interpret the news, and make everyday decisions. Data analysis is important in the sciences and social sciences in high school and beyond.

In Grades 3–5, students created picture and bar graphs. In Grade 6, students have analyzed data displayed in various ways. Now students learn to organize data in appropriate representations such as dot plots, histograms, and box plots. They display the same data using different representations. By comparing different graphs of the same data, students develop an understanding of the benefits of each type of representation.

In later grades, students will continue to study measures of central tendency and variability and use them to understand sets of data. They will also continue to learn how to display data effectively.

Ready *Teacher Toolbox* Teacher-Toolbox.com

	Prerequisite Skills	*6.SP.B.4*
Ready Lessons	✓	✓
Tools for Instruction	✓	✓
Interactive Tutorials		✓ ✓

CCSS Focus

6.SP.B.4 Display numerical data in plots on a number line, including dot plots, histograms, and box plots.

STANDARDS FOR MATHEMATICAL PRACTICE: ***SMP 2–7*** *(see page A9 for full text)*

AT A GLANCE

Students create a dot plot and use it to draw conclusions about the data.

STEP BY STEP

- Tell students that this page models how to use a dot plot to draw conclusions about data.
- Have students read the problem at the top of the page.
- Work through Explore It as a class.
- Once students draw the dot plot, discuss ways they can check to make sure they recorded the data accurately.
- Ask student pairs or groups to explain their answers about the graph and the data it shows.
- As students describe the graph and draw conclusions about the data, encourage a variety of comments. Help students express their observations fully and justify their conclusions.

SMP Tip: Students attend to precision (*SMP 6*) when checking their graphs for accuracy. Stress the importance of recording each number once in the correct place.

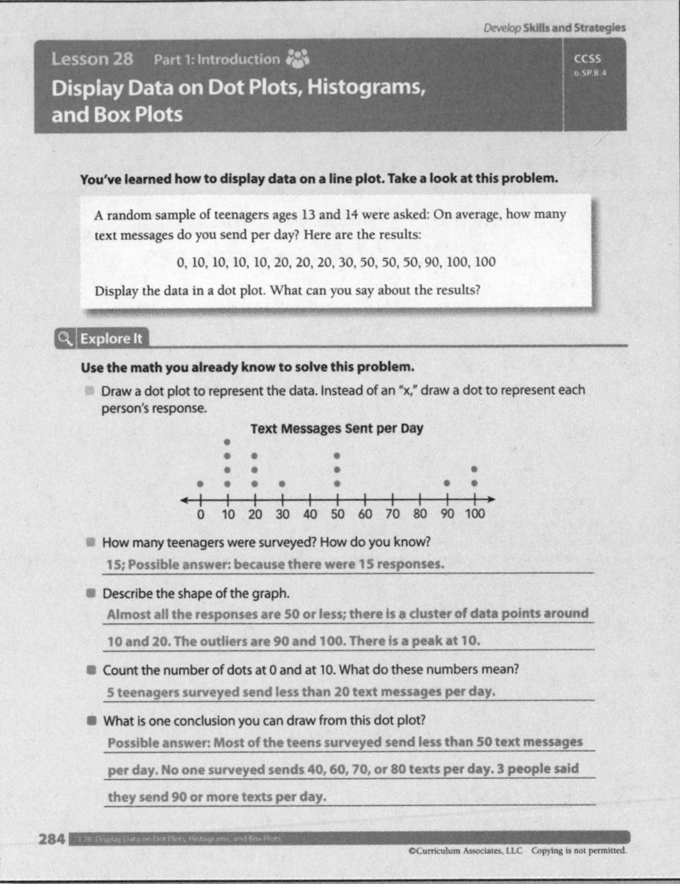

Develop Skills and Strategies

Lesson 28 Part 1: Introduction

Display Data on Dot Plots, Histograms, and Box Plots

CCSS 6.SP.B.4

You've learned how to display data on a line plot. Take a look at this problem.

A random sample of teenagers ages 13 and 14 were asked: On average, how many text messages do you send per day? Here are the results:

0, 10, 10, 10, 10, 20, 20, 20, 30, 50, 50, 50, 90, 100, 100

Display the data in a dot plot. What can you say about the results?

Explore It

Use the math you already know to solve this problem.

- Draw a dot plot to represent the data. Instead of an "x," draw a dot to represent each person's response.

- How many teenagers were surveyed? How do you know?
  15; Possible answer: because there were 15 responses.
- Describe the shape of the graph.
  Almost all the responses are 50 or less; there is a cluster of data points around 10 and 20. The outliers are 90 and 100. There is a peak at 10.
- Count the number of dots at 0 and at 10. What do these numbers mean?
  5 teenagers surveyed send less than 20 text messages per day.
- What is one conclusion you can draw from this dot plot?
  Possible answer: Most of the teens surveyed send less than 50 text messages per day. No one surveyed sends 40, 60, 70, or 80 texts per day. 3 people said they send 90 or more texts per day.

284 L28: Display Data on Dot Plots, Histograms, and Box Plots

©Curriculum Associates, LLC Copying is not permitted.

Mathematical Discourse

- *Is it easier to draw conclusions from the list of numbers or from the dot plot? Explain.*

  Students' preferences will vary, but many will prefer the dot plot because it gives a visual representation of the data.

- *What other methods can you use to present the data to help you draw conclusions? Explain what each method is and what information it would give.*

  Students might describe different types of graphs and how to make them. They might also talk about statistical measures such as the mean, mode, median, and range.

AT A GLANCE

Students learn to display data using a histogram.

STEP BY STEP

- Read Find Out More as a class.
- Talk about the idea of grouped data. Explain that grouped data are useful when it is not necessary to know the exact numbers and is a summary of the results.
- Look at the histogram. Call students' attention to the labels on each axis of the histogram. Have them explain what each axis shows.
- As students discuss the difference between a dot plot and a histogram, have them go beyond the mechanics of making each. Encourage them to talk about the types of data that would be best displayed by each as well as the types of conclusions they can draw from each.

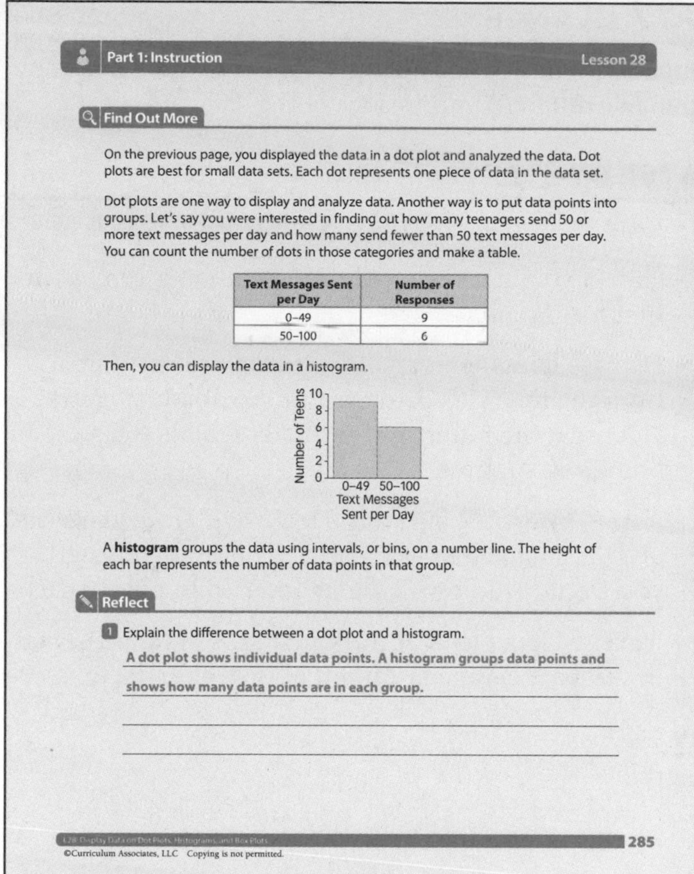

Part 1: Instruction Lesson 28

Find Out More

On the previous page, you displayed the data in a dot plot and analyzed the data. Dot plots are best for small data sets. Each dot represents one piece of data in the data set.

Dot plots are one way to display and analyze data. Another way is to put data points into groups. Let's say you were interested in finding out how many teenagers send 50 or more text messages per day and how many send fewer than 50 text messages per day. You can count the number of dots in those categories and make a table.

Text Messages Sent per Day	Number of Responses
0–49	9
50–100	6

Then, you can display the data in a histogram.

A **histogram** groups the data using intervals, or bins, on a number line. The height of each bar represents the number of data points in that group.

Reflect

1 Explain the difference between a dot plot and a histogram.

A dot plot shows individual data points. A histogram groups data points and shows how many data points are in each group.

L28: Display Data on Dot Plots, Histograms, and Box Plots 285

©Curriculum Associates, LLC Copying is not permitted.

Hands-On Activity

Make a dot plot and a histogram using the same data.

Materials: poster board, markers, sticky dots, rectangular sticky notes

- Prepare a poster board for a dot plot and another for a histogram. Title each "Hours Spent Watching TV Last Weekend." On the dot plot, draw and label a number line from 1 through 24. On the histogram, mark a number line with the intervals 0–4, 5–9, 10–14, 15–19, and 20–24.
- Have students estimate how many hours they watched television the previous weekend. Give each student a sticky dot to record their response on the dot plot and a sticky note to record their response on the histogram.
- Have students compare and contrast the two graphs. Have them think of two questions that could be answered by either graph, two that could only be answered using the dot plot, and two that could only be answered using the histogram.

Real-World Connection

Suppose researchers want to know what it is like to be a middle-school student. What questions could they ask that would receive numerical responses?

Examples:

- How long do you spend doing homework, watching TV, playing sports, reading, playing video games, doing chores, or other activities?
- How many times a month do you go to the movies, the mall, the park, the museum, or other destination?
- How much allowance do you get?
- How many pairs of shoes do you have?

AT A GLANCE

Students study two histograms that show the same data but give different impressions of the data.

STEP BY STEP

- Read the problem at the top of the page as a class.
- Have a volunteer relate the information given by the first histogram.
- Discuss how the intervals in the table are different from the intervals displayed in the first histogram. Note that the number of responses totals the same in both presentations.
- Ask: *Why are the intervals 0 to 20 and 21 to 40 instead of 0 to 20 and 20 to 40?* [If you want to record a 20, you wouldn't know in which interval to put the 20.]
- Have students look at the second histogram. Discuss how its appearance is different than the first one.

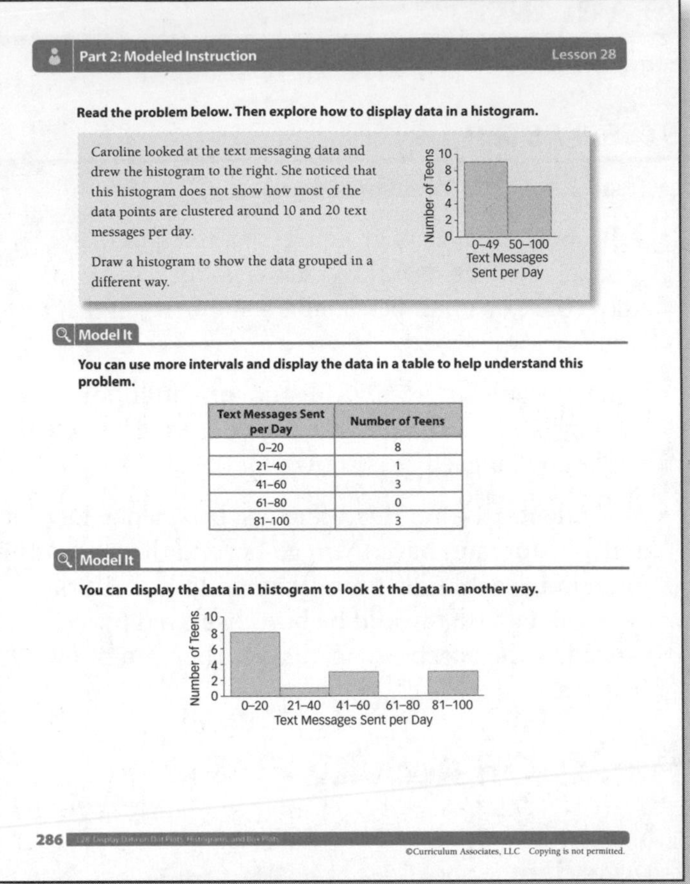

Part 2: Modeled Instruction Lesson 28

Read the problem below. Then explore how to display data in a histogram.

Caroline looked at the text messaging data and drew the histogram to the right. She noticed that this histogram does not show how most of the data points are clustered around 10 and 20 text messages per day.

Draw a histogram to show the data grouped in a different way.

Model It

You can use more intervals and display the data in a table to help understand this problem.

Text Messages Sent per Day	Number of Teens
0–20	8
21–40	1
41–60	3
61–80	0
81–100	3

Model It

You can display the data in a histogram to look at the data in another way.

286 L28: Display Data on Dot Plots, Histograms, and Box Plots

©Curriculum Associates, LLC Copying is not permitted.

Mathematical Discourse

- *Is there a rule that says how large to make the intervals in a histogram? If so, what is it?*

  No, there is not a rule.
- *What could be a problem if you make the intervals of a histogram too large?*

  Students might say that if the intervals are too large, the histogram will not show how the data cluster.
- *What happens if you make the intervals too small?*

  Students might express the idea that if the intervals are too small, there will be so much separate information that it will be hard to draw conclusions.
- *How do you decide how big to make the intervals?*

  Students might say that they would see where the data cluster and find intervals just small enough to show such clustering.

AT A GLANCE

Students revisit the problem on page 286 and analyze the new histogram. They will compare it with the original histogram.

STEP BY STEP

- Read Connect It as a class. Be sure to point out that the problems refer to the problem on page 286.
- Have students summarize the information given by the labels on the axes. Discuss why the information is necessary for reading the histogram.
- Have students describe the visual impression given by each histogram and the advantages of each. When they express their preference for one or the other, encourage them to give solid reasons for their choice.

SMP Tip: When students discuss which histogram shows the data most effectively, they must construct viable arguments and critique the reasoning of others (*SMP 3*). Remind students to give reasons for their choices and relate their reasons to the types of information gained from each histogram.

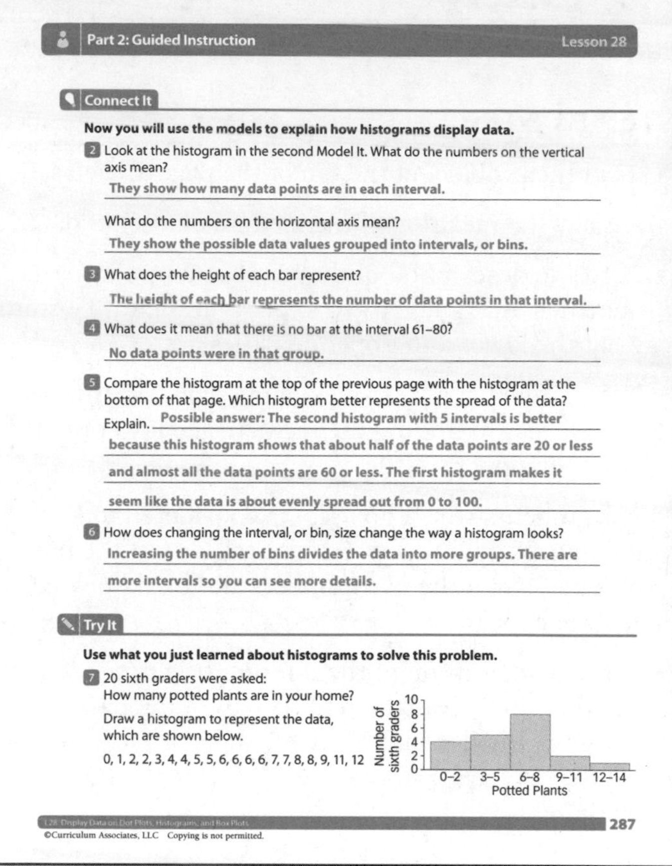

Part 2: Guided Instruction Lesson 28

Connect It

Now you will use the models to explain how histograms display data.

2 Look at the histogram in the second Model It. What do the numbers on the vertical axis mean?
They show how many data points are in each interval.

What do the numbers on the horizontal axis mean?
They show the possible data values grouped into intervals, or bins.

3 What does the height of each bar represent?
The height of each bar represents the number of data points in that interval.

4 What does it mean that there is no bar at the interval 61–80?
No data points were in that group.

5 Compare the histogram at the top of the previous page with the histogram at the bottom of that page. Which histogram better represents the spread of the data? Explain. **Possible answer: The second histogram with 5 intervals is better because this histogram shows that about half of the data points are 20 or less and almost all the data points are 60 or less. The first histogram makes it seem like the data is about evenly spread out from 0 to 100.**

6 How does changing the interval, or bin, size change the way a histogram looks?
Increasing the number of bins divides the data into more groups. There are more intervals so you can see more details.

Try It

Use what you just learned about histograms to solve this problem.

7 20 sixth graders were asked:
How many potted plants are in your home?
Draw a histogram to represent the data, which are shown below.
0, 1, 2, 2, 3, 4, 4, 5, 5, 6, 6, 6, 6, 7, 7, 8, 8, 9, 11, 12

L28: Display Data on Dot Plots, Histograms, and Box Plots 287
©Curriculum Associates, LLC Copying is not permitted.

TRY IT SOLUTION

7 *Solution:* See the histogram shown; others with different intervals are possible; students may tally the data and decide on intervals. They then may draw a histogram to display the data.

ERROR ALERT: Students whose histograms do not reflect the data may have tallied it incorrectly.

AT A GLANCE

Students see how to use a box plot to summarize data.

STEP BY STEP

- Read the problem at the top of the page as a class.
- Review the meaning of the median of a set of data.
- Read the description of the lower and upper quartiles. Ask students to explain in their own words what the lower and upper quartiles are.
- Look at the list of text-messaging data. Go through the process of finding the median, the lower quartile, and the upper quartile.
- Ask students why a box plot is considered to be a five-number summary. Have them look at the box plot and name the five numbers and explain what each one means.
- Read the definition of the interquartile range (IQR). Say that the IQR is the middle half of the data. One fourth of the data are below it, and one fourth of the data are above it. Have students locate the IQR on the box plot.

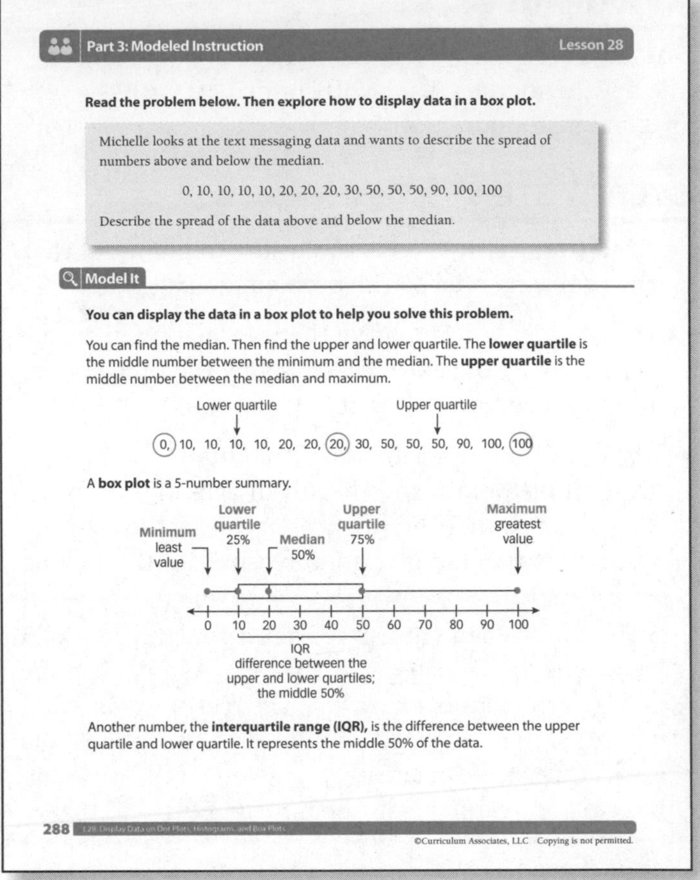

Part 3: Modeled Instruction Lesson 28

Read the problem below. Then explore how to display data in a box plot.

Michelle looks at the text messaging data and wants to describe the spread of numbers above and below the median.

0, 10, 10, 10, 10, 20, 20, 20, 30, 50, 50, 50, 90, 100, 100

Describe the spread of the data above and below the median.

Model It

You can display the data in a box plot to help you solve this problem.

You can find the median. Then find the upper and lower quartile. The **lower quartile** is the middle number between the minimum and the median. The **upper quartile** is the middle number between the median and maximum.

A **box plot** is a 5-number summary.

Another number, the **interquartile range (IQR),** is the difference between the upper quartile and lower quartile. It represents the middle 50% of the data.

288 L28: Display Data on Dot Plots, Histograms, and Box Plots

©Curriculum Associates, LLC Copying is not permitted.

ELL Support

- Display the numbers 2, 3, 1, 5, and 8. Have students tell you how to write them in order. Discuss the meaning of *lowest or least*. Have students identify the least number and label it. Discuss, identify, and label the *highest* or *greatest* number. Do the same with 3, the *middle* or *median* number.
- Go over the vocabulary again, having students say each term aloud. If students have some mastery of the terms, introduce *minimum* and *maximum*, displaying those words as well.
- Display the numbers 4, 8, 11, 12, 15, 17, and 20. Call on students to name the *greatest,* the *lowest*, the *median*, and so on until they have practiced all the words.

Mathematical Discourse

- *How can you find the median of a set of data?*

  Students should say that you put the data in order and find the middle number. If there are two numbers in the middle, you average them.

- *How can the steps for finding the median help you find the lower and upper quartiles?*

  Students should say that you look at all the numbers below the median and then find the median of those numbers. That number is the lower quartile. You repeat this process for the numbers above the median to find the upper quartile. In other words, the lower quartile is the median of the numbers below the median, and the upper quartile is the median of the numbers above the median.

AT A GLANCE

Students revisit the problem on page 288 and analyze the box plot in terms of the data.

STEP BY STEP

- Read Connect It as a class. Be sure to point out that the problems refer to the problem on page 288.
- As students answer the problems, have them relate the box plot to the actual data that it represents.
- When needed, explain terms used in the problems such as *spread* and *lines extending from the box*.
- Summarize by saying that the middle 50% of the teenagers sent between 10 and 50 texts. One fourth of the teenagers sent 10 or fewer texts, and one fourth sent 50 or more.

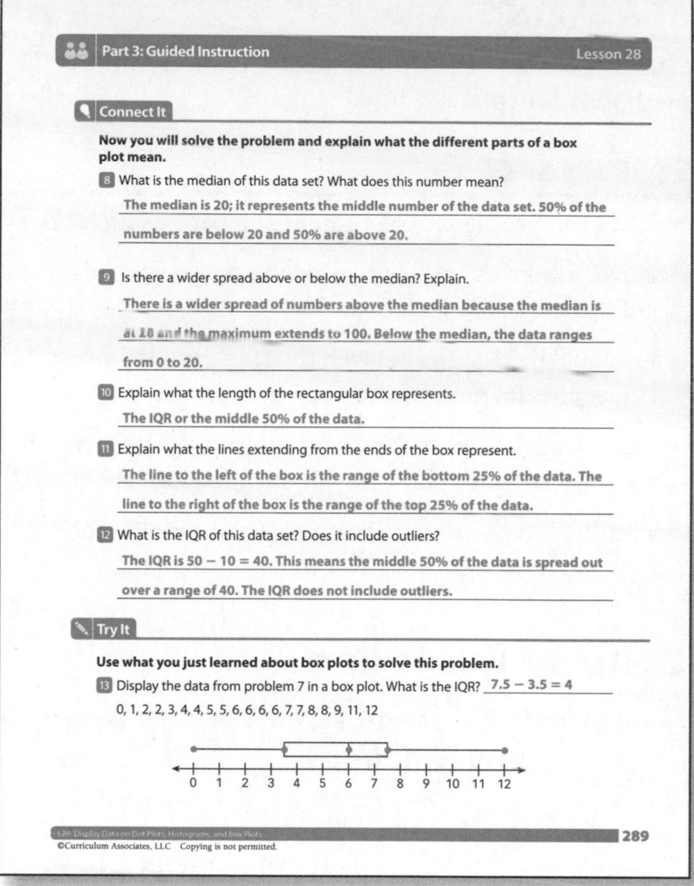

Part 3: Guided Instruction Lesson 28

Connect It

Now you will solve the problem and explain what the different parts of a box plot mean.

8 What is the median of this data set? What does this number mean?

The median is 20; it represents the middle number of the data set. 50% of the numbers are below 20 and 50% are above 20.

9 Is there a wider spread above or below the median? Explain.

There is a wider spread of numbers above the median because the median is at 20 and the maximum extends to 100. Below the median, the data ranges from 0 to 20.

10 Explain what the length of the rectangular box represents.

The IQR or the middle 50% of the data.

11 Explain what the lines extending from the ends of the box represent.

The line to the left of the box is the range of the bottom 25% of the data. The line to the right of the box is the range of the top 25% of the data.

12 What is the IQR of this data set? Does it include outliers?

The IQR is 50 − 10 = 40. This means the middle 50% of the data is spread out over a range of 40. The IQR does not include outliers.

Try It

Use what you just learned about box plots to solve this problem.

13 Display the data from problem 7 in a box plot. What is the IQR? **7.5 − 3.5 = 4**

0, 1, 2, 2, 3, 4, 4, 5, 5, 6, 6, 6, 6, 7, 7, 8, 8, 9, 11, 12

L28: Display Data on Dot Plots, Histograms, and Box Plots 289
©Curriculum Associates, LLC Copying is not permitted.

Visual Model

Illustrate the spread of data displayed in box plots.

Use these descriptions to produce and display three box plots:

First box plot: Narrow interquartile range and narrow upper and lower quartiles.

Second box plot: Wide interquartile range and narrow upper and lower quartiles.

Third box plot: Narrow interquartile range and wide upper and lower quartiles.

Tell students that the box plots represent class scores on three tests. Discuss what type of test results each box plot would show.

TRY IT SOLUTION

13 *Solution:* Check students' graphs. The IQR is 4; Students may find the difference between the upper quartile (7.5) and the lower quartile (3.5).

ERROR ALERT: Students who wrote 11 added the upper and lower quartiles; students who wrote 12 found the range instead of the interquartile range.

AT A GLANCE

Students are given a set of data and explore three methods of displaying it.

STEP BY STEP

- Read the problem at the top of the page as a class.
- Have volunteers describe the characteristics of a dot plot, a histogram, and a box plot.
- Look at the dot plot. Have students explain what types of information they can get from it.
- Have students examine the histogram. After they do so, have them explain how it summarizes the data.
- Finally, have students examine the box plot and explain how it shows the spread of the data.

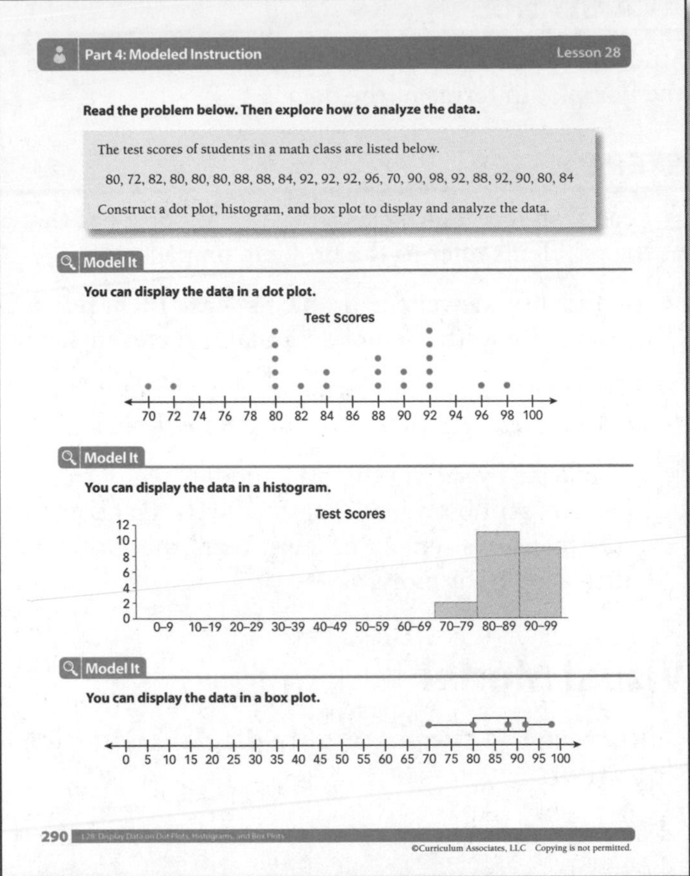

Part 4: Modeled Instruction Lesson 28

Read the problem below. Then explore how to analyze the data.

The test scores of students in a math class are listed below.

80, 72, 82, 80, 80, 80, 88, 88, 84, 92, 92, 92, 96, 70, 90, 98, 92, 88, 92, 90, 80, 84

Construct a dot plot, histogram, and box plot to display and analyze the data.

Model It

You can display the data in a dot plot.

Model It

You can display the data in a histogram.

Model It

You can display the data in a box plot.

Concept Extension

Visualize the shape of various graphs based on a description of the data.

- Describe three card shops to students.

  Shop A: Cards range from $1 to $5 with many cards at each price.

  Shop B: All cards are $2.00, $2.50, or $3.00.

  Shop C: Most cards are bargain cards for $1 or fancy cards for $5 with only a few mid-priced cards.

- Have students think about how a dot plot would look for each shop. Have volunteers sketch and display their ideas. Discuss whether the shape fits the description of the data.
- Have students think about how a histogram would look for each shop. Again, have them share and justify their ideas.
- Finally, have students consider how box plots would look for each shop. As students share their examples, discuss how the upper and lower quartiles and the interquartile range would change in each situation.

Mathematical Discourse

- *What are two conclusions you can draw about the data using the dot plot?*

  Students' responses will vary. As students respond, have them refer to the dot plot to show why they drew that particular conclusion. Ask others whether they agree, disagree, or have questions to ask so they can understand the speaker's conclusions.

- *What are two conclusions you can draw about the data using the histogram?*

  Students' responses will vary.

- *What are two conclusions you can draw about the data using the box plot?*

  Students' responses will vary.

AT A GLANCE

Students revisit the problem on page 290 and analyze the advantages of each type of graph.

STEP BY STEP

- Read Connect It as a class. Be sure to point out that the problems refer to the problem on page 290.
- Students should consider all three graphs when answering each question. In addition to naming the most effective graph for each use, have them explain why it is not possible to get the information from the other graphs.
- Have students summarize what is useful about each type of graph.

SMP Tip: As students consider which graph is most helpful for a specific purpose, they are learning to model with mathematics effectively *(SMP 4)*. Encourage them to think about what information they are trying to communicate and which graph communicates the information best.

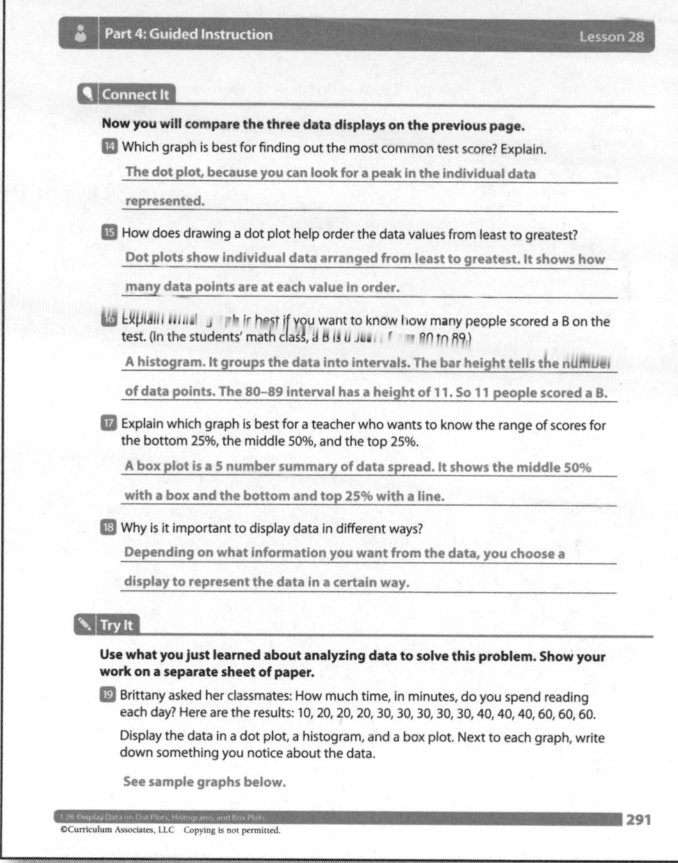

Part 4: Guided Instruction — Lesson 28

Connect It

Now you will compare the three data displays on the previous page.

14 Which graph is best for finding out the most common test score? Explain.

The dot plot, because you can look for a peak in the individual data represented.

15 How does drawing a dot plot help order the data values from least to greatest?

Dot plots show individual data arranged from least to greatest. It shows how many data points are at each value in order.

16 Explain [illegible] is best if you want to know how many people scored a B on the test. (In the students' math class, a B is [illegible] 80 to 89.)

A histogram. It groups the data into intervals. The bar height tells the number of data points. The 80–89 interval has a height of 11. So 11 people scored a B.

17 Explain which graph is best for a teacher who wants to know the range of scores for the bottom 25%, the middle 50%, and the top 25%.

A box plot is a 5 number summary of data spread. It shows the middle 50% with a box and the bottom and top 25% with a line.

18 Why is it important to display data in different ways?

Depending on what information you want from the data, you choose a display to represent the data in a certain way.

Try It

Use what you just learned about analyzing data to solve this problem. Show your work on a separate sheet of paper.

19 Brittany asked her classmates: How much time, in minutes, do you spend reading each day? Here are the results: 10, 20, 20, 20, 30, 30, 30, 30, 30, 40, 40, 40, 60, 60, 60.

Display the data in a dot plot, a histogram, and a box plot. Next to each graph, write down something you notice about the data.

See sample graphs below.

L28: Display Data on Dot Plots, Histograms, and Box Plots 291

©Curriculum Associates, LLC Copying is not permitted.

TRY IT SOLUTION

19 *Solution:* Check students' graphs and observations; Students may tally the data and use them to make each type of graph.

ERROR ALERT: Students whose graphs are inaccurate may have tallied the data incorrectly.

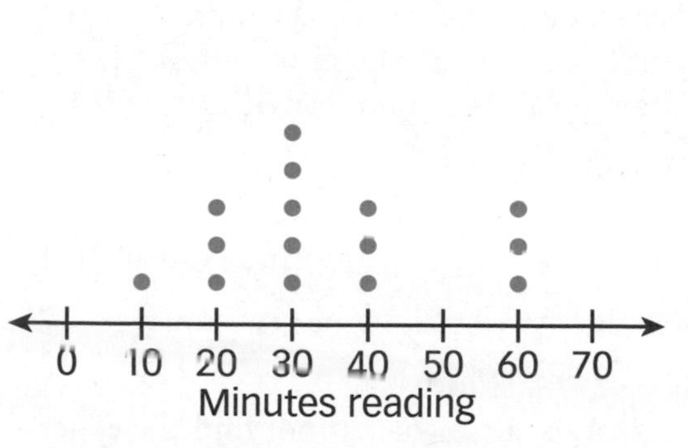

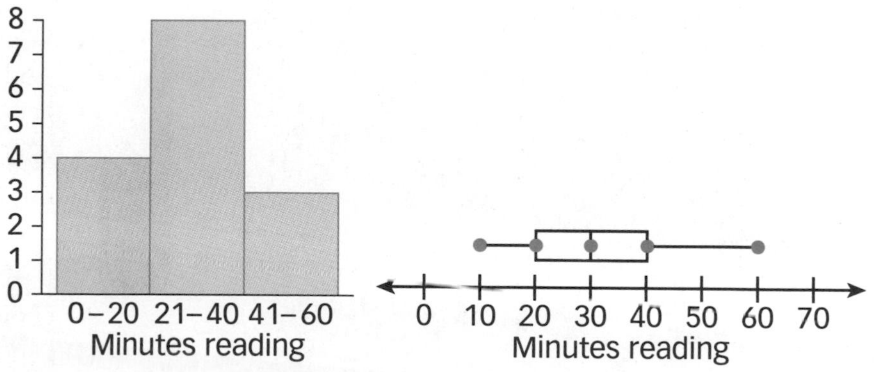

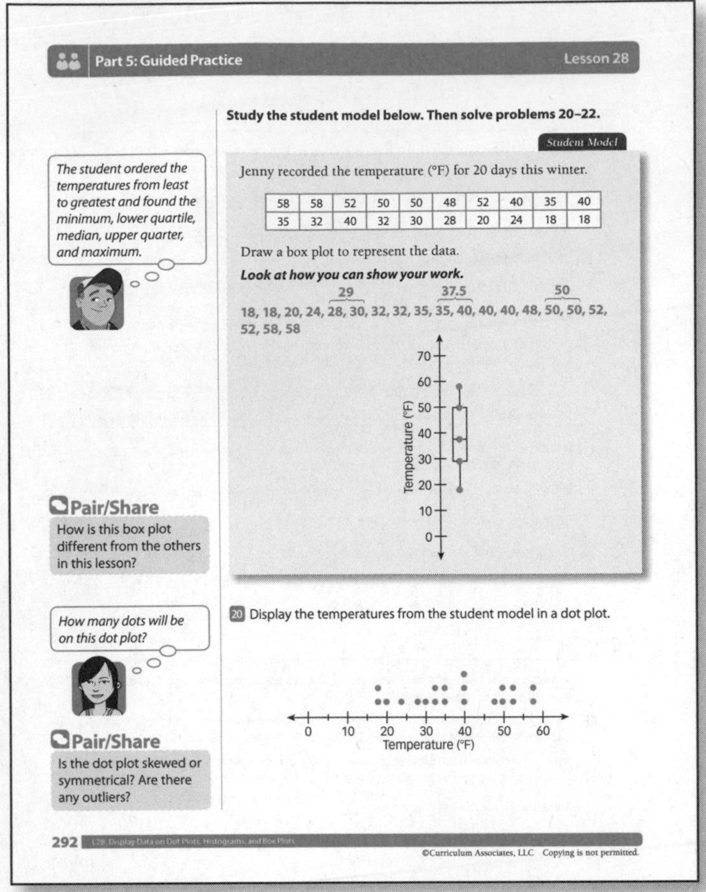

Part 5: Guided Practice Lesson 28

The student ordered the temperatures from least to greatest and found the minimum, lower quartile, median, upper quarter, and maximum.

Study the student model below. Then solve problems 20–22.

Student Model

Jenny recorded the temperature (°F) for 20 days this winter.

58	58	52	50	50	48	52	40	35	40
35	32	40	32	30	28	20	24	18	18

Draw a box plot to represent the data.

Look at how you can show your work.

29 37.5 50

18, 18, 20, 24, 28, 30, 32, 32, 35, 35, 40, 40, 40, 48, 50, 50, 52, 52, 58, 58

Pair/Share
How is this box plot different from the others in this lesson?

How many dots will be on this dot plot?

20 Display the temperatures from the student model in a dot plot.

Pair/Share
Is the dot plot skewed or symmetrical? Are there any outliers?

292 L28: Display Data on Dot Plots, Histograms, and Box Plots ©Curriculum Associates, LLC Copying is not permitted.

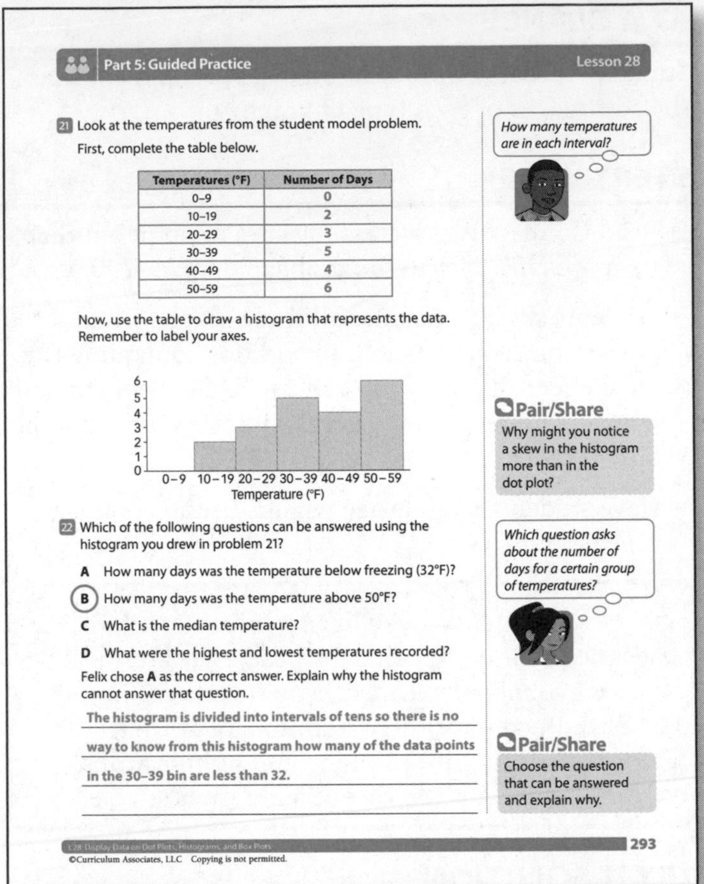

Part 5: Guided Practice Lesson 28

21 Look at the temperatures from the student model problem.
First, complete the table below.

How many temperatures are in each interval?

Temperatures (°F)	Number of Days
0–9	0
10–19	2
20–29	3
30–39	5
40–49	4
50–59	6

Now, use the table to draw a histogram that represents the data. Remember to label your axes.

Pair/Share
Why might you notice a skew in the histogram more than in the dot plot?

22 Which of the following questions can be answered using the histogram you drew in problem 21?

A How many days was the temperature below freezing (32°F)?

(B) How many days was the temperature above 50°F?

C What is the median temperature?

D What were the highest and lowest temperatures recorded?

Which question asks about the number of days for a certain group of temperatures?

Felix chose **A** as the correct answer. Explain why the histogram cannot answer that question.

The histogram is divided into intervals of tens so there is no way to know from this histogram how many of the data points in the 30–39 bin are less than 32.

Pair/Share
Choose the question that can be answered and explain why.

L28: Display Data on Dot Plots, Histograms, and Box Plots ©Curriculum Associates, LLC Copying is not permitted. 293

AT A GLANCE

Students display data using different types of graphs.

STEP BY STEP

- Ask students to solve the problems individually by drawing the type of graph asked for.
- When students have completed each problem, have them Pair/Share to discuss their solutions with a partner or in a group.

SOLUTIONS

Ex The numbers are listed in order, and the quartiles and median are indicated. A completed box plot is shown.

20 *Solution:* Check students' dot plots; students could solve the problem by showing the data with dots and a number line. ***(DOK 2)***

21 *Solution:* See students' tables and histograms; students could solve the problem by tallying the data and drawing a histogram. ***(DOK 2)***

22 *Solution:* **B;** Felix could not be able to tell the number of days the temperature was below 32°F because the data were grouped in intervals of 10°F.

Explain to students why the other two answer choices are not correct:

C is not correct because you cannot find the exact median with grouped data.

D is not correct because grouped data do not show the exact minimum and maximum. ***(DOK 3)***

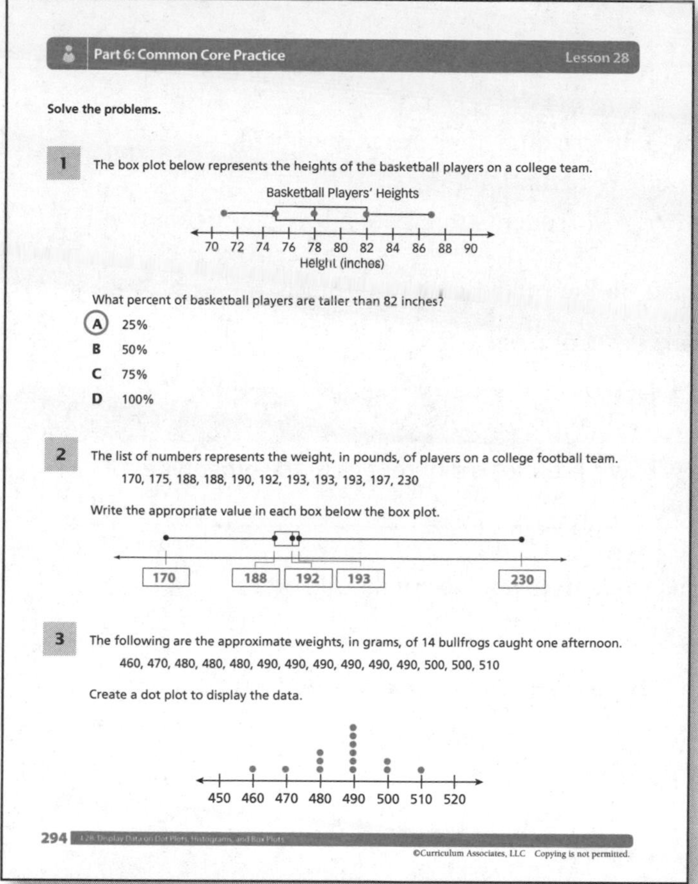

Part 6: Common Core Practice Lesson 28

Solve the problems.

1 The box plot below represents the heights of the basketball players on a college team.

What percent of basketball players are taller than 82 inches?

(A) 25%

B 50%

C 75%

D 100%

2 The list of numbers represents the weight, in pounds, of players on a college football team.

170, 175, 188, 188, 190, 192, 193, 193, 193, 197, 230

Write the appropriate value in each box below the box plot.

3 The following are the approximate weights, in grams, of 14 bullfrogs caught one afternoon.

460, 470, 480, 480, 480, 490, 490, 490, 490, 490, 490, 500, 500, 510

Create a dot plot to display the data.

294 L28: Display Data on Dot Plots, Histograms, and Box Plots

©Curriculum Associates, LLC Copying is not permitted.

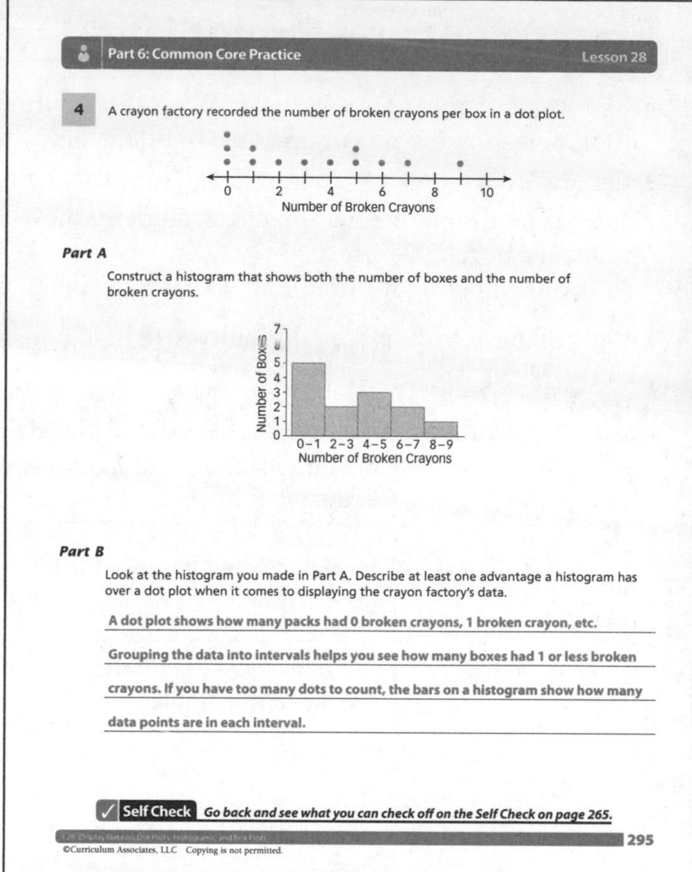

Part 6: Common Core Practice Lesson 28

4 A crayon factory recorded the number of broken crayons per box in a dot plot.

Part A

Construct a histogram that shows both the number of boxes and the number of broken crayons.

Part B

Look at the histogram you made in Part A. Describe at least one advantage a histogram has over a dot plot when it comes to displaying the crayon factory's data.

A dot plot shows how many packs had 0 broken crayons, 1 broken crayon, etc. Grouping the data into intervals helps you see how many boxes had 1 or less broken crayons. If you have too many dots to count, the bars on a histogram show how many data points are in each interval.

Self Check Go back and see what you can check off on the Self Check on page 265.

L28: Display Data on Dot Plots, Histograms, and Box Plots 295

©Curriculum Associates, LLC Copying is not permitted.

AT A GLANCE

Students use and draw graphs to answer questions that might appear on a mathematics test.

SOLUTIONS

1 *Solution:* **A**; Note that the data described are greater than the upper quartile, which is the upper 25%. ***(DOK 1)***

2 *Solution:* 170, 188, 192, 193, 230 (from left to right); The minimum is the least value, the lower quartile is the median of the lower half, the median is the middle, the upper quartile is the median of the upper half, and the maximum is the greatest value. ***(DOK 2)***

3 *Solution:* See student book page above for possible student dot plot; ***(DOK 2)***

4 *Part A Solution:* See student book page above for possible student histogram.

Part B Solution: See student book page above for possible description. ***(DOK 3)***

Assessment and Remediation

- Ask students to create a box plot using these numbers: 2, 3, 4, 6, 0, 1, 7, 3, 1, 3, 5.
  [Box plot showing minimum: 0, lower quartile: 1, median: 3, upper quartile: 5, maximum: 7.]
- For students who are struggling, use the chart below to guide remediation.
- After providing remediation, check students' understanding. Ask students to create a box plot using these numbers: 1, 6, 2, 5, 4, 2, 0, 6, 2, 4, 1.
  [Box plot showing minimum: 0, lower quartile: 1, median: 2, upper quartile: 5, maximum: 6.]
- If a student is still having difficulty, use ***Ready Instruction, Level 5,*** Lesson 23.

If the error is . . .	Students may . . .	To remediate . . .
a dot plot or histogram	not understand the differences in the types of graphs.	Review how a box plot is different from the other types of graphs.
min.: 2, l.q.: 4, median: 0, u.q.: 1, max.: 5	have neglected to order the numbers first.	Remind students to put the numbers in order.
other incorrect key points	not know how to find the median and quartiles.	Review the technique for finding the median and quartiles.

Hands-On Activity

Make a human box plot.

Materials: paper, markers, tape

Label separate sheets of paper with these terms: *Minimum*, *Lower Quartile*, *Median*, *Upper Quartile*, and *Maximum*. Display an unlabeled number line.

Have students record the number of people who live in their home (or the number of people in their family) on a sheet of paper. Have students stand and arrange themselves in a line from least to greatest.

Identify the 1 or 2 students in the middle. Give the middle student(s) the paper labeled *Median*. Find the lower and upper quartile, giving those students the appropriate papers. Give the students at each end of the line the *Minimum* and *Maximum* papers. Have all the other students sit down.

Discuss the numbers needed on the number line. Number the number line. Have students still standing tape their papers above the appropriate points. Have volunteers explain how to complete the box plot.

Challenge Activity

Conduct a survey and display the results using different types of graphs.

Working individually or in pairs, students should think of a question that classmates can answer with a number less than 30. Students should ask at least 15 classmates the question and record the results.

Students should first organize the data using a dot plot. Then they should decide on reasonable intervals and draw a histogram to display the data. Finally, they should create a box plot that shows the distribution of the data. Remind students to include a title and labels for all data displays.

Students should write a paragraph listing conclusions about the data that they can draw using the dot plot, histogram, and box plot, respectively.

Lesson 29 (Student Book pages 296–305)

Analyze Numerical Data

LESSON OBJECTIVES

- Interpret a set of numerical data by noticing and describing patterns and deviations.
- Understand mean absolute deviation (MAD).
- Determine variability (IQR, MAD).

PREREQUISITE SKILLS

- Find the mean and median of a set of data.
- Describe the range, spread, and outliers of a data set.
- Graph data with dot plots, histograms, and box plots.
- Understand absolute value.

VOCABULARY

There is no new vocabulary.

THE LEARNING PROGRESSION

An understanding of data analysis is important in today's world. Employees must understand and use data in many careers. We use data to make choices as we buy products and make healthcare decisions.

In Grade 6, students learn to find measures of center and variability. They also expand the types of data representations they use beyond the picture and bar graphs they learned in Grades 3 through 5.

In this lesson, students use dot plots, histograms, and box plots to examine the spread of data and the effect outliers have on the mean and median. They also find the mean absolute deviation (MAD), a measure of variability.

In later grades, students continue to analyze data using measures of central tendency and variability. They will use various methods to display data effectively. As students extend their study of statistics, they will build on the skills and concepts learned in Grade 6.

Ready ***Teacher Toolbox*** Teacher-Toolbox.com

	Prerequisite Skills	6.SP.B.5a, 6.SP.B.5b 6.SP.B.5c, 6.SP.B.5d
Ready Lessons	✓	✓
Tools for Instruction	✓	✓
Interactive Tutorials	✓✓	

CCSS Focus

6.SP.B.5 Summarize numerical data sets in relation to their context, such as by:

a. Reporting the number of observations.

b. Describing the nature of the attribute under investigation, including how it was measured and its units of measurement.

c. Giving quantitative measures of center (median and/or mean) and variability (interquartile range and/or mean absolute deviation), as well as describing any overall pattern and any striking deviations from the overall pattern with reference to the context in which the data were gathered.

d. Relating the choice of measures of center and variability to the shape of the data distribution and the context in which the data were gathered.

ADDITIONAL STANDARDS: ***6.SP.A.2, 6.SP.A.3, 6.SP.B.4*** *(see page A42 for full text)*

STANDARDS FOR MATHEMATICAL PRACTICE: ***SMP 2–5*** *(see page A9 for full text)*

AT A GLANCE

Students describe a set of data using the mean and median.

STEP BY STEP

- Tell students this page models using the mean and median to describe data.
- Have students read the problem at the top of the page.
- Work through Explore It as a class.
- Have a volunteer explain how to make a dot plot. Stress the need for accuracy.
- Have students describe the spread, then suggest what the spread might mean in the context of the problem.
- Ask student pairs or groups to explain their answers for finding the outliers, the median, and the mean.
- As students compare and contrast the mean and the median, have them explain how the shape of the data illustrates the similarities and differences between the two measures of central tendency.

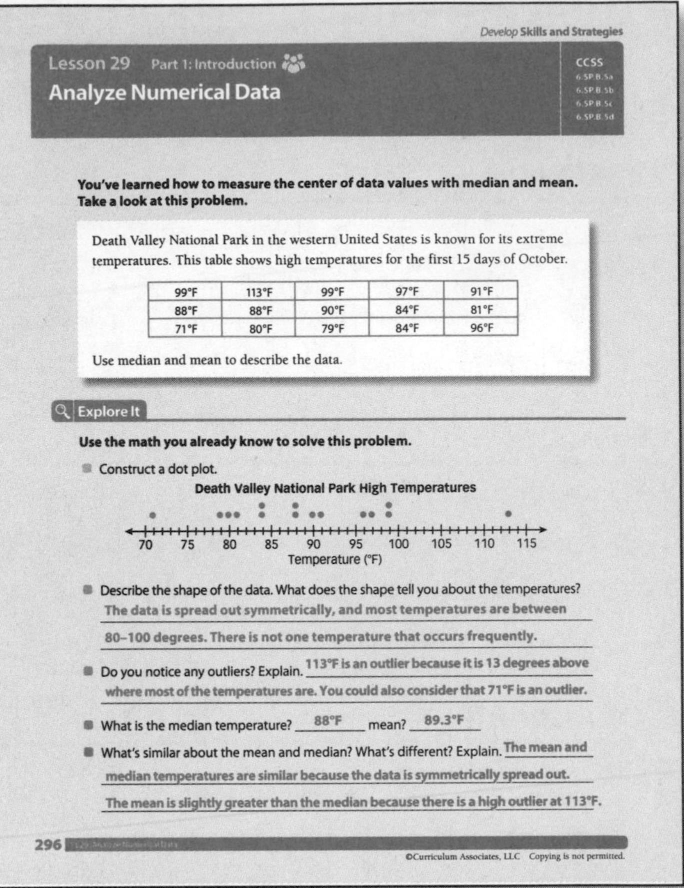

Develop **Skills and Strategies**

Lesson 29 Part 1: Introduction

Analyze Numerical Data

CCSS 6.SP.B.5a 6.SP.B.5b 6.SP.B.5c 6.SP.B.5d

You've learned how to measure the center of data values with median and mean. Take a look at this problem.

Death Valley National Park in the western United States is known for its extreme temperatures. This table shows high temperatures for the first 15 days of October.

99°F	113°F	99°F	97°F	91°F
88°F	88°F	90°F	84°F	81°F
71°F	80°F	79°F	84°F	96°F

Use median and mean to describe the data.

Explore It

Use the math you already know to solve this problem.

- Construct a dot plot.

- Describe the shape of the data. What does the shape tell you about the temperatures? The data is spread out symmetrically, and most temperatures are between 80–100 degrees. There is not one temperature that occurs frequently.
- Do you notice any outliers? Explain. 113°F is an outlier because it is 13 degrees above where most of the temperatures are. You could also consider that 71°F is an outlier.
- What is the median temperature? 88°F mean? 89.3°F
- What's similar about the mean and median? What's different? Explain. The mean and median temperatures are similar because the data is symmetrically spread out. The mean is slightly greater than the median because there is a high outlier at 113°F.

296 L29: Analyze Numerical Data

©Curriculum Associates, LLC Copying is not permitted.

ELL Support

- Call 7 students to line up in the front of the class.
- Ask the class to name the student in the center. Say that *center* is another word for "middle."
- Ask the students to stay in the same order, but to spread out. Discuss the meaning of *spread.*
- Have all the students move close together except for one on an end who should move away from the others. Explain that this student is an *outlier.*

SMP Tip: Students can use dot plots to help them understand a set of data. Encourage them to use dot plots and other appropriate representations as tools for visualizing data and drawing conclusions about them (*SMP 5*).

Mathematical Discourse

- *Why is it often helpful to make a dot plot as a first step in analyzing data?*

  Students might say it is a quick way to order the numbers. They might also say that it is a good way to study the spread and look for clusters of numbers.

- *Would you rather use the table or the dot plot to find the median? How about the mean? Explain why.*

  Students' answers will vary. Many might say the dot plot is easiest to use for finding the median because you can count points to see which number is in the middle. They might also say that the table is easiest for the mean because it doesn't matter what order the numbers are in when you add them. Be sure all points of view are explained.

AT A GLANCE

Students examine the effect of an outlier on the mean and median of a set of data.

STEP BY STEP

- Read Find Out More as a class.
- Have a volunteer explain how the data set on page 297 is different from the data on page 296.
- Have students compare the dot plots on pages 296 and 297 and then predict how the change of one temperature will affect the mean and the median values.
- Based on student answers to the Reflect directive, discuss why the mean changed but the median stayed the same.

SMP Tip: Students learn to reason abstractly and quantitatively as they compare sets of data with and without outliers (*SMP 2*). As you work through examples, have students predict the shape of the data before they actually graph it. Then discuss how close their predictions were to the actual results.

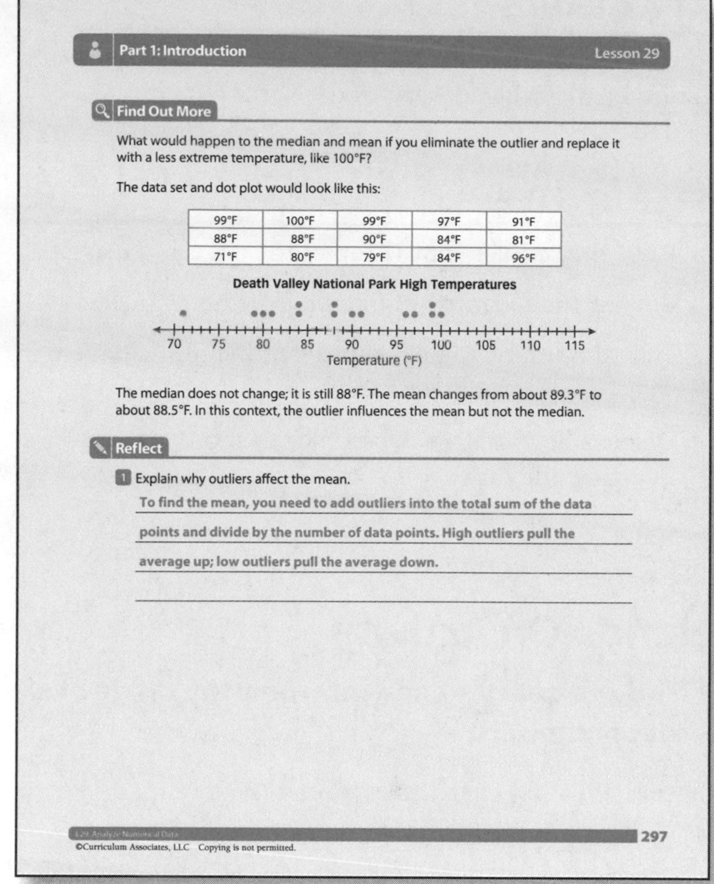

Find Out More

What would happen to the median and mean if you eliminate the outlier and replace it with a less extreme temperature, like 100°F?

The data set and dot plot would look like this:

99°F	100°F	99°F	97°F	91°F
88°F	88°F	90°F	84°F	81°F
71°F	80°F	79°F	84°F	96°F

The median does not change; it is still 88°F. The mean changes from about 89.3°F to about 88.5°F. In this context, the outlier influences the mean but not the median.

Reflect

1 Explain why outliers affect the mean.

To find the mean, you need to add outliers into the total sum of the data points and divide by the number of data points. High outliers pull the average up; low outliers pull the average down.

Real-World Connection

In many jobs, people use information from what happened in the past to make decisions about what they will do in the future. What are some of these jobs? What types of decisions are affected by past numbers?

Examples: An event planner deciding how much food to buy; a medical researcher deciding if a new medicine is curing people; a school superintendent deciding how many teachers are needed at each school; a traffic planner deciding where new stoplights are needed; a coach deciding which players are the top scorers or defenders.

AT A GLANCE

Students use models to help them visualize how the interquartile range describes the variability of a set of data.

STEP BY STEP

- Read the problem at the top of the page as a class.
- Review the meaning of *interquartile range (IQR).*
- Talk about how to use an ordered list of the data to show the interquartile range.
- Discuss how to draw a box plot to show the interquartile range.

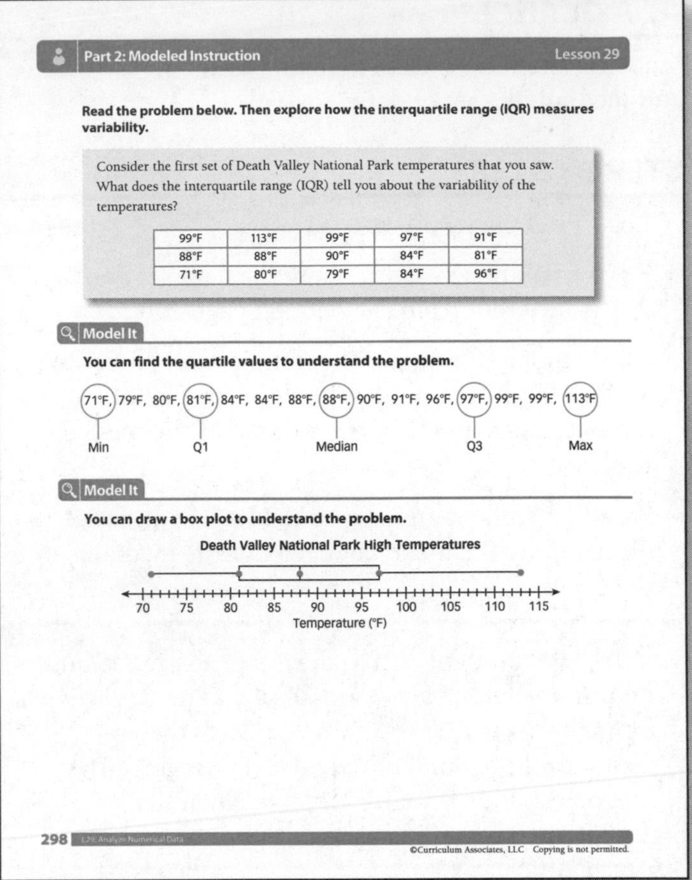

Part 2: Modeled Instruction Lesson 29

Read the problem below. Then explore how the interquartile range (IQR) measures variability.

Consider the first set of Death Valley National Park temperatures that you saw. What does the interquartile range (IQR) tell you about the variability of the temperatures?

99°F	113°F	99°F	97°F	91°F
88°F	88°F	90°F	84°F	81°F
71°F	80°F	79°F	84°F	96°F

Model It

You can find the quartile values to understand the problem.

71°F, 79°F, 80°F, 81°F, 84°F, 84°F, 88°F, 88°F, 90°F, 91°F, 96°F, 97°F, 99°F, 99°F, 113°F

Model It

You can draw a box plot to understand the problem.

298 L29: Analyze Numerical Data ©Curriculum Associates, LLC Copying is not permitted.

Hands-On Activity

Find the quartiles and interquartile range of a set of numbers.

Materials: playing cards without the face cards.

- Give each student 12 cards. Each student should put the cards in ascending order and then divide them into 4 groups: the lowest fourth, the second fourth, the third fourth, and the highest fourth.
- Model the term *quartiles* for the groups. Call on students to describe the cards in each of their quartiles.
- Ask students to focus on the two middle groups. Note that those cards are one-half of all their cards.
- Have students find the card representing the lower quartile and the card representing the upper quartile. Have them find the difference of the two cards. Tell them the difference is called the *interquartile range*, or *IQR* for short.
- Redistribute the cards so that each student has a different set of 12. Have them find the quartiles and interquartile range independently. Have students pair up and check each others' work.

Mathematical Discourse

- *What are the five important points on a box plot? What does each point tell you?*

  Students should name the minimum, the lower quartile, the mean, the upper quartile, and the maximum. They should explain what each value means relative to the data. Listen for phrases such as "the lowest 25%," "the middle temperature," and "the highest temperature."

- *Do you only have five points on a box plot? Do the other points matter? Explain why or why not.*

  Students should explain that the other points do matter because they determine the five key points. Those five points are spread out through the quartiles, with 25% of all points in each quartile.

AT A GLANCE

Students revisit the problem on page 298 and use a box plot to analyze the data.

STEP BY STEP

- Read Connect It as a class. Be sure to point out that the questions refer to the problem on page 298.
- As you discuss each question, ask students to restate responses given by other students in their own words. Allow time for clarifying questions.
- Review the significance of the interquartile range (IQR) in the context of the data.
- Discuss why replacing the outlier affects the range but not the median or interquartile range.
- Have students consider when they would be most interested in the interquartile range compared to the range.
- Have students share their responses to problem 5. Use their responses to increase classroom understanding about what the median and the IQR indicate about the entire data set.

SMP Tip: When students explain what various statistical measures mean and predict how changes in the data affect those statistical measures, students must construct viable arguments and critique the reasoning of others (*SMP 3*). Encourage students to help each other express their ideas clearly, using proper mathematical terminology.

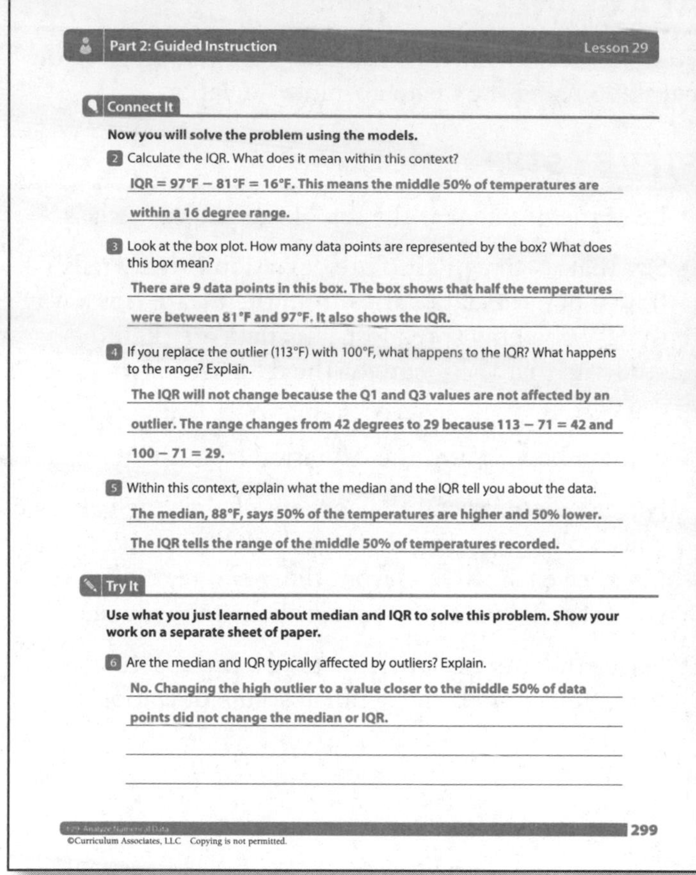

Part 2: Guided Instruction Lesson 29

Connect It

Now you will solve the problem using the models.

2 Calculate the IQR. What does it mean within this context?

IQR = 97°F − 81°F = 16°F. This means the middle 50% of temperatures are within a 16 degree range.

3 Look at the box plot. How many data points are represented by the box? What does this box mean?

There are 9 data points in this box. The box shows that half the temperatures were between 81°F and 97°F. It also shows the IQR.

4 If you replace the outlier (113°F) with 100°F, what happens to the IQR? What happens to the range? Explain.

The IQR will not change because the Q1 and Q3 values are not affected by an outlier. The range changes from 42 degrees to 29 because 113 − 71 = 42 and 100 − 71 = 29.

5 Within this context, explain what the median and the IQR tell you about the data.

The median, 88°F, says 50% of the temperatures are higher and 50% lower. The IQR tells the range of the middle 50% of temperatures recorded.

Try It

Use what you just learned about median and IQR to solve this problem. Show your work on a separate sheet of paper.

6 Are the median and IQR typically affected by outliers? Explain.

No. Changing the high outlier to a value closer to the middle 50% of data points did not change the median or IQR.

L29: Analyze Numerical Data 299

©Curriculum Associates, LLC Copying is not permitted.

TRY IT SOLUTION

6 *Solution:* No. Changing the high outlier to a value closer to the middle 50% of data points did not change the median or IQR.

ERROR ALERT: Students who answered "yes" may have confused median and IQR with mean and range. Outliers affect both the mean and the range of a data set.

AT A GLANCE

Students see how to analyze data from the problem on page 296 using the mean absolute deviation.

STEP BY STEP

- Read the problem at the top of the page as a class.
- Say that the mean absolute deviation (MAD) tells how much the data varies from the mean. It is a way to describe how spread-out the data are. Remind students that the mean for the data set shown is 89.3.
- Study each column in the table. Have students explain how to find the deviation from the mean.
- Have students recall the concept of absolute value as you explain that the absolute deviation is the distance each value is from the mean regardless of whether that value is above or below the mean.
- Have students explain how to use the absolute deviations to find the mean absolute deviation.

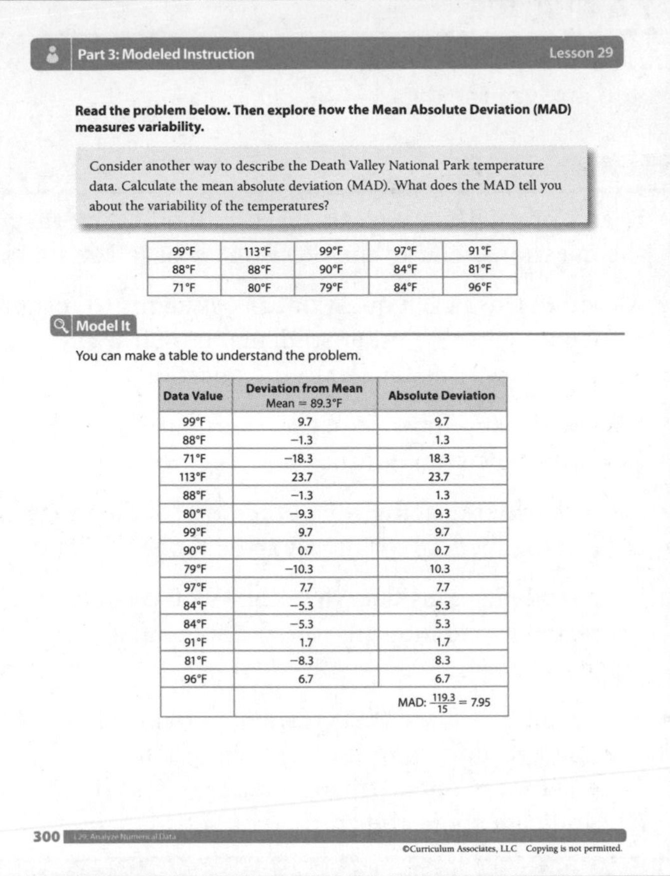
Part 3: Modeled Instruction Lesson 29

Read the problem below. Then explore how the Mean Absolute Deviation (MAD) measures variability.

Consider another way to describe the Death Valley National Park temperature data. Calculate the mean absolute deviation (MAD). What does the MAD tell you about the variability of the temperatures?

99°F	113°F	99°F	97°F	91°F
88°F	88°F	90°F	84°F	81°F
71°F	80°F	79°F	84°F	96°F

Model It

You can make a table to understand the problem.

Data Value	Deviation from Mean Mean = 89.3°F	Absolute Deviation
99°F	9.7	9.7
88°F	−1.3	1.3
71°F	−18.3	18.3
113°F	23.7	23.7
88°F	−1.3	1.3
80°F	−9.3	9.3
99°F	9.7	9.7
90°F	0.7	0.7
79°F	−10.3	10.3
97°F	7.7	7.7
84°F	−5.3	5.3
84°F	−5.3	5.3
91°F	1.7	1.7
81°F	−8.3	8.3
96°F	6.7	6.7
		MAD: $\frac{119.3}{15} = 7.95$

300 L29: Analyze Numerical Data

©Curriculum Associates, LLC Copying is not permitted.

Visual Model

Illustrate variability using line plots.

- Sketch two line plots on the board. Each number line should extend from 20 through 30.
- On the first number line, put one dot over the 23, two dots over the 24, five over the 25, two over the 26, and one over the 27.
- On the second number line, put one dot over each number.
- Have students discuss how the line plots are the same. Note that they are both symmetrical and centered around 25, so the mean and median would be 25 for both sets of data.
- Ask students to explain how the line plots look different. Tie the idea of a greater spread to greater variability or deviation from the center.

Mathematical Discourse

- *Use your own words to describe what the mean absolute deviation (MAD) tells you about a set of data.*

  Listen for responses that the MAD describes how spread out the data are. A data set for which the MAD is low is one where each value is close to the mean value. If students are uncertain, use data sets from previous pages to review and discuss.

- *How does using a table help you find the mean absolute deviation?*

  Students may say that having the data in a table keeps the data organized. They might also say that the table reminds them of the steps they must use.

AT A GLANCE

Students revisit the problem on page 300 and discuss the significance of the Mean Average Deviation.

STEP BY STEP

- Read Connect It as a class. Be sure to point out that the questions refer to the problem on page 300.
- As you talk about the mean average deviation, stress that *deviation* refers to how spread-out the data are.
- Have a volunteer explain the difference between high variability and low variability. Discuss why outliers increase the variability.
- Make sure students understand that the mean measures the center of the data, while the MAD measures how spread out the numbers are.

Concept Extension

Apply the concept of mean absolute deviation to real-world situations.

- Have students visualize two bags of potatoes. The mean length of the potatoes in each bag is $4\frac{1}{2}$ inches. The MAD for one bag is 2; the MAD for the other bag is $\frac{1}{2}$.
- Discuss what the MAD means in the context of the potatoes. You want to buy potatoes to make mashed potatoes. Ask if the MAD should influence your decision as to which bag to buy.
- Have students picture two boxes of square tiles. The mean length of the tiles in each box is $4\frac{1}{2}$ inches. The MAD for one box is 2; the MAD for the other box is $\frac{1}{2}$.
- Discuss what the MAD means in relation to the tiles. You want to buy tiles to re-tile your shower. Ask if the MAD should influence your decision as to which box to buy.
- Have students think of situations in which consistency is not important and others in which it matters greatly. Discuss why knowing the mean absolute deviation can be helpful.

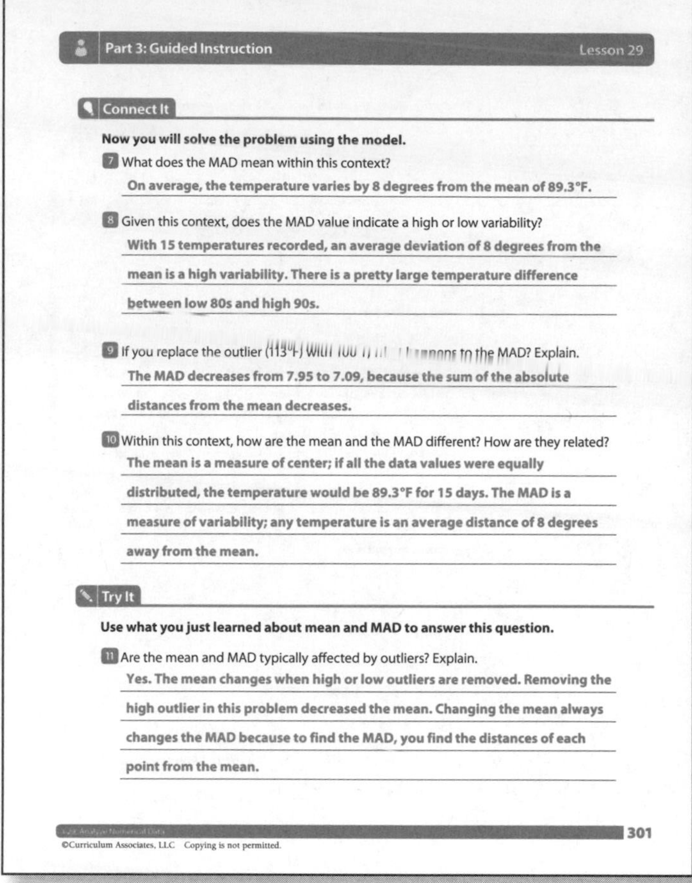

Part 3: Guided Instruction Lesson 29

Connect It

Now you will solve the problem using the model.

7 What does the MAD mean within this context?

On average, the temperature varies by 8 degrees from the mean of 89.3°F.

8 Given this context, does the MAD value indicate a high or low variability?

With 15 temperatures recorded, an average deviation of 8 degrees from the mean is a high variability. There is a pretty large temperature difference between low 80s and high 90s.

9 If you replace the outlier (113°F) with 100 [illegible] happens to the MAD? Explain.

The MAD decreases from 7.95 to 7.09, because the sum of the absolute distances from the mean decreases.

10 Within this context, how are the mean and the MAD different? How are they related?

The mean is a measure of center; if all the data values were equally distributed, the temperature would be 89.3°F for 15 days. The MAD is a measure of variability; any temperature is an average distance of 8 degrees away from the mean.

Try It

Use what you just learned about mean and MAD to answer this question.

11 Are the mean and MAD typically affected by outliers? Explain.

Yes. The mean changes when high or low outliers are removed. Removing the high outlier in this problem decreased the mean. Changing the mean always changes the MAD because to find the MAD, you find the distances of each point from the mean.

L29: Analyze Numerical Data 301

©Curriculum Associates, LLC Copying is not permitted.

TRY IT SOLUTION

11 *Solution:* Yes. The mean changes when high or low outliers are removed. Removing the high outlier in this problem decreased the mean. Changing the mean always changes the MAD because to find the MAD, you find the distances of each point from the mean.

ERROR ALERT: Students who answered "no" may have confused mean with median.

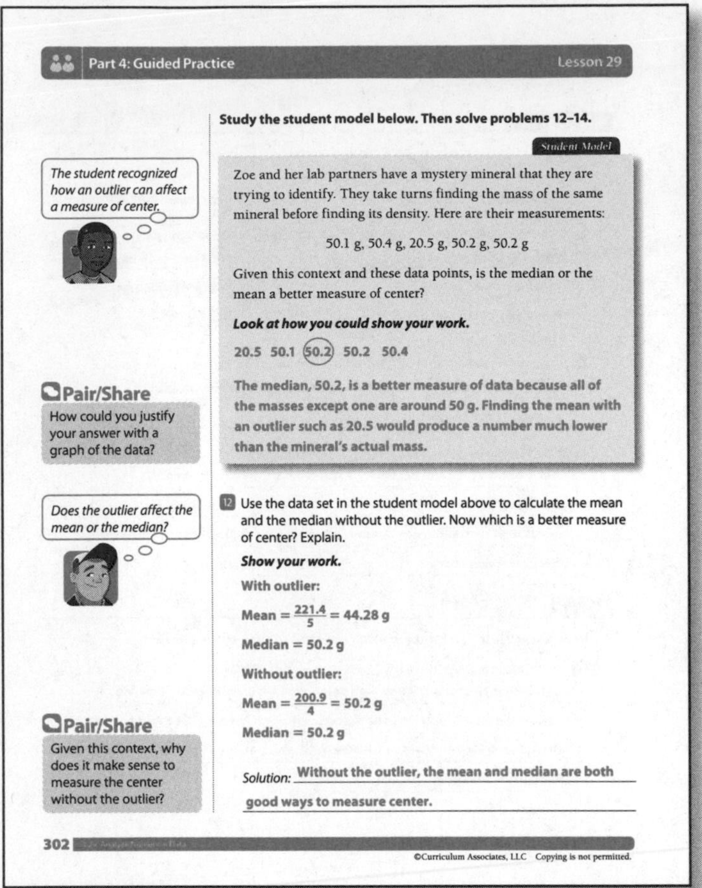

Study the student model below. Then solve problems 12–14.

The student recognized how an outlier can affect a measure of center.

Student Model

Zoe and her lab partners have a mystery mineral that they are trying to identify. They take turns finding the mass of the same mineral before finding its density. Here are their measurements:

50.1 g, 50.4 g, 20.5 g, 50.2 g, 50.2 g

Given this context and these data points, is the median or the mean a better measure of center?

Look at how you could show your work.

20.5 50.1 (50.2) 50.2 50.4

The median, 50.2, is a better measure of data because all of the masses except one are around 50 g. Finding the mean with an outlier such as 20.5 would produce a number much lower than the mineral's actual mass.

Pair/Share
How could you justify your answer with a graph of the data?

Does the outlier affect the mean or the median?

12 Use the data set in the student model above to calculate the mean and the median without the outlier. Now which is a better measure of center? Explain.

Show your work.

With outlier:

Mean $= \frac{221.4}{5} = 44.28$ **g**

Median = 50.2 g

Without outlier:

Mean $= \frac{200.9}{4} = 50.2$ **g**

Median = 50.2 g

Solution: **Without the outlier, the mean and median are both good ways to measure center.**

Pair/Share
Given this context, why does it make sense to measure the center without the outlier?

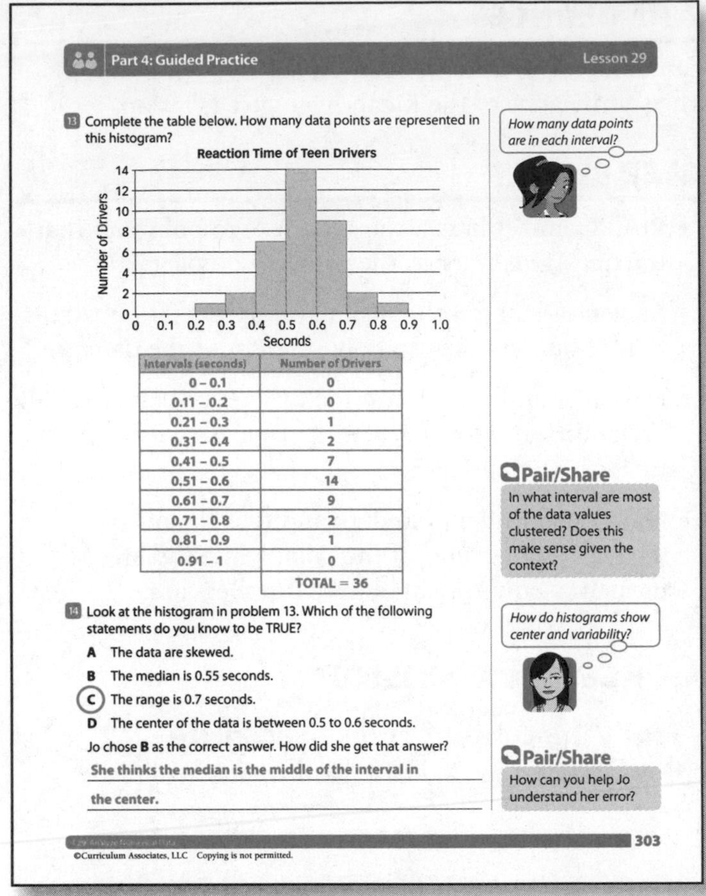

13 Complete the table below. How many data points are represented in this histogram?

Intervals (seconds)	Number of Drivers
0 – 0.1	0
0.11 – 0.2	0
0.21 – 0.3	1
0.31 – 0.4	2
0.41 – 0.5	7
0.51 – 0.6	14
0.61 – 0.7	9
0.71 – 0.8	2
0.81 – 0.9	1
0.91 – 1	0
	TOTAL = 36

How many data points are in each interval?

Pair/Share
In what interval are most of the data values clustered? Does this make sense given the context?

14 Look at the histogram in problem 13. Which of the following statements do you know to be TRUE?

A The data are skewed.

B The median is 0.55 seconds.

(C) The range is 0.7 seconds.

D The center of the data is between 0.5 to 0.6 seconds.

Jo chose **B** as the correct answer. How did she get that answer?

She thinks the median is the middle of the interval in the center.

How do histograms show center and variability?

Pair/Share
How can you help Jo understand her error?

AT A GLANCE

Students solve problems using measures of center and variability.

STEP BY STEP

- Ask students to solve the problems individually using graphs and tables when possible.
- When students have completed each problem, have them Pair/Share to discuss their solutions with a partner or in a group.

SOLUTIONS

Ex An ordered list of the numbers is shown to demonstrate that most weights are around 50 g. The mean is not as good of a measure because 20.5 is an outlier. The median is the better measure of center.

12 *Solution:* Without the outlier, the mean and median are both good measures of center; Students could solve the problem by finding that both the mean and median are about 50.2. ***(DOK 2)***

13 *Solution:* 36; Students could solve the problem by finding and adding the frequency of each interval. ***(DOK 1)***

14 *Solution:* **D**; Jo assumed the median is the middle of the center interval.

Explain to students why the other two answer choices are not correct:

A is not correct because the data clusters around the center.

C is not correct because the exact maximum and minimum values cannot be determined from the histogram. ***(DOK 3)***

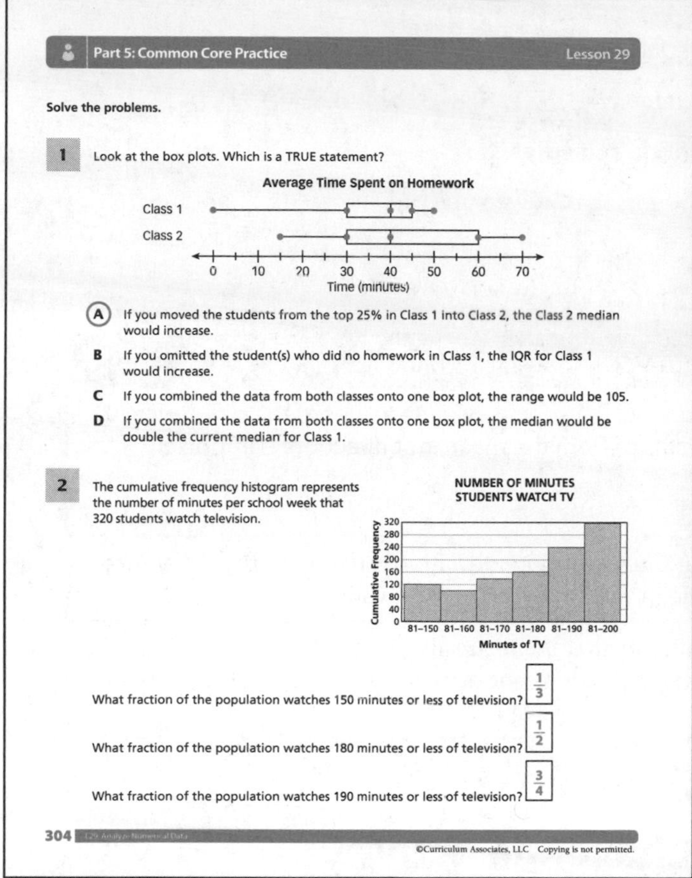

Solve the problems.

1 Look at the box plots. Which is a TRUE statement?

(A) If you moved the students from the top 25% in Class 1 into Class 2, the Class 2 median would increase.

B If you omitted the student(s) who did no homework in Class 1, the IQR for Class 1 would increase.

C If you combined the data from both classes onto one box plot, the range would be 105.

D If you combined the data from both classes onto one box plot, the median would be double the current median for Class 1.

2 The cumulative frequency histogram represents the number of minutes per school week that 320 students watch television.

What fraction of the population watches 150 minutes or less of television? $\frac{1}{3}$

What fraction of the population watches 180 minutes or less of television? $\frac{1}{2}$

What fraction of the population watches 190 minutes or less of television? $\frac{3}{4}$

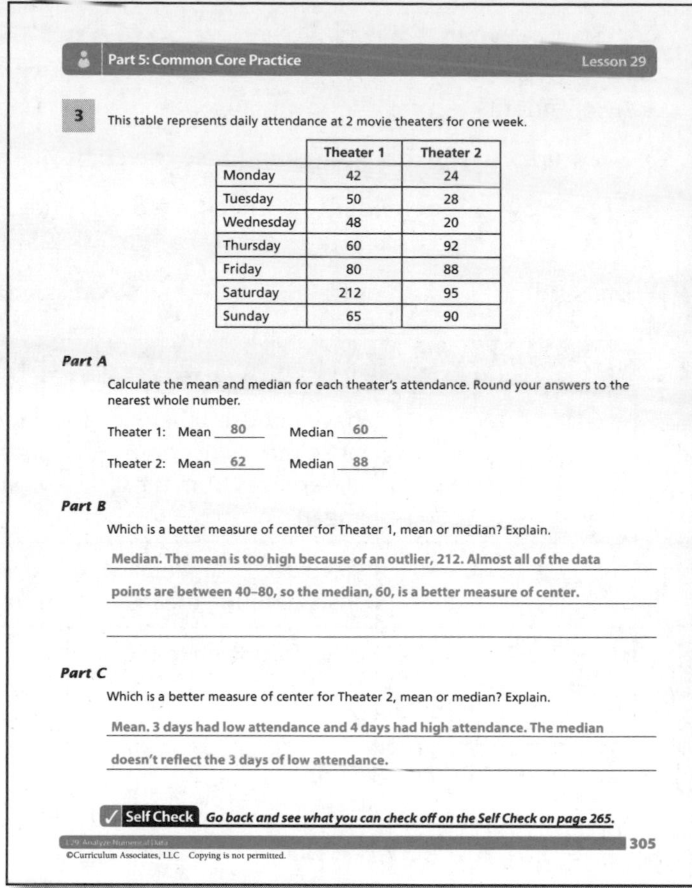

3 This table represents daily attendance at 2 movie theaters for one week.

	Theater 1	Theater 2
Monday	42	24
Tuesday	50	28
Wednesday	48	20
Thursday	60	92
Friday	80	88
Saturday	212	95
Sunday	65	90

Part A

Calculate the mean and median for each theater's attendance. Round your answers to the nearest whole number.

Theater 1: Mean 80 Median 60

Theater 2: Mean 62 Median 88

Part B

Which is a better measure of center for Theater 1, mean or median? Explain.

Median. The mean is too high because of an outlier, 212. Almost all of the data points are between 40–80, so the median, 60, is a better measure of center.

Part C

Which is a better measure of center for Theater 2, mean or median? Explain.

Mean. 3 days had low attendance and 4 days had high attendance. The median doesn't reflect the 3 days of low attendance.

✓ Self Check *Go back and see what you can check off on the Self Check on page 265.*

AT A GLANCE

Students use graphs and measures of center and variability to solve problems that might appear on a mathematics test.

SOLUTIONS

1 *Solution:* **A**; Adding more values that are greater than the median of Class 2 would increase its median. ***(DOK 2)***

2 *Solution:* $\frac{1}{3}$; Divide 120 by 320.

$\frac{1}{2}$; Divide 160 by 320.

$\frac{3}{4}$; Divide 240 by 320. ***(DOK 1)***

3 *Part A Solution:*

Theater 1: Mean: 80; Median: 60

Theater 2: Mean: 62; Median: 88

Part B Solution: median; See student book page above for possible student explanation.

Part C Solution: mean; See student book page above for possible student explanation. ***(DOK 3)***

Assessment and Remediation

- Ask students to find the mean absolute deviation of this data set: 3, 7, 1, 8, 8, 4, 3, 1, 3, 2 [2.2]
- For students who are struggling, use the chart below to guide remediation.
- After providing remediation, check students' understanding. Ask students to find the mean absolute deviation of this data set: 2, 7, 5, 4, 6, 5, 4, 7 [1.25]
- If a student is still having difficulty, use ***Ready Instruction, Level 6,*** Lesson 27.

If the error is . . .	Students may . . .	To remediate . . .
0	have not used the absolute value of the differences from the mean.	Remind students to use the absolute values of the difference because distance from the mean, not direction, is important.
2	have used the median instead of the mean.	Review that mean absolute deviation is based on the difference from the mean value, not the median value.
22	have forgotten to divide.	Remind students that the *mean* absolute deviation is an average, and the total of the differences must be divided by the number of values.

Hands-On Activity

Explore the effect of spread on the mean and the median.

Materials: drawing paper, sticky dots

On a sheet of paper, have students display the following sets of data on dot plots using sticky dots.

Graph 1	Graph 2	Graph 3	Graph 4
5, 5, 5, 5, 5	1, 5, 5, 5, 9	5, 5, 5, 9, 9	1, 1, 5, 5, 5

Next have students find and record the mean and median for each set of data and label them below the number lines of the graphs.

Discuss the following questions:

- If one data value is increased and another data value is decreased by the same amount, how do those changes affect the mean? The median?
- If two data values are increased, how do those changes affect the mean? The median?
- If two data value are decreased, how do those changes affect the mean? The median?

Challenge Activity

Find and compare mean average deviations.

Materials: number cubes

Have students think about the results of rolling a number cube several times. Discuss the range of outcomes and the probable mean. Then have them consider the results of rolling two number cubes several times. Finally, have them predict which trial would have the greatest mean average deviation.

Have students work in pairs to find, record, and analyze two sets of data. Direct them to roll one number cube 10 times and record the results. Have them find the mean of the results and then the mean average deviation. Then have them roll two number cubes ten times and find the mean and MAD for those results. Have students compare the results of the two trials.

As a class, discuss the results. Have students compare the results with the predictions they made at the beginning of the activity.

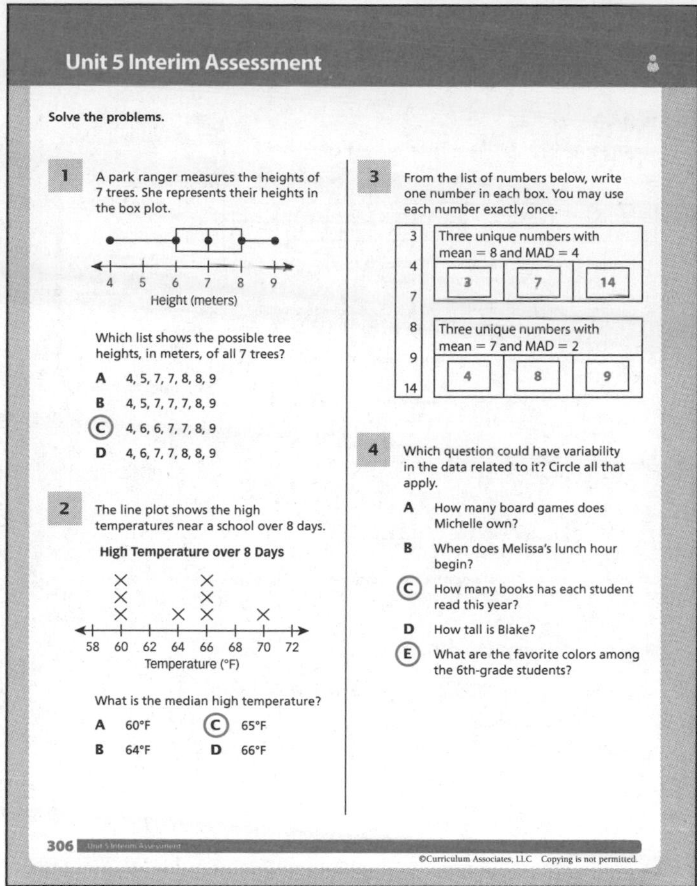

Unit 5 Interim Assessment

Solve the problems.

1 A park ranger measures the heights of 7 trees. She represents their heights in the box plot.

Which list shows the possible tree heights, in meters, of all 7 trees?

A 4, 5, 7, 7, 8, 8, 9

B 4, 5, 7, 7, 7, 8, 9

(C) 4, 6, 6, 7, 7, 8, 9

D 4, 6, 7, 7, 8, 8, 9

2 The line plot shows the high temperatures near a school over 8 days.

What is the median high temperature?

A 60°F

B 64°F

(C) 65°F

D 66°F

3 From the list of numbers below, write one number in each box. You may use each number exactly once.

3, 4, 7, 8, 9, 14

Three unique numbers with mean = 8 and MAD = 4: 3, 7, 14

Three unique numbers with mean = 7 and MAD = 2: 4, 8, 9

4 Which question could have variability in the data related to it? Circle all that apply.

A How many board games does Michelle own?

B When does Melissa's lunch hour begin?

(C) How many books has each student read this year?

D How tall is Blake?

(E) What are the favorite colors among the 6th-grade students?

306 Unit 5 Interim Assessment ©Curriculum Associates, LLC Copying is not permitted.

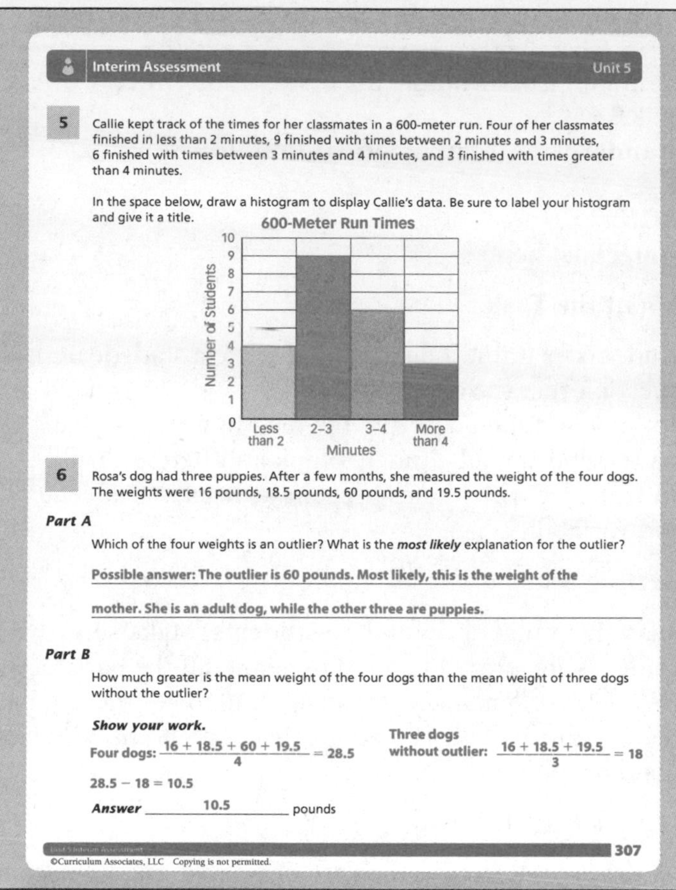

Interim Assessment Unit 5

5 Callie kept track of the times for her classmates in a 600-meter run. Four of her classmates finished in less than 2 minutes, 9 finished with times between 2 minutes and 3 minutes, 6 finished with times between 3 minutes and 4 minutes, and 3 finished with times greater than 4 minutes.

In the space below, draw a histogram to display Callie's data. Be sure to label your histogram and give it a title.

6 Rosa's dog had three puppies. After a few months, she measured the weight of the four dogs. The weights were 16 pounds, 18.5 pounds, 60 pounds, and 19.5 pounds.

Part A

Which of the four weights is an outlier? What is the ***most likely*** explanation for the outlier?

Possible answer: The outlier is 60 pounds. Most likely, this is the weight of the mother. She is an adult dog, while the other three are puppies.

Part B

How much greater is the mean weight of the four dogs than the mean weight of three dogs without the outlier?

Show your work.

Four dogs: $\frac{16 + 18.5 + 60 + 19.5}{4} = 28.5$

Three dogs without outlier: $\frac{16 + 18.5 + 19.5}{3} = 18$

$28.5 - 18 = 10.5$

Answer 10.5 pounds

Unit 5 Interim Assessment ©Curriculum Associates, LLC Copying is not permitted. 307

SCORING GUIDE AND ANSWER ANALYSIS

1 *Solution:* **C**; For the set 4, 6, 6, 7, 7, 8, 9:

- least value: 4
- lower quartile: 6
- median: 7
- upper quartile: 8
- greatest value: 9 ***(DOK 2)***

2 *Solution:* **C**; For the set 60, 60, 60, 64, 66, 66, 66, 70, the median is (64 + 66) ÷ 2 = 65. ***(DOK 1)***

3 *Solution:* 3, 7, 14; To find the mean, add three numbers and divide by 3. To find the MAD, find the distance each of the three numbers is from the mean, add them, and divide by 3.

4, 8, 9; To find the mean, add three numbers and divide by 3. To find the MAD, find the distance each of the three numbers is from the mean, add them, and divide by 3. ***(DOK 2)***

4 *Solution:* **C**; The number of books read by each student will vary from student to student.

E; The favorite color of each 6th-grade student will vary from student to student. ***(DOK 2)***

5 *Solution:* See student histogram above. To get complete credit, students must include a proper title and labels (1 point), appropriately number the *x*- and *y*-axes (1 point), and draw all four bars correctly (1 point). ***(DOK 2)***

6 *Part A Solution:* The outlier is 60 pounds. See student book page above for possible student explanation.

Part B Solution: 10.5; Find the mean weight of all four dogs (28.5), then find the mean weight of three dogs without the outlier (18), and subtract the latter from the former (10.5). See student book page above for possible student work. ***(DOK 2)***

PERFORMANCE TASK TEACHER NOTES

Common Core Standards: 6.SP.A.1, 6.SP.A.2, 6.SP.A.3, 6.SP.B.4
Standards for Mathematical Practice: SMP 1, 2, 3, 4, 5, 6
DOK: 3
Materials: none

About the Task

Students examine a data set and write a statistical question that the question could answer. They make a dot plot and then describe the data in terms of shape, center, and spread. Students look at different displays and analyze which ones best show measures of center and variability.

Getting Started

Read the problem aloud with students. Make sure students are aware of and understand all the parts of the task. For students who are struggling to get started, have them identify the least and greatest data points and plot them on a number line.

Completing the Task

Students need to read the data presented in the table and think about a viable statistical question that could result in that data set. Ask them to look at the numbers closely and think about questions they might ask friends that could be answered using these numbers. ***(SMP 2)***

Next, students construct a dot plot of the data. Ask them to think about how they can ensure that each data point is represented and not repeated. As students begin to describe the shape, center, and spread of the data, encourage them to use as many precise terms as they can to identify measures of center and variability. ***(SMP 6)***

Finally, students need to identify the data display that is the best visual model for measures of center and the one that is best for measures of variability. Make sure students are making a solid case for their choices. ***(SMP 3)***

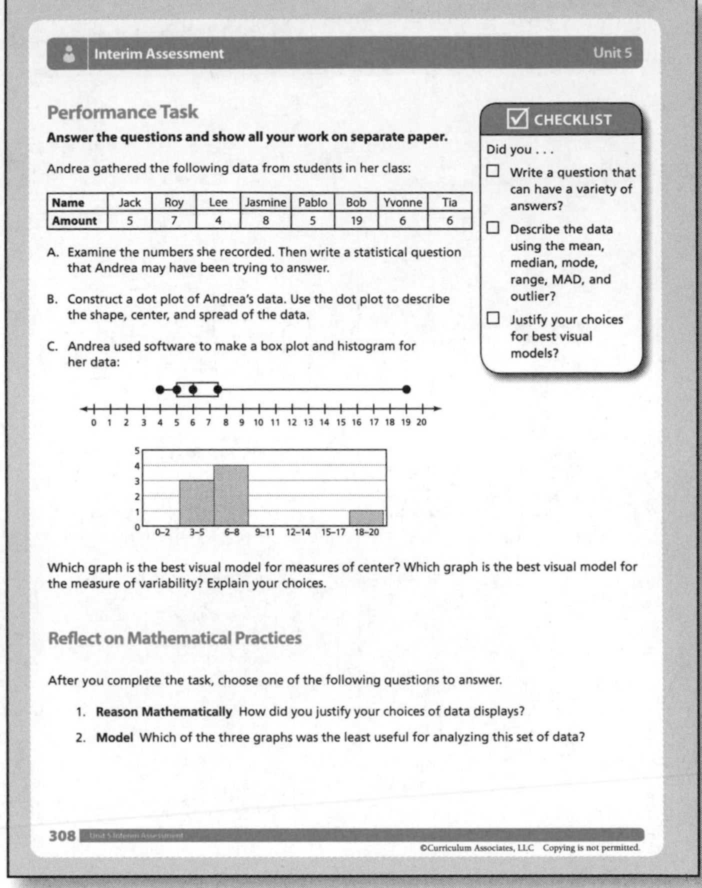

Interim Assessment Unit 5

Performance Task

Answer the questions and show all your work on separate paper.

Andrea gathered the following data from students in her class:

Name	Jack	Roy	Lee	Jasmine	Pablo	Bob	Yvonne	Tia
Amount	5	7	4	8	5	19	6	6

A. Examine the numbers she recorded. Then write a statistical question that Andrea may have been trying to answer.

B. Construct a dot plot of Andrea's data. Use the dot plot to describe the shape, center, and spread of the data.

C. Andrea used software to make a box plot and histogram for her data:

Which graph is the best visual model for measures of center? Which graph is the best visual model for the measure of variability? Explain your choices.

CHECKLIST

Did you . . .

- ☐ Write a question that can have a variety of answers?
- ☐ Describe the data using the mean, median, mode, range, MAD, and outlier?
- ☐ Justify your choices for best visual models?

Reflect on Mathematical Practices

After you complete the task, choose one of the following questions to answer.

1. **Reason Mathematically** How did you justify your choices of data displays?
2. **Model** Which of the three graphs was the least useful for analyzing this set of data?

308 Unit 5 Interim Assessment

©Curriculum Associates, LLC Copying is not permitted.

Extension

If some students have more time to spend on this problem, you can have them solve this extension:

Andrea used software to find the mean, median, mean absolute deviation, interquartile range, and range of the data. The results are in the table below. She wasn't sure if she used the software correctly. Which values from the software are correct and incorrect? Explain.

Statistic	Value
Mean	7.5
Median	6
Mean absolute deviation	7.5
Interquartile range	3
Range	15

PERFORMANCE TASK SAMPLE RESPONSES AND RUBRIC

4-Point Solution

A. A statistical question Andrea may have been trying to answer might be, "How many first cousins do you have?"

B.

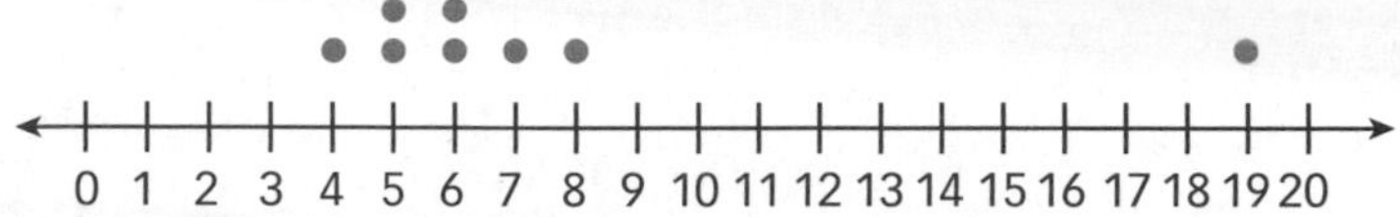

The dot plot shows that data point 19 is an outlier. With the exception of the outlier, the data are clustered close together. Since most data points are clustered near lower values, the graph is skewed right. There are two modes, at 5 and 6. The median is 6 and the mean is 7.5. The range is 19 − 4, or 15. The MAD is $\frac{24}{8}$ or 3.

Data Value	Deviation from the Mean	Absolute Deviation
5	−2.5	2.5
7	−0.5	0.5
4	−3.5	3.5
8	0.5	0.5
5	−2.5	2.5
19	11.5	11.5
6	−1.5	1.5
6	−1.5	1.5
	Total	24

C. The dot plot best displays the measures of center. You can see that 5 and 6 are modes and the median is 6. On the box plot, only the median is obvious. You cannot determine measures of center from the histogram. The box plot best displays measures of variability. You can see the median, interquartile range, and minimum and maximum values.

REFLECT ON MATHEMATICAL PRACTICES

1. Look for an understanding that the data displays must clearly show the measures of center and variability. ***(SMP 2)***
2. Look for responses that are justified. For example: The histogram is the least useful since it shows intervals, not exact values for measures of center and variability. ***(SMP 4)***

SCORING RUBRIC

4 points The statistical question is appropriate. All answers are correct, and explanations and the dot plot are complete and accurate. The student correctly found all measures of center and variability. The justification for best choice of visual model is reasonable.

3 points The statistical question is appropriate. There are minor inaccuracies in the answers or explanations. The dot plot is well constructed, but one data point may be inaccurate or missing. The student correctly calculated most measures of center and variability. The justification for best choice of visual model is reasonable.

2 points The statistical question is missing or unreasonable. The dot plot has some errors, and some of the measures of center and variability are correct. The student may have chosen best visual models, but did not justify the choices.

1 point The student's responses are incomplete and mostly incorrect. The dot plot and measures of center and variability are missing, incomplete, or inaccurate. The student did not justify the choices for best visual models.

SOLUTION TO THE EXTENSION

The mean, median, and range are correct. The mean absolute deviation is 3, not 7.5. The interquartile range is 2.5, not 3. The median of the lower quartile is 5, and the median of the upper quartile is 7.5: 7.5 − 5 = 2.5.